W9-ACA-757

GOING AWAY

A Report, A Memoir

A Houghton Mifflin
Literary Fellowship Book

Other Houghton Mifflin
Literary Fellowship Awards

To E. P. O'Donnell for *Green Margins*
To Dorothy Baker for *Young Man with a Horn*
To Robert Penn Warren for *Night Rider*
To Joseph Wechsberg for *Looking for a Bluebird*
To Ann Petry for *The Street*
To Elizabeth Bishop for *North & South*
To Anthony West for *The Vintage*
To Arthur Mizener for *The Far Side of Paradise*
To Madison A. Cooper, Jr., for *Sironia, Texas*
To Charles Bracelen Flood for *Love Is a Bridge*
To Milton Lott for *The Last Hunt*
To Edward Hoagland for *Cat Man*
To Eugene Burdick for *The Ninth Wave*
To Herbert Simmons for *Corner Boy*
To Philip Roth for *Goodbye, Columbus*
To William Brammer for *The Gay Place*

By Clancy Sigal

GOING AWAY

A Report, A Memoir

1962
Houghton Mifflin Company • Boston
The Riverside Press • Cambridge

Also by Clancy Sigal
Weekend in Dinlock

Second Printing

Library of Congress Catalog Card Number: 61–10778
Printed in the U.S.A.

Except for certain well-known public figures all of the characters in this book are fictitious and any resemblance to actual persons, living or dead, is purely coincidental.

Now two days before his death, writes Mrs. Chapman, he kept murmuring, "A soldier lay dying, a soldier lay dying." I bent over him to catch the words, and he repeated the first four lines of "A soldier of the Legion lay dying in Algiers," adding, "*But there is lack of nothing here,*" in a voice of deep feeling. But later, when semiconscious, he began saying, plucking at my fingers, "I want to take it away, I want to take it away!" "What?" I asked. "The pillow?" "No," he said. "The mute, the mute. I want to play on the open strings."

Dialogue at the bedside of the dying moralist, John Jay Chapman; quoted in Edmund Wilson's *Triple Thinkers*

These are not catastrophes that I went out of my way to look for — these were my friends; moreover, these things happened not during the depression but during the boom.

F. Scott Fitzgerald, *The Crack-Up*

GOING AWAY

A Report, A Memoir

The person whose narrative appears here was an American, with a crew cut and a 1940 Pontiac sedan automobile, whose childhood had been spent in many cities. Both his mother and father, before they separated, had been trade union organizers. He had grown up chiefly on the West Side of Chicago, a gang boy, a zoot-suiter and a neighborhood leader in a radical youth organization. At twelve he had been a Catholic. In 1944, at the age of seventeen, he volunteered for induction into the Army, choosing as his branch the infantry. While in basic training he volunteered again, this time for the parachutists, but withdrew his application on second thought. Two years later, a staff sergeant, T/3, he went AWOL and hitchhiked through the country from Camp Kilmer, New Jersey, until he struck the Skid Row section of Los Angeles, where he lived for a time. He received an honorable discharge from the Army and then took up his parents' vocation and went to work for the Amalgamated Vehicle Builders–CIO in Detroit. Anticipating the results of a convention dispute which was to decimate his faction, on the advice of his betters he enrolled as a freshman student at a state university in Los Angeles. He majored in American History and was editor of the campus newspaper until the student body turned out to sack him because of a current political controversy. As soon as his last exam was over, he left the university without waiting for his diploma. The Korean war broke out and in New York he worked inside a small avant garde record company patronized by an heiress. When the unit collapsed he took a succession of odd jobs and was eventually hired by a Hollywood studio.

It was his custom, between jobs, to go on the road, and this he did again upon severing his connection with the studio. After wandering freely, he became a journalist. Then a cabdriver. Then he led an abortive strike of 16-mm film cleaners. On the same day that he was hired as a riveter in a non-union factory, he applied for and received a position with a motion picture and television agency near the Sunset Strip, Hollywood. His two years with the agency were successful and lucrative, and on his birthday he gave notice and then went to bed for several weeks with an illness diagnosed as mononucleosis, "student's disease." He returned to settle his affairs at the agency and then drove across the country in a red-and-white De Soto convertible. In Boston, arrangements were made to publish his book, and on the day the shelling stopped in Port Said and Budapest he took sail for Europe, like so many young Americans before him, to write an autobiographical novel. Except for a short tour of duty as an occupation trooper in Germany, he had never been to Europe. He was twenty-nine years of age.

I woke up early, about five, and began to write. Fifteen minutes later I changed over to a Scripto pen and lined yellow paper. Nothing happened. I sat at my desk and then went into the kitchen and made myself a breakfast of corn flakes, a banana and coffee. I put on "Dippermouth" by Louis and several old Bunk Johnson records but couldn't get going again, either at the typewriter or on the yellow paper with a Scripto pen. I tore out a sheet of paper and began to write a letter. "Dear Tad and Hilda: I am a dead battery. I can be artificially recharged only by physical contact with people. Can I come and live with you for a while? Love," and I signed my name. I put a stamp on the envelope and then tore it up. Then I sat around until a decent hour and began phoning various people, at their homes or work. Not many of them were eager to talk. I had alienated many more friends than I realized. Then I sat by the telephone waiting for it to ring. It did, twice. Both times I shouted into the phone and scared them off.

The apartment was warming up. I prowled it and flicked on the television set several times, and then I sat down at my desk, cleared away the typewriter and paper and sat writing my name for about an hour as fast as I could. I cried for a while and then slept. The telephone woke me. It was Gorman, calling from work, asking me did I realize that two people we had known died over the weekend.

I told him I knew all about that. My personal lawyer, from overwork, and Georgina, Laura Collins' maid, of a heart attack in Laura's house. Gorman said why did I have to enumerate them. I said it was because I didn't want him to think I wasn't hep, *au courant*. He said it depressed him thinking about those two dead people and that I probably felt worse because I had known them even better. I said, Gorman, did you ever stop to think, death has no smell, it is a pressure on the temples. Gorman asked me if I wanted to go to a brothel on the Strip. I said no and he hung up. The only reason he wanted to go to the brothel was that he had fallen in love with one of the girls. Gorman was in a rotten mess. He should have stayed in Montreal studying philosophy on the G.I. Bill; he was a dry, fat man and I had helped set him up in business as an agent. I had warned him against it but he said it would kill him to go on being a Douglas Aircraft timekeeper all his life. I declared that he had a shopgirl's idea of Hollywood, and he said better spurious glamour than none at all. Gorman had a first-draft novel which he refused to finish. I read it once; he could write. But his twin boys masturbated in public, he was paying alimony, his present wife blamed him for taking her away from a promising career in light opera (she said) in Canada, and he had become one of the most deliberately crude men in the business, and unsuccessfully. He had an office and a secretary but I knew he was bringing home about twenty dollars a week. Also, he had gotten into the habit of falling in love with teen-age girls, like this chippy on the Strip, for whom he had just bought a new cloth coat. I never knew quite how to appraise the mocking element in his unexpectedly ferocious sense of humor, I'm not sure he did either. When Jimmy Dean, the actor, died in a crash it was Gorman who phoned me at four in the morning to tell me the news and say, Daddy's dead. What're we going to do?

The only times he ever really became angry were when I advised him to leave Eleanor, his wife. Nobody I ever knew had ever seen Gorman raise a hand in anger to anyone, and that was a little rare in our crowd.

Fifteen minutes later Gorman phoned again. He was in trouble at Fox. He had quoted them a price on a newly published novel and now they said they wanted it. But he had neglected to sew up representation on it. In fact, he hadn't even asked New York yet. He was almost crying again, this time out of worry. He asked me to write a personal special-delivery letter, or better, wire the New York agent, asking that he be given representation. That was the kind of fix he never used to get into at Douglas Aircraft. I said okay, I would. Then I made a long-distance call to the New York agents, lied a little and got them to agree to take Gorman as the motion-picture rights agent. They were suspicious over the phone, wanting to know why I didn't lock it up for Sol Benedict. I said that I wasn't working for Benedict any more and that I was getting a private commission. To have told them the truth would have soured the deal. So, feeling that I had betrayed my former employer, they hung up, superior. I phoned Gorman and told him he had the book but only if Fox sustained their offer and made it firm. He said that Fox hadn't exactly made an offer, only an inquiry. I asked him where he had gotten the price he had quoted me and he said that was the price he quoted the studio. I said, Gil, that was the first time you have ever lied to me. And he said, I've got to start some time. I hung up.

I watched afternoon television all day, ate some tuna fish for supper and then went to a meeting, up in Laurel Canyon, of the editorial board of the *Gulflines Review*. For several years I had been carping at the *Review*, and now that the political situation had changed (or "altered") they wanted to talk to me.

The meeting was in the house of a rich psychiatrist with whom I had worked on a Ban-the-Blacklist-in-Hospitals committee. The editorial board consisted of two blacklisted screenwriters, a Chinese poet, my friend Brendan Montagu, also a poet and once a Rhodes scholar, and a few others. Very solemnly, and without referring to past quarrels, they offered me a spot on their board. A year ago I would have given my eyeteeth to move in on the magazine; now I listened to their proposition and it meant nothing. I had lost my taste even for bush league vindictiveness. They told me what they were planning for the next issue, and, pushing the knife in, I said I would consider coming in if they would reprint two of the political chapters of Orwell's *Homage to Catalonia*, a translation of a certain Polish existentialist poem, and if they deleted the planned chapter of Congressman Vito Marcantonio's *This Is Where I Stand* and in addition the tribute, as written, to Paul Robeson. I was pretty drunk. After some arguing, they agreed to drop the Marcantonio piece and renegotiate the style of the tribute to Robeson, who I said was a darling of a man but a political mongoloid. The wife of one of the blacklisted screenwriters called me a white chauvinist and I said coming from the likes of her that was a compliment. I had no need to do that. These were good people. But I didn't apologize. The basement room in which we were meeting was full of strain, and I had done it. And this time to no overriding purpose. I leaned forward and said, Look, I'm sorry but I think it would waste your time if I came on as one of the editors. Nobody said anything so I got up and left and drove home.

When I got home the phone was ringing. I grabbed it, not even knowing who I hoped it was. It was Buddy Terhune, one of "my" writers from the agency. He said he wanted my advice about whether to stay with the agency now that I was no longer there, and was I going into business on my own? I told Buddy that he would have to get someone else to advise him about his life and business matters now. He sounded aggrieved, as only North Carolinians can. What's the matter, ol' cock? I thought we were friends too, he said. I mean, he said, that we seemed to had gone well beyond a purely business relationship.

How could I tell him? That he was a nice guy but that I liked to choose my own friends, and not keep friendships as the instruments of agency policy, which ours was? I told him to keep his shirt on and that I would meet him for lunch at Scandia's day after tomorrow and we'd talk it over. He said that made him feel better and oh, yes, did I know that yesterday morning Irene Viertel had been taken away to the state hospital at Norwalk? What? I said. That's right, Buddy replied. Night before last Beverly Hills cops found her walking along the street with no clothes on. I said no, I hadn't known.

He said, Poor kid, and asked me to be sure to meet him at Scandia's and hung up. I went into my bedroom and turned on the television set. I felt so ill I thought my stomach would fall out. Two nights ago I had seen Irene, in her house on the Palisades. She was a thin, frightened girl, a farm girl from South Dakota, who had married an art gallery owner, a friend of mine who spent most of their time together reminding, bitterly reminding Irene of how stupid she was. The terrible thing was, Irene was stupid. Just not very bright. But she was pliable, and polite; she used to phone me a lot, just to talk, and two nights ago I said that I would come up to the house. She wanted to talk. She said nobody ever really wanted to talk to her because they felt she had nothing to contribute. In my heart I agreed with them. That night she wanted to talk. And I didn't want to listen to her. So I picked her up, unprotesting, and carried her less than one hundred pounds up to her bedroom, and even as I was kissing her she kept whispering, You're somebody I can talk to. Several hours later, apparently, she had taken it into her pitiful little head to go walking in the nude on Wilshire Boulevard. How in God's name did she get down there? She had no car. Her husband had never let her learn to drive. And now she was in Norwalk. Oh, Jesus. I shut my eyes and kept shaking my head but that didn't make things any better for Irene. I knew I would not visit her. I realized that what I regretted most was not having made a more plausible excuse that night. Why was I feeling so horrified, so utterly paralyzed by shame? Hers hadn't been the only hand I had held right up to the gates of Norwalk.

After a while I got up and tried to write another letter, this time to an old friend, Nick Melly, whom I hadn't seen for ten years, not since Chicago. I tore that up too. Then I went into the small photographic darkroom I had fixed up next to my study and climbed a chair to rummage in the shelves. I took down the .45 Navy service automatic which I kept at my house for Howard and turned out all the lights in the house and sat in my new Swedish-style fabric chair and thought. The telephone rang again, and I sat with the .45 in my hand in the dark room in the garage apartment and let it ring. I couldn't have moved out of my chair to go to anyone's assistance even if I had wanted to. The thing is, I didn't want to. For the first time in my life I could think of nobody whose assistance I wanted to go to. I kept the lights off and transferred the .45 from one hand to another, whistling, for some reason or other, "Jersey Bounce," the Tommy Dorsey version. Then I rang up Eric Pomeroy, a poet I know, and gave him the address in Norwalk where Irene was. He groaned but when I told him the circumstances he said he'd hop right over there. Eric was an ex-Alcoholics Anonymous who got kicked out of his chapter for trying to move resolutions about the Rosenberg case, but he still likes to do things like this for people.

I was so tired I couldn't move. I tossed the gun on the couch and lay down on the other couch in my living room. I knew I wouldn't do anything with it. It wasn't even loaded. I lay in the dark for a while and then I got up and stood on the chair in my dark room and took down the two clips of .45-caliber bullets. I went downstairs and dug a hole in the garden and buried the clips. And then I thought that was a pretty silly thing to do and dug up the clips and put them in my pocket and walked down to the corner of Doheny and Melrose where there was a large empty lot. The street was quiet and moonless. I broke open the clips and spent a few minutes hurling the bullets off into the darkness. Months later, in Paris, I got to worrying if a stray kid might come across them and hurt himself, so I wrote a letter to the Maintenance Department, Beverly Hills City Hall, asking them to send out a man to look in the weeds. I hope they did.

Then I went home and stayed up watching *Desert Victory* on TV, took a few more drinks and went to bed. It had not been my day.

•

The present narrative opens on the day which was to prove his last at the agency in Hollywood . . .

I awoke early in my apartment and rested quietly for an hour. Then I phoned my office to say that I would be in. Lucy, my secretary, was pleased, and said that she was thinking of getting married. We gossiped a few moments, then I got out of bed, slowly, and took a cold shower and shaved my beard off. I had let it grow while I was seeing nobody. I regretted seeing it go and made a game of shaving, first removing one sideburn, then half a mustache, then the other sideburn, until all that was left was half a mustache on a clean-shaven face. I looked like a mad Albanian peasant. I was laughing so hard I had to sit down on the edge of the bathtub.

I put on my charcoal-brown suit. I dressed neatly and carefully while listening to some of my jazz records. George Mitchell's "Tin Roof Blues," which many people take for Louis, and Brubeck's "Perdido," I put on twice, and then I went downstairs from my garage apartment and out to my car. I said hello to the woman from the yellow stucco house in front who was hanging wash in the garden we shared. "Sweet day, isn't it?" she said. It was what she said ten months out of the year whenever we chanced upon each other in the driveway. She and her family were from Eau Clair, Wisconsin. They stayed up watching television until one or two most every morning, a set of grandparents, husband and wife, three children. As I always did ten months out of each year, I smiled and agreed. It was very warm and sunny with hardly a breeze to move the leaves in the trees lining the quiet, sun-blasted street.

My car was still there. I loved it. Sixteen years old, with a crushed-in rear end, a torn right fender and a hood that was liable to fly open at speeds exceeding forty miles per hour. None of the original paint was left; before I bought it someone had scraped it down to its original rusty gray metallic finish which it must have had before it went under the paint spray at the Flint factory. Under the hot sun it look gruesome. My friends always said it was the kind of car hacked-up bodies of domestic murder victims were left in. I loved that old car. It ran smooth as cream. Coming back from my daily rounds at the film studios in the valley I used to beat Cadillacs and Lincolns because my car was so quick off the mark at traffic signals, not like those sluggish Firedome Eight battleships.

[9]

The top of the car was spattered with bird droppings and buds from the overhanging cedar tree under which it had been parked for the past month. I rolled down all the windows to air it out. I got in but it wouldn't start. I wasn't worried. It seldom did after inactivity. I got out and raised the hood and twisted the idle screw forward. When I got back in, the motor started instantly. The idle screw: it was that kind of car. I pushed open the wind vent and let the motor idle a few moments. Then I started for the office.

I felt very good driving my car for the first time in a month. I took the long way round, just to get the feel. It made the Clark Drive hill up to Sunset Boulevard in third (I had bought it for $100 after the salesman let me take it over Laurel Canyon pass without changing gears), and I turned north on the Strip towards the office, feeling better and better. The late-morning traffic was light. The Solomon Benedict Building was built into the middle of a palm-lined, grassed-up cul-de-sac where Burton Way intersected with Bedford Way and Santa Monica Boulevard. The cul-de-sac was called, legally and officially, Benedict Square. I turned in to the company parking lot and nosed in diagonally at my number, 38, between a new Chrysler convertible and a 1956 creme-and-green Cadillac belonging to fellows at the office. My car always stood out like a bloody sore thumb in that parking lot filled with gleaming new models, Lincolns, Jags, even a Mercedes, none of them ever over two years old. Status is peace carried on by other means. I had withstood a lot of pressure in not turning my old car in, and finally my bosses had put a good face on it by pointing out the old Pontiac to visiting firemen as a curio, the implication being that, of course, I had the money for a new car but felt queerly for that old wreck. Which wasn't so far from wrong either.

"Hey, stranger, where you been all our lives!" I crossed the street and shook hands with Andy and Joel, who ran the gas station across the boulevard from the agency. They were war friends, wiry and peppery, in their early forties. They had married once each, and now they were living with Joel's mother, who cooked for them and was a physiotherapist at a Jewish hospital. Joel owned a small boat which he kept down at San Pedro. For over a year he kept asking me to come sailing one weekend, and when I finally did we weren't out an hour before we ran into a small fleet of Yugoslav tuna tugs with colored lamps and gay flags hanging all over them. Joel hollered over and got us invited aboard two of the tugs lashed to each other. Those Slavs were jumping. Steaks, slivovitz, the works. It was their national feast day or something. We went down into one of the tugs and stayed all day, eating and drinking and singing to an accordion. The captain asked Joel to marry his daughter and Joel said sure, any time. Everybody pounded everybody else on the back and yelled "*Muy drug*" all day long. I had a ball. Joel was so drunk that one of the Yugoslav tuna sailors had to take his boat back for him. Joel's buddy, Andy, was even smaller, and a pugnacious man. He owned the parking concession for the night club next door to the gas station, and his right hand tended to be bandaged from slugging drunken playboys who cracked wise about the Jews. He was thinking of going into the picture-frame business because the oil company that controlled the property on which the station sat had decided to close out the business. Neither Andy nor Joel was bitter. "It's the way the ball bounces," shrugged Joel. "It's their way of making a living," said Andy. The friends were excellent mechanics and also thieves. Whenever my car needed repairs they fixed it up practically for free. But let a Cadillac or Lincoln roll in with a dirty spark plug, if they thought they could get away with it the boys would rip out the transmission and give in a bill for $400. That's how they were. During the war, they had been artillery officers in the Pacific. Once, over Buna, both had been flying as artillery spotters when their plane ran out of fuel and crashed to the ground. They were proud of the incident and liked to talk about it.

"Where you been, boychik?" chirped Joel. Sick for a while, I said. "Sick hell," rasped Andy, "he's just enervated on too much pooo-oo-nn tang." This like to broke the boys up laughing. I must have been paler than I thought. They were being gentle. Joel said, "Say, boychik, what's this I hear about you leaving the office?" He nodded at the four-story pale blue penthouse building across the boulevard. "Say it ain't so, Shoeless Joe." I said yes, I had given notice, though I hadn't decided just when. It might be months. My bosses were amenable. Some wanted me to stay. The consensus was, there was no rush.

Andy said disgustedly, "Ah, you're a hothead. You need a psychiatrist. A good job like that." Joel asked, with real concern,

"What'll you do?" I thought and said, I'm not sure. Maybe look around.

Joel cocked a quiet look at me. "*Mishuga*, jobs like that don't grow on trees. Go first to a headshrinker. Andy and me went last year and he said we ought to leave Mama, remember, Andy? The *goneff*. He's never tasted Mama's *knadlach*. Still it was worth it for the laughs. I dated his receptionist until I found out she was going to him too. It's a funny world." A car drove up to the gas pumps. It was a new Imperial. Maybe it had a dirty spark plug. Joel and Andy jumped to service it, all smiles and chatter. I started to walk away. I heard Andy say, mournfully, "Hey, mister, you're leaking oil bad." I crossed the street. Just before I went into the office Joel shouted, "We'll miss you, boychik!" I waved and went inside and walked upstairs.

It was like stepping into a jungle of cold air. The air-conditioning was on. At the moment I did not feel like facing my assembled colleagues, and slipped into my private office just off the third-floor corridor. I closed the door behind me and pulled the venetian blinds and snapped on the floor lamp. Lucy had gotten everything shipshape for me. I sat down in my red leather chair and looked through the interoffice memos piled in my IN tray. Then I buzzed Lucy. "G'morning, sweetie," she crackled through the box. "You know, there's a meeting."

She always said it like that to me, half reprovingly, and also to let me know that she knew I was very bored by the ceremony of the Monday morning meeting. Of course, I said, come on in with your notebook. I sat back. Lucy, discreet person that she was, came in by the hall door. She was, as usual, brightly dressed and made up, her coal-black hair done up in a new-look bun, her large bright eyes heavily mascaraed. Lucy was almost fifty and had a seventeen-year-old daughter who played tennis and was doing badly in school. We talked about her problems a lot. A few months ago I had recommended a remedial teacher, a friend of mine who had been thrown out of the Pacoima school system for "past activities." Esmeralda, my friend, had been good for the girl, and Lucy had been grateful to me. She was always being grateful for something, starting with our first week together when she knew I wanted to get rid of her. Slowly I had come to like and respect Lucy. She was a lady, a confused lady, a chronic, quite secret alcoholic and way, way out on some crazy limb of her own. She had braveness. And, also, she had persisted in liking me even though I didn't treat her well those first few weeks. Later on, I realized just how clever she was. Though frightened and a little mousy now, she had been around a great deal. When we finally got to know each other we used to sit around in the afternoons laughing together while she told stories of her lovers. She was very fast at shorthand and bloody awful at typing. But she was my right arm. I could tell Lucy anything. She was the person I had bequeathed my apartment to.

She remained at the door. "Hello, sweetie, how do you feel?" Not half bad, I said. I got up and kissed her on the cheek. She began to cry. I had learned not to become angry when she did that. "I'm not sad, you know," she said. Sure, I said. She sat down on the couch and began, skillfully, to wipe away the tears. How was it, being Les's secretary? I asked.

She looked up and grinned, showing those marvelous white young teeth of hers. "Don't ask," she said. "I think he hates me." He hates everybody. How's everything around here? I asked. She gave me a run-down, what clients had departed, what new clients had come in, who was squabbling with whom, which secretary was sleeping, or militantly not sleeping, with what agent. Normal, I said. "I suppose that's one word for it," Lucy said.

I sat on the desk and told her I wanted to dictate a short letter before I went to the meeting. Lucy was great. She never once asked me when I was going to leave. The letter had been bothering me for weeks, all the time I was lying in bed and growing my beard and watching television from 8 A.M. to one in the morning, getting up to go to the bathroom or make myself a sandwich in the kitchen. I had even taken my phone off the hook.

It wasn't an important letter, merely to a corresponding agent in New York to tell him that one of my clients had gone east. It had been on my mind. The client in question, a writer-director, wasn't poor but I liked him. Also, for himself, he needed work. I consoled myself that he had probably pulled a good job his first week in New York, but I didn't like the fact that I had delayed this long, out of laziness. Before I'd gotten sick, I had been doing things like that. If it hadn't been for Lucy checking up on me I probably would have done more. Okay, I said, here goes. She flipped open her pad and I dictated the letter, making up an excuse for the delay as I went along. Lucy took shorthand with her legs crossed and in perfect posture. It was only last year that she had graduated secretarial school, and she was always trying to do things the correct way, even when she was half crocked. She had, considering her small body, rather long and beautiful legs. That was one thing, I don't think she knew I liked her legs. All the while I was dictating the telephone and buzzer kept going. Lucy told them I was out.

I got up and straightened my tie. Lucy asked, before I went down to the meeting, would I go out and say hello to Shirley, my other secretary. I said I would, later. Shirley was eighteen and cute. She had visited me during my illness and had gotten into bed to watch the Democratic convention on TV with me. We had taken off our clothes and fooled around and not much else, the kind of thing you stop doing at her age. Shirley was a nice *hamisheh* but I didn't feel, in view of our history, like putting her first on my list of hellos. I did not tell Lucy any of this. She had been advising me for months to get it over with already with Shirley, and I wasn't much in love with the prospect of my two secretaries coffee-klatsching over my sexual regressions. Not that I had any assurances they weren't already, anyway.

I said Geronimo! and slipped out the door. I had to walk down the stairs and out the side door to get in through the ornate front entrance. It was hot as a stove out, and the sun striking the cement pavement of the cul-de-sac like to blinded me. Just in case Joel and Andy were waving from the gas station, I waved back, and then the pneumatically operated door swung open before I touched it. It was that kind of thing, later to be found in the American Express building in Paris, which gave me the creeps. Involuntarily, as I always did upon entering the ground-floor suite where the agency brass lived, I hunched my shoulders slightly and went into a kind of subtle crouch.

"Benedict Agency, good morning . . . Benedict Agency, good morning," droned the switchboard operator, Rita, whose boyfriend was one of Mickey Cohen's hoods. Rita was attractive in an inquisitive, bulky way, but men, including myself, stayed away from her. "G'morning, lover," said Estelle, the slim, harebrained receptionist, "where ya been keepin'?" Estelle had just got married and had had to fight her fiancé, an orthodox Balkan from Riverside, who insisted that she shave her head before the wedding ceremony as a good wife should. Keeping cool, honey, I replied. I reminded myself to ask Lucy if she was serious about getting married.

Walking past the rows of desks I said hello to the secretaries and answered questions about my health. The doors to the private offices were open, their inhabitants already in the boss's office for the meeting. I noticed that all the interoffice memos in the IN and OUT trays were lying face down. That was a new rule, to prevent clients from reading what the agent said about them. Clients who dropped in unannounced always complicated an agent's job. Hermione, the outlandishly brawny office manager, stopped me. "How do you *feel?* Everybody's been *so* worried about you." I said, Hermione, I feel just fine, and then stepped into the ceremony of the Monday meeting.

*

Everybody was there, in Sol's newly decorated Swedish-modernistic warehouse of an inner office, with its three-legged chairs and ceramic tables and originals on the walls and suffused lighting and the Brancusi out in the mosaic-tiled garden back of the slatted picture window. All the agents were there too, pads and pencils out, ties off, some unshaven, sipping coffee or munching Danish delivered daily by Sol's private baker. Only two women were present, Sol's faithful secretary, Natasha, and Laura Collins, head of the literary department and Sol's partner. The atmosphere of thinly concealed tension had a neutralizing effect: the men were demasculinized and the women defeminized. All three of Sol's telephones were off the hook. The Monday morning meeting was sacred, used by the owners of the firm to learn what had been happening during the previous week and to present to the agents the "situation in depth," as Laura liked to call it. It was also the meeting to discuss problems, plot strategy and where the agents had to confess in public about their promises and boasts on the previous Monday. Tomorrow's Tuesday meeting, in Laura's office, concerned literary department problems solely. Wednesday morning the agents met again down at Sol's for a "vulnerability" meeting: to try to detect, by joint conspiracy, which Hollywood stars were the least happy with their agents and most open to "The Approach." Thursday morning was the television meeting, where the new pie in the sky was cut up. Friday there was no meeting. The agents could relax.

". . . and I'm glad to announce that Horace Mock's wife called to report Horace is resting comfortably at Cedars of Lebanon," Sol was saying as I walked in. Heads turned towards me and Sol looked up. "Glad to see you again," he said.

Glad to see you, Sol, I said, taking my place with three other agents from my floor on Sol's expensive gold-threaded Italian-imported couch. "Also," Sol resumed, "it is my misfortune to tell you that Bob Sylvester died over the weekend. Natasha, send the usual flowers." "Gee, Sol," piped up Stanley, head of the television department, "I saw Bob only two weeks ago." "No," said Mal, the wiliest of the ground-floor agents, "that can't be right. He's been in a tent that long." "Oh," subsided Stanley, almost in a grumble. I picked up my pad and pencil (embossed, like all the others, with my name in raised, sequined letters) and made a doodle. On the other side of the large, parabolic room the two agents I worked most closely with acknowledged my presence, Les with an automatic wink, Howard with a secretive grin. Howard was going with a hysterical Cajun, a Louisiana swamp woman he had met at A. B. Mayer's funeral, and I let them use my apartment in the afternoons because he lived so far out, at El Segundo. He was a bug on small-arms hunting but had to keep his .38 in the office for fear his ladyfriend would get at it. She had once been an attorney but wasn't much of anything now except a case. Howard was my best friend in the office.

I made more doodles while the meeting got down to business. Laddie, the ex-paratrooper whom everybody but Howard disliked (Howard found a reason to like everybody), nudged me warningly. I wrote down an obscenity on the pad and showed it to him. He showed me the finger surreptitiously. Laddie every Monday morning announced how he was going to bring Frank Sinatra into the agency. By now it was an office joke.

As far as I could tell, the meeting was going off smoothly enough. Sol, the president and chairman of the board of the agency, a former dry-goods peddler from the East Side of New York, was keeping a sharp, sad eye on his grammar: whenever he forgot himself with a

"Goddammit!" it was usually a sign that someone in the assemblage, not excluding himself, had goofed. He wasn't using any "Goddammits!" this morning. But you never could tell with Sol. Sometimes, to everyone's relief, he forgot. But also sometimes, when he forgot, Natasha was at his elbow with a coy sibilant reminder, "Mr. Benedict, last week you asked me to remind you about Sophia Loren's new contract," and if Sophia Loren hadn't yet signed her agency contract some agent was bound to catch it in the neck. Everybody in the room except the owners of company stock feared Natasha. She didn't mean anything by it. She was only doing her job. And watch as closely as we could, none of us agents could ever detect the slightest glimmer of a smirk of satisfaction on Natasha's open, American face when she unlocked a can of peas.

It was Sol's custom to open the Monday morning meetings not with a prayer but with a soft, lugubrious report on which of the Hollywood moguls was sick, dying or dead. For the agents this pensive little service performed the duty of letting them gather their wits, gauge the boss's temper, prepare their pitch and pop a Miltown down the hatch. That was over now. Business had begun.

"Okay, fellas," said Sol, "what're our worries?" An unheard, collective sigh rippled around the room as legs stretched out, bodies fitted into chairs. The first to speak up was Chubbie, a stockholder by virtue of his mother's having lent Sol money in the early days. He usually spoke first on Monday mornings in order to impress the company directors with his right to keep the stock and also on the principle that he who buys the first drink is ever afterwards remembered and seldom asked again. Chubbie had a psychosomatic eye twitch but otherwise would have made a perfect shoe salesman. He was a religious faddist. This year it was Vedantism, and he came to the office earlier than anyone else in order to listen to a Vedantist radio program on Station WBDO out of Salt Lake City; his wife, a friend of mine, abused and laughed at him. "We're in trouble with A.," said Chubbie, mentioning an aging lady star. "Lazner Agency is romancing her hard and I think she's going to leave us."

"What's the matter, fellas?" demanded Sol. "Why can't we get work for this lady?" Several agents, including myself, reported their efforts at the studios to get A. a job. Sol broke in. "What about Wilfred Morganstern at Metro? Christ, they used to be married. Don't he believe in old times?"

Mal Miller, the smooth swarthy agent who covered M-G-M, muttered, "I'll work on the *momser*. But you know, Sol, let's face it in the confines of this room. She's an old lady. Dry skin. Eyes. You know. Steady Eddie Lopat, he got old too, went to Baltimore."

"Okay," said Sol, "we keep trying. Laura, give her a few things to read. It'll keep her occupied." Laura Collins replied, "She don't want to read, Sol. She wants to work." Laura adjusted her Hattie Carnegie pearl-gray hat and straightened her severely tailored Balenciaga suit. She wore a hat in the office, always a soft felt slouch.

Sol said, "All right, so she wants to work. Find her a property." Laura raised her eyebrows. "So then what. We going to buy it for her?" Sol thought a moment. "Nah," said Sol. "Better she should go to Lazner. That bum."

Mal said quietly, "Sol, then there's B.," mentioning a medium-rank male star.

"Natasha, find out his contract dates. Mal, relax. I know he's a problem. It's only because he wants to play Beethoven and Schweitzer and crap like that. But he's not in bad shape, objectively. Subjectively, let him go to a psychiatrist. He's got no keeping money. He falls into jobs Palance won't have. Four or five independent pictures, 65G's plus 25 per cent, like Robert Ryan, and he's got an insurance policy for life."

"Okay," said Mal, "but he's still worried. And when he's worried I'm worried. Chubbie, give me a hand next time he drops in. He likes you." Mal knew Chubbie resented him for coming into the agency after Chubbie and pulling in three times the amount of business. Discreetly, Mal shivved him, but when out in the open was magnanimous and seldom let an opportunity pass to ostentatiously give Chubbie a pat on the back. It cost him nothing and anyway you never could tell when Sol would start getting sentimental over the sons of those who had befriended him.

"Next case," said Sol.

"C.," said Jack, the resident company lawyer, a phlegmatic, unemotional negotiator who was reputed, on no hard evidence, to have won his share of the agency in a Palm Springs poker game. He was less of a lawyer and more of an agent now than any of us. "Remember how we decided to dump him last week? I asked him to come in. But one look at that mouth and I was afraid to offer him a release. I thought he'd hit me. Mal, call him and dump him."

"Thanks a lot," said Mal. Everyone laughed quietly.

"Oh, before I forget, you all know," said Sol, "that Robert Sherwood died over the weekend." Howard said, "So did Bernard DeVoto."

Les said, "Well, Princeton beat Yale."

Tony, the big ex-football player from Southern Methodist with a beautiful evangelist wife who went to the Tia Juana bullfights every weekend, said, "D., Sol. It's like butting my head against a wall." "What is it, the money?" asked Sol.

"She keeps wanting a hundred thousand," said Tony.

"Bring her down to earth," cut in Jack. "There's nobody who's a hundred-thousand-dollar mother in the business today."

"So put her back on a horse," said Sol.

Les said, "E., Sol." Sol was surprised. "What about him? I thought we were working him." "Sure," said Les. "But commissions still going to MCA, not us. Do we want it that way?" "Look," said Jack, the lawyer, "his contract with MCA expires a year from now. Let's keep him working on single stupids and then lock him up in a term contract somewhere."

"He wants a term contract now."

"So don't get him one."

"Fellas, anything for F.?" requested Mal. Round the room a series of negatives from twenty agents. "Sol," said Mal, "she's a problem all right. She *hocks* me nice. But it's still *hock*ing."

"Let's put her in television," said Sol. "She's finished in movies."

"She don't want television. She hates it."

"Does she hate to live? Take her out to lunch and start insinuating. Next case."

And so it went. The problems, the dilemmas, the traffic jams, the emergencies and crises and panics. As the meeting went on, Sol's temper shortened. He grew tougher. A large part of him hated the business now that he was almost a millionaire. He thought he belonged at a higher station in life and cursed his early lack of education. About once a month he would come into my office and I would give him a list of books. The last time we had met on the street he said, "You know, kid, *Tom Jones* is marvelous. Art. I hope nobody makes a picture of it." I liked him. Considering that, on balance, I had lost him more money than I made him, he had been good to me.

In the middle of the agents' reports he burst in with a long, passionate speech about how the picture business was dying and how the agency must adapt to television. Since everyone in the room knew that the agency had had the jump gotten on it in television by rival agencies, and was fighting a losing battle, and had heard the same fervent speech every Monday for the past year, we just waited. When Sol was spent, we got down to business again.

"Metro needs two women for their new war script. Who we got?" "We'll put in G. and H." "No, we don't collect commissions on them." "Who we got?"

"Also a young boy." "Push I." "Do we collect on him yet?" "Not until January, Mr. Benedict." "Forget it until then."

"Did you mail the contract to J., Chubbie?" "No, Sol, not yet. I wanted to look at it first. His wife is a lawyer." "You're learning, Chubbie."

"Look, Sol, I did all I could to get K. into the Warners picture. Walter Buck opposed her." "I don't believe Walter Buck opposed her. He ain't got that much power any more. He's a yellow bastard."

"They don't like L. at Universal. I can't give him away."

"M., she's like A., a *kluge*. I can't handle her cursorily."

"C'mon you fellas, you ought to go to U.J.A. dinners. We do lots of business there."

"N.?" "She's happy. Don't want to work." "But I want her to work."

"O. just got a face lift. Eyes, ears, mouth and nose. She says she looks very pleasant now, and will we try again?"

"UA provides fifteen thousand dollars. P. gets fifty thousand and fifty thousand deferred, guaranteed five weeks, our choice director fifteen thousand same guarantee."

"I told you once, I told you twice, don't solicit new clients on company stationery. It ain't legal." "Sorry, Sol."

"Q. calls me every day, no small talk, just, 'What's doing kid?'"

"R., he's a bum and no use us kidding Paramount. Get him eight weeks at seventeen-five and five thousand deferred and we're all happy."

"Laura, advise S. to tell Roger Orr he hates the book. Orr don't trust nobody who doesn't insult him."

"Honestly . . ."

"Frankly . . ."

"Sincerely . . ."

"A thousand a week." "Laura, how'd you do it?" "Twisted his arm, that's how." "One thousand. Laura, you're a sweetie."

"Braverman wants T. to make p.a.'s." "Fuck 'im. Ruin his career. What's in it for him?" "Money. Braverman will pay." "That's different. Find out how much."

"You all know, it's the artists who are the crooks, not us. Steal, steal."

"I read the script. What do you want me to say, Sol?" "Say what you want. It's a fine script."

"Let's dump him too, Sol. He's a cryer. Oh what a whiner. *Grizzuhs. Grizzuhs* alla time. Talks about the past. I been there. I don't want to talk about it."

"Tell him eighteen days. He won't check it."

"Naw, it's not horseshit, whoever said that?" "I read the damn thing." "Okay, so?"

"He's a bum. I wouldn't let him step into the office. Phony!"

"I gave him the pitch right there in front of the MCA agent."

"Cohen is vindictive. Three and a half years to go on the contract; the boy's in a cage. He's *dead* dead."

"U. A nize boy. Devious."

"You just can't relax, fellas. Inscribe it on your hearts."

"Mike Connolly called, Sol. Asking questions about V.'s politics. What'll I tell him?" "Screw Connolly. The heat is wearing off. No, be polite. Tell him to talk to V.'s lawyer, we don't know nothing about politics around here. I'm giving a sigh, fellas. Lemme tell you about these Communists. I wish I had them back. Best writers, best guys, best commissions, worked steady month in and month out. Who cares who they gave their money to. One day we lost all of them because of creeps like Connolly. Best guys. I'm giving a sigh, fellas."

"W., Sol. They won't hire her unless they screw her or think they can. I told them no chance." "There's always a chance." "Ah, why don't they merge with Polly Adler."

"How you going to sell X. to RKO?" "How else? Spit like crazy."

"The only way to be completely honest is to cheat him without his knowing it."

"You made the deal, Chubbie. Now live with it."

"He won't slim down, Sol. Sings better fat. Hell of a thing, got to shoot right away."

"Y. should see the loony picture. Take him with you. No, better not. Too close to home."

"He wants to believe things, always looking at the sky. A liar."

"Anybody with a low handicap can get to him."

"Somebody's lying, Mal." "Somebody's always lying, Sol."

"Z., how come we can't move her, fellas? Who's asleep?"

"A^2 is bitching me. I took him to lunch and romanced him — " "His last picture he was lucky to be taken to lunch."

"Can't budge her, Sol. Got great loyalty to Bartlett." "They messing around?"

"They got to pay for first look at the book. Make everything off the record. But get an offer."

"I told B^2 it was great." "Did you read it?" "Of course not."

"We're playing a little poker game."

"Just keep working on him, he'll plop."

"All about psychoanalysis and crap. Very interesting. Sell, yeah, sell good."

"Will he back us up?" "Yeah. To the wall."

"A giant is a cockroach compared to him."

"You're absolutely right, Sol."

"Thank you, Chubbie."

Sol made his final pitch about television and then, a little tiredly, said, "Okay fellas." The meeting broke up. Some of the boys came around to ask about my health, and I asked after their families. Laddie grinned disagreeably, "Wish *I* could get sick for a month."

I said hello to Natasha, shook hands with Sol and went upstairs to the third floor. I opened the door to the waiting room and went through it as quickly as decency allowed. I kept my eyes straight and blank, as if passing pustulated beggars. This time of the morning

his wife Leonie." To the Plodgetts he said, referring to me, "My colleague used to be a distance runner. He knows all about you and has spoken to me of your records."

Howard was a nice guy but he could spitball with the best of them, not with the suave geniality of the money boys downstairs but with his own special brand of quiet, tidy lies. I didn't know Plodgett from Adam. I shook hands with Plodgett and his nervous, pretty wife, telling them what a pleasure it was to meet them and had the Plodgetts, I asked, attended the recent NCAA decathlon elimination at the Coliseum, which was the way I guessed Howard wanted me to start in on Plodgett. One of the things you had to be in the agency was quick on the uptake so that when you walked into a room containing a client or a prospective client you gave the immediate impression of having for the past twenty-four hours been utterly absorbed in his welfare. Howard always said it was okay to do this because it was no skin off anybody's nose and made everyone feel good. When I first came to the agency I used to argue about it but then I saw his point. Right now, Plodgett was visibly preening because he thought I knew who he was, or had been, and he said no, he and his wife had been to a temperance convention in Omaha last week and had missed the Coliseum event. He didn't, he said, get as much chance as he would have liked to go to track meets, doing the Lord's work. I smiled with blank earnestness and remembered who he was. Vincent Plodgett, prewar Olympic 220-low hurdle, 440 and dash man who had been one of Rickenbacker's Tokyo raid boys, got shot down over Manchuria, spent half a thousand days in a prisoner-of-war camp, escaped, fought some more, took to drink, got saved by Billy Graham and had just written a book about himself.

Howard said, "We've been fortunate enough to sign Mr. Plodgett to a representation contract. We were just talking about what price to put on *Mercury Fallen*." This was Plodgett's book. It had not been a best seller but hadn't done too badly, considering a literary market glutted with God, and when one or two of the film studios had put out feelers Howard had jumped in to wrap up rights. Howard sober, which was often, was quick on things like that. A representation contract meant that he had had to buck competition from other agencies; to get Plodgett to sign he had promised that we would sell him as a writer on the picture of his book. This was always untrue. The last thing producers wanted in their hair when they bought a book was to have the original author around, particularly corn-fed amateurs like Plodgett. At purchase time, if it ever was, things could become slightly unpleasant when the author found himself boxed out. After trying several formulas, Howard and I had agreed the one that worked best was to get tough and lay it on the line to the author, did he want a sale or not? They always came around. But first we all had to go through a song and dance.

Obviously Plodgett and Howard were new to each other because Plodgett was doing a lot of loud talking without including any of the facts of life. How he wanted only Gregory Peck to star, and Director So-and-so because he was a temperance man, and how he, Plodgett, had worked out a first-draft screenplay flashing back before titles to an incident in his father's life. Howard just stood there, with Mr. and Mrs. Plodgett in two easy chairs, nodding in his understanding, calm way. He was plastered. I didn't know how. At the meeting downstairs he had looked okay, and that had been only fifteen minutes ago. It was impossible but there it was. Not that Howard could be detected. He always did it with vodka, never slurred and never took liberties. You had to know Howard to tell.

Plodgett was going on, how much the book meant to him, how important it was to have a film made worthy of the theme of a man's regeneration, all that. I interrupted and asked Plodgett if a minimum price had been set on the book. He frowned.

"I'm not one of those who pretends money is nothing," he said, "but the spiritual aspects have to be looked at." I told Plodgett I was not one to lose sight of the spiritual aspects.

Mrs. Plodgett said something. "My husband," she said, "is extremely involved in the spiritual aspect of that book." She had the pronunciation of a five-and-dime salesgirl and was very pretty in a staring, thin way. I assured Mrs. Plodgett that the agency shared her reverence.

Several things struck me about the Plodgetts. He had the eyes of a fanatic, and she kept saying "spiritchool." We got around to talking about Plodgett's personal life. He said that his first "profound experience" had been in a solitary-confinement shack in Manchuria which he shared with a man who was now a sanitation engineer in Kenosha.

"Oh, and that's something I wanted to bring up," he said, "about Walter the man in this Jap shack with me. It was one of those contraptions where you couldn't stand up or sit down. Hot. Also worms and Death Watch beetles in there. It seems he's making to sue me if I make this picture without getting his say-so." "How much will he settle for?" asked Howard. "Oh, he doesn't know," said Plodgett. "Oh yes he does," said Mrs. Plodgett. "Ten thousand dollars. I talked to him on the phone," she said.

"Well then," said Howard, "we'll simply tell the producer, whoever buys it, to cut out the solitary-confinement sequence."

"Oh, you can't do that," protested Mrs. Plodgett.

"I'm afraid she's right there," assented Plodgett. "Like I said, that was my first profound experience and why no picture about me would make any sense at all without that put in it. No sir." Howard looked at me and we all talked about this man Walter from Kenosha for a while, and Howard promised to write and try to use reason. "Reason hmph," said Mrs. Plodgett. Mr. Plodgett went back to the spiritual aspects. How he had married the present Mrs. Plodgett when she was an heiress in Texas, had gone off to war, and when he'd come back started beating up on her.

"He used to beat me terribly, didn't you, Vincent?" said Mrs. Plodgett. "Yes I did," said Plodgett heartily. "I was just plain no good. Drank like a fish. Three, often four quarts a day. Leonie over there paid, I didn't do a stitch of work for two years, and when she wouldn't buy my drinks why I'd just whup her."

"Yes," said Mrs. Plodgett.

He went on some more, describing the spiritual aspects of his past, how he stumbled into a tabernacle and heard Billy Graham for the first time, how he went back home and smashed all the whiskey bottles until his hands bled and then searched through the city until he found Billy Graham in his hotel room. "Right there in that hotel room Mr. Graham and I knelt to pray and I took the pledge. I grabbed hold of Mr. Graham's lapels so hard I got blood all over his suit, but he didn't seem to mind a single bit. Now I go all over the country giving talks against drink. I got a dull response with my first talk. I tacked on a new ending and now they pat me on the back and . . . don't give me whiskey for Christmas presents."

Howard and I laughed politely. I started to ask Plodgett what new ending he had tacked on to his talk, I get interested in such matters, but Howard cut me short. I had performed my function of letting the client know that more than one agent in the office was interested in him. I left Howard's office as the Plodgetts were beginning to ask some surprisingly astute questions about motion picture studios.

When I got back to my office I found a list of phone calls I was supposed to make back to people who had called me. I settled down to it. The first was a writer, Cullen Pope, who shouted, "I've been waiting a month and a half to tell you I'm leaving the agency, honey, unless you find me a job in seven — s-e-v-e-n days." I told him to cool off, it was a slack period. I didn't much like Cullen and I didn't much like going out to find him work, but I had brought him to the agency, in fact he was my first big catch and I felt a responsibility. But it didn't make me like him any the more. The second call was to a producer married to the star we had discussed at the downstairs meeting whose face had been lifted. The producer wanted me to find a story for her.

"Get me a story," he demanded, "where this guy walks in and slaps the shit out of her in the first scene but we don't know why. See?" The third call was to an old friend of mine, Louis, who was back on a studio shooting floor after eighteen months at Chino minimum-security for trying to solve it in the early mornings by stealing cars he didn't need. I liked Louis and his wife. We had been to college together. Now, courtesy of a psychiatric parole, he was a "grip" at the studio where he had once been an assistant director. It was Louis' idea of "how to fight back." He was writing an article, on commission, about what it was like, for the *Readers' Digest.* Louis had submitted a western screenplay to me some time ago. He urged me over the phone to sell it hard. "I know it isn't quality," Louis said, "but I want you to go overboard for this. It's important to me. You know as well as I that it's enthusiasm that counts."

The fourth call was to a novelist whom I had taken out to the night clubs last month, on Laura's orders, when he came out on a $1500-per-week job. We'd gotten drunk and he'd told me all about his childhood in Iowa, and when he got out of the taxi he'd fallen flat on his face and getting up said, "You must detest my work." I said I did. Now we were talking long-distance and from New York he wanted to know when he could be coming back to Hollywood for a job. The fifth call was to a director at Paramount who had come over to my apartment a couple of weeks ago to ask my advice on an anti-Red story the studio wanted him to do. He was a House Committee testifier, including the name of the first man to give him a job in Hollywood. Up at my place he had told me he wasn't so much worried about the anti-Red angle but there was a Mexican kid in the story and he wanted to know would the agency back him up if he shot a story which also included anti-discrimination. Now he was merely asking after my health. I made a few more calls and then went into Laura's office for a talk. She and Stanley, the head of the television department, who owed me $33 which Howard said I would never see, were hiding in her office, with the blinds down, and peeking out the windows dodging a rival agent who was coming over to settle a four-way hassle with NBC. It was a delicate situation and would remain so until somebody's lie proved weakest. Laura and Stanley were skulking around, signaling to someone outside. Buzz told me they were barred to all visitors, especially the rival agent, who was representing NBC. It was a little complicated because he had once worked for the Benedict agency and knew Laura's style. Nobody had much time for me, they were still crouching around and lifting the blinds and making hand signals, so I told Buzz to tell Laura to let me know when she was free.

Christopher, the Negro handyman who had been working for the agency for eleven years and made $58 a week, was in my office, amiably moping about with a broom handle. He had once been an athlete but was beerbellied now. Once, I used to try to get him to join NAACP, but we never talked about much now except jazz. Christopher had a dream of forming his own combo. He hung out at Joel and Andy's garage across the street. We schmoozed around, and then a client burst in from the corridor. I hated that but there was nothing much I could do. Christopher gave me a big daddy-o wink behind the client's back and dozy-doed out.

This client was a big-money woman — $2000 a week on a guarantee — with whom I had a relationship of sorts. The bohemian daughter of a lumber town baron, she was now commercial, pinched. I made my first reputation in the agency by bringing her back to the fold after she strayed. I did it mainly by talking Thackeray with her. It was just that she was temporarily sick of illiterates. I am not outstandingly literate, but Thackeray was "my" man at college. The office believed I had saved her for us by spitballing and I never disenlightened them. Her name was Amanda Schorr. She had a reputation because she had worked on expensive pictures and because of her money. But she was always in trouble owing to being such a slow, unimaginative worker, and we usually had difficulty finding her a job but we always did because, in the last resort, a producer knew that any script done by Amanda would hang together.

She was in a good mood. She was working, at an independent, true, but working. She had with her a tall broad-chested young man with a blunt *sabra* face whom I recognized as a New York writer brought out to do the latest Jimmy Dean but who had been switched over, after the accident, to a Sal Mineo. I had tried to get him with a $750-per offer but MCA lapped me with this Dean story for twice the figure. Amanda suggested we all go to lunch. I made two more phone calls, one to an agent to warn him that the client he was romancing had another five years to go on his contract with me and he, the agent, would be working for nothing, the other to a producer at Allied Artists to say that the author refused to climb down on price, which was embroidering it only somewhat.

I ducked my head in Buzz's office and asked if Laura was free. Buzz said, "They're still in there playing cowboy and Indian." I said what I had could wait.

We went down in Amanda's car, a modest little Oldsmobile Eight with electronically operated everything, but had to drop the New York writer off for a psychiatrist's appointment. On the way we had been talking about the tattoos on the writer's wrists. I recognized them as pachuco gang marks, and the writer had said yes, he had had himself tattooed in order that he might share a deeper empathy with the boys in his script. Even so, he wasn't half bad, that writer, and I was sorry he wasn't joining us.

We lunched at Gingirelli's on Hollywood Boulevard. I had liver and onions, Amanda ordered some special soup, some special toast, and a weird salad. She was a finicky eater. What she really had invited me out for was to read a novel for her and backstop her judgment on whether to buy it. Like many Hollywood writers, she had run out of ideas and was now in the business of buying books to adapt. We talked about the novel, and then she talked about how she got started in pictures. Shortly after Pearl Harbor, a famous director, then a newly commissioned colonel, had come all the way out from Washington to get her into an Army film unit on the basis of the one and only novel Amanda had ever written. The Colonel had then promptly forgotten Amanda but Amanda said she learned a lot from the Colonel doing menial jobs on location for a documentary about treatment of combat fatigue. I had seen the film in college. It was the best, least compromising film the Colonel made, then or since. I am told the War Department refused issuance to civilians. Amanda spoke at considerable length about her respect for the Colonel, "who taught me to revere life," about her compassion for mental patients, about the pitiable state of mind of the crew shooting the picture. In the middle of her telling me how much she loved the Colonel and the ordinary man, the waiter came by with the wrong salad and Amanda screeched out of her seat, "You stupid man! That's the second time you made the same mistake!" When the waiter went away, Amanda told me how much she pitied the Digger Indians of California, about whom no film had ever been written. Amanda said she was dreaming up one now.

After lunch I went back to the office by taxi. All along Hollywood Boulevard there were big signs in drugstore windows: WE HAVE MILTOWN. I asked the driver if he'd made his nut for the day and he glared at me as if I were from the vice squad. Except for the secretaries, the office was completely empty when I returned. The agents were all making their rounds. Buzz told me that Laura and Stanley were off somewhere and Laura wouldn't be back until later. I talked with Lucy, leaning my elbows on her desk. Then I gave her the day off. She didn't want the day off and gave me a peculiar look but I told her to take it anyway. Then I went and locked myself in my office. It was quiet, with the blinds drawn and everyone but me on their rounds.

I sat for quite a time, thinking about things. Then I picked up the phone and asked Estelle to give me a line to Oscar Bush, the story editor at Worldwide Studios. As soon as he got on he started spieling, which was what he always did with agents to get them off balance. Oscar lived with two uncles and took kickbacks from writers he hired and, unlike story editors elsewhere, was an important man on the lot. "Y'know, this play, *The Bad Seed*," he said over the phone. "Never'll make a movie. Why not, let me tell you why not. Because the people in the small towns will throw rocks at it. You cannot attack the sanctity of the home and get away with it. And the same goes for the story you tried to sell me—" Oscar, I said.

"Yes, what is it?" he replied.

Oscar, if I see you again I'm going to knock the crap right out of you. I hung up. I must have had a smile on my face for the next ten minutes.

Next I pulled out a piece of paper and carefully wrote down a list of people in Hollywood I wanted to say goodbye to. I gave the list to one of the girls outside and asked her to keep the calls coming. There weren't many. Just a few special people. A censor over at M-G-M, the story editor at Warner's, a secretary who'd worked at Republic for eighteen years and whose name really *was* Jane Doe, a studio guard at Hal Roach, a feisty old woman reader at Columbia, a venerable agent at Famous Artists, the head waitress at the Universal commissary, the assistant story editor at the same lot and an actor at Fox. The people who had been nice to me. Just as I got through with the calls, I could hear the agents, one after another, tumbling back into the office, slumped (I knew) exhausted, fiercely figuring. Several people tried my doors but I had them locked. I sat back and thought some more. I smiled off and on, like a neon sign, and I couldn't seem to stop it. I sat and thought. Then I reached out and placed both hands, palms down, on the double row of interoffice buzzers stapled to my wall. I picked up the intercom and listened to the agents in the other offices say "Hello? Hello," a score of querulous, fatigued, wondering voices skimming into each other. I used to do that sometimes when I was bored. I listened to the agents say hello to each other and then put down the intercom to carefully make out another list. I had to think about this one. I wanted to remember all the women I had slept with in the past six months or so. After I made out the list, I put the phone on "private" and dialed the numbers myself.

Then I called a few more numbers, the secretary of the Citizens' Committee to Preserve American Freedoms, on whose board I occasionally sat; Alain, a kindly young homosexual tart who was an "inker-in" for Walt Disney; an old friend at North American Aircraft; a French horn player I hadn't seen in about a year; Gorman my agent protégé, and some poker buddies. They weren't all in and where I could I left messages. When I went out into the outer office-well it was loud and busy, all the agents on the phone or dictating memos. I walked all the way back to Howard's office where he broached this idea once again, his pet idea of a burial ground at sea. He had been a PBY pilot in the war and he couldn't get it out of his head that millions were to be made because many people, he felt, wanted to be buried under water. I told Howard I was clearing out and he said he was sorry to be hearing it. We shook hands. I went out and into Laura's office. Buzz called through and said Laura might be held up at NBC until six or seven. I didn't feel like waiting that long, so I wrote a note and left it on her desk. Then I went into my office, collected a few of my things and went down to my car.

I drove out of the agency parking lot, crossed Santa Monica Boulevard north up to Sunset, then slowly west. I turned up Tigertail Road, past the movie star mansions, weaving in and out of the fretwork of twisting roads and streets in that part of Beverly Hills, until I came to Rio de Oro Road and took it to the top, where the cemetery is. I parked under some eucalyptus and folded my arms over the steering wheel and rested my chin. It was about six in the evening and very hot. I had my coat and tie off on the seat beside me. From where I was parked on the hill under the tall flat trees I had a view of the university, my old university. It was spread out on green lawns, sloping easy lawns, the rust-colored neo-Renaissance buildings casting shadows on the square stone quad. I hadn't expected to see many students around but there were. I remembered it was Registration Week. The campus was larger, and the new buildings more modern, than when I was enrolled. In the athletic field scrub teams were scrimmaging. I sat and stared at the university for a long time. Then I started up the car, rolled down to Sunset Boulevard and crossed it. I parked behind Haines Hall and got out and walked around. It was a Southern California dusk, and everything was dark now. Most of the students had gone home. I walked up to where The Gully had once been, to the various class buildings I remembered. I saw nobody I had known, of course. By now it was too dark to recognize anybody. The people I passed were just dark forms. I stood in the center of the quad and then I went back down the hill to Haines Hall and tried to get in the back door. None of the doors were locked. I ducked behind a pillar on the loading platform to let Tex, the custodian, pass. I waited until I heard him go through the kitchen door out back. Then I went upstairs, through the women's lounge, to the offices of *The Daily*. The entire building was deserted. I went into the editor's office and didn't turn on any of the lights but stood at the window and watched where the sun had gone down. In the little cubbyhole next to the editor's office the A.P. machine hummed and bumped. I sat down in the editor's chair, behind a vintage Underwood typewriter, and draped my leg over the typewriter rest. That was the way I used to think and write my editorials. The carillon in the tower of Luther Burbank Hall up the hill struck nine o'clock. I got up and went back downstairs. As I was getting into my car Tex came onto the loading platform and shouted, "Hey you!"

In the afternoon, the next day, I met Alain for lunch at Scandia's. Every three or four months we came together like this. Actually, we had a great affection for one another, but the way we lived could not stand the strain of seeing each other more often.

Lunch with Alain was always fun. He was very courteous and charming and filled me up on gossip. Alain was a very nice boy, by standards of his kind, I am told. He was Dutch, and always superbly, extravagantly dressed. Today he had on beltless black trousers, a red waistcoat cross-hatched with red and silver seams, a pale yellow shirt with a string tie and an expensive-looking blue jacket. I loved Alain's clothes. He could get away with anything. Whenever we met at parties we were always happier to see each other than anyone else, but as I said the different ways we lived our lives made anything more impossible. Alain was what I guess you might call a whore. He lived in the swimming-pool house of a successful garment manufacturer who paid his bills and didn't make too much of a fuss whenever Alain went off to the other boy who kept him. Alain and I never talked about the way he lived. He had been selling himself, more or less, ever since the war. He was not beautiful, except in his body which was always tan and lithe; he had a moon face and wore spectacles and I had never seen him do an unkind thing. I wore specially for lunch the $90 beige cashmere jacket Alain had given me. Manufacturers often favored him with clothing in exchange for his appearing in their product at social occasions, and if the cut wasn't perfect or the fabric stupendous he would pass it on to his friends, including me. He always said I wore clothes like an ape, but I knew my wearing the cashmere jacket pleased him. A couple of months ago Alain and I had taken two girls up to Yosemite. The girl Alain had taken had been in love with him. She was an heiress and was trying to marry him. We had spent three days in a double room in the mountains. Alain had been amiable with the heiress but the weekend almost ruined her. In some ways she had been a splendid girl. She did nothing to spoil our weekend.

Over whiskeys, I told Alain that he should stop seeing the heiress, who was also a good friend of mine. Alain said that he liked her as a friend. He said, I don't take money from her, or love from her. I told him he was breaking her up. He said surely I was exaggerating. He did not, he said, make that kind of friend very easily these days, and he did not like the idea of giving her up. I said that at the minimum he should not promise her anything in a moment of weakness or affection. Alain was a very affectionate boy. He smiled that grave, fond smile of his and promised he would not promise her anything. When we got up after lunch, he said, That's a nice jacket but you look terrible in it. We shook hands and he said if I ever got to Holland I should look up his brother in Utrecht. I said if I ever got to Holland I would.

In the evening I gave a party for myself at the house of Joan Buchanan. Four or five days before, by mail, I had asked some people to come to my party. Some were those I knew now; others I hadn't seen in a long time. About thirty people came.

None of them was sure about why I was giving the party, but neither was I except that I wanted to get them all into a room, the people who had been most important to me, one way or another, so that I could look at them. Maybe I wanted to say something to them. Before the party, I had composed a little speech, saying that I was going away for a while and why I was going away, but of course I didn't give it. The people came and we drank and talked and then they went away.

About half of them were people I knew from Hollywood, and half of them political friends. The Hollywood friends took it like any other party, and had a good time and left early. The politicals were extremely formal, though not unfriendly considering that several of them weren't on speaking terms with me. Of course we didn't talk politics. You don't talk war to the shell-shocked. They knew I had invited them to this party because I wanted to get acquainted again, and they knew that they would probably have to learn to go to many such parties as this, and for some of them, like Daisy Hanberry and her husband, it was something of an experiment.

Daisy was a top-drawer Red in Los Angeles, a big and homely woman with the largest feet I ever saw on a woman. She was a professional youth leader, one of those thrown up by the National Youth Administration back in the thirties. When the campus Reds used to climb up my back, on my opportunism or chauvinism or whatever it happened to be that month, I used to go to Daisy, who controlled them, and ask her, in a kind of a joke, both of us smiling, to get them off. The joke was that neither of us ever admitted, openly, that she was the boss. For a few months, in fact, when all the others in L.A. were retired into jail or hiding, she had been King Kong. She could never quite get it out of her head that blood was not about to run in the streets, but otherwise she wasn't so bad. I liked her husband a hell of a lot. We got along pretty well. He had been a metals stress man at North American Aircraft and on his way to what I believe is called managerial eminence when he met Daisy who persuaded him it was immoral. He had given up his job, and gone into book selling and married Daisy. He even joined the party for a few months but had to get out because of his sense of humor. How those two, Daisy, with her lumbering unsmiling personality, and her husband, ever got on nobody knew. I think he loved Daisy. Well, anyway, Daisy was at my party. She was drunk and staggering around looking into people's eyes and saying, "My God, all those years. My God, all those years." She couldn't talk of anything but Khrushchev's speech at the 20th Congress in Russia. Her husband was pretty embarrassed by it all. Finally she came and put her arms around me and said, "Will he ever forgive me?"

I knew who she was talking about. Kevin-John O'Sullivan, her aide-de-camp and the local Red sachem on our university campus, whom Daisy had driven out of the party for some offense like white chauvinism, which was the fashion just about then. The real reason he was kicked out was his drinking. He used to drink a bottle of hootch a day and I suppose the New York people thought he was a weak link in their security chain. But they could have done it better, instead of just one night inviting him to a meeting and the next morning there he was, without a comrade to call his friend. He went to hell fairly fast, visiting me once to say, unconvincingly, that maybe it was all for the best, at least he was reading for the first time in his life. He said, "I don't have a friend in the world any more. But I'm reading for the first time in my life." He asked me to give him a reading list, and we sat up all night while I told what I thought he should look for in each author. Then I took him to a streetcar and we shook hands. But it hadn't gone well with him. The government must have heard that he had been bounced, because they visited his employer, an insurance agency, and got him fired, then began coming around to his apartment to ask questions. The thing is, with Kevin-John drinking, and feeling lost, I wasn't all that hopeful he would keep his mouth shut. The party probably had a point there. But still they didn't have to kick him out that way. I think when they kicked Kevin-John out was when I decided they could go chase themselves. We lost all track of Kevin-John. Last I heard he was working for a sporting goods manufacturer in St. Louis.

Daisy kept slobbering on my shoulder, asking me if Kevin-John would forgive her and did I have his address so she could write asking forgiveness. I know the way I'm putting it down makes it sound awful, but the thing is, Daisy was really sincere: towards the end most of the party brass were a little out of their minds.

Her husband couldn't do a thing with her. Then Midge came over and spoke quietly to Daisy and she pacified herself. Midge was a big fat steelworker whose father owned my favorite drive-in bowling alley over in Sherman Oaks. I had known Midge since Chicago. He had just come out of jail on a trumped-up contempt charge, I thought, but he said no, I had mixed him up with someone else, he was back in circulation now because some sort of legal time limit had run out on him. I hadn't seen Midge for years. He did party work in the steel mills over near Avalon Boulevard, and like a lot of the old Chicago people was mistrustful of me. He wasn't too intelligent but was very loyal, to just about everything. Funny thing. His father, who owned the bowling alley and, in Chicago, had been a cop, had decided a long time ago that a revolution in America was in the cards and so had sent Midge, at about age seven, to Black Hills Military Academy. Nobody ever knew how Mr. Ginsberg ever maneuvered that; I think it had something to do with his having served in the same division with the Commandant of Black Hills in World War I. So Midge learned how to be an upper-class officer nine months out of the year for six years, and his father and he talked Communism for the summer vacations, and when Midge was seventeen he went into Tanks. He fought all through North Africa, Sicily and France. He was not the kind to get medals. After the war he went into the steel mills. He wasn't a militarist or anything like that, and in some ways was dopily sentimental, but he was capable of killing without crying. I had once seen him knock a Christian Fronter halfway across a street with one blow to the chest.

Midge and I tried to calm Daisy down, which she did by getting sleepy, and then her husband took her away. I said something innocuous, and Midge's wife, Lucille, spat, "What makes you think you're such an intellectual?" It embarrassed Midge. I felt foolish. But the more I tried to explain myself the harder Lucille looked and finally I said in exasperation, Oh for Christ's sake, Lucille, the ball game's over. I thought she was going to slap my face. She said, "Maybe for you it is. But not for a lot of others." And she walked away. Midge shrugged. He said, "You shouldn't have said that, old sock." Then he tried to talk politics, going all the way back to the Korean war. I said, What the hell, Midge, in another minute we'll be fighting. "Yes," he said, "I guess you're right." He said goodnight, and then he and Lucille took Daisy and her husband home.

That was the sort of party it was. I apologized to Joan for the inconvenience. I couldn't tell whether her delight over being the hostess came from one of her dexedrine kicks. Before I fixed her up with her present boyfriend, Arnold, her habit was to phone me at three in the morning to say that she was coming off the dexedrine and that she was scared. And then she would come over to my place, driven by the Negro maid Corda, and I would give her some sleeping pills and she would go to sleep next to me, mumbling like a baby.

In her own way, she was in deep too. She had been Homecoming Queen at the university and just about the most beautiful girl on the campus. When I was king she was queen.

I had neglected studies for Joan, a sorority girl from Montana who had started out to know me as a lark and a thumb-to-the-nose to Delta Delta Delta. This was when the sorority girls had orders, I mean really orders, not to have anything to do with me. They could lose activity points. That year, we didn't feel comfortable with any of our friends, and in retrospect I think it had something to do with our belief that we should feel something for each other, since our coming together was, if not natural, expected by everyone, but we never really did. We used to take long drives in the fog, especially for some reason I've forgotten, out to Ventura, away from all our friends. Half Jewish, she was in a "good" gentile sorority and feared exposure. She was not courageous but was foolhardy, riding horses on the beach and taking bets on high dives, that sort of thing. She had grown up on a ranch and could hunt, ski and ride, none of which I did. Finally Joan's family made a marriage for her to a surgeon back home in Billings. She rebelled and married the university football hero.

About a week before she became engaged we sat on the lawn outside the library and she gave me back my books, most of them Marxist, or Shaw's *Prefaces* and Morris' *News from Nowhere*. She said, If I keep on reading the books you give me I'll be spoiled for the Junior League, I'll never be able to go back. I asked her if she wanted to be a Junior Leaguer and she said no, not particularly, but what alternative did I offer? She had me there. The next week, as I say, she became engaged to this football hero. About six years later, in L.A., when I had gone to buy a sweater for my girlfriend's birthday in I. Magnin's, I met Joan again. She was in bad shape. Still beautiful, sturdy and brown, but had this very unfortunate habit of talking about her husband's sex. The thing was, she had had the same effect on me. She was unbelievably beautiful and had a blown-up magnificent figure, but nothing. Just nothing. I wondered whether it was because we all sensed this hysteria in her. Through the years she had tried all the routes: art school, nymphomania, marijuana, and for a couple of months sneaking out of the house to work as a hat-check girl in a night club. Her husband was now a corporation attorney and they had this big house in Culver

City, with a maid and a nanny and a two-car garage, just the sort of marriage she had been bred up for, A Marriage As Big As the Ritz. Well, I don't know. I told Joan at the time that she ought to face up to her folks, particularly her father, who was a bastard on wheels. Joan said she couldn't, she insisted she was waiting for him to die and didn't want the will changed. Maybe it was an alibi. She seemed all right the night of my party in Culver City. This boy I fixed her up with — not until, I hasten to add, an unfortunate weekend we had up at Lake Tahoe where I ran into this same trouble that her husband had, the first time *that* had happened to me, and I hope the last, in my life — was an old pal, five foot two inches tall, half a head shorter than Joan and looking like a bulldog genius. He was a violinist at one of the studios and occasionally with the L.A. Philharmonic. When I knew him at college he played the violin like a madman: dark, gaunt at five foot two inches, cynical. I had been in the habit of treating him like a kid brother, but when I gradually saw that he played better than I wrote I stopped that. Now I supposed Arnold was halfway to marrying Joan. It looked good. He was slow-moving and from the easy way he held himself I didn't suppose he had run into my trouble with her.

Both Joan and Arnold were a little nervous, they said, as they kept looking out the windows whenever a car went slowly past in the street. Joan's husband was going through that stage where he was threatening to shoot Arnold. I had known him in college. We had run track together.

At the party tonight, people came and people went, and after Daisy went home nobody made any more speeches. Nobody got too drunk either. Everyone was being damn polite to one another. So I never made my going-away speech. When the house was empty I told Arnold and Joan to go to bed, I would clean up, and they said, after a nice little protest, leave everything but the ashtrays and bottles. They went upstairs. Arnold came down and said if Joan's husband suddenly showed up not to get into a mix-up with him, just to call out. Then he went back upstairs. I wondered if Joan's husband would show up. I hoped not. I didn't feel like staying up all night and talking about life with a corporation attorney. I went around the rooms emptying the ashtrays and then someone came onto the front porch.

I went to the door. It was a pretty girl, not more than nineteen, who had come to the party with one of my writer friends. She asked if anyone was around and if she could help me clean up. I was feeling lonely and miserable as hell, but not nineteen. I told her to go home. Then I went into the kitchen and started washing glasses. Outside the kitchen window the garden was dark and quiet. In the cloudy moonlight I could see a cat rummaging in the barbecue pit. The house was still. I said to myself, what the hell. It had been that kind of party.

I didn't leave Los Angeles right away. For the next two weeks I thought of "putting my affairs in order" but mainly what I did was to get on a binge of personal excess. I used my apartment as headquarters but didn't stay in it much. I drank a certain amount, spent a number of nights playing poker in Gardena, all-night sessions, hung around the "Lighthouse" in Hermosa Beach listening to Shorty Rogers and Barney Kessel, and I tried going on marijuana but finally settled on two dexedrine spansules alternating with tuinals. There was not very much sex in this two-week period. I visited with a few old female friends, an Alcoa shop steward with a cleft palate and an old newspaper associate, but we just talked a lot. I looked up another old friend, a former nurse from Sawtelle who'd set herself up as a prostitute over on Bunker Hill, and we took her car down to Balboa to have shrimp Napoleon at Victor Hugo's only to find the place had burned down when we got there. On the way back to L.A., she dropped me off at the "Lighthouse" and I picked up a nice Chinese girl. We fooled around all the next day and then I went home with her to Venice, where she and some girl friends had a strange setup with some football players from S.C. I stayed there a couple of days and then left. Not so much because it was getting rough, as boring. Three or four is company, but seven or eight is a crowd.

I remember sitting up with them one of those nights and trying to explain patiently, I mean without patronizing them or anything, how the Third International might never have gone off the tracks if only they had listened to Rosa Luxembourg. I would like to have known, for instance, just what Radek and Bukharin felt when Rosa said her piece about overcentralization. I didn't know. Maybe they had said certain things. Maybe in a hundred years they would let us know what Radek and Bukharin had said.

I remember just before going to sleep on that particular night trying to tell one of the girls, not the Chinese one, that when you came right down to it, what had happened to the leadership of the Comintern was nothing less than a holocaust. Of the five people who had signed the Twenty-One Points, only Lenin had died of natural causes (I hope), the other four murdered. I kept asking this girl if the Revolution had to murder its sons as a general rule and all the time, and she seemed to think about this at least as seriously as when one of the USC football boys asked her whether she preferred the quick-kick punt or a quarterback sneak through the middle of the line on the fourth down a yard to go if you were still in your own territory.

I thought I might be able to sweat it out in The Haig or the Hula Hut, but the music in both places was dreadful. Wardell Gray was in London and Mulligan was in jail. Ory was just a clown over at the Beverly Caverns and though I knew Billie Holliday was in town at a club on Western Avenue, I didn't have the heart to go. I called up my old friend Gene, who was also my dentist. He had been a flier in the war. In 1948 Gene and I had flown over the campus in a hired Piper Cub and dropped Wallace-for-President leaflets. In 1949 he had re-enlisted in the Air Force but now he was all right. Marriage had taken the starch out of him but he was still a good man to listen to music with. We went over to Robertson Boulevard, near my house, and heard Tal Farlow. There were too many mirrors in the place. I took Gene out to an all-night drive-in bowling alley in Sherman Oaks where we threw a few lines at two bits apiece, and the proprietor and I argued about Lenin. The proprietor was a fat little toughie whose son, Midge, had been under Smith Act indictment and had come to my party. It was the view of Leon, Midge's father, that to leave the working class was to abandon it, to betray it, and if the shoe fits I should wear it. Leon was a good old boy. His bowling alley was a curious place, a hangout for the leather-jacket motorbike set but almost any night you could see a prominent Communist and sometimes his wife in there in sneakers and floppy shirt. It is the least sinister bowling alley I know.

Gene went back home to his wife and I went down to the Hotel Louisiana in the center of Skid Row where I had stayed once. I phoned the Chinese girl but she said she didn't like the section of town I was in, I should come out to her place, all the football players had gone up to play Oregon State. I drove out to Venice and stayed in the flat above a fried-shrimp joint just off the ocean for the next three days, the Chinese girl, two of her girlfriends and myself. Occasionally a sallow-faced young punk used to drop in, and sit drinking in the kitchen and cry, actually weep. He wore a shoulder holster but I never got close enough to tell if the gun was real.

On the following Saturday evening I had a social engagement.

From Venice I went over to Steve Halley's house in Benedict Canyon, the Reverend Stephen Halley, to hear my friend Marty tell about his trip to New China. We were sitting in the parlor, Steve and his wife Helga, Essie and Harold and myself, sipping wine when Marty came in, looking slimmer and fit, in G.I. trousers and a black cotton shirt he had bought in Peking.

Marty had with him three television scripts of a show he was going to do, "under the table," about a beautiful woman doctor in the Yukon. "I don't know," he sighed, "if I can ever do this kind of thing ever again." He tossed the scripts, carefully, on the couch. He sat in an easy chair and we asked him questions. He had been away for two months and had just returned the previous afternoon. The date to hear him in Steve's house had been made the day before he flew out to Hong Kong. Already he had three scripts to do. I should explain that Marty is a blacklisted screenwriter, an Australian, who has lived and worked in Hollywood for many years. For almost as long as he has lived in Hollywood he has been one of the three party spokesmen on West Coast cultural matters. He has never pretended not to be a Communist and when called before the J. Parnell Thomas Committee had been the only one of the screenwriters to reply "Yeah, what of it?" Blacklisted, he had lain back on his bank account and thought up ideas for television shows, almost all of which were successful. His latest series was called something like "Me and Her and the Little Sister." Marty was a comedy writer.

We settled down to listen.

"China," Marty said, after kissing Helga and Essie, "is fabulous. All my dreams of Communism are come true there. No kidding." Marty's voice was low and serious and wistful. "I want to take my kids there," he said. "I want them to see it. There's absolutely nothing like it, absolutely nothing." He looked at us and shook his head at us, the benighted ones.

"Well," he said, "you know the mood I left in. The Twentieth Congress had done such things to me I never thought I would survive as a Communist. I was knocked all to hell. I had believed in Communism, I had fought for Communism, and you know." This was, I knew, Marty's newest pitch, frankness with the liberals, don't hide anything, fraternity and mutual confidence on the left. He had fought with the British battalion in the Spanish civil war. He had been sent to Catalonia. After being promoted to political commissar he had sent men to their deaths. His own comrades, he used to tell us. Just plain guys like me, he used to say. He liked to say things like that in front of the wives of other men, he seemed to take a mild pleasure in it. I never knew whether to believe Marty's guilt-ridden harangues, but Essie and Helga did. "But China, China," said Marty, "has made a new man of me. You must see it. You must."

Marty declared that he had been depressed by Moscow. The porters had accepted tips. He didn't like their accepting tips. The Russians, he said, ah, I didn't swing there at all. Those tips, the bureaucracy. They almost sent him back because he didn't have an entry visa. But we should have seen them hop when he told them he had an invitation from the Chinese Ministry of Culture. "The TU-104's," Marty said, "are magnificent machines. Four hundred and fifty miles an hour. Thirty-eight thousand feet up in the air. Fantastic, in Omsk and Cutsk, the people wear the same clothes as my mother, my old Jewish mother from Russia now in Melbourne, and in Omsk there was a fleet of forty TU-104's and in Cutsk twenty." Marty shook his head and laughed. "In Moscow we got out of a Russian TU-104 and into a Chinese TU-104. The stewardess had a fly swatter in her hand and killed six flies. You know, there are no flies in China." He gave us that elaborately casual, half satiric, half Daumier-lawyer grin of his which is the unfathomable secret of his soul. "I didn't see one fly. They put a bounty on them or something."

Marty told us that he had refused a well-paying film job in Italy in order to make the trip to China, and when he had told the Chinese film officials that he was losing money on the deal, in four days, *four days mind you,* they had arranged through a bank in Geneva for funds to cover his overdraft. They paid him promptly for his work but not munificently by the usual standards, because they were so hard up for foreign currency. Press photographers and high officials of the film industry had greeted him in Peking. A girl had come forward to give him flowers.

"You know what the first thing my interpreter said to me, you guys?" asked Marty. "I went into the little building for people just coming off the plane, and there was this interpreter, the one who went everywhere with me, he stepped up to me, and do you know what the first thing he said to me was? 'We have surpassed the United States in oats production.'" Marty surveyed us triumphantly. "The very first thing," he said. The news had come out the day Marty landed in Peking.

Marty had come down with a virus in transit from Russia, and he had gone to a Peking clinic for shots. While waiting for treatment, he said, a seven-year-old boy on the same bench had looked up at him and asked if he was a Russian. The interpreter had said no, Marty was an Australian by birth. The little boy had insisted Marty was a Russian, and when Marty told the interpreter to tell the boy that okay, he was a Russian, the little boy, who was sitting with his mother, said, I am only seven years old but I want to be the first Chinese to go to the North Pole, what was the age at which this could be done and would Marty fix it up?

Marty leaned back in the chair and smiled at us. "Ah found religion," he said.

Again, I said.

"Smart guy," he replied.

Marty and I were enemy friends. He liked going around Hollywood telling people I was an FBI agent. About a year ago I had cornered him at a party and taxed him with this. Marty had grinned, sheepishly, and stuck out his hand for me to shake, saying, Ah forget it, I discussed it with my psychoanalyst and he says it was a malicious thing to do.

"You don't understand," Marty leaned forward to us fiercely. "There's going to be a great leap forward there." Several times Marty brought up the great leap forward. In production, he said, in agriculture, everywhere. "Do you realize," he said, "that in four or five years China expects Communism. Not Socialism, Communism." We looked disbelieving. "The communes," Marty said. "They're new. To eliminate the contradiction between town and country, between mental and manual labor. I visited some north of Peking. Small factories, with smelters you could put your arms around and large fields of rice."

Decentralized, I said. Much smaller targets.

"Don't give me that capitalist shit!" Marty cried. "You ought to see those rice fields. Rice so thick you could walk on it like a carpet. Fantastic. New methods. A great leap forward. They're learning. They won't make the same mistakes, you'll see. I want to take my children there."

I told Marty that while he was away Mao Tse-tung had made a speech estimating that 300 million Chinese might be lost in the next war but that it was a war China would win. Marty said, "Yes, I can say the Chinese are preparing for war. They expect a war. Just before I left, three million, gosh you should have seen them, three million people demonstrated in Peking. I was in a cab when I heard the noise of the crowd. I got out and looked. It made me a little nervous. They marched through the city. It took them all night. They don't hate the American people, mind."

Just the ruling circles, I said.

"Okay, wise guy," Marty said. "It's not like the goddamned fucking Russians. Everywhere I went a distinction was made between Dulles and Eisenhower on the one hand, and the peace movement in America, the trade unions, the masses."

Were the Chinese, we asked, interested in the American Left? Not at all, said Marty. They asked him no questions about America or England or Australia. "They're too involved in making their revolution," he said. "They weren't interested in anything else."

"What about the family?" Essie asked. "The women."

"The family," Marty said, "I don't know nuttin' about. I didn't see. But they've got no bureaucracy there, I can tell you. Three months out of the year writers, artists, managers of factories, go out to fields or factories and work. A manager makes just a little bit more money than a worker and they're going to keep it that way, I have confidence. The women, that's interesting. I never thought

Chinese women were beautiful. But boy, and how, are they! But I was celibate for two months. The Chinese are puritans. I was afraid to make a pass at a girl, honest. They even got jail sentences for adultery." He grinned. "Celibate for two whole months.

"The big news, though, is that it runs sideways. Ha, ha." We suffered patiently while Marty made a few jokes like that. Marty had been wounded in Spain by an Italian mortar shell which had burned him and gave his nose and lips a roasted flattened appearance.

I asked him if the writers or factory managers resented going out to work a quarter of the year. On the contrary, Marty said, they loved it. "It strengthens their ties with the people," he said. "It gives them something to write about. One of the writers he says, to me, 'You know, you have periods when you just don't write.' 'Sure,' I said. 'The three months,' this Chinese writer says, 'with the people enriches our lives, prevents barriers.' "

I said, what if the three months comes at a time when the writing is going well? Marty said, "Cocksucker.

"Oh yeah," Marty resumed, "I ran into Chou En-lai. In an elevator. My interpreter told him what my work was, and we got off on the ground floor and talked for about twenty minutes.

"Chou," said Marty, "is a real sweet guy. A wonderful smile. I asked him about the possibility of war. He said, unfortunately there is a distinct possibility of war. He said they would fight for Quemoy and Matsu. On Formosa he indicated they could wait."

We got into an argument with Marty. He said the Chinese were girding themselves for war but that Mao's occupation of one thousand miles of territory in northern Burma was not meant as a provocation. I said none of us in the room disputed Red China's claim to the offshore islands, but that Burma was altogether a different matter, and we just wondered about the timing of the bluff, if bluff it was. "It ain't no bluff," Marty said proudly. "Those people will fight. The party is preparing them for nuclear war. They expect to lose half their population but they are convinced it will mean the end of America, and of capitalism."

"Oh jolly," Harold muttered.

"Well, yes," said Marty. "The Chinese are charming, wonderful, gentle people. But in the demonstration, for the first time I saw them angry. They were really angry. How long do you think they can go on having their people killed by Chiang's shells?" he demanded angrily. Sure, I said. Helga, Steve's wife, said, "Gentle? Have you ever read *Man's Fate?*" Which one is that? asked Marty.

The people of China, Marty said, love the Party. He didn't, he said, see the jails or ask about them. "For the first couple of weeks I asked just the questions you are. Remember my mood. Twentieth Congress, you know. But then I stopped asking questions. You just don't know what it is. Miracles are taking place.

"At first, me too, I asked about civil liberties and all that. But nobody seemed very interested." And then he said he saw that these questions were irrelevant beside the fact that the people of China who had once starved now have enough to eat. Jesus Christ, Marty, I yelled, in another minute you'll be talking about mistakes and errors. "You're falling for the crap, boy," he said.

When he asked about Ting Ling, the "rightist" writer, he was taken to meet her. "She said to me," Marty said, "that she had been mistaken about some things but that she still felt she was right about other things. And she was writing. And they were publishing her. And she wasn't in jail."

Essie, who was a part-time teacher in zoology at the university, said, "She was a while back."

"I don't know anything about that," said Marty. "She wasn't when I saw her. She said she could write freely and be published." Did you talk privately to her? I asked. "No, it was at a big party." "Civil liberties, the opposition," he said, "don't make too big a thing of it. It was explained to me that the people in opposition had been reconditioned, most of them had come from the old way. And what difference does it make anyway? What does it matter, artists, writers, let them drop dead today, the people of China are eating." (Marty himself had done one novel in the thirties and then ceased serious writing.)

We asked more questions. He could give no figures but would, he said, give us literature he had brought back. "The communes will bring Communism," he assured us. "It will pop up all over the place, first here, then there. Wait and see. From each according and all the rest of it. Wait and see if it doesn't. There is no coercion. The people love the Party. Everybody is too busy for nonessentials. It was beautiful, fellahs, just plain beautiful. I want to take my kids."

"What about psychoanalysis?" asked Helga. "They don't have it in China, do they?"

Marty grinned ruefully and slumped in his chair, suddenly a more familiar Marty. "Well, Helga, you know, not everything is perfect." We all laughed. Marty said, "I must get my psychoanalyst to go there. It would help him. That was funny. I tried talking about psychoanalysis to the Chinese and nobody was interested. I even told them about my mama and papa and nobody was interested. Wonderful country.

"But fellahs, one thing I'm telling you. I came back determined to rebuild my links to the working class. The American working class. I don't know how yet. Maybe I'll join the Democratic Party. Gosh, I'm sleepy. You people ask the same questions I did. Then after two weeks—boom, no more questions. I want to take my kids there."

When Marty left Steve's house, Helga said, "Marty forgot his scripts." I ran down the path to give the scripts to Marty starting his Buick convertible. He gave a little laugh and said, "Those. Well, I suppose I'm back, eh kid."

Then he drove away.

I returned to Venice, and on a Sunday afternoon I went to my apartment and packed. I called some friends and told them to come in next week and take anything they wanted, and then I called Lucy and told her she could take possession any time after tomorrow and not to worry if people she didn't know descended and walked out carrying things. I called my closest woman friend but she was having an affair with a studio publicity man so there wasn't very much to say. Then I called Esmeralda, the tutor of Lucy's kid.

Esmeralda and I had been to college too. She had a dry, mature, analytical mind; we used to dispute issues. After college, she had "gone into industry" and then she started teaching in a high school, which is what she wanted to do. Esmeralda and I had never been close, she had never trusted me politically, which for her meant personally, so when she showed up one afternoon at my apartment during my illness I was surprised. She had always been, as a matter of pride and basic nature, taciturn but that day she talked her head off. She told me she had dropped by on her way from her psychotherapist, a boy named Alvin who had also been in the college gang. I knew Esmeralda was embarrassed to tell me she was going to a psychiatrist; one of the few things that united us in the old days was our jokes against it. I had asked her why she was going and she said that she had fallen in love with a fifteen-year-old student and couldn't get him out of her blood, and had broken off her engagement to one of the gang. (We intermarry in our lot.) The way Esmeralda and Alvin (his psychiatrist) worked it out, Esmeralda had a power complex. I told Esmeralda I wasn't sure I bought that but she gave me one of those hooded, wise wait-until-it-happens-to-you looks, and what could I do? In the old days she never would have done that. Up in my place she had talked a blue streak until we were interrupted by Gorman, my agent-protégé who had insisted on hanging around. That afternoon was the last I had seen of Esmeralda. I got her on the phone now, but she was cold and hostile. I told her to give my regards to Harris, her fiancé, and she said she would.

About midnight I phoned Maurice and Julia Lathenas, a young French couple introduced to me by Hollywood friends. Before I had fallen ill, the Lathenases and I had gone around together. They were in America on vacation. I had given them the tour around L.A. introducing them to factory workers, and they had invited me to come to Paris some day.

I spoke to Maurice and asked him if he still wanted someone to drive his rented red-and-white convertible to New York. He said yes he did, he and Julia were going out by plane. I told Maurice I would drive it for him, tomorrow morning, would he leave the keys in his mailbox? He asked me if I wanted to come over for a drink, and I said no, I'd see them in New York. Julia came to the phone, and then Maurice agreed he would leave the keys. I packed my things and lugged them out to my car. Then I sat up in my apartment all night. Near dawn, I phoned in a telegram to my friend Henry, telling him he could have my car which would be parked outside the Lathenas place in Beverly Hills.

The De Soto convertible was parked on Doheny Drive. As promised the keys were in the mailbox of the rooftop garden apartment which the Lathenases were renting. Without waking them,

I wrote them a note, thanking them for the car. Then I went downstairs and transferred my baggage from the Pontiac. I left it standing there on Doheny Drive.

It was a dark, cool Los Angeles dawn. I decided not to take Sunset Boulevard past the university out to the beach highway. All that was over now. I went west on Olympic Boulevard to Westwood without stopping through mist and blinking traffic signals. The university was just over the rise to my right but this time I did not feel anything.

Traffic was light and fast, the boulevard almost clear of cars. The De Soto's motor was cold and it responded sluggishly but I knew it would handle better later in the day. The Lathenases had assured me that they had sent it in for a check last week.

I drove faster, past the sleeping factories, past Packard Bell where I had almost gone to work as a riveter, past the glowing kilns near Sawtelle and deserted streets and the sixty-foot-high female leg about which I had once written a story assuring all American Wire Service readers that it was a faithful replica of Marie Wilson's. I wondered if anybody remembered Marie Wilson any more. I had last seen her in a funny picture with Martin and Lewis at Loew's 72nd Street in New York. I had last seen Jerry Lewis a few weeks ago on the Paramount lot. He was playing catch with one of his yes-men and zinging the ball in, laughing all the time.

I dipped the De Soto down to the coast road. The air was deep mauve and the mountains in front of me rising out of the sand were dim mauve. The air was thin and cold. I rolled down the window to let it wake me up. I felt muffled, dazed. The air whistled past the window. Other cars whipped past me silently. Only the slow trucks made a noise. The mountains seem to fringe me in. I was leaving Los Angeles, departing a crater on the moon, unreal, an image in a half-waking dream.

The coast highway, so well remembered. Now in another context. Going away. And then suddenly the crater I am driving up is on the moon, and the moon is to my left, low now, dipping towards the water, white, iridescent, casting its pale light like something on a garage calendar. Past Will Rogers Beach, past memories.

At Tapia cut-through I stopped for a red light. The cars from the valley moved down and around past me, like an automated morain, towards Santa Monica and Venice, early-shift employees full of flesh, in new cars, going to work. That, too, I am leaving behind. I won't be going to work for a while. I want to turn around and follow them to work, to some office or factory somewhere. My gaze follows the winding road up Tapia. That is where my mountain is, the place high up above the sea on one side and the valley on the other, stupendously silent except for the strong wind and sometimes the thin voice of someone's radio in a house down in the valley. There is a bronze plaque on the pinnacle of that mountain, put there by the Los Angeles Water Board. I was shown how to get to that mountain by Jos, back in college, before she married. I used to spend a lot of time there.

The traffic signal flashed green. The moon disappeared beyond a mountain up forward. The highway was clear. I stepped up to 70. For no reason, I remembered the spot on the beach I had passed a mile or so back. I hadn't paid much attention at the time. It was just off where Sunset runs into the coast highway. I used to drink behind the rocks there, sometimes alone, and then go swimming. Once, one of the police troopers from the Malibu station walked right down to the water line and flashed his light towards me. They didn't like people swimming with no clothes on. He yelled at me. I didn't yell back, but circled around in waist-high waves and waited behind a rock for him to move away. When he did I dashed for my clothes. He never did find me. In the old days Chuck and I used to go drink in the rocks and swim at night. The girls we liked best to take had been Roy and Maxine. They had been good old girls. Chuck and I used to flip a coin for which one. Chuck is married now, living with his wife and new babies in a house in Glendale. His wife is tough and loyal, except that she gossips over the washline to the other wives and says that Chuck always wants it too much. I was sorry Chuck had to get married. He came to my place, when I was living near Angel's Flight and driving a cab, a week before he got married, to ask me if he should. The girl he had really liked he had broken with over politics. She had been a socialist from Bennington. The night he came over to ask about getting married I told him that if he waited a year or two the political situation would change so drastically that he and this girl from

Bennington would be able to make it easier. He replied that he was almost thirty-five now and couldn't afford to wait. I told him what the hell was he asking my advice for if he had made up his mind. He said that he was asking advice because he didn't love the girl he was going to marry but wanted a family. Chuck had been a Marine rifleman at Iwo Jima. We used to play football on the asphalt street outside the Co-operative Barracks near the university. He played the line with a cigarette dangling out of his Hunky mouth. I was sorry to see him getting married. We used to kill a lot of time behind those old rocks. The last girl I had taken there, while I was still a little sick, had been a freckle-faced young actress ten years younger than me. All I did was lie on the sand, and drink, and cup her fantastic young face in my hands and look at her. When she started to cry I took her home. Her mother phoned me at four that morning and raised an awful row because I had brought her nineteen-year-old girl home so late on the eve of her going to England to train at the Royal Academy of Ballet. Her father, said the mother, was of a mind to cancel the trip. We had words. Actually, I liked the mother, a rather beautiful woman who was engaged in writing an epic poem about Oscar Wilde and who was married to one of my clients. When I had been in form I never would have had anything to do with daughters of clients. It was a stupid situation but worked out. She finally did go off to the Royal Academy.

I kept the De Soto at 70 and stopped remembering. The small, slatted beach houses sped by, patches of gray ocean, mist-ridden hills, one or two highway bars. That was it. I was out of Los Angeles. Over on my right, a string of Mexican workers walking along the railroad abutment paralleling the highway. Hello, world! I waved to them but they didn't see me. Gradually, the cold cramped feeling dissolved away; the knot in my stomach unreeled at seventy miles per hour, leaving behind a spoor of vague regrets and new vows. Right out of the blue, that old on-the-road blast of exultation hit me. I was free again.

*

I switched on the car radio. A new pop song. "Que Sera Sera." What will be will be. That's right. The news came on. The commentator reported pickets fighting a truck bearing strikebreakers at a Chicago meat-packing plant. I wondered which one it was. I knew some of the union guys at Armour's. I was suddenly eager to go and see for myself. I hoped the strike wouldn't be over by the time I arrived in Chicago. I decided to visit Paul and Helen. Paul was in Chicago now and could tell me about the strike. I began to sing to myself.

Just outside Oxnard, I pulled over to the side of the road, got out my address book, satisfied myself and drove out to a yellow stucco house on the edge of town. It was a nice house, with a flower garden in front and hedges on all sides, a very respectable, prim, middle-class house.

Stirling came to the door, in his robe, sleepy and perplexed. I opened the screen door, and said, Come on out for a coffee, Stirling. He gave me a queer look and said, "It must be awfully important for six in the morning." He had me there. I said, Look, I'm leaving town, come on out for a coffee. He said, "Okay, wait in the car, I'll be right out."

It didn't surprise me, Stirling's not inviting me in. He had always been afraid of me. You see, Stirling Adams is a Negro. But a special kind of Negro. An American Negro on the make. With one difference. Most Negro fraternity boys — of whom Stirling is almost the archetype if not the prototype — aspire to the Black Bourgeoisie. Not my pal Stirling. He wants into the *white*. And he has just about done his nut, as the English say, to get in.

I first met Stirling when he was only one of several hundred Negro students at the university: clean-limbed, moderately athletic, what we call "clean cut." The kind of Negro you can invite into your home if you are one of the majority of white people with a strong but refined bias. He had a genius for inhabiting the middle ground between toadying and forwardness. He was well behaved. But he also gave off an aura of self-respect. This fooled me for a long time, until I saw that my old Stirling was nothing more nor less than a damn California politician. Mark my words, he's going to be a Congressman. He is riding the wave of the future. Perhaps I better explain what I mean.

By common assent, we Americans have made the Negro, in quotes, our Prime Moral Problem. Now to my way of thinking, this is sentimental nonsense. Assuredly, the place of the Negro in American society — and let's not kid around with euphemisms; what I mean is, the application of political, economic and moral pressures at all levels of society so as to ensure the elementary rights to all Negroes (desegregation, demiscegenation, depoll taxation, the *lot*), including the right of the Negro workers to truly enter the working class and the right of the Negro middle class to take its education where it wants to without having to pay the massive costs in neuroses and that godawful *mittelklasse* stuffiness of which they are so capable, and, yes, even if we do have to send in troops to keep the kids in school — the place of the Negro in American society is a critical problem. But it is not *the* problem. *The* problem has to do with us, the whites, and not the Negroes.

Now, among many liberals, progressive and radicals this is a gentle heresy. I think this is because the liberals (without permission, I will use this as a generic term), the liberals, unable to solve the priorities on their plate, in a cul-de-sac, have turned to the one problem that does look as if it *can* be solved within the context of contemporary American existence. Which is fine and good, and I say good luck to us. But if I may say so, humbly (don't you believe it), there are also a few small things such as the Cold War, bureaucracy and uprootedness within a compulsively competitive ethos, and in fact how the majority can live a sane and decent life in today's America which the liberal and left intellectuals have a tendency to scamp in favor of questions more easily put and easily answered. Far easier to mail money down to Reverend King in Montgomery than to stand up at your local Democratic Party meeting and suggest a rapprochement — hush! — with Red China; much easier write a letter of protest to the local daily rallying to the support of a "security risk" wrongfully accused than gather with your fellow citizens to work out the problems of unhypocritically putting military security in harness with the right of meaningful dissent (I don't think it can be done, but at least we can *try*). Far, far easier to buy a new house, a new television, a new record player than to sit back and devise how to *live* with these things when all our traditions and impulses are against it.

That's why we have this thing about the Negro now. No, not we. A great many unpolitical, unliberal and unsophisticated Americans have, in the past few years, become seriously exercised over the situation of the American Negro. I do not speak of them for theirs is a painful and innocent response to the presentation and discovery of an open wound. I mean the liberals, the ones who know something of the score. Their reasons for taking up the cause of the Negro — and often *only* this cause — is not suspect, but does bear looking into. Is it an easy way out? I think so.

Anyway, as I was saying, when the liberal chooses to block up his libido in this fashion, it is inevitable that he choose the Negro — who has been historically selected to take his place *now* anyway — his Bride of the Month. During the next few years what we are going to see in America is the emergence of another Talented Tenth among Negroes who will, really, for the first time step up on the rostrum with the whites and not be condemned in perpetuity to a sort of sociological odd-man-outism, such as Jackie Robinson, Marian Anderson and Paul Robeson have had to endure. Already, some of the younger Negroes I know speak of these pioneers with an affectionate, patronizing indulgence. It is natural.

Now, to me, one of the fascinating things to come will be the character of this new Talented Tenth. They are going to have a rough time, interiorly speaking. They can, and probably will, appropriate the characteristics of the white professional class: mortgages, moribundness, blandness, tweedy and pipe-smoking exurbanite pleasures, if so they can be called. Now, that is probably what a Polack or Mick working-class boy would do. But these new ones, they are *Negro*. They have a rich, thick, terp-smelling tradition of spontaneity, of imposed cohesion, of (enforced) community. What is the Talented Tenth going to do about that? Since 1619, when Black Anthony Johnson, the first of the "twenty and odd Negers" set foot on American soil from a Dutch ship at Jamestown, the American Negro has had three and a half centuries in which to perfect his insights into white hypocrisy. Can he lose these overnight? Somebody like my friend Stirling sure does try.

About a year after I got to the university, Stirling went out for the cheerleading team. Now, you have to understand that being a cheerleader, one of only five, at a university whose football games draw upward of 50,000 a week in season to the L.A. Coliseum, is a *serious* job. For the entire length of the game, half an hour before it also, you have got to prance up and down like a madman, with four other madmen, and try to get a horde of college and ex-college students to yell, shriek, punch the air and go through Futurist gyrations in a systematic pattern which sometimes makes me feel as if we, and not the football team, are the reasons why we come out every Saturday afternoon in the autumn. I enjoy it. But you have to admit, it is something of a pagan ceremony, with us vigorously praying at the feet of a totem whose pinnacle is a squad of eleven more or less stupid young men dressed in shoulder pads, yellow-and-white jerseys and fierce scowls. Well, if you are a cheerleader, you are a category of priest officiating at this ceremony, and if you are one of those sitting in the cheering section and do not follow the directions of this priest I cannot describe to you the glares you will get. When I first came to the university, as a matter of principle I and some of my friends from the Co-operative Barracks would muscle our way into the cheering section just so we could sit among all those vacuous smiles and saddle shoes and blazing white shirts under the hot, glaring sun and drink gin and stubbornly not cheer. It was a childish thing to do, but it had something to do with that by now forgotten phenomenon, the Campus Revolt of the Returned Serviceman, of which the less said the better, inasmuch as some of us have turned respectable, me included. One Saturday, however, we made a mistake — myself, Chuck Podolny, Joe Bishop, Zack Washburn (a Negro but a different kind), Dick Feingold, Henry Carleton, a few others — and started to cheer for Stanford, the other team. Maybe we would have gotten away with it, except that this was a Big One. The winner was to go to the Rose Bowl, to play Notre Dame. The first time we sent up a cheer for the opposing side nothing happened except that a mass of surprised empty faces turned up to us (practically everyone in the cheering section belonged to a fraternity or sorority; aside from initiation this was their ritual of rituals). The second time we did it, however, about a ton of fraternity flesh fell on us from behind. My God, there was a fight. And it wasn't over in a hurry, either. So you see what I mean about football games and cheerleaders. And that's what my Negro friend Stirling Adams became. They couldn't keep him out, even though there had never been a Negro cheerleader at our university. The reason they couldn't keep Stirling out was that he was more fraternity than the keenest "frat" boy. He was a paragon of Greek Row virtues: socially nimble, alert, "sincere," amiable, not too pushy, not too bright, not too athletic — and very, very careful not to date white girls. This latter habit of his disgusted me.

My last year on the campus I was editor of the daily newspaper and Stirling was secretary of the Inter-Fraternity Council. Between us, at least in theory, we ran the show on the student side. I say theoretically because it was an appropriations year at the state legislature, and the university administration was not about to jeopardize its relations (delicate at best) with Sacramento by permitting the student editor his traditional prerogatives. The atmosphere on campus was unpleasant. Student democracy was breathing its last, to die finally in defense of a faculty which had not the courage to defend itself against a political means test imposed by a Board of Governors so conservative as to be downright embarrassing. (Embarrassing is here an operative word. Within twelve months of my graduation one governor was refused confirmation to high public office by the U.S. Senate by reason of his deep embroilment with oil interests; another was indicted in his capacity as a senior trade union official for misuse of funds; a third governor, a Hearst editor, remained a Hearst editor.)

The moment the Governors brought out their loyalty oath you could not stub your toe on the quadrangle lawn without starting controversy. But the old cause was doomed, the ship was sinking. There were petitions, mass meetings, student strikes, suspensions. But someone in Sacramento or Washington had pushed a button, and we all sensed we would have to bend the knee sooner or later.

Stirling, and many like him, the majority in fact, did not see it this way. The university was for them a step up. If you said market place of ideas to them they nodded in a cheery, friendly way. If you said defense of free learning, they grinned as though a crypto-Communist had stepped out of a niche in the wall and whispered the words into *your* ear. It was hopeless. As naïve as it sounds, I had come to the university in order to find out what intellectual freedom really meant — in the most selfish terms, to see what was in it for me — only to arrive on the scene when freedom, in its most basic and utilitarian sense, was being butchered to death by an imposing Unpopular Front of business alumni, Los Angeles newspapers, panic-stricken administrators, Greek Row storm troops, liberals who had suddenly adopted the world view, political Governors, and an *ohne mich* student body. It was like some of the poet-tourists I had heard about who, holidaying in Spain, were thrown into the defense of Madrid before they had a chance to learn the language. That was how it was for me. No sooner had I arrived than I was pitched into a battle for the defense of something which I did not yet understand.

Stirling proved chicken-hearted in all this. By careful and well-planned stages he had progressed to the point where he could run as a candidate for Inter-Fraternity Secretary (the only student office that counted: council president was a girl and a figurehead) and receive the backing of both the campus Left and its arch-enemies, Greek Row. He was a portent of things to come, was our Stirling. I used to tell him this, in the bar on Pico Boulevard we used to go to before he became too frightened even to be seen talking to me and he used to grin, thinly, back. For a long time I thought that grin meant he knew what I was talking about; now, I don't know. As I say, I think I allowed Stirling credit for too many brains. (Much later on, in England, I was to meet a young West Indian who was so much like Stirling — except much brighter — that I sometimes had to make a physical effort to remember his name was Reg Meany and not Stirling Adams.) Incidentally, I did not vote for Stirling when he ran on a campus-wide ballot for Inter-Frat Secretary. It was what finished the campus Left with me. They said I was a "white chauvinist." But what the *hell,* Stirling was playing it so cool he would not even speak out against racial discrimination in student housing. A portent, as I say. A young, black Ike Eisenhower. Who knows — maybe some day we'll find Stirling president of the United States. Honest to God, it would not surprise me.

That last year on the campus, when we shared and almost dominated Student Activities Building, I tried to influence Stirling openly in all manner of ways. That's when he started becoming anxious about me. I used to stroll down the corridor from my office to his, vault the railing behind which his pretty sorority secretary sat, and go into his office and say something like, Say, Stirling, when are you going to start dating white girls? Or, When are you going to put in for honorary membership in the white race? It used to drive

Stirling wild, but the way he showed it was to show his teeth in a grin and ask me politely how things were going. I tried to get him moving on all sorts of issues, but he just wouldn't *move.* On anything. He wanted a nice, peaceful year as the first and only Inter-Frat Secretary in the nation who was a Negro, and then he wanted to use this as a step to business school and then to a junior-grade Ralph Bunche job with the State Department. The one thing he did not want was for anybody to rock his boat, and the one thing I wanted was to not let him get away with it. It may sound crude, or even cruel, for me to have spent so much time reminding Stirling he was a Negro, but it really killed me the way he practically *fawned* in the face of his Greek Row friends whom we both knew were racists in their hearts. Still, it wasn't so uncivilized that we didn't go drinking from time to time. Most of the time when we passed in the pleasant antiseptic corridors of Haines Hall we would greet each other almost on the sly, as if we knew what the other's game was. I knew his, but I never really knew what he thought mine was. Anyway, we had this secret, unspoken compact, the gist of which was a curious friendship. Except for the time when he became frightened, we each of us felt good to see each other.

And then of course things happened to spoil it. I led a staff newspaper strike and we won; the next term I stretched my luck just a little too far, and this time the administration abruptly stepped in to run the paper with scab fraternity boys. Stirling refused to take a hand, despite the closest thing to a popular uproar we had had on that campus since the Academic Senate, with near-unanimity, voted to acquiesce in the Board of Governors' loyalty oath. When it was time for him to vote his principles on the Student Council Stirling turned his hand against me.

At the time I felt sorry for him; I mean, I wasn't angry. I still do feel sorry for him, because afterwards whenever he saw me, he would give me one of those shameful grins such as you only see on deep South Negroes in domestic service after you've caught them in the liquor cabinet. The thing is, Stirling, no matter how deferential and white he behaved, had never before put that kind of grin on his brown, handsome face.

I wasn't the only person to be "on" to Stirling. Many of the other Negroes were; they regarded his spectacular rise with mixed contempt and respect. They suspected they would, each in his way, have to pay Stirling's cost, sooner or later. Those campus Negroes were about the only Negro group I have not wanted to be a member of; they were a fairly dull and conformist lot. Maybe they had themselves a ball when they went back home to the ghettos of Central Avenue and Watts, but on the University campus they watched their step too damn much. I know they had to. But it didn't make it any easier to be with them, and I wasn't, much.

You see, like many Americans, I would like to be part of a Negro family. Don't get me wrong. I am not like these pseudo-hip characters who immolate themselves in the Negro race which, if you ask me, really *is* Jim Crow in reverse. I know that's how most Negroes feel about it. Well, I take that back; I feel fairly certain that's how they feel. Because, no matter what you hear to the contrary, no white person in America, unless happily miscegenated, is *au courant* with either the mass, collective voice of the Negro people or the private emotions of one. Anybody who says differently is telling himself, and you, stories. I know perfectly well that it sounds somewhat fatuous to say I want to be *in* with the Negroes, but that's the truth, so help me hannah. I don't want to *be* one, just be *with* them and be accepted. I have a long, involved theory about why many Americans want to be accepted by Negroes which I do not wish to go into right here. Speaking for myself, it is because it would make life *simpler* for me. This has nothing to do with the noble savage doctrine. The Negroes I know — mostly northern people — are the most sophisticated individuals I know — or at least were until the past few years, when they began to have "opportunities." (Emotionally speaking, God help the American Negro once he starts up the Willy Loman trail.) By sophisticated, I mean they have had more time than I, and my second-generation immigrant pals, to perfect their defenses against the truncheons, rubber and figurative. Any attempt on my part to explain further must necessarily sound romantic and simple-minded, and I think I will desist here, although it may occur to me later. The thing is, Negroes live a *dense* life. That is how I once lived and how I would like to live again.

A few minutes later, Stirling came out of the house dressed in sneakers, jeans and a T-shirt, and got into the car beside me. I hadn't seen him so informally dressed in years. In fact, I hadn't seen him for about two years now, and hadn't had a serious talk with him (if we ever had one) in six years. All I knew was that he was living with his aunt and was working as a trainee executive in San Diego.

I drove out to Ventura Boulevard. Stirling was uneasy. He was wondering why I had called on him, and at that moment I was wondering the same. So I just repeated, I'm leaving town and I thought we would have a cup of coffee together. You could almost see him make the physical effort, shaking himself together to drag himself back those six years to a time when we had been sufficiently important to one another to merit this kind of gesture. (I see it as a gesture now, but it seemed natural enough to me then.)

I said, Relax, there are no petitions in the car. He didn't laugh. Well, you can't always expect the old jokes to work. And then I knew why I had come out here to Oxnard. I felt that I was giving Stirling his last chance to be a person; I felt that just by seeing me he would become suffused with the kind of heavy, pale sadness that had been my constant companion these past weeks and which his old, formidable wall of cautious amiability would not be strong enough to resist. I was, to put it mildly, probably a little crazy.

I pulled into the parking lot of an all-night restaurant, and we went in to sit at the counter for coffee. Stirling was still suspicious but not cold. Patronizing, if anything. I didn't mind. He always used to do that, because he always thought I was trying to recruit him into something.

I asked him about himself, and he mumbled something. I said, For Christ's sake, Stirling, I'm going away, I may not see you for fifty years, we used to get on in a queer way, and I wanted to see you. He smiled and said, "You always were the rudest bastard I knew." Ah, that was better. He began to talk. What he said was a little surprising. He had graduated from the university a much publicized and recommended figure, the darling of the administration, Greek Row and the business community, to whom he was their own very special Negro. He had decided not to cash in immediately but to play for the long haul. Instead of taking one of the many jobs offered him by white firms, he decided to go to business school, flunking his first and third year. Somehow, and against his will, and despite hard work, he had regularly found himself on the bottom of the academic pile. By availing himself of special tutors, he had only just managed to graduate, whence he took a job as a trainee executive in an impeccable San Diego investment office, it being generally assumed that when the time was ripe he would step forth in some more considerably exalted position of liaison between white and Negro worlds. Thus far, according to what Stirling was telling me, it had not happened, and he had begun to spend more and more of his time doing work for the National Association for the Advancement of Colored People. He spoke slightingly of the Urban League and similar modest-reform Negro groups. I had to smile.

He felt, he declared, very militant about Negro rights now. I said, Stirling, you'll feel militant until someone offers you a plum job. He said, "That is fucking unfair, man." I explained to him that I did not mean he was a sell-out artist, because he was not. But he did have, I told him, a superb instinct for timing, usually, and he would probably be lifted high up by the next sociological wave. I laughed and said, All you need, Stirling, is patience. He laughed, too, and said, "You are a rude and reassuring bastard." Still, I felt sorry for Stirling. He *had* worked hard and still he hadn't made it. He had outsmarted himself. He had counted on his talents for accommodation being called upon during a smooth transition (without Little Rocks) from second- to first-class citizenship, and instead history had played him a dirty trick. But leave it to old Stirling, he was climbing on the bandwagon, the NAACP gravy train. Trouble was, I could see a situation where no sooner would Stirling adjust to a period of violent wrenches in Negro-white relations than there might, as can happen in America, set in a period of relative peace for which he would find himself unfitted. Maybe not. His single genius was for not going out on any limb too far.

So we had coffee and I drove him back to that little yellow house, said goodbye and drove back on the highway, heading for San Francisco. My talk with Stirling had been neither satisfactory nor unsatisfactory; he was as involved with himself, almost narcissistically, with his reasons for premature failure as I was burdened by a sense of shooting out into space without knowing for a certainty if I should land anywhere. Wherever it was I came to rest, if I crossed an ocean I knew it would have to be in a country gentle and formal, if such a country existed.

At seven in the morning I went out of Oxnard at eighty miles an hour.

Past Oxnard, I stopped at a gas station to take care of the De Soto. Gas, oil, tire pressure, check the luggage in the rear, buy a pair of sun goggles, get a good look at the car. It was last year's model, and clean, and ready. When I started up I felt very good. I was primed.

Sixty, seventy, eighty up the coast highway. Man. Zigzagging red light in my rear-view. I pulled over. The cop got off his motorcycle and said, "You have any idea how fast you were going, mister?" I called him sir, and we had an absorbing conversation about speed and death. He gave me a ticket in the name of the township of Ventura. I thanked him, and he sped on ahead of me. I put the ticket in the glove compartment and found six Beverly Hills parking citations. All made out to Julia Lathenas. The Lathenases had been living it up.

Just before Santa Barbara, I walked into a drive-in hash house. I could tell from the clothes and sunburnt faces I was coming into ranch and farming country. The men were in Stetsons and work shirts. They all had creased faces and small eyes. The old feeling of alienness returned to whonk me, but only for a moment. I began to listen to their talk.

On the road again. The plunge into Salinas Valley, white-hot, broad high hills of dry yellow and burnt brown, serried patches of stark green. And gangs of dark-skinned men whose backs only were visible in the fields. I stopped twice to talk in broken Spanish to the field hands. Not very much was said. They were too suspicious. A few miles south of San Jose a third attempt was broken off by the sudden screeching arrival of either the owner or foreman in a pink Cadillac. He was angry. He said, "What do you want around here?" As I started to go, he yelled, "My people get top dollar in this neighborhood . . . If all the writers in this fucking state would go to hell . . ." I didn't stay around to hear the rest. The Mexican fruit pickers enjoyed it enormously. It irritated me. Nobody had ever called me a writer before just on first meeting.

I went over an overpass in the direction of Palo Alto, passing the campus, with its sandstone Romanesque buildings and roofs of red tile, a mile outside the city. Near the center of town I parked and locked the De Soto and walked around until I found the address I had written on the crumpled envelope in my hand. It was hot and sunny.

Both Del and Kate were at home in their new, tiny apartment, lazing around. They were surprised to see me and opened up some cans of beer which we sat around drinking in the warm, gloomy apartment. They were both dressed in swim suits. They asked me about Rafe Hawes, who was my oldest friend, and I had to tell them that I hadn't seen Rafe in six months.

Del nodded. They had seen Rafe last month when he drove through on a holiday in Oregon. They said he was tooling a new big Buick. All he could talk about, they said, was his job. I know, I said. That was one of the reasons why we stopped seeing each other. He was ultra-respectable these days, living all alone in a big new apartment half a mile from where I lived in L.A., alone with his new black pile carpet and 21-inch television set and drugging himself on paperbacks and drive-in movies and his job, which I had to admit was a good one. Starting out as a management trainee, he was now a rising young luminary on the "labor relations team" of General Motors. He lived alone and ate alone and did not go out with girls or see his old friends. His laugh was becoming harsh and hysterical and he talked about nothing but his job. He was beginning to hate workers. Especially, he detested workers who bought furniture on credit. I mean detested. His father had once been a *bracero*, and both of his brothers were sheet-metal workers in Texas.

I had first known Rafe in Chicago, when he was living with my first dialectics instructor, Alan Pick. We both had gone to the William Lloyd Garrison School, where Rafe's sleepy pose of noncommitment infuriated Alan, our mutual teacher, who had seduced Rafe about three years before. I hadn't known anything about that at the time, and only learned about it when I went to live with Rafe, and Del and Kate O'Hara, in Brooklyn, when the Korean war broke out. Rafe had taken me out to Central Park one morning and told me about it, and also that he was through with that kind of life because it had no percentage in it for him. I remember being shocked and that was when we started hurting each other. I tried as hard as I could but I never could quite treat him in the same way, putting my arms around him and all the rest, and that hurt him fiercely so that he never forgave me. By the time I had become grown-up and un-American about this it was too late, and he was already giving me the harsh, acid laugh.

I had lost touch with Rafe after Chicago, all through the war, and Detroit; and then halfway through my last semester in college he had shown up, from nowhere, to wait on his mother's death. He hadn't seen her for years.

I was studying late in the Memorial Library, with a few of the friends I had met that last, different semester, when I looked up from *The Faerie Queene* to see this tall, broad-shouldered cat-eyed Mexican coming up the aisle. He didn't smile when he sat down at the table opposite me, just moved the green-shaded lamp away so that he could see me and said that his mother was dying and would I go over to Boyle Heights with him. He didn't look at my friends Kenneth and Jessica. It had been five years since I had seen him.

I drove Rafe in my old '36 Plymouth. It was a bad evening. The Plymouth conked out on La Brea Avenue, and we had to take three buses out to Boyle Heights. For the next three days we lived together in his mother's shack, while she was attended by a doctor and a Mexican priest. She had been a terminal cancer patient at L.A. County Hospital and when she asked to go home they had let her. She was a fat little old woman who slept most of the time except when the doctor, or the priest, or Rafe was present. When she was asleep Rafe used to argue bitterly with his two brothers from Texas. He hated them as he had hated his father, who was a prosperous official for the nationalized oil industry in Mexico.

For three nights Rafe and I stayed up. Gradually, I became frightened; Rafe grew calmer. I knew that trick of his, freezing himself and pretending not to care and making stupid wisecracks about important things. His mother died while the priest and doctor were away and the two brothers were up at the corner tamale stand, on the afternoon of the fourth day. Rafe went into her tiny room where she had crucifixes and Mariana stuck all over the newspaper-plastered walls. He came out in a minute and sat down on the bed beside me and said, "She's bleeding all over." I said we should do something. He said no, the doctor allowed that was how it would happen. I could hear her moving around in there, bleeding and not saying anything, and when I couldn't stand it any longer I stood up and went to the door of her little room. "Get your hand off the doorknob!" Rafe roared. I did, and then everything went quiet. In a few minutes Rafe got up and smiled. He went to the icebox and said, "Here, have a Pepsi-Cola." He sat down at the kitchen table and began to talk, about movies and sports and cars. He kept offering me Pepsi-Colas and I had to keep saying I wasn't thirsty. When his two brothers showed up, I told Rafe where he could find me and I took the buses to my stalled jalopy on La Brea Avenue.

Rafe didn't tell me when he departed L.A. but I received a letter from him just before I left the university telling me that I had a place to stay in Brooklyn if I ever went east. Six weeks later I was living in North Gowanus in an attic room with Rafe in a dirty old house rented by Del and Kate and another couple, Big Tom and Gina Lorenzo. All their friends, and then mine, in this period, were construction workers, underfed musicians or Negroes. There was even a young Indian from the nearby Caughnawaga hangouts, a high-steel man like so many in that colony.

Both Big Tom and Del had been in the war, in jail, and in the first-round strikes after the war. Big Tom was quizzical and oblique and had a cauliflower ear from the Peekskill riot; Del, who was built like a small truck, had almost lost an eye there. He was a former jazz sax player and junkie and was now a construction laborer in Big Tom's crew. We used to stay up nights eating pizza and arguing politics. Rafe and I spent three weeks looking for an apartment together in Manhattan, but he kept finding fault with everything we saw. Then, one morning, he went away to one of the Al-Can Highway projects in Canada with the Caughnawaga high-steel man. After he went away things went to pieces in the house. Gina Lorenzo was the first one to become scared. This was late in 1950. An FBI man came around, to inquire about someone else, and the panic was on. Gina insisted on getting rid of all the controversial books. Everything we did we did in the name of Gina's peace of mind and pregnancy. Her husband, Big Tom, just stood by and clucked his tongue. Finally it came around to me. Gina hinted that I ought to find a room for myself. She delegated Del O'Hara to pass the word.

I left the house in North Gowanus and didn't see much of the Lorenzos and O'Haras after that. Gina and Big Tom had their baby and moved out to Denver. Rafe served his time on the Al-Can Highway and came back to the States to lie his way into General Motors as a management trainee. We drifted apart in Los Angeles until it became impossible to talk to each other. Every time I opened my mouth he started defending himself. It just didn't seem worth it. I didn't even say goodbye to him when I left L.A. this time. That Caughnawaga Indian, I never saw him again either.

Over the beer, Del said that he and Kate did not hear from the Lorenzos any more. There had been a third child and Big Tom was a confirmed lush now from Gina's nagging. Kate put it down to Gina's having been a European refugee. She said that Gert had never lost her fear of the FBI. (All they had ever done, you know, was to sell *Daily Workers* in Greenpoint.)

Del had a funny story to tell in that connection. After New York, he and Kate had moved out to San Francisco where Del began learning the air-purifying business. He swore to me it was a high science once you studied it. He started out as a ventilator scraper and worked his way up until he was pricing jobs for his firm which made him top boy in one of their purifying teams. One week, Del submitted a bid on a building in central San Francisco and beat out four other atmosphere-clearing firms. His boss promoted him. Then Del discovered that the building he had successfully bid to purify was the FBI headquarters, and that he would have to submit to a loyalty quiz. There could be no backing out. So the FBI ran a security check on Del while he and Kate sweated it out. The FBI gave Del a clean bill of health. Kate said that when Del came rushing home to announce the news they had spent the entire evening laughing out of sheer relief. Del had been one of the most prominent Communists, and then Trotskyists, in Brooklyn, and the only thing the FBI had come up with was that in 1948 some Virginia highway patrolmen investigating a minor traffic mishap had discovered Wallace For President leaflets in the back of his car. When questioned by the FBI about the incident, Del had sworn that the car had not been his, which was true, and he went on to purify the air in the building, nervously. But it had made them so uneasy that Del quit his job and moved with Kate down to Palo Alto where they were beginning to make a good living selling religious articles. Both Del and Kate were atheists. Del said he liked selling religious articles. It gave him kicks to spend all day talking to priests, he said. In another year they would have enough money to make a baby. Kate frowned. I remembered. The O'Haras and Lorenzos and Rafe and I used to discuss it over pizza in North Gowanus. They had a problem. Del's gun was too large. Kate was always a little frightened of it. I had seen it. She had good reason to worry. I didn't bring up the subject this time.

We talked about old times. They said that all the Brooklyn Reds were out of politics now, still scared. Carol, our Negro friend, was in prison on a narcotics rap — part true, part frame. It was she the FBI had come around about. All the old comrades, they said, were frightened. Monty and Rickie, who used to come over for pizza, had divorced over the issue of their black poodle, The Monk, named after Thelonius. Rickie insisted that The Monk sleep with them. The little dog used to raise a boner every time it walked into a room where Rickie was present, Monty testified in Domestic Relations Court. Monty was now in a TB sanitarium in upstate New York, and Rickie had set up on Orchard Street as a whore. Rickie had always been a peculiar girl. She was a rich girl from New Haven, accustomed to college proms and football players and local polo hotshots, and the first time she laid her eyes on Monty, a fat, balding, unhealthy-looking junkie, she started talking him into marriage. When she finally beat him down she went to live in New York City and became a high-fashion *Vogue* model and started to commit suicide. She had slashed her wrists so many times that each wrist looked as though a piece of white rope had been tied around it. In *Vogue*, she was always photographed with gloves on. She was brunette, petite and very pretty. She almost always came out winner in our poker games.

Del said he wouldn't be surprised if Rickie had turned FBI informer, and I said I didn't think so, she wasn't that sick. Kate made a sign of the cross. We drank more beer. Kate said she had sent three letters to the Lorenzos and had them returned from Denver. Then she began to cry. The Lorenzos and O'Haras had been best friends for a long time. Del and Big Tom had met in a stockade in France in the war when Tom was up on a narcotics charge, and Del in for twenty-four hours on a technical murder charge. While on sentry duty he had shot and killed a G.I. who refused to answer his challenge. Del would talk about anything except that. I learned it from Rafe.

I told Del and Kate I had to go. They said sure, they understood. Del gave me five dollars for a subscription to a new socialist magazine and asked me to have it delivered to a box number in a wrapper. I told Del this made me very sad. Del laughed in that ex-hophead way of his and said, "That's the way the ball bounces, man."

"You don't play trumpet any more," screamed Kate, her eyes still wet.

I said goodbye.

Del said, "That's the way we get our kicks, man."

I cut through to the coast highway again and rode it, at lessened speed, all the way to San Francisco, stopping off once in Watsonville to have a chat with an old friend who ran a health food store. He used to edit a lumberworkers' newspaper up in Canada between the wars. He was an old man now, an IWW, and all he wanted to talk about was the evil of candy. He told me his wife died last year.

When I got into San Francisco I phoned Earl and Minnie. Earl answered and said Minnie was doing a rush job but that I could stay over if I wanted.

I went over to their place, an apartment in the trough of a valley of houses, and Earl and I talked politics. Earl was one of the handsomest men I ever knew, a big shock of rust-red hair and a freckled, chiseled face and marvelous teeth. He was vain, but Minnie used to tell me that he treated her well. She was twenty-two and he was forty-five or something; he had three children, two of them in movies and the other a pole-vaulter for Covina High. Earl had once been a back room boy for the Progressive Party, a non-Red Red stricter than the Reds. The worst type. He was still defending Stalin. Not explaining, defending. While waiting around for Minnie we agreed that left-wing politics in America was shot. He said he was making Halloween masks and practical jokes now, on a subcontracting basis, and might go into business on his own. He still went to meetings of one kind or another but his heart wasn't in it. He had once given politics to Minnie but now, he said, he wasn't much interested in educating her, he wasn't so sure of the answers any more. I never thought I'd live to hear Earl say anything like that.

In the middle of talking Earl got up and switched on the TV to watch "Dragnet." Then Minnie came in and we sat around drinking wine. She had to go back to the cutting room (Minnie was a film editor of industrial documentaries) to supervise some negative cutting, and Earl and I drove up to Twin Peaks and watched the lights of the city until we became sleepy. Earl said he missed his kids down in L.A. and asked me to come across the bay with him tomorrow to help him buy a used Chevrolet station wagon. I said I didn't know much about station wagons and he said he knew less. I had never known Earl so humble. It disturbed me because there was a time when I thought the only intact thing in Earl was his arrogance and when that went everything else would go too. But so far, except for his drinking a little more wine than he used to, he seemed much the same.

In the morning, Minnie rehearsed in the living room on her harp (she was in an amateur philharmonia) and Earl and I drove to Berkeley to look over this station wagon. I crawled under but I couldn't tell anything one way or the other. My instinct told me it was a lemon, and I told this to Earl, but he said his instinct told him the opposite. Months later, when I was living in Paris, he sent me a letter to say that the station wagon had dropped its transmission box on its first trip south.

In the afternoon, I dropped in at the ILWU office to talk to the assistant editor of the union newspaper. He was a blacklisted screenwriter. He described his new novel to me. It sounded very bad, the kind of novel writers tend to write after working too long for the studios. He was bitter and told me a long story about how, when the Committee was after him, he had gone to a famous movie star for a small loan and had been turned down even though they had been in the same Army platoon together. I asked him for a job on the paper and he said no, he was being fired himself next month. Before I left, he pointed out to me the church across the street. There was a pane missing in the stained-glass window. He said it was generally assumed that that was where the FBI spied on the union building. A year ago, the union had sent a Catholic longshoreman around to the church and he had come back to say that the room behind the missing pane of glass was barred and locked.

I had lunch, by appointment, with the research staff, the director, two assistants and a woman. Like most union research people they were shrewd and capable. At the moment they were passive and skeptical but receptive to what I had to say. We had been writing to each other, and this was our first meeting. They were interested in my correspondence with Professor Cole at Oxford. When they found I hadn't brought The Message they grew restive. I told them that there was no formula to straighten the spine of the Left, that left-wingers could no longer look to the old-timers for leadership, but this they knew already.

After lunch, I took a stroll around the Embarcadero. San Francisco was turning out, as always, an undiluted joy. I always brought fine weather with me. I talked to the guys in a hiring hall, and we had a big laugh over Harry Bridges switching his political registration to Republican. They didn't take it too seriously. "What in hell," said a shorty, "Kefauver's campaign manager was the prosecuting attorney at Bridges' last trial." "Yeah," said another longshoreman, "it was Harry's way of getting back. Cute." Nobody took the switch seriously, including the staff members I had lunched with. I told them I had seen Bridges in the corridor of the union headquarters and they asked me if he had any bandages on him. I said no, he was smiling and not too badly marked. (On the day before my arrival, Bridges had been assaulted by two of Harry Lundberg's goons in the lavatory of a bar in Sausalito.) I listened to the boys in the hiring hall reminisce about the General Strike. The dispatcher said, with firm authority, that this was the first time in twenty years Bridges had been the object of physical attack.

I bummed around the waterfront and tried to get into the Tin Angel but it was too early, and I found it locked. I went over to Pier 11 and waited for Sam, an old friend. He came out with a bunch of longshores at whistle time but didn't give me too happy a hello. Sam had helped me get a warehouse job at Safeway Stores when I quit hacking, but had never quite believed my story about being fired by the personnel manager after only a few days. The truth was, I had been, because I had lied on my questionnaire about never having been to college, but I might have quit anyway.

Sam had been disappointed because he figured to caucus me for floor steward and eventually we would lead the local union together. Later, when the Teamsters were trying to raid the warehouse, I used to take time off from my job at the Benedict agency to go down and distribute leaflets on San Pedro Street. But I don't think, in Sam's mind, it ever made up for my getting fired. And anyway I had some books of his back down in L.A. which I had never returned. He was a surly bastard on any count. I had met him after the Navy had dishonorably discharged him at Treasure Island, for reading the wrong books, the ones I read, and I had been sent by a wire service to do the story. Sam was from Tennessee and had married the local mayor's daughter who was then disowned. I liked his wife, who was very good-natured and useless.

Sam took me to his local union headquarters and we sat around talking. The local president and treasurer were there. They said other unions could join the newly merged AFL-CIO but the west coast longshoremen would remain independent. "If we go in," said the treasurer, "labor won't have a conscience any more." There was general agreement. Afterwards, we had a few drinks in a bar around the corner and talked about Bridges and his having gotten beat up in Sausalito. The guys were more surprised than angry.

Minnie and Earl were busy that night, and so I made the rounds. I didn't have a girl in San Francisco and I was lonely, but it was better than anywhere else not having a girl. There were many young couples on the streets, including an impressive number of Caucasian-Oriental alliances. I have never seen much of that anywhere except in San Francisco. It is the best city in America (and will obviously become less so the more it is advertised as such, even here, unfortunately). The houses are old from the outside and it's not easy to tell the slums. I went around the North Beach dives, The Cellar, Vesuvio's, Miss Smith's where I listened to Bechet on records and the barkeep telling me lies about his role in the Mexican revolution to come. I saw a nice girl in the Anxious Asp but she didn't see me. In all the official bohemian joints the kids were better dressed and stiffer-faced than on my last trip. Vicariousness institutionalized, dipping their pinkies in. I went and made a phone call to Sam but he said he and his wife were having a fight, so I went out to the Tin Angel and listened to Turk Murphy and began to feel pretty blue. The happier the jazz the bluer I felt. Finally, I went home to Earl and Minnie's. Earl was up, at one in the morning, and having a steady ball in front of the TV. He asked me to join him and I did. We talked about politics. Earl was depressing when he talked about politics; we depressed each other. I went to bed.

In the morning I drove out to Oakland to look up Rita and Whitey, but the landlady said that they had gotten a divorce, and that Rita was back down in L.A. working on a newspaper. Then I had a talk with Saul Silverman. Saul had a big house now, overlooking the bay, and was doing well in union insurance. A few years ago, with others, he had been forced off the staff of his union and now spent most of his time flying up and down the west coast servicing various unions in a business way. He was fat, wry and disappointed. "Radicalism," he said, "has vanished from the union movement. All the guys talk about is sex, baseball and cars." He also told me that two of the unions he serviced had just signed four-year contracts with management. We talked about the catastrophic decline in socialism, how militant unions were settling for labor peace, and the mortgage on his house. I persisted in trying to pinpoint ideologies and he said, finally, with impatience, "No more thought, no more philosophy. Just pork chops." He was grimly determined to hold on to what he had and not to sacrifice much of it in the name of the death rattles of a moribund movement. Saul had discovered home, children and family.

Later in the evening, Minnie had to go back to the cutting room and Earl dragooned me into attending, on pass ticket, a $50-a-plate Democratic Party dinner. Earl said with a lame grin, "You have to work somewhere, boy."

We drove down to the Fairmont Hotel in a '55 Olds. The driver was a friend of Earl's who was doing publicity for Stevenson. He was a slim, good-looking deceptively young man who said he used to work for the Food & Agricultural Workers Union and before that for one of the New Deal agencies. The woman beside him was tremendously made up to cover the ten years, perhaps more, difference in age. She wisecracked a lot, sadly, and I liked her. Earl whispered that she wanted to marry him but that he was lush and had a wife.

When we got into the car I saw that he had dark, shadowed and despairing eyes. I asked them if they wanted to go over to Berkeley after the banquet to hear a new high school "mainstream" trio I had been told about. They said they'd like to, but he had to stick close to the guest of honor. We separated in the lobby of the hotel, and the minute her friend left her she looked like a lost child. "I wish I could sit with you and Earl," she said. "But I have to stay with the local brass. God, how I hate the publicity game."

Senator John (I beg your pardon, Jack) Kennedy was feature speaker. The front man's front man, the apotheosis of candidacy, the ultimate in political pin-ups, handsomely boyish, careless hair, easy smile, is for courage, a splendidly filmable war record, a pretty wife, rich reactionary folks and just enough of the controversial—his Catholicism—to infuse his supporters with the requisite pugnacity. What's the matter with ya, bud, ya against freedom o' religion? Except that, my God, Kennedy's speech in that banquet hall: never in my life have I sat still for such unbelievable nothing. He raises platitudes to the level of a high, metaphysical art. For no particular reason I thought of Saul, the unionist-turned-businessman I had seen earlier in the afternoon. Poor bastard. Try as hard as he might, he still cannot disguise, for all his laconicism, his thirst to work and sacrifice for others. All around us, at banquet tables, were sitting well-heeled Democrats who, God help the nation, were gazing at this Kennedy creation with admiration, men and women both, even adoration. I felt physically nauseated. I looked over at Earl. He wore a thin smile on his handsome, aging face, but I didn't know what it meant.

I couldn't take it any longer, and I whispered to Earl that I would meet him back at the house. All the people at my table, especially a pretty, middle-aged Democratic Central Committee type who had told me she was from Bakersfield, looked very accusingly at me as I got up and went out. Old Earl wasn't quite dead. He said, audibly, "Stay for ice cream." I laughed. Kennedy, the speaker, stopped in mid-sentence up on the dais, and I beat it out of there before anyone got the idea that I was a GOP *agent provocateur*. I sat down in the lobby and planned a large volume to be entitled "Profiles in Snollygostering" and ate a Suchard choclate bar and then moseyed into the hotel record shop and asked for a Lennie Tristano. The man behind the counter wore two small buddhas as cuff links and said he had never heard of the gentleman.

I asked him if he had ever heard of Chu Berry and he looked insulted so I didn't press the point. Outside the hotel the fog had rolled in white and wet and cold. I didn't know what to do with myself. I went back into the hotel and phoned up Clem Silver and told him I was in town. He said for me to wait for him. I had a couple of drinks in the small bar until someone tapped me on the shoulder: the young-old publicity man for Stevenson who had driven us down to the hotel. He had been drinking by himself in a dark corner. He asked me why I wasn't in the banquet room, and I said I had been overwhelmed by emotion. "Yeah," he said, "yeah, me too," and he stumbled gloomily back to his red leather, dark corner seat. I didn't want him to think I was a smart-aleck. I went over and said, What the hell, we all have to make a living. He looked up and gave me a wan smile. "You're talking to the converted," he said. We had a drink together, and he said his happiest days had been lying up in a base hospital in Dorset, England, after being run over by one of his own tanks in the Charenton peninsula, reading old *New Yorkers* and organizing a creative writing course for injured combat troops. He was feeling pretty lousy when I left him. We made up to meet again but I never did see him again.

Clement was waiting for me in a brand-new Ford convertible under the marquee. I told him to come in for a drink, and he said no, Marya was expecting us. So we drove all the way out to his place in Oakland. They had a new house, split-level, on modish stilts, on the edge of a development, and most of the way out there Clement talked about the roadway he was building from the main road to his garage. When we got to his house in Oakland Marya was waiting for us with beer and sandwiches, and so were their two kids, a boy and a girl. They were angry kids, furious all the time, and Marya soon sent them to bed. Clement and Marya and I sat around talking.

He was working for good money now as a professional collector for one of the ethnic minority groups. He said it was all very skillful, very polished, their operation, and he was getting to meet all the big deals in San Francisco, the clergy and shipowners, people like that. I said, Jesus Christ. He toasted that. Marya looked uncomfortable. I wanted to tell her not to worry, that I wasn't going to make trouble. She was about fifteen years older than Clement, who was a few years older than I, and both kids were hers by him. Clem was one of those terrific-looking Austro-Germans who look like ski instructors. We had known each other since 1945 in Washington where he had an OSS assignment.

Clem's father had been killed by a shell in the Karl Marx buildings in Vienna in 1934. At seventeen Clem had gone to fight in Spain, and after that had set up in Paris under the aegis of some committee or other as liaison with the Austrian and German undergrounds. In 1939 the committee, which was more or less a Comintern front, fired him, and Clem joined the French Army under false papers. He was captured in 1940 by the Germans — the only time in his life, he said, when he was so frightened he shat — and with three or four others managed to escape to Sweden. He tried establishing contact with one of the Comintern anti-Fascist cells in Stockholm but the word about him had already gotten around (that he was possibly a Nazi agent), so he came to America, volunteered as an infantry private and finally ended up with one of the D-Day divisions. After he was invalided back from England, they discovered he knew how to speak six languages and so he received this assignment with OSS in the Pentagon. When I was working for G-2, Dissemination, at the War College, I used to go to a lot of wild OSS parties and that's where Clem and I met, just before V-J Day. Pete Mitchell, the French-horn player, was one of us then. Now all Clem wanted to talk about was building his goddam road, that and the mortgage. I wasn't drunk or anything, but I told Clem I wasn't interested in his mortgage. Marya walked out to get more sandwiches and Clem asked me to take it easy, things had been a little rough around the house recently. Then he launched into a long, Germanic explanation of why the Left was finished in America, how its inhabitants had been swept off the stage of history, and all the rest. He also did a rather intelligent analysis of the 1948 Wallace campaign. Clem had been one of Wallace's bright young men. I told Clem I got his point. When Marya came back her eyes were red. I wanted to put my arms around her but I didn't know her that well. Clem and Marya took me on a tour of their house, and then I asked him to take me back to town. Marya didn't ask me to stay the night, but Clem did.

We didn't say much to each other on the long ride back. I told him that inasmuch as we wouldn't be seeing each other for a while there was no point to his sulking. He replied that I shouldn't come around people's houses and criticize the kind of lives they were leading. I said a mortgage and a road to the garage wasn't a way of life, and when was the last time he had read a novel? Clem was one of those phenomenal readers who used to go through two a day. He gave me one of his little-boy sunburnt grins and said, "Okay, okay." I told him that didn't make me feel any better. So we quarreled. He was being charming as hell which only made me angry. He wanted to drive me out to Earl's but I made him put me down on Powell Street. He said, "Goodbye you sonofabitch," but he was smiling. We shook hands, and then he drove away. The fog was very thick. I walked around until I found a drugstore open and I phoned Sam and asked him to come down and have a milk shake. Sam was sore, as usual. In cold and precise terms he informed me that it was one-thirty in the morning and did I know that? I told him I knew that, but I wanted to talk to him which, strictly speaking, wasn't true. I felt like talking to somebody. Sam asked me what about his books down in L.A., and I said for Christ's sake I didn't feel like talking about his goddam books. He kept saying he had lent me those books on honor and trust, and finally I promised to see to it he got them back. That was the end of our talk. He said he had to go to work in the morning and I said okay, I'd see him another time.

I thought of going over to Coit Tower or Miss Smith's and maybe picking up one of the college girls. But it seemed too far to go just for a college girl who probably wouldn't be there anyway, and a lot of jazz from the Mexican bartender about his scheme to infuse the Partido Revolucionario Institucional with insurrectionist fervor. I stood on the foggy street corner hollering for a taxi until one came and took me home. All the way in the taxi I felt lousy. In fact, I felt dizzy. A real, physical dizziness. The cabdriver had to turn around and ask me several times for the address, and when I got out of the cab I had to sit on the bottom of Earl's steps until the nausea went away. The cabdriver knew I was feeling sick but didn't even look at me when I gave him his money.

I let myself in the house with the key Minnie had given me. I sat in the dark living room and tried to think. Then I took the telephone into the hall closet, closing the door after me, so as not to wake Earl and Minnie. In the small dark confine of the closet I fumbled until my finger caught the last hole. I told the operator I wanted to call long distance, Los Angeles. She asked me who the party was I wanted to call in Los Angeles and I hung up. I didn't know. I walked out of the closet, put the phone back on the hall table, made up my bed on the front-room couch and went to sleep.

I slept late. Minnie woke me up and we went down to Earl's shop to have lunch with him. On the way down in my car Minnie said she sometimes got fed up on Earl, his preening and his drinking, but she thought she was more stuck on him now than when they got married. "I'm crazy, but I love the bastard," she said. I know that should have made me feel good but it didn't, especially. I wished Earl had left the Democratic Party banquet when I had.

Earl's shop was on a top-floor loft, and when you first walked in, all you smelled was fresh paint and sawdust and all you saw was a small sea of Halloween masks. Earl had three people working under him making masks, all profit-sharing partners, and one old refugee Magyar contriving practical jokes in a small well-lighted room all of his own. There were also three or four wax nude mannequins in the place; Earl repaired them. Earl said business was picking up. He explained just how Halloween masks are created and made, and the part that fascinated me was the way Earl and his profit-sharers all sat around, with deadly serene expressions and tried to figure out what face would be most representatively gruesome next year. While Earl and Minnie were off having a small argument, I wandered through a forest of plastic unpainted masks and sat down at the feet of a dumb goddess whose perfect legs would never wither. I ran my hand down the leg of the mannequin, and Earl's employee, a Negro, who was screwing its head on, smiled queerly. Gives you thoughts, I said. He said he had been working for Earl a year and he still had thoughts. But he still smiled at me queerly.

Just before we went out Earl showed me a painting of a Florentine landscape which had been done, he said, by Seymour Costa. Seymour and I had been to college together when he had won $5000 in an Oh Henry! chocolate-bar contest he had entered after picking up an Oh Henry! wrapper in the gutter. Earl said Seymour was painting and writing in Rome. Seymour had been a card in college. He had wrestled for the team and made money on the side by working for a bookmaker. They had a system. Several afternoons a week Seymour drove down to Santa Anita track and booked a seat at the very top of the grandstands. Just as soon as a race finished he would flash the result, using two small red flags, to a man in the track parking lot who communicated by two-way radio with the Los Angeles bookmaker. When Seymour wasn't working at the track he was always trying to get up poker games in the office of the campus newspaper. He and his wife had a cooperative cheating system; everybody in the office knew about it, it wasn't too clever, but as far as I know nobody ever faced him down about it. In fact, the only real trouble Seymour had was when he started stealing new textbooks from the newspaper office at the start of each semester. The sports-page boys cornered him finally and told him they weren't sure who was taking their books but if the books weren't returned by the next morning they would wipe the floor with Seymour on general principles. Naturally, he returned the books. (In fact, someone else was stealing the books, but in view of how much Seymour had taken us for, at one time or another, in his poker games, this was something of rough justice.) In many ways, Seymour was a charming fellow, and the painting, of the hills below Fiesole, was not, as they say, untalented.

Earl and Minnie and I had lunch in Chinatown. There didn't seem much to say. Minnie had to go to the cutting room, and Earl had to go back to work. I went back to their place and took my time getting my things together and putting them in the convertible. Then I wrote out a note to both of them, wished them a lot of luck and left some money to cover food. I got into the car and drove down to the Embarcadero. It was busy in the afternoon, ships being unloaded. I drove back and forth a few times and then stopped for a drink in a bar on Stockton Street. I took out my road map and studied it and listened to a couple of longshoremen talk about *On the Waterfront* starring Marlon Brando. Then I went to the car and drove it up the block to a garage to fill up on gas and check everything. They were busy in the garage and I decided to take care of it on the road. Then I went on the road.

*

I was caught in an early rush of cars out of the city, and I started sweating all over. My throat felt dry. I wanted to go, and go fast. It was better, swifter, on the freeway past the bay. Once I hit the bay freeway I don't feel nostalgic or regretful about leaving San Francisco. There was a thirty-minute delay in Richmond while the police and a wrecking gear cleared the upward slope of a sedan-truck collision. The cars were lined up for miles on both sides of the highway. From where I sat I could look over all Richmond and I realized, for the first time, what a sprawling industrial complex it was. I cut out of the line of cars and went into a diner and ate a greasy pork chop. I almost pushed it away, then remembered what the food would be like everywhere on the road and decided to get used to it again because at the end of the line would be my biggest test of all, the ultimate in man's inhumanity to man, Howard Johnson's.

Inside the diner, I got to talking to a bunch of truckers at the far end of the counter. We all agreed that Warren Spahn was good for another five years of big league ball and that all cops, anywhere, under all circumstances were sonsabitches. A newspaper boy walked in and said the wreck on the road up ahead would be cleared in ten or fifteen minutes and that the man and woman in the sedan had been killed by the truck. I bought one of his papers, a *Chronicle*. There was a big black headline: "Hungarians Revolt Against Reds." I read the story. It said that mass demonstrations were taking place in Budapest against the Rakosi regime. The demonstrators, according to the *Chronicle*, were demanding more democracy and a withdrawal of Soviet troops from Hungarian territory. Before the newsboy went out I bought two more newspapers, both of which had wire-service stories that were datelined Budapest but obviously had been written in Vienna.

I got into the car again and backed it into the service station next door to the diner and asked the attendant to take care of her. While he was doing it, I sat in the car and watched the traffic crush inch forward up the sloping highway and thought of a conversation I had had in Barney's Beanery in Los Angeles last week with Joe Garfield, a blacklisted scenarist friend of mine. I had said that I thought the East German workers would revolt pretty soon now, that Poznan was not something that happened and then everybody forgot about. Joe became very angry. He said the chief, in fact the only issue to worry about was war and peace. Sure, I said, and the world was round too. Did I, he demanded, think that Ulbricht would turn guns on the workers? I said he was goddamned right Ulbricht would. For months I had been arguing with Garfield and his wife, Jean, and with their friends that something was going to bust loose soon in Eastern Europe and that when it did the chances were better than 50-50 that the Communist regimes would put down the insurrections in blood. But somewhere in my heart I didn't believe it.

The attendant came by and said my right rear spring was weak. I asked him if he thought it would last three thousand miles, and he looked doubtful. I got out and asked him to spread a tarpaulin on the ground. I crawled under the car and examined both sets of springs. The left was all right. The right had sprung a crack, in the metal and not the joint. I got out and brushed my hands and told the man it would last across the country. I hoped so.

Slowly, blowing my horn, I inched across the down-swinging traffic into the opposite lane. A truck driver waved me in and I fought the stream going faster. Near the crest of the hill we passed the wreck. The truck was a long-distance moving van and was off the road but not badly damaged except for the front end. The sedan, a postwar Plymouth, was a tangled mess with oil all over it. It had burned out. Where the collision had occurred a deep rut was cut into the highway which several booted highway cops waved us around. Over the crest of the hill the traffic picked up. Within a quarter of a mile I was in speed, whipping past the huge oil refineries that are outside Richmond. Usually a wreck on the road makes me nervous for the first ten or fifteen minutes. But I didn't feel a thing. This surprised me. Even when I was covering the daylight accident beat for American Wire Service, which meant virtually living on Highway 101, where three and four-car pile-ups in the fog are not unusual, I never became used to it. Always, after two or three minutes of inspecting the wreckage strewn across the highway or wrapped around a lamppost, and interviewing the police, I began to get very cold and to tremble. Once my teeth chattered so badly I had to drive all the way back to the office to type out the story because I couldn't phone it in. Some of the other reporters interviewed the survivors. I never had the stomach; I got all my data from the cops on the scene.

The highway outside Richmond plunges and rears past the big refineries and then straightens out over the mountain ridge and slides into Sacramento. I was surprised there were no hitchhikers or boomers on the road; it was still picking season. Maybe, I thought, everybody really is making money. I kept wondering why I hadn't felt anything when I looked into that blackened wreck back near Richmond, and I touched one hand to my face. No, it was warm. Maybe I was growing hardened. Maybe old.

I knew the highway like anything. It was an auxiliary home to me, and had been ever since the war. I had walked it, hitchhiked across it, driven everything from a '38 souped-up Mercury to a brand-new Cadillac on it. In through Vallejo, in the Napa valley, I just slowed down. It was a hot fruit town which I had first seen when I had driven Slim Robinson up here about four years ago. Slim was a college boy then, and during this vacation he had hired out as a bodyguard to the chief organizer for the AFL Lettuce Workers Union which was conducting a drive to sign up workers, mostly Mexicans. There were also a great many Japanese in the neighborhood, most of whom had been in internment camps during the war and had to fight in the courts to get back their land. I never met any because most of them had their own places and stayed strictly away from union people.

I had checked in overnight in a motel with Slim, and about five in the morning three sheriff's deputies had shown up and arrested Slim for being drunk and disorderly which was quite humorous when you know that Slim was a teetotaler. The deputies left me alone, and later in the day had let Slim come back to the motel. He reported that no one had roughed him up; it was, according to the union officials Slim was supposed to bodyguard, just the way of the Employers Association of letting him know what the score was. I had to hand it to Slim. He was not a fearless young man; but he stayed up around Vallejo for three months, even missing the first week of university term. When he returned to Los Angeles Slim told us that it hadn't been as violent as he expected. About a month before he arrived, the growers' association had set a pack of vigilantes on some Mexicans, and in the fracas a Mexican had died, it was generally assumed of heart failure. AFL headquarters had made a stink to the Justice Department, and by the time Slim got to Vallejo several FBI agents were around the place, which cramped the vigilantes' style. Most of the time, Slim said, all he did was write and mimeograph leaflets, though once or twice he was called upon to "belly bump" in the picket lines. He was a huge, hard-living boy who, I am told, has taken a Ph.D. in social statistics and married a rich social worker also huge. We used to buddy around together in the old days, when my girlfriend was a schoolteacher in the Pasadena system and his a Bennington College anthropologist who walked around all day and all night (out of term) in leotards. Her name was Sue and she looked swell in the leotards. The only thing "wrong" with Sue was her father, who used to come to our parties to get drunk and smash windows with his elbow and recite all the verses to "They're Hanging Danny Deever in the Morning." I always felt sorry that Slim hadn't married Sue; she would have helped make more of a man of him. The last time I had seen Slim, in New York, he had told me that I was a fool to stay with politics. His exact words were, "The grabbing is good now. Grab." Old Slim was okay, just slightly a whiner.

Right outside the Vallejo city limits I slowed down to the speed limit and went very slowly through the center of town. Vallejo and Salinas are my two least favorite places in California. I never heard of a lynching in Salinas but every time I went through I always expected one from the look of the faces of the men who hung around the main street. It was irrational to indict Vallejo for the demerits of Salinas, but that's the way I felt about the place.

At the junction with Highway 99 I was tempted to turn north for Red Bluff where my friend E. J. Birdsong lived now.

It was several years since we had last seen each other, but we always wrote. E.J. was a good old boy. We had gotten to know each other while taking advanced infantry training down at Camp Howze, Texas, when the war was still going. E.J. once forwent a pass in order to stay with me a whole weekend, when the company commander sentenced me to seven straight days in the latrine removing new M-1's from their cosmoline wrappings. After I came back from Germany, AWOL and about twenty-eight days from listing as a deserter, I hitchhiked out to E.J.'s house in Cache, Oklahoma. It was a white-painted house with five white stars painted on the blue roof, that had been given to the family by the government in recognition of the services of E.J.'s grandfather in bettering Indian-white relations. E.J.'s grandfather had been chief of the last band in the Comanche nation to surrender at Fort Sill. E.J. was something of an Indian nationalist and was not particularly proud of his grandfather, whom he saw as a little bit of a traitor. I had lived in that house for near on to two weeks, along with what seemed like eleven families, all with eleven children apiece. Then E.J. and I had cut out, bumming around and fruit-picking; we separated in the Hotel Louisiana, Los Angeles, just before I made my try for separation papers at Camp Beale. About five years ago, when I had the easiest job of my life, lying on a couch and reading books all day long for Liberty Pictures, he had come through town and I'd put him up at my place. Then we lost touch. Last I heard he was a used-car salesman in Red Bluff, California, which was as near as I could make out a hundred and twenty miles north of Highway 40 junction out of Vallejo. I felt like seeing E. J. Birdsong. I parked the car outside a filling station and made a long-distance call to Red Bluff. It probably would have taken only five minutes to get through to New Delhi; Red Bluff took fifteen. The person who answered the phone at E.J.'s house said he had quit his job and left town about two years ago and nobody knew where he was. I thanked the woman and hung up. And then I remembered where E.J. was. Walla Walla.

I pointed the De Soto towards Sacramento and picked up speed on the highway. I was leaving behind the lush valley greenness and hitting the patches of semi-aridity. The highway was empty except for the lumbering oil trucks which I kept catching up on. I decided to keep driving in the night and by-passed Sacramento, which is another town I dislike, by taking 40 North through Roseville and Auburn and up into the mountains. I loved the approach to the Sierras. The sun was going down behind my exhaust pipe and the snow-capped range had that bluish gray which most California painters I know never could quite catch. The approach itself is slow, long and loving, out of green country into scrub country, each mile raising you a little higher, a little cooler, so subtly that you are well into the Nevadas before you are aware of it. You turn one bend and it is night and you must switch on your headlights; around the next bend the sun still hits the road. I had been worried all the way out of San Francisco, but not any more. Everything would be fine. I felt terrific and was getting hungry again. That was always a good sign.

I drove through the Sierra, fast and carefully, and some time after midnight I pointed down into the Donner Pass. In the middle of the pass, as it began to climb up again, I drove off the side of the road where my headlights picked out a small picnic ground. I stopped the car and got out and sat down at one of the wooden picnic tables. It was cold up here, cold and full of the night, with very bright stars and tense, moaning silence. All I could hear was the wind through the Pass. I sat at the table and shaded my eyes from the occasional truck or car as it came up around the bend in second gear and disappeared into the darkness. Like most other History Majors I had written a paper on the Donner party. I supposed every rational person had his own special area of mysticism. The Donner Pass was mine. Three times before, twice in a car and once on foot, I had stopped in the Pass to spend some hour or two. So I sat, wrapped in aloneness and night, growing less and less conscious of the occasional headlight, and pretty soon I was talking to some of them. I had done a lot of research on the Donner party, from the morning they left Salt Lake until, fatally, they split up on the cannibalistic snows, and I remembered all of the names and ages of several of the families. Tonight I spoke mainly with the leader, Captain Grimble, and Moses Snyder, who had lived on parts of his wife and dead son when the snows closed in. I had written my paper on the relationship between Captain Grimble and Snyder in attempting to explain Snyder's character.

After a time no headlights appeared on the road, it was as sad and terrible and peaceful as the night they must all have realized that they were lost and no help would be coming. I got up from the picnic table and went back to the De Soto. I locked myself in and turned on the radio. A news broadcast reported a night of heavy fighting in Budapest, against whom and for what it was not yet clear. Then a disc jockey came on to advertise a sale tomorrow morning at a local butcher and to play Mantovani's "Dancing in the

Dark." I sat in the dark car whose only glow came from the Motorola radio and thought about the Donner party and whoever it was dying in Budapest and E. J. Birdsong, and for I don't know how long, in each rhythm to whatever songs the disc jockey played, I got them all mixed up in my mind, with E.J. and me on snow-tufted rooftops shooting at something and taking orders from Capt. Grimble. I became rather lost in it and when it began to spread out from behind my jaw, it worried me a little and I turned on the ignition, and rolled out onto the highway in second gear.

To remove the hum from my jaw and throat I drove very fast, eighty and ninety on the straightaways, and slowed down when the road began to go down. By the time I could see the flickering lights of Truckee I was all right. I coasted down into the town and found an all-night drive in. I had lost my hunger but made myself eat. The waitress, a nice woman with a scar across her nose, and I talked. There were not many customers in the place at that time of the night. In the dark shadow of the Donner Pass she told me about her husband, the chef, and how they had come to work in this place after two years in Alaska. The only thing she ever read was the *Reader's Digest*, she said; she got the habit in Alaska and couldn't break it. She expected to be leaving Truckee for The Dalles next year. She wanted a house and a baby, and she blushed when she told me she couldn't have a baby. Her husband came out, a sturdy little chopper in chef's suit. We gassed a while and the husband asked me, half in joke, whether I wanted to go out to The Dalles with them. He would need someone to help build the house in exchange for room and board. I thanked him mightily but said I had to go on. They asked me where I was going. I said if I knew I would tell them. He said, "Don't be a sucker, if you come to The Dalles with us you can make a life for yourself. We'll get you married up there. In fact, I know a girl." His wife touched his arm and said, "Dan, he knows what he's doing." That's just the point, I told her, I don't. "People like you," she said. "They make me cry." Dan waited for three customers to leave, then shut up shop. His wife said, "Dan, it's not as if you owned the place." Dan winked at me and we all went in back, to the kitchen, and sat around drinking. That kitchen was the cleanest and neatest I had ever seen in a restaurant. I asked them who they were voting for. They said they never bothered about politics. The only thing in the world they were interested in, Dan said, was building that house and loving each other. His wife blushed furiously. Dan got up and bent over and kissed the top of her bosom. She didn't try pushing him away. It was one of the nicest things I had ever seen in my life. Dan started to break out another bottle when I said I had to go. They walked me out to the roadway and stood with their arms clasped around each other, waving at me, and I stopped the car and got out and waved back. Then I drove on.

I arrived in Reno shortly before dawn after racing through a stretch of desert. The desert around Reno in the night always depressed me, and it did this time too. It plays optical tricks, especially just before daylight. An hour of steady, fast driving and the sheen of headlights on the atmosphere makes it look as though the road were strewn with white boulders. There is absolutely no sound whatever and pretty soon you don't even hear the swish of your own tires. At any moment you expect to just fly off the edge of the world. I turned the car radio on full blast and that kept me going until I rolled over the next hill and down towards Reno, which was, as usual, wide open, its neon lights flickering, for all the world like a cow-town on Saturday night.

Though there are many towns in America which I dislike, I think that Reno is the only one I fear. I fear it more than Las Vegas which at least has the excuse of attempting a touch of the Roman orgy. But Reno is not like that. It is, as far as I can tell, the only town that exists solely in terms of its economic function, gambling. Gamblers are zombies. The least sexual beings in the world. My dad was one. It was four-thirty in the morning and the main street, and streets leading off it, were crowded with shiny new cars. I drove slowly through the center of town and down a side street to Jack's Pot o' Luck, a minor gambling hall inhabited mainly by slot machines and the zombies who play them. I had found Junior, dealing faro and blackjack in a small corner here the last time I had been through, a year ago. Junior was not exactly a friend. We had once collaborated on a screenplay. About a cowboy who is afraid of guns and a lady ranch owner who is afraid of men. While writing it, we thought it was very funny and touching; we kept Katherine Hepburn and Humphrey Bogart in our minds all the time. Junior was a famous crook in Hollywood. He stole from everybody and was writing a verse novel about his childhood in Muscogee. On the first night of our collaboration I told him I had heard of his reputation and I brought out a contract right then and there. He laughed very hard and signed it and I mailed it, registered, to myself. I found Junior easy to work with if he was locked up legally that way. At that time he was married to a ballet dancer who was so terrified of pregnancy that she made him wear a double condom while she wore a contraceptive device herself. Junior's wife never liked me because she thought I believed she was stupid. I did believe she was stupid. In terms of pure distilled stupidity she was a world-beater but I was disappointed in myself that she should know that I thought so. She wasn't a bad girl and very good-looking. I was one of the minority who thought she was excellent as a dancer. She also could do Martha Graham, but possibly without the right degree of muscular austerity, because you could get excited watching her. She was a Jewish girl who looked Negro. Junior finally left her for a rich woman who had a number of children and a swimming pool in Palm Springs and was living, in addition, on her husband's alimony. I knew her husband too. We had a regular old circus in those days. The screenplay never sold.

Amidst the racket of clacketing, whirring slot machines and the sleepy mumble of a few dealers, I walked around looking for Junior. The manager couldn't even remember his name. I fell to talking to several men in Stetson hats who were standing around the Coca-Cola cooler. One and all, they told me that Eisenhower saved the country and would continue to do so. I looked out the window and saw numbers of people congregating on the corners and even on the low roofs of the motels across the street. I asked the men in Stetsons what was up. They said that in a few minutes the AEC was setting off a nuclear device over near White Sands, at Mercury. That was the phrase one of them used, nuclear device. I asked him if he meant an atom bomb, and he looked at me. I was a square. We all walked out of Jack's Pot o' Luck and up the street to watch for the glow.

When we got to the street corner one of the men said he was going to climb a roof for a better view. The others told him he could get just as good a view from the street, that the announcement had said this was to be an unusually big one, but he left us anyway. "Sam's like that, isn't he?" said one of the Stetsons to me. I agreed Sam was like that. Then they all began to talk like experts, like sitting members of the Atomic Energy Commission. They asked each other what kiloton range the device was likely to be, sniffed the wind to comment on the favorableness of weather conditions, and mused about whether the "shot" would be high or low level. I asked what time the atomic bomb would be exploded. They stared at me again. I had done the square thing. I excused myself and called it a nuclear device.

One of the men put his hand on my shoulder and said, "Son, there ain't no call for you getting sarcastic. That's the only thing that stands between us and the Russians. If they fought fair it would be a different thing, believe me." He was the largest and oldest of the men in Stetsons. I asked him if by fighting fair he meant that the Russians had more men than us. Without consultation, they all decided I was a foul ball and conversation ceased forthwith. We stood together on the street corner and waited.

A clear, yellowish dawn was beginning to come up in the east. Behind us, none of the neons went off. Small knots of people collected on the street corners, and a few of the south-facing windows in the small hotels had faces in them. Here and there a party on a rooftop. Gamblers and slot-machine players began drifting out of the clubs to watch. Others, on the street corners, unable to wait, hurried back into the clubs. One of the Stetsons disattached himself quietly and went into the Palace of the Golden West to play the slot machines. Everybody's attitude was watchful but not tense. There was a lot of quiet joking around, as before the bride appears. "There it is!" a woman shouted.

An intake of breath swept the crowds, followed by a babble as the eyes caught the white glare that spread over the whole dawning sky, a sharp, slow splurge of light that brought forth appreciative Ah's from the crowd. One of the Stetsons said, "God, that's beautiful." As the glow whitened and spread and blotted out the ridge of rising sun, the babble died down and the faces on the people became serious and drawn. Several people said, "It's a big one." When the new harsh light did not go away, several looked frightened. The light was high and wide but was far away and not reflected against the white cement walls and the white, tense faces of the watchers. The glow spread and weakened. Not many people spoke. When it began to merge with the rising dawn people began to break away and go back into the joints.

I left the company of the Stetsons, who were lounging on the street corner, staring off at nothing in particular, chewing on toothpicks and smoking cigarettes.

I walked into the Palace of the Golden West. The Stetson was still there, glued to his slot machine. He had made a big killing in dimes and he looked glumly excited. He hadn't even come out for a look. I asked him why he hadn't come out for a look, but he kept feeding dimes into the machine and pulling the lever like a mechanical man, shifting his eyes only to dart a cold glance at me. One of the hostesses, who was plastered against the plate-glass front, was still looking off to the southeast. The joint was half full of customers at the slot machines. Only a few had gone out for a look. The hostess said, "It sure does make a person wonder, doesn't it?" I said it sure does. I went over and lost a dollar's worth of dimes in one of the machines, then went out to the sidewalk and walked around the center of Reno for a while. Then I bought an early morning newspaper in front of an all-night drugstore and went into an all-night diner for breakfast. According to Reuters, said the *Nevada State Journal,* the revisionist Nagy had taken over the premiership of Hungary from Hegedus. The new government, under Nagy, had invoked the Warsaw Treaty and was inviting Soviet troops to help pacify the uprising.

The counterman had the radio tuned in to a disc jocky and I asked him what the latest news was. He said he turned off his ears whenever the news program came on. The radio was blaring "Love Me Tender" by Elvis Presley. I finished my breakfast. The man sitting next to me asked me if I had seen the flash. I said that I had. He seemed satisfied. I paid for my meal and walked back to the street corner. By now it was early morning, a clear warm morning, and the streets were empty. Nobody was around. Even the joints were beginning to close up. The Stetsons had scattered. I walked around the bleak, blinking streets thinking about Hungary.

In an alleyway a woman in a black shirt-blouse and a checked dirndl skirt called out to me harshly. That was something new in Reno. Probably she was drunk. I told her I had to go on. And I did.

I stayed on Highway 40 heading for Salt Lake City. I kept glancing to my right, south toward Yucca Flat, waiting for a flash. It seemed impossible to me that traffic should move so normally, that trucks and cars should be lined up so usually in front of the gas stations, that the expressions on the faces of the drivers coming towards me should be so empty of meaning as they concentrated on the road. Why weren't they all glancing over their shoulders south to Yucca Flat? Why weren't they scared? I was. I was so scared that I stopped off in Sparks and bought two bottles of aspirin. I was cold and trembling so I drove a way out of town and parked in the desert and slept for a couple of hours. I kept the radio on while I slept.

Better, awake, I switched off the radio because I didn't want to weaken the battery and also because I didn't want to hear the news which kept repeating that the situation in Budapest was confused. The road dipped down towards Carson Sink and I took 40 along what used to be the California emigrant trail. It was all pure desert now. Nothing green. Scrub and high hot sun. Following the Humboldt River, I turned off at the Winnemucca junction of Highway 95 and headed due north. I drove straight into the desert and by early afternoon the highway north was almost deserted. I was going north fast, away from the glow of Yucca Flat, towards a town I knew and loved. I crossed the Oregon border doing ninety-five and feeling fine in myself, not tired, in country that was wide and yellow and clean. North, north, up into the desert highlands, through the old sand-papered mountains and down into the Jordan Valley, patches of lush green where they had put in irrigation. The De Soto was doing fine. There was a slight tear in the fabric of the top which kept flapping bad sounds into my brain, and as soon as the sun was cool enough I lowered the top and drove into a torrent of clean desert wind, slowing down into Idaho and crossing the Snake River bridge at one hundred, my foot hard down on the accelerator, the clean dry wind a roar in my ears and not a car in sight beyond the big brown bluffs. This was Cheyenne and, before they got horses, early Comanche territory, north country, the southern border of Nez Percé country, in the Salmon River Mountains. At Caldwell I stopped the car where a plaque said that the Oregon Trail crossed Highway 95. There was also a restaurant drive-in and a drive-in movie. I looked at a map I'd picked up in a local gas station. The highway followed the old Trail. I drove along it, out of Caldwell, into fertile irrigated land, following the Snake along the rugged gorges and flat plains, into higher country, along the Idaho border looking into northeast Oregon. I was now on Highway 30 North, roaring up into the Blue Mountains, approximately the same route taken by Lewis and Clark. High elevation orchards and wheatfields.

I was in timber and fishing country now, going eighty along the tops of the red gorges. Up ahead were the great national forests. The highway narrowed and there was a great deal of repair work; I slowed down. As soon as I did I almost lost control of the car when a lumber truck rounded a bend and came towards me. The De Soto swerved into the truck's lane but I pulled it back in time and heard the truck driver call me a name. I felt a strong temptation to go and lie in a ditch somewhere but I kept going until my head cleared. I switched on the car radio which said that it was not yet known whether Soviet troops would respond to Premier Nagy's call for intervention.

Near Pendleton I stopped the car to inquire of a group of men on the highway what the trouble was. A nearby ambulance was just getting into low gear. One of the men said they were deer hunters and Les Buckler had accidentally shot himself in the leg. Another man asked me if I was a reporter from the Pendleton *East Oregonian*, and I said yes, we always tried to get to where the news was happening fast. They started giving me queer looks, those hunters, and I followed the ambulance all the way into Pendleton. Following the ambulance made me feel better for some reason, and in the middle of town I turned off onto Highway 2 heading into the dusk. I drove steadily until the sun went down behind a great national forest on my left and I followed the signs until I arrived at Walla Walla State Prison.

*

When I tried to drive past the cement island a guard stepped out and said that no visitors were permitted after three in the afternoon and that, in any event, I would have to arrange for permission well beforehand. I turned around and drove into Walla Walla and registered at the first hotel I came to, which was the Marcus Whitman Hotel, the most expensive one in town. After shaving and washing up and refusing to turn on the radio in the room I went downstairs and had a heavy meal and then into the bar.

Most of the local businessmen drinking at the bar said they were Eisenhower supporters, naturally. I asked some questions about the prison which nobody in the bar could answer. The bartender said, "We've all been living here for so long we don't think about it much." I asked the bartender, whose name was Philip Gracious, if he ever thought about what it meant to go without women for fifteen years and he asked me if I had just got out. I said, with conviction, yes, I'd just gotten out. He said I should not entertain morbid thoughts, and that my whole life lay before me, I was still a young man. I agreed. He reached under the bar and brought out a copy of *Love Or Perish* by a man named Smiley Blanton. I told Mr. Gracious that when I was a kid the only people named Smiley Blanton who admitted it in public were the men who played the grizzled sidekicks of Johnny Mack Brown and Ken Maynard. We got to arguing over whether either Brown or Maynard had ever had a sidekick in his films. I said that I had worked for years in Hollywood and that there was very little about pictures I did not know. Philip Gracious, the bartender, said he was impressed by my exploits but to name one picture where either Johnny Mack Brown or Ken Maynard, or for that matter Buck Jones or Tom Mix, had ever had a permanent sidekick. He said he did not want to be unfair, I did not have to give the titles but only a recognizable outline of the plot. He said he could remember western plots like his own name. Finally, I had to admit I could think of none. He was gracious in victory and offered to buy me a drink. I accepted and allowed as how it was very significant that cowboys today needed sidekicks. I said that we could make a cool million by writing a new song to this theme, the title would be "Togetherness on the Range." He said that no song had a chance these days that did not feature heavenly choirs and sing it up with God. It disgusted him. He said Smiley Blanton was disgusted too, and that he, Philip Gracious, wanted me to have his book, as a personal token. I said I did not want to take his ballast away from him, and then I got sore and said that I had lived this long without Smiley Blanton and I could live some more without him and what the hell kind of name was that anyway. Philip Gracious looked hurt and turned away to serve other customers. I was doing better than usual. At least I hadn't *attacked* Smiley Blanton, I assured myself. But old Philip Gracious still was offended. I signaled for him to come over and I said, Look, you go to your church and I'll go to mine. He replied it was no skin off his nose. I said, For Christ's sake, Mr. Gracious, it's stupid, really stupid, for us to be arguing the finer points of popular divinity when at any moment Russian soldiers. When. When.

He gave me an experienced look and I said, Don't worry, I'm not drunk. But he didn't believe me.

A little fat businessman named Harold Cherry came over and introduced himself from where he had been feeding coins into the Wurlitzer and playing the kind of tune Smiley Blanton disapproved of. Harold Cherry was the proprietor of Walla Walla's largest paint and varnish emporium. He said that he guessed I was a public pollster. A what? I asked. A man from the Gallup polls, he said. He had heard me asking earlier in the evening how everyone was going to vote. I said I was doing it only to settle a bet with a friend in Los Angeles who had wagered me there were more Democrats than Republicans in Walla Walla, Washington.

Harold Cherry said cheerfully, "You've won yourself a bet, mister, come on over and meet the wife." We sat down in a red leather couch near the Wurlitzer and Harold Cherry stuck in about a dollar's worth of change just to keep things friendly and alive, he said. Mrs. Cherry had, for some reason, an evening gown on. She said no, it was a cocktail dress. I said it was most attractive. Harold Cherry looked pleased. Mrs. Cherry was a blonde and not young and quite dreamy. Mr. Cherry said his wife often got into moods near the Wurlitzer. I said, Do either of you feel one way or the other about the door being shut on soviets plus electrification in Budapest, and Mrs. Cherry smiled gently and said, "Land's sakes of course not." She was really very sweet. I said, Well that's taken care of, now we can be just folks.

We sat around talking for an hour or so, and then Mr. Cherry said he had a hard day's driving to Spokane tomorrow to purchase some varnish wholesale and he would have to go beddy-bye now. He said beddy-bye. We said goodnight to him and wished him well. When he was gone Mrs. Cherry and I moved over to the bar where Philip Gracious maintained his distance, sulking. I said, for Christ's sakes, Mr. Gracious, stop sulking. Mrs. Cherry and I had several drinks. She kept telling me that I reminded her of her eldest son, Matthew, who was at the Air Force Academy. I said that was very interesting. She really was a good-looking woman. I touched her cheek with my hand and in this same, dreamy, detached voice she said, "My husband is a very odd man. He wants you to kiss me and touch me. He says that one day he would like to watch." I stopped touching her cheek. We had one more drink and then Mrs. Cherry went upstairs to Mr. Cherry. I fed the Wurlitzer a half hour's worth and sat down in one of the rear, red leather seats and drew circles on the Formica table and sat in the dark and drank and thought about Mr. and Mrs. Cherry. Mr. Gracious had to tell me twice that he was closing up. He didn't look as if he wanted to be asked to have a drink with me so I didn't ask him. When I left the copy of *Love Or Perish* was gone from the top of the bar.

I drove out to the prison early the next morning and asked at the warden's office if I could see my good friend E. J. Birdsong. I said that I knew it was irregular but that I might not be through this part of the country for quite a while. When I flashed my obsolete press card and talked about researching a film about prisons, they finally let me see him. I have visited friends in several prisons in America, but this prison at Walla Walla had the only visiting room that looked as though a set designer had put it up twenty-five years ago for *The Last Mile*. This was not a visiting day and E.J. and I were pretty much left to ourselves, except for a single guard who lounged in an overstuffed chair on a platform and read *Daring Western Stories*.

How have you been keeping, Indian Bird? I said.

He said, "It's a nice surprise, I wasn't expecting any visitors."

I told the Indian Bird I was passing through. He said, "Where to?" and I said I wasn't sure yet. He said, "Like in 1946."

Yes, I said, just like in 1946 . . .

The soldier boy, Tech/3, was AWOL.

Unmolested, he had walked out the front gate of Camp Kilmer, New Jersey, and had gone to visit friends in Paterson, New Jersey, where his mother and father had once organized a long and fruitless strike of fabric weavers. Then he kept walking, to Durham, North Carolina, to go visiting some more.

Being in the South affected him, and he decided to use what little money he had to take a train to Chattanooga, Tennessee, where as a child he had gone barefoot and nigger-baiting; and in Chattanooga he took the incline cable car to the place he knew best, Lookout Mountain, to the promontory of Pulpit Rock where with one of the veterans of the Confederacy, commonly known hereabouts as the Old Bugler, deaf and lunatic, he had sat out the dying afternoon on a bench.

They sat overlooking a valley which had once been the location of a tactically decisive bayonet charge.

Behind them, the descending whine of the cable car. Left behind, only a few visitors, uninterested, after the first glance, in the old man and the soldier boy who, though they sat several feet apart on the wooden bench, had achieved a tenuous and furtive contact the dimensions of which would have required keener eyes than were represented in the husband and wife from Nashville, the family from the city below with their two small children and the Negro refuse collector more involved in keeping to the shade of trees on Pulpit Rock than eavesdropping on what was not anything yet of the old man's dribbling recollections. The air around the two of them on the bench seemed thick with the arresting and cessation of time.

Perhaps ten minutes passed in just this fashion, the Old Bugler and the Tech/3 sitting on the same bench with only one of them acknowledging the other's presence by his wonder if the old man was asleep, dreaming awake or dead.

"Old Bugler? Sir? Old Bugler?" the soldier boy called, low.

The flesh above the eyes where once there had been brows

twitched imperceptibly, as though to brush away an unseen fly, or child's hand. The soldier boy did not want to touch the old man. He moved closer on the bench. In silence they stared out together at the valley.

"Old Bugler," the soldier boy said, "I've got bad trouble."

Thus, all afternoon, he spoke his heart to the deaf and motionless old man.

". . . but I don't know. Something keeps telling me not to go back to Chicago, to leave it alone." The soldier boy chewed stubbornly on a blade of grass, half remembering how he and Cecil and Wilson, as boys, used to go down to the river and eat the special salty clover growing along the banks. "Way I feel right now, I'd just as soon stay up here on this damn rock till winter comes."

"Yes . . . Till winter comes. Both us." A whispered lament, a piece of the wind, not a human voice.

The soldier boy sat up with a startled sigh. He stared at the man who had heard his confession.

At a discreet distance, the Negro groundskeeper, so bent and wrinkled in his own right that he might have been one of the slaves whose rights had been in dispute that cloud-shrouded August day in 1863, edged towards them, wishing to explain something the young white gentleman appeared not to understand. The octogenarian sat frozen in a precise, instant posture of honorable surrender. Prickles thrilling on his neck, the soldier boy stood away from the bench and awaited a movement.

"What's the mattah, boy. Ol' Bugle let one go?" The groundskeeper yelled and yipped with laughter.

At that moment, the incline cable car brought the Old Bugler's caretaker — son, friend, hired man, kind man? — too naturally torpid, too sleepy and spiritless to acknowledge a joke which had been standing between the old Negro groundskeeper and himself for so long it had grown noisome. "If'n he c'n fart by hissef, he c'n walk by hissef!"

The cable car brought them all down to ground.

Inside the enclosure at the foot of the mountain the soldier boy watched after the Old Bugler shuffling away, without sign, without word. The cable car's motorman shut the door of his vehicle and pulled at the accordion gates of the enclosure. "All right, soldier, time to get a move on."

The soldier boy looked up. Pulpit Rock emerged sharp, almost gleaming in a fortuitous ray of late afternoon sun; and with a movement of sky, a tattered flag of cloud grew dark and shadowy, a place of inlaid ghosts and cannonballs rusting in the wood of stately oaks and the rustle of a thousand bugles.

"Sure thing, mister. I've got to get a move on!"

And the move he got on he no longer tried to borrow a purpose for, but went in the direction he woke up facing, sometimes traveling five hundred miles in a single day only to wonder at fall of night what in *hell* was the hurry, he had nowhere to go. Yet, at times, for two, three days running, he found his blood and thoughts racing. Who had a clock on him? Nobody but the Judge Advocate's Department of the U.S. Army, and that was nothing he was in such an all-fired rush to set his time to. But he was in a rush; beyond the Mississippi was a new vastness to him as exciting and potential of adventure (perhaps even a lucky stroke of salvation) as it had once looked to Marquette and Pike and Frémont and Big Bill Haywood. Westerly he went, on the fringes of the first lap of the wave that was to carry whole demographic chunks of America to the Rockies, to the Pacific, away from the known and old and tried to the new that was already (though none knew it) turning tarnished, the truly last frontier turning green at the edges before anyone could lay a firm hand on it.

His mother's forebears had walked into new country behind a moldboard plow, his father had come in steerage, and steerage was good enough for the AWOL son of a half-Irish publican's daughter and a Byelorussian troublemaker. Anyway, is there such a thing as steerage, in a good late September when a clean G.I. uniform will catch you a highway ride quicker and freer than a ticket on The Chief?

Westerly. Away from Pulpit Rock, and the confession he had made there now only a burr with broken needles somewhere under the scalp of his mind; scuffing back-country dust of back-country roads on his G.I. brogans to a junction at 231 where another hitchhiker warned watch it boy there's bulls across the line in 'bama lustin' for our skulls; so he turned north, riding and walking and keeping an eye out for city cops and MP's and country cops in three equal parts, up the trunk of Tennessee State, by-passing Murfreesboro to brood on the fields of Armageddon known as Stones River where Mendenhall's artillery had done its work so well that only an unpicturesque puzzle of chomps of meat and shards of bone was left to piece out that which they never were able to do, one out of six of Breckenridge's Johnny Rebs so blasted to pieces gravediggers got impatient and shoveled the correct weight into holes and tagged the holes with the names of the missing. Stones River, had the Old Bugler been there? No, he couldn't have been, not if he hadn't seen a bayonet used until Chattanooga.

The soldier boy kept going, beginning to like the way he was living, forgetting even to count the days which slipped past him like the telephone poles which brooded on his lonesome passage to God knows where he didn't; west again on 70 N because it carried heavier traffic until he remembered it would take him to Nashville and he was by-passing the invite of the big towns this trip, thank you just the same, shrewdly ducking through the gullies and woods where Hood had yipped at Pickett's heels, who had outnumbered him ten to one, until Thomas could break away from Murfreesboro, snap Jackson's neck, galled Pickett, shrewd Hood, shrewd soldier boy, taking the side roads and no roads, sleeping in the fields and begging his food at back doors of beat-up old farmhouses as lonely in the scrub fields as he knew he had every right to be, and wasn't, except sometimes when he saw a pretty girl and got a sudden keen sparking out of his belt buckle to tarry a bit but couldn't; he'd gone to a lot of gangster films in his day and if there was one thing the soldier boy, Tech/3, knew it was stay away from the dames when you're on the lam. Still, he couldn't very well throw cold water down his pants every time he passed a sweet-titted thing; so he kept on yearning and kept on walking, ceasing neither, not even when the lady of the house, somewhere east of Paris and west of Blytheville, obediently washed his shirt and sewed on the ruptured duck he had bought in the last town for fifteen cents (if the Army of the United States wouldn't discharge him, by God he'd discharge himself), showing him an extreme courtesy (but not extreme for those hospitable parts, stranger) in a town called Hopkinsville, Kentucky; bam bam thank you ma'am and then oh Jesus Sam that's my husband and out the back window he dove in a style so traditional he knew he was going to laugh even before he rolled onto the roof of the chicken coop, remembering he hadn't been in Advanced Infantry Training for nothing, hitting the ground in a neat double roll that would have made his commanding officer weep with pride just as the man of the house drove up early from produce market, running like crazy hell so he fled into a slow old dirty old river and waded out laughing so hard he thought sure the angel in charge of damfoolishness would surely be holding his ears and planning to make life difficult for him over this if nothing else. So there he sprawled on the west bank of an east Arkansas river, wet and covered with green scum, the laughter so hard and new it was the quickest way to dry off, lying under the dead oaks, and thinking how he'd once thought these things happened only in the eight-pagers he and Fifie and Schloime sold one winter on consignment around Hanson Elementary until the night Fifie sobbed that juvenile authorities had been to his house, and the two of them had to go out at one in the morning to sadly bury all their inventory in a frozen fastness of Douglas Park, using a World War I bayonet and a kitchen knife to hack out a hole in the snow-covered ground. Fifie and Schloime. The soldier boy lay back, homesick, so ill with it it occurred to him Jake Arvey's Chicago was the only home he was ever likely to have had, and with the river scum so thick on his G.I. trousers cultured flowers might have sprung from the vicinity of his loins had he encountered a good stiff rain, he pointed himself towards the nearest highway heading due north, bumming it and looking it, white trash driven by a wayward wind but not careless enough to knock on the doors where he'd be welcomed most warmly, in the Negro villages flanking the Mississippi; passing through poor white country he was no more a refugee and hard bankers than any of them, but he kept away from Negroes who would warm him and feed him and talk about him and nothing he could do to stop them.

Due north, Chicagoward. Highway 61, no less, if you please, traveling by night and sleeping by day ever since the morning a bored deputy in Fayetteville, Arkansas, took down his name in a little book on general principle but had been too damned bored to ask past the ruptured duck for papers. Shrewd soldier boy, successful spy in enemy country, he found highways in the dark now the way mountain witches find water fifty feet under, the way Indians find game, the way the FBI finds its man, God forbid. Highway 61, in every year and every model of prewar Ford, Chevvy and Dodge (Packard, Buick, Chrysler, you joking?), in the cab, on the roof, inside the truck, inside outside and on the edges of trucks, half tons, full tons and quarter tons, once on the running board and twice on the fenders of Rios, White Motors, International Harvesters, Diamonds and Fruehauf trucks, vans, lorries and hybrids, paying off in the two kinds of currency he could manage, sharing the wheel and listening to the lonely talk of lonely drivers on the lonely night highway.

He didn't know it but he was catching up. All he knew now was that he had been away longer than it seemed.

Lord, the people he met and the troubles he heard, and not a peep about his own since Pulpit Rock.

A yard-goods drummer with a cheating wife *and* a cheating girlfriend, what was a man to do, it was this crazy war destroyed the moral fiber of the nation, danged if it didn't.

An honest-to-God grayhaired drummer who looked like anyone's daddy, even yours, stuck away in a Cape Girardeau roadhouse orchest-e-ra when he was so sure one good break would take him to the sweet wily glare of, at least, Woody Herman; tooling a Model A, *with super-charger coils*, with a gold-star flag, of a type displayed in lace-curtain front windows by bereaved mothers, fluttering from his Aphrodite radiator ornament and a supply of big-time breaks in a small black medical bag snug under the front seat. This drummer was cheating on nobody but life. The gold flag, he cried, was for dear departed himself.

Things were bad enough without little black bags, and the soldier boy thanked the man a hundred miles south of Cape Girardeau orchest-e-ra, not raising his thumb again until he saw the gold star flag disappear over the next hill because he didn't want to hurt the feelings of the man who had found out so well how to hurt his own.

Migrating season for miseries and musicians. A cowboy singer up from the Panhandle, except he wasn't a cowboy, wasn't a singer but might have been the other from the way he kept offering to borrow tay-in dol-lahs like the soldier boy should of been ish-amed of hissef fer bein' so uncharitable as to talk, in such levitous tones, about blood from turnips and such, why *don't* a young feller, vet'run too Ah see, would've been in mah-sef except fer spots on mah lung which jes' missed bein' recorded by one of the more prominent companies, "Draft Exempt Blues."

Texas season too. This one the gen-u-ine article, oil rig man, just wanderin' until he could forget what crude smelled like, then he'd be ready to go back to the fields, did it every year, just couldn't stand that greasy-cream smell more than eleven months out of the year.

A truck driver with seven children and one wife, further comment superfluous.

A wall-eyed gray-haired lady who looked like Whistler's Mother and acted like Whistler, had the menopause, thought she was being driv crazy and wouldn't soldier boy like to put a pause to her menopause? Lady, you could be my mother. Mind your manners, I ain't.

A young priest with no troubles he wanted to talk about. But there's no law against guessing.

A farmer from Missouri who didn't know the war was over.

An aircraft worker from Paducah who knew it was and was worried.

A leaf colonel in the Signal Corps who was going back to found the biggest automatic laundry in Fargo, North Dakota.

A droop-eyed young poet in a droop-chassied old Chev, going home to the farm in Niles, Michigan, after two years at Tulane University because the Rhodes scholarship he'd won in 1943 couldn't be done in wartime England.

A motorcyclist with a death wish, and a truck driver with piles who didn't stop talking about it from New Madrid to Sikeston; a truck driver with boils on his spine and a truck driver with sciatica; by south of St. Louis soldier boy had become world authority on the ailments, aliments and implacements of every teamster, truck and muck driver in the whole wide state of Missouri.

A man in Hupmobile taking his son to a clinic in Ste. Genevieve. The son had "the evils" and was tied with hemp rope to the door handles. Giggling, he sounded more sinister than his old man.

Soldier boy, no expert on nervous illness, guessed the kid had cerebral palsy.

A foreman in a Little Rock dyeworks whose hands were stained blood-red and who said he had grown up with Harry Truman but wouldn't be voting for him after that speech about drafting railroad workers who were on strike.

The mayor's son of, well what's the diff now, why besmirch the fair name of he who has no doubt met a glorious end in some public urinal, zipping along in a 1940 Lincoln on vacation from Yale winding up a lecture on Plato meant to put someone maybe soldier boy in his place by offering a proposal which might have proved irresistible under a slightly altered genetic circumstance, say if one of them had been a girl, officially.

A Negro wagoneer who claimed he cried two days running when Roosevelt (Franklin Delano) died, and looked to be pretty dubious if he or the world would ever recover.

A Fundamentalist parson who had memorized Churchill's blood, tears and sweat speech.

A gloomy gus in a shrimpy red Ford, laid off from a place called Willow Run, jobless and wifeless and friendless and just plain tired of being less. I got a gun in the trunk and I'm gonna use it on myself in Sain Loo, he promised. What do you want to say such things for mister, you ain't scaring me. Don't need to that, I'm scared for both of us. Soldier boy decided that maybe gloomy Gus wasn't kidding. He told the man what he'd heard down the road, they were hiring over the line at West Frankfurt. Still, he wouldn't read any of the newspapers for a few days, just in case.

A mile outside city limits, St. Louis, a red-haired giant with a face the color and size of a pumpkin pulled up and said, You maybe looking fawr work, young man. Maybe. Got a gas station jes' around the bend and need a night man, $22 a week, three dollars a day, either way you want it, and a cot to sleep on in the back. So for the next ten days it was soldier boy, pump monkey without portfolio, had to listen to Redhead Neville's ignorant talk whenever Redhead Neville took a mind for it which was sometimes 3 A.M. sharp. Neville was the largest, fattest, stupidest, selfishest, slowest most redheaded boastful blissful bastard soldier boy had ever known, and didn't even have a good heart, but what he didn't know about fixing motors just wasn't worth knowing and had the added advantage of being just too damn stupid to wonder why soldier boy never made that mile up past city limits and generally was not available for comment when the state or county cops came around for a friendly hooraw. Redhead Neville had only two gears, sleeping and bragging. He could, would and did brag about any and every single activity he had ever committed since memory, like he was his own doting mother, from the Not Quite Honorable Discharge he had from the Regular U.S. Army, from the number of years it took him to get out of "slow school" to his fat wife's cooking, the size of his shoes and the size of his dong (same), how in all this world what he hated most were the middling, piddling people, the uppity niggers and the officers; he called soldier boy Shorty and charged him fifty cents a night for the cot at the bottom of the grease pit.

Soldier boy was fired as he was hired, quick and blustery weather was made of it, but with less explanation and walking away from St. Louis soldier boy could see the big redhead figuring a way to boast about *that* but would ever wonder why his employer never talked big about the one thing that justified him taking up so much space on an overcrowded planet, what he could do with motors. They say in Missouri, and elsewhere, it takes all kinds.

Soldier boy came away from St. Louis with $17 in his pocket and a Greyhound bus ticket to the house of the Indian Bird, E. J. Birdsong.

"Indian Bird! Indian *Bird!*" he called across the freshly painted white picket fence squaring the big, porticoed house with the white stars painted on the blue-colored rising sun side of the sloping roof. E. J. Birdsong had said that the house was given and paid for by the government in recognition of a conciliatory attitude on a complicated grasslands transaction. It had porticoes and large squat pillars and a porch running around three sides. It was situated at the end of a dirt road outside Cache, Oklahoma. It was early morning.

"Indian *Bird*."

"I'll be go-to-goddam," calmly declared E. J. Birdsong, coming out the screendoor and ambling down the steps and across the ingrassed red-dirt yard. He had on a blue work shirt against his oxblood-colored skin and tight blue jeans and homemade openwork sandals.

"That's right, E.J. You get my postcard?"

"The one from New York?"

"Uh-huh."

"No. Never got it."

They laughed and shook hands over the white picket fence.

"How does it feel to be out of uniform, E.J.?"

"I never was in," said the Indian Bird, eying the ruptured duck.

E.J. opened the gate and said, "It's no white man's setup here, sergeant."

"I'm not a white man any more, E.J."

"If you got a sad story, paleface, we better honor it here. The tepee is full of conservative squaws."

"Indian Bird, when are you scheduled to stop talking like that?"

"Like what?"

"Oh well."

The two boys squatted in the red dust of the big yard in front of the house. The sun was strong. "What's that?" Soldier boy pointed to the white stars on the blue roof.

"Big white stars," said E.J., carding red and yellow dust through his thick brown fingers. "One of Tonto's ideas." E.J. always called his grandfather, the last chief of the unreservationed tribe, Tonto.

Sitting in the yard they renewed things between them. It felt good. E.J. seldom showed his emotions; when he liked people he looked directly at them as they spoke, otherwise his eyes were usually planted six inches above their heads, meaning he didn't give a damn about them one way or another. With his curly, oily black hair and big chubby brown face and small bee-stung mouth and a rounded almost button nose he didn't much look like a traditional Indian, but E.J. said that in the old days the tribes used to raid deep into Mexico, occasionally as far as Chihuahua, and always some Comanches in the next generation had the soft Mexican look. The Mexicans, he said, used to call September the "month of the Comanche moon," so regular were the raids.

"I'll tell you, Indian Bird. The Army, I just decided it would be the wrong thing."

"Uh oh, a legal thing. I don't want to know about it. Even if I ask you don't tell me." He raised himself standing from a cross-legged squat in one lithe movement. "I'm thirsty too." They walked across the yard and up the steps together.

The first thing soldier boy thought inside the screen door was how could the house appear so drowsily quiet from the outside and hold so many people inside at the same time.

It was like a boardinghouse, or a hotel. The only difference seemed to be that no owner or proprietor was on hand to maintain order.

"Kind of loony in a way," said the Indian Bird, nonapologetically.

The first floor was divided by a long corridor, or hallway, running the entire length of the back of the house, paralleling the outside porch. A dozen doors, presumably leading to rooms, were encrusted in the wall at even and precise intervals. Each door was woodworked into baroque curlicues like a medieval church entrance.

Both ends of the ground-floor hallway opened onto doorways without doors spilling out precipitately, without benefit of stairs, into the yard and around which were clustered children, or rather the small shadows and silhouettes of them, since the hallway was dark except for the daylight pouring in at both ends.

The entire section of the first floor, to the left, fronting the yard was taken up by an enormous parlor. At the moment, this room, the dimensions of which were those of the downstairs section of an Army barracks, was bustling with household activities. From a broken-down couch in front of the room's only window, a slim young woman was feeding numerous children not all of whom had Indian skins. In the far corner of the enormous room, facing a wall the design of whose paper was no longer visible except as decaying brown snakes in black nests on brown paper, stood a narrow table on which two somewhat older women were ironing clothes from a huge bundle at their bare feet, oblivious to the nude calendar above their heads dated 1937.

In the center of the room an old gnarled lady squatted on the floor contemplating but not working a primitive weaving frame on which nothing was stretched. On the steps leading from the porch to the room three women sat mending and gossiping. All along the near wall women stood at corrugated iron tubs filled with what looked like tallow, dipping their hands in up to the elbows and working a colored, viscous fluid which coated their arms. The predominant noise of the room was a chakkering hum which seemed to emanate more from the walls than the inhabitants. All the women wore cheap print dresses. Some had fairer skins than the soldier boy. Some of the women stopped work to notice him.

"Visitor," said E.J.

Few of the children looked like E.J. They were the sons of the raiders, not the raided.

E.J. took his friend upstairs. He pointed to a room the size of the downstairs parlor and enclosed by three-quarters high partitions. "Kitchen," said E.J. "Latrines out back." He went over and spoke to a fat woman looking at them from the entrance to the kitchen. When he returned he said, "You're in like Flynn. I told them you're sixteenth Cree. Makes it easier on me."

They were standing at a hole in the wall at the back of the house. Someone had forgotten to put in the door, and the drop was a sheer thirty feet to the weeds below. Out there, resting in a tin-can and trash-littered back yard was an outhouse with a dusty invitation to EATS painted on one side and the windows covered with cardboard and red dust. It was a railroad-car diner such as truck drivers frequent at the side of highways. On both sides of the outhouse were small clumps of trees and behind the trees an oil well. More precisely, an oil pump, its black, rusted elephant head nodding to a slow dreamy chug-chug beat.

"Wait a minute," said E.J. and disappeared into one of the indentations along the hall. He emerged. "C'mon."

The room into which soldier boy walked was square, small and almost dark. A short fat woman in a print dress sat on a bed. She examined him while holding an infant in one hand and *True Love Affairs* in the other. The room was neatly arranged, two pastoral scenes hung in glassed frames on the walls, the floor was swept, the other bed made up and a small library of books and magazines on the window sill. The window was boarded up from the inside, and the room was lighted by bulbs in a miniature crystal chandelier stuck in the ceiling.

The woman was a private hymn to overlapping folds of rich brown flesh. "My boy says you're going to stay up here a spell."

"Yes ma'am, if it's all right."

"Get him something to eat, Indian Bird," she said, using the name E.J. had acquired at the hands of whites in the Army.

Outside in the corridor, with the door shut, soldier boy asked, "Is that your mother?"

"I think so," said the Indian Bird.

High tea was served downstairs in a communal dining hall adjoining the parlor, on long clean board tables.

Afterwards, the two Army friends went behind the outhouse where the Indian Bird chased away some children. It was cooler out here, in the shadow and hearing of the oil pump.

E.J. said, "A thing or two you ought to know before the Mencken come in."

"The who?"

"Men-kin." E.J. rolled over on his stomach. "I don't believe I ever did tell you about this setup, did I? Guess not. I wasn't born in that house but I might as well have been." He paused and laid his brown cheek against the earth, fitting himself into it as he would a woman. "Ol' Tonto is the cause of it all. I'm his great-grandson, one of twenty-three. Well anyway something like that.

"He died in 1913, got his grave about half a mile back in the trees there, go and visit it if you like, buried with his horse, shield and lance. Ol' Tonto, he wasn't a Christian, wasn't much of anything except Comanche. Like you know, he was the final chief to come on in, that was in 1879, had four United States armies chasing him, wintered in the Palo Duro Canyon and when the government agreed to a—a what do you call it? armistice—no, amnesty—he brought the band in to Fort Sill. His people were what I am, Antelope band, was down to less than a hundred maybe two thousand soldiers on his ass.

"Ol' Tonto, he didn't much care for reservation life. Especially when a bunch of friggin' Texans got together to kill the Indian agent and scare the bands off the Brazos. The government and Quakers finally got most Comanches, and some of our cousin Kiowas, settled around Anadarko but Ol' Tonto he just took off, on his lonely. Rode halfway through Texas to visit his mama's burial place. She was white. Now don't go giving me that look, if you want you look it up at the Oklahoma State Historical Society, got someone there doing a book on him.

"He was a real piss cutter, Ol' Tonto. Going all that way into Texas alone. Way I see it, he meant to get killed. He was a warrior and a thief and there was no place for him on the reservation and he like to get himself killed off but didn't want to do it himself. Have to remember, he'd been raiding and killing all up and down West Texas the two winters before he came in. He was *known* in Texas. To make a long story short, he got back alive and with a wife, a little ol' Mex gal. Wife Number Two, already had one in the Sunshade band. What with him being white and all, I mean half white, and having the prestige of coming in last, wasn't long before they set him up as a tribal judge and then Number One Chief, which he never was before. A lot of the old-timers didn't care for that too much, when they knew him as a wild young horse thief who was always cutting out of war parties, especially if they was vengeance ones, but they didn't have much say in the matter by this time.

"By this time, it occurred to Ol' Tonto to get rich. The reservation law was that each man had his own piece of land, which nobody could get used to because they'd always thought of this whole damn country as property of whoever used it. Well, not really property. Indians don't believe in property, not the way you do, or even maybe the way I do. Great-granpa caught on first, about this land business being personal, and he started buying it all up. We none of us are sure where he got the money but by this time two of his daughters had married local cattle men, and maybe there. When the law was finally changed to allow Comanches to sell their land it turns out Ol' Tonto owns half the reservation. At heart he was still a thief, he sold that land piece by piece to ranchers and even back to the government, until he was just about the biggest character in this part of the state. Got this house for signing a treaty, forgot which. Had learned to talk English and hire lawyers and soon he had six wives. Adopted a boy run away from the circus. Even talk of running him for Senator. Rode a big white horse in the inaugural processions of two Presidents, McKinley and Roosevelt. The first one. When Roosevelt visited here they went hunting together.

"A showpiece Indian. Independent as hell, feisty enough to get himself a seventh wife at near to eighty, but still a showpiece Indian. A bunch of the churches tried converting him, Baptists, Catholics, the whole lot. But the old man wouldn't have none of it. Had his own religion. Something called Native Indian Church.

Everybody sit around in an old tepee chewing mescalin. Ol' Tonto, he brought it back with him from Mexico on the ride back from Texas. You want, I'll get you some. Anyway, at first he just wouldn't talk to the parsons. Then, maybe he knew he was going to die soon, he began saying yes to all of them. When he finally kicked off they was all hollering to bury him, regular old scandal when it was done tribal.

"Anyway, he left behind eight wives, about a thousand kids and grandkids, a supply of blood kin to last to Armageddon. He didn't leave no will or anything like that, so the money and what was left of the land was divided out. The house, that one, was left to Ol' Tonto and his heirs in perpetuity, nobody much cared to live in it at first, ghosts of things, but come the depression two things happened: a lot of the family got poor and a little oil was found out back, not much, just enough to bring back some of them.

"I don't know if it's too easy a setup to understand. All the blood lines are fouled up. When Ol' Tonto passed away, his brothers didn't take over his wives, which is how the nation used to take care of widows in olden days. So the cousins and nephews all slipped into line and got dealt out the wives; of them, the eighth one, the chief wife, wasn't having any of that noise, she wanted a real life brother or nothing, which was difficult considering his one and only brother had been killed in a raid to steal some horses at Fort Sill long before. Fact is, she was a shrewd ol' squaw, she made a pitch for all Ol' Tonto's fluid assets. She told the government she was the only legal wife, said polygamy was illegal which it always was, except to keep the old Chief's good will nobody ever made him get rid of any. Got all solved when the last wife up and died, county sheriff came out here trying to prove unnatural causes, like to near caused a riot. Well, just when the old boy's money was probated, or whatever, Ol' Tonto's wives got to fighting over the house, biggest one around at the time. What would you do if you had to be the judge and decide between seven women? Don't get it wrong. The wives got on with each other, that's the way it works with Indians. That only made it worse, for a white judge, the women each wanting to live in the house and saying she had given Ol' Tonto the best satisfaction and that's why she deserved it. The youngest wife even tried marrying up with the Chief's adopted son, the white boy, but he went away after the funeral and never came back. You'll see some of his kids around here.

"The judge in Oklahoma City passed the buck to the Indian Court which all found out later he shouldn't've done because the house was federal property only leased to Great-granpa. The Indian Court, minus Ol' Tonto, did the only intelligent thing it could do, made the house belong to all the wives, and that's how it's been since, I don't remember the year, 1915 or something."

Soldier boy asked if all the women hereabouts were wives, or descendants, of the Chief.

"Don't know for sure myself. Expect so. Every summer a family or two moves in, and one or two goes away, so as I say it's pretty mixed up. Just about the time school starts welfare usually comes down trying to sort everybody out but I guess all they're looking for is TB and incest. They ought to know Indians by now. I'll show you your room. How long you want to stay?"

Come evening, the men trooped in from work, looking like a beneficent practical joker's war party, quiet bronzed squat men in suntans and overalls and shirts, perhaps thirteen of them, with their bronze Indian faces and fat noses and wide untall bodies, tired men coming home from work to a big house with big white stars on the blue roof.

Dinner was well-organized. Some sat with their families at the two communal tables in the parlor, now miraculously cleared of laundry and excess children, some out back, picnic style, under the trees, some softly in their rooms. As the men trooped into the parlor, E.J. said, "They ain't exactly what you would call warriors. But they're still bowlegged. Ain't one of them been on a horse in years and they still got legs fitted for a horse. Comanche isn't so damn good without a horse and never was. Just a dirty old fat old redskin, couldn't hit the side of a barn door at twenty yards even in the old days, whole damn nation's got glaucoma. You remember, took me two extra weeks to qualify on the range. But you just put a Comanche on a horse. I don't guess we'll ever get on horses any more. I don't guess so. They got us stuck away in councils, and in schools, in this house, even got a lobbyist in Washington. We don't even know we're Comanches any more. We would if we lived in Texas. They still hate our guts down there. Up around here, it's the thing to have a little Comanche in you, why you can't hardly run for Governor without claiming to some."

The Indian Bird and soldier boy went out and sat down on the porch steps, after dinner, when the sun had gone down and the stars were out in the dark night.

Soldier boy asked Indian Bird what he was going to do now, what he wanted to do, now he was a civilian.

"You'll laugh," said E.J. Birdsong.

"No, I won't."

"All right. Once a year the whole mess of us gets invited down to a little town in North Texas, just across the border. This town is named after Ol' Tonto, they even got a little ol' spur railroad named after him, and one or two of the big stores. The annual celebration of the founding. It's a regular Wild West hoedown, I hate it, always have, treat us like monkeys and make us wear Indian costumes from J. C. Penney's. A lot of the young folks won't wear the costumes any more, and I reckon they'll stop inviting us one of these years. We go because we think we should, and anyroad we get paid for it by the Texas State Chamber of Commerce. The best thing that happens all day is the ceremonial ride, commemorating the ride Ol' Tonto took through that part of the country after he surrendered and expected to get himself killed. At first the ride, which is from one end of town to another, was done by one of us, alone, slow, bang through the center of town, proud as hell, Texans could see he was spittin' in their eye. Later on, they made a regular circus of that ride, big flashy white horse and acrobatics and a whole troop of the Texas Rangers strung out behind. Past few years they begun hiring trick riders because none of the family know how any more. That's what I want to do. Every goddam year I want to be the one to ride in that parade, and do it so proud and fine that they wouldn't even want to put those sonofabitch Rangers in the same parade. I want to bring back that ride to the way it should be done."

Soldier boy said that was good, but what he had meant by his question was what E. J. proposed to do with his future. E.J. rather misunderstood.

"How'll I spend the rest of the year? Well I'll tell you. The rest of the year I just want to practice up for June 25th. That's what I want to do." He stretched. "Maybe in between June 25th I'll do rodeo work. Boy, I'm sleepy. You?"

Later that night a familiar combination of soft shrill bugle notes drew soldier boy out of his room. From the nonexistent cutaway door in the second-floor hallway he looked out into the darkness. The musical notes faded away. E. J. Birdsong joined him in the sawed-out doorway.

"Who was that playing Taps?"

"That's Little Olly. He's in the school band. Not bad for a kid."

"He do that every night?"

"Olly this year. Four years ago it was my turn."

Soldier boy laughed. E. J. Birdsong said, "Listen, paleface. Don't knock the tribal customs. Before Ol' Tonto died he gave out he wanted Taps played for him every night."

"Forever?"

"He didn't say anything about stopping."

E. J. Birdsong moved away, then returned. "At first the old people had it done because they thought if they didn't Ol' Tonto's ghost would come back and do them coyote magic. The ones that came right after them did it because they thought it was part of the legal will. So it goes."

"You mean, honoring your great-grandfather's memory?"

"Little Olly, I don't believe he's even heard of him."

One cold dark morning, two weeks later, the two of them, the Indian Bird and soldier boy, took off. At a road junction, several miles away, one of them said, "I wasn't ready to come home anyway."

We hitchhiked up into Wyoming and down to California, working here and there, and finally we settled down at the Hotel Louisiana on Sixth Street in Los Angeles. People call this part of the town Skid Row. E.J. already had his honorable discharge, and we waited down on the Row for my ninety days to be up until I would be listed as a deserter. We were drunk much of the time, and then we teamed up with Axel Kane and Adolph Tucci, also two young veterans. Axel, a stocky crop-haired Swede-looker, had been a lieutenant with Graves Registration in the Pacific "steppingstone" campaign. He had landed back in San Francisco six days after his wife, a student doctor, committed suicide; he walked out of the Army General Hospital in the Bay Area into which he'd been inserted and made his way to the Row where he was buddying with Adolph Tucci. Adolph was a wiry Italian-American type, very quiet and almost studious, whose only joke in life was that he had taken off in an airplane fifty-seven times and never landed in one. He had been a paratrooper in Tunisia, Sicily, southern France and had also been at Remagen. His general had taken a liking to him and insisted on having Adolph along as a "good-luck charm"; Adolph's last combat jump had been made in Belgium with his fractured left arm in a plaster cast and a machine pistol cemented into the plaster. We used to sit on the curb outside the free-dinner Gospel Church on Los Angeles Street and laugh like hell every time Adolph said, "I been up in a plane fifty-seven times but never landed in one." The Row was full of people like us in 1946. Eventually, on the eighty-first day, I sneaked an honorable discharge through Camp Beale, in northern California, in a way which is too complicated to go into here. I was content to stay down in the Row, rooming with E.J. and working at odd jobs, but he said it was no way to live, that he did not want to be a postwar bum, and he left Los Angeles to work the rodeo at Riverside and later returned to Oklahoma. Axel and Adolph I met again at the university, where they were both married, Axel instructing in political sociology and Adolph studying for the law, but the Indian Bird and I just wrote Christmas cards to each other for nine years . . .

*

We didn't talk about what E.J. was in for, which was bank robbery. Last year Adolph Tucci had sent me the news clipping. The Bird had pulled only one previous job before they nailed him. He said, "I know it's hard for you to visit me, because you live so far away." Now, we talked about this and that, and the guard let us alone for nearly two hours. He didn't mention the annual ride down in North Texas in memory of his great-grandfather. I didn't mention it, either.

E.J. said that he was being a good prisoner and that he expected to be out in another five years, in 1961, not 1964. I said, That's good, Indian Bird. He looked fatter, he said, because of the food, but in general he couldn't complain. He sounded very offhand and detached about the whole thing and kept asking questions about my life. I didn't give him too many straight answers. It's not easy to talk to someone inside the wall about your life outside if he has always expected great things of you.

E.J. looked away. He never could tell the difference between pride and shame; I suddenly remembered how stiff-necked he used to get over some little crack of mine. Indian Bird, I said, it isn't easy to describe how I live.

He said, "Forget it, it's just that it's goddam easy to describe how I live. No offense to you, but visitors make it harder for me. I let the folks come up twice a year."

I said, I'm sorry, I didn't mean to make it harder for you. He said, "No, no, you didn't know."

We talked a while longer and then the assistant warden came into the visiting room to tell the guard to tell me to go. E.J. and I stood up. I said I was sorry the wire-and-glass fence prevented our shaking hands. He smiled and said, "It's all in the mind, man." I said, I'll be seeing you, Indian Bird. He said, "Sure thing."

I followed the assistant warden out to my car in the driveway in back of the warden's office. He asked me when I was coming back to start my research for the film, and I said tomorrow morning, and I drove away, and kept driving until I hit Colfax, Washington, on the Palouse River, in wheat country. The newscast said unconfirmed reports were that Russian troops were massing on the Hungarian border.

I tried by-passing Spokane but hit all the wrong roads and then it started to rain and I found myself skidding along muddy rural paths and asking directions every quarter of an hour to Coeur d'Alene. I felt very bad about the Indian Bird. The truth was, I wanted to get right inside that prison and stay a while with him.

Late in the afternoon I became lost and stopped the car under a drumming, thrashing October rain at the end of a half-finished road in the middle of a lumber forest. You could see pieces of machinery in the trees. I listened to the rain, until, click, I began to hear an onrushing, ominous and oddly soothing music. I tried shutting my eyes but something prevented them from closing, as if sticks propped them up. I reached over to turn off the radio but it was already. I listened to the brain music, hoping that by turning to it full-face it would, as it had in the past, become inaudible, but it did not, it simply became louder, so I slouched deeper in the seat, kept the motor running and waited for it to go away.

I went to sleep very quickly, banging my head on the door handle. When I awoke it was still raining; I backed the De Soto out of the unfinished road, in reverse through the mud for about a quarter of a mile which woke me up completely. I felt okay, and crossed the state line into Idaho in the late afternoon, linking up with Highway 10 outside Coeur d'Alene.

Coeur d'Alene has a romance all of its own, different from Cripple Creek and Telluride. Driving, I saw right through the dairy farms and fruit orchards to a beautiful mountain region where the hard-rock miners had fought pitched battles against federal troops, against company finks and state militia vigilantes, in one of the great industrial civil wars. Coeur d'Alene, the Western Miners Federation, the Industrial Workers of the World; it started here, at the north end of Coeur d'Alene Lake, the gulches and canyons I was cruising over, in memoriam, had once heard the tramp of invading, strikebreaking troops, had once seen the sudden bright blood of that now vanished breed, the worker who dreamed of setting free his own and all other classes, the miner who in the flickering light of the bunkhouse candle read Rousseau and Shakespeare, Ingersoll and Henry George, Marx and Gibbon. It was here, in a town now given over to commercialized pastoralism, with high school kids in jeans sucking milk shakes through straws and jived-up stock cars rattling around the clean, tidy streets, that in the great violent strikes of 1892 and 1899 thousands of miners were flung into barbed-wire camps and held without trial for months. It was here that the westerner broke his head against the copper bosses' will — the country of Joe Hill and Haywood, of Moyer and Pettibone and of that great unsung Johnny Appleseed, Pat Reynolds, Socrates to Haywood's Plato; the birthplace of all those thousands of other Johnny Appleseeds who went up and out to spread the gospel of One Big Union. Other men may have their Yorktowns and Little Big Horns and Gettysburgs. For me, and my family, to rank with Haymarket and Lawrence there was always Coeur d'Alene, where the pioneer dream was killed.

*

I hung around town most of the day. It did not displease me that there were no monuments to the strikers, no commemorative plaques. Some day there would be — as there were at Shiloh and Valley Forge and Pulpit Rock. I talked to nobody. I made my meals out of cheese and sandwich meat I bought at grocery stores, and then in the late afternoon I cruised around Coeur d'Alene asking questions until I found what I was looking for: a large white-slatted house set back from the street in a clump of scrub trees, at the foot of some sort of old mound or hill which lay behind it — 1065 Ashford Street. Midge had given me the address at my party. I got out of the car and locked it and walked through the open front gate and up onto the white-painted porch. Two people inside the living room saw me, young people, and came out. It was funny. She recognized me right away. But Cal looked blankly at me for about a full half-minute before he spread out his arms, like some spindly towering prophet and whooped, cocking his wizened Jewish head to one side in that unintended half leer which was really the only way he ever had of meeting his own surprise — "*You old asymptote!*" He danced and capered around me and we pounded each other on the back and arms. His wife leaned against the door slat with her arms folded. I said hello and she said hello. Old Cal just couldn't stop capering and giggling. He had changed all right.

With his wife unsmilingly walking behind us, Cal told me to come into the kitchen with him. I said to his wife, Can I help you make any coffee? Cal and I sat around the kitchen table and he asked me what I was doing up in that neck of the woods. He was beginning to be a little suspicious, I think. I said that I was passing through. "What do you mean, passing through? Nobody ever goes through Coeur d'Alene just passing through."

To save a lot of breath, I said I was on a vacation and touring around, and that Midge had given me his address. He seemed satisfied by that, and we left it at that. So we sat around the kitchen table drinking coffee and talking. Not with his wife, though. She was pretty much left out of it. I'd met her only once, in L.A., and we didn't care for each other. She was a harsh-faced working-class girl, the daughter of needle-trades people, who I thought was just plain vulgar. I don't know, maybe Cal thought she was some sort of essence of working class. He had a thing about the working class, and even though he had worked in mills and factories since he had come out of the Army, eleven years ago, he always thought of himself, I think, as a *petit bourgeois,* because his father had been a lawyer. Midge and Cal had come back from the war together and were practically married off the boat. I didn't mind Midge's wife so much, she was all right, but Cal's wife, Haviva, was a rough old cob. Right now she was screwing up her face and searching her mouth with her tongue for a bad tooth or something. She was not my dream girl.

Cal surprised me by knowing what, more or less, I'd been doing all these years. Such as he was, he exaggerated some of it. By the time it reached him, for example, that abortive little lockout of seven 16mm-film cleaners was blown up into a major industrial strike in the studios. I was surprised, also, that he was so friendly. But then I began to see that he was being friendly on the old basis, that it was as though we were seventeen and singing together and walking by the lakefront at night with Nick and Stu.

It was funny, in a way, looking back on it, the four of us. It was in the middle of 1945, the war in Germany had just shut down shop, and Cal and I were in different Army camps about one thousand miles apart. Stu was somewhere in the Merchant Marine.

At about the same time we heard that the fourth one, Nick, had had an arm blown off near St. Lo, we also heard, Cal and I, independently, some crazy rumor concerning the formation of a new Republican Army to fight Franco. Now, this rumor, or a variation of it, about a resurgent Loyalist force, had (and has) been circulating ever since 1940, but for some reason it was told to me in such a way that this time I believed it. I was doing advanced infantry training at Camp Howze, Texas, and I received a letter from someone, I forget who, causing me to take off that weekend on a train for Chicago and drop in at the offices of the Anti-Fascist Refugee Appeal where I said that I wanted to go to Spain. I was a Pfc in the Army just then. I really expected to be sent, is the point of this vignette.

They almost laughed at me. The other point of the story is that while I was there, on my second visit to the office because I thought that perhaps they had information about Spain they didn't know me well enough the first time to impart, in walks Cal, asking for the same thing. I remember we didn't laugh about it at the time. He had come from a field artillery outfit in Arizona. We really had wanted to go to Spain. And we were terribly disappointed. Ever since we were old enough to know about it, we had been anticipating an anti-Franco insurrection, and sometimes, in Chicago before we went our separate ways, we used to sit around and talk about what we would do in Spain. We all had known people who had fought with either the Lincoln Battalion or the International Brigades, and it was something we wanted to do. I had a cross-eyed cousin, an organizer for the farmworker's union, who had been with an ack-ack battery in the defense of Madrid, and some nights we would go over to the Near North Side and visit with my cousin Archie and ask him to tell us stories. Afterwards, we would sit on some front stoop in the summer evening, watching the traffic go by, and talk about what we would do in Spain. We had it all figured out. Stu, who had weak eyes and was generally unreliable politically (he sang folk songs, was dominated by his family and, one way or another, was always in trouble with girls), Stu was to put on shows and skits behind the lines, or be a doctor, or something. (He never much cared for the way we slotted him; that last summer he actually spent a few weekends in Oak Park taking instructions on the rifle from a man he paid and who claimed to have been an instructor for the Rainbow Division in the first war.)

Cal was to be the political commissar and writer of radio propaganda. Nick, small and agile, was to be a courier. I was to be a battle commander. It looks childish the way I'm putting it down. None of us ever got to Spain. The anti-Franco revolt, I suppose, the four of us are still waiting for. I'd still go. Stu, maybe, wherever he is, selling Rice Krispies and toilet paper in Fort Wayne, Indiana, last I heard, would too. But not Nick, I think. Nor Cal any more.

At the kitchen table Cal slumped back and was serious a moment: he stopped doing all those gestures and inflections we had all done, which had bound us, at seventeen and which he had become full of the moment he saw me coming up the front steps. He reported that Nick, minus his arm, was in Chicago and doing social work. He called Nick a bleeding heart. I said, You're not one of them who starts to hate your friends who decide to go back to university. Cal slumped even further down, spreading out his long lanky Lincolnesque legs and said, "I am."

"Oh what the hell," he said.

His wife put down her coffee cup and just plain walked out of the kitchen.

Cal said, "You know, I used to work down in Butte. In one of the smelting plants. Two, almost three years, and then the FBI came around and they canned me. But it wasn't something the boys in the union felt they could fight on, because by this time my faction was losing out in this particular local." Now Cal did not exactly tell it this way. He used words like police agents, stooge of the bosses, relationship of forces within the top leadership, and so on. The way he had been talking when we were seventeen. The more he talked, in fact, the more I saw that it was not merely the fact of seeing me that had sent him back twelve, thirteen years for all the facial gestures and verbalistic excesses with which to meet me; this had really become his rhetoric over the years. Not in daily life, but whenever he was inspired by a new situation. Asymptote, for instance. My God, I hadn't heard the word used that way for a long time. It was what the Corpuscle Quartet used to call other people, and themselves, when they were politically deviating. In higher math an asymptote is a line that simply goes off somewhere on its own and winds up in infinity, or at least that's what I think it is. Nick first started using the word to describe me in an argument. This was when he and I were busy hating each other, for some crazy reason, or no reason, at the height of activity in Chicago. Even today I wouldn't want to say for certain why that had happened. The Group, with the Corpuscle Quartet, the four of us, as the nucleus, was barreling along with tremendous efficiency, eating, sleeping (chastely) and arguing with one another until one day, it seemed, Nick and I just got to hating. Or rather, one night. We were all up at Stu's, his parents away for the weekend, and sitting around on the floor, talking politics, and Nick and I looked at each other across the room and started disliking and envying each other. We both knew it. At the same instant. The jokes we began to play on each other for the next three or four months were cruel until gradually they tapered off as we all went into the Army and lost touch if not track. I lost my hatred for Nick, but not his for me, that I knew.

The thing about this is that it never came to a quarrel, we never discussed it, and I don't think Stu or Cal, or any of the girls, were ever aware of it. They all seemed to accept much more readily than Nick or I that we should be rivals.

Cal was telling me what it was like to work as a coremaker in a Butte foundry. Even after all this time, I couldn't get used to the idea of him doing heavy manual labor; I couldn't think of anyone more born to be an intellectual. Cal was the boy who had recast me into an atheist by talking to me on a Douglas Park bench in Chicago until four in the morning after I left the church. He was a relentless and contemptuous logician, and I think that the main reason I returned to atheism that night, after lapsing into religion, or something like religion, for a couple of years, was that Cal got up from the bench and walked off saying, "I'm disgusted with you." He could put a quartful of righteous scorn into what he said. He was by instinct thoroughly rude, with friends hardly less than opponents, but I think even then we recognized that this rudeness had an utterly serious, cauterizing political function. We none of us ever looked upon Cal as superior, but as a sort of transmitter of superior ideas, and in that perhaps we were unfair to him, and denied him a certain salute which might have, obscurely, released his blocked, and then desiccated, emotional energies. He and I had gone through high school together, not being particularly close, Cal interested in his studies, I not giving much of a damn one way or the other. He was tall, pimply-faced, gangly, ugly as sin, with a thin Jewish face and big awkward hands and a way of handling himself, physically, which made you think he had a touch of some nervous disease. He didn't jitter, he just threw himself around. He was terrible at games, Nick Melly and I were the best, and it was awful to see him play baseball. Fortunately, he didn't often try. It was Cal who was the bookreader of all of us, the master dialectician, the brooding sharp-tongued thinker, the agit-prop commando, the transplanted *yeshiva boccher*, the Marxist Talmudic scholar. Cal's fate, in another time, would have been, should have been to stormily debate the abstruser points of a dying theology. I don't know, without wanting to be too facile, perhaps he was.

Obviously the thing for Cal to have done after the Army was to get into some university and whack the daylights out of the phony scholars in his department, eventually establishing himself in an isolated and independent treetop somewhere within the academic grove. What he did was to marry a needle-trades girl as coarse as old dirt and go into an L.A. foundry for a stretch of five solid years. I saw him only once in all that time, at the christening of his gigantic black-haired baby in a patio out in Eagle Rock. Everything about that day was ruinous though I think I was the only one who thought so. Because, you see, Cal was someone who might have achieved a noble, if excoriating stature, if only he had had the guts to accept a few more years of lonely misery, of the kind of monastic waspishness combined with pseudo working-class bonhomie which was his special shield against life. Well, he didn't.

Cal's wife was a Communist out of socialist parents; but I don't think Cal knew what a gruesomely, fanatically conservative girl he had married. What I had most against her was that she had let him begin a history course at the University of Nevada and then allow him to cancel out. I wasn't there at the time, but I feel in my bones that Cal wanted, possibly desperately, someone to remonstrate with him. And it wasn't as if she didn't have the equipment. She had brains, probably enough brains to know that Cal would have completely outgrown her in another two years of university. Perhaps I should state my prejudice. I hate women who take men away from their work, for whatever reasons, even if the baby is dying. I know there's another side to the story, and maybe somewhere in this narrative I'll find reason to be a little fairer. But Cal was my friend.

So there we sat, me mainly listening while Cal laughed and slapped his thin bony knees and resorted to expressions I'd forgotten we used. I felt like saying, Hell, Cal, why don't you just talk to me. But then I saw that it wasn't something he was putting on for my benefit, it wasn't with any effort or pain that he was reaching back for his shield. This is how he had been all the time since the Corpuscle Quartet broke up. He had helped equip us with a way of looking at the world, with a necessary kind of coldness, and we had given him that which he was constitutionally incapable of acquiring by himself, a working-class rhetoric. But, it coarsened him. I mean, Cal was not really capable of understanding working people. Or people of any kind. He was a book man. I was sorry we had lost touch. I felt, listening to him now, that had Stu and Nick and I gone out to Nevada we might have persuaded him to stay at the university. (In fact, at the time I wrote a letter to them asking if they would come with me to Nevada. Nick never replied and Stu said no.)

I told Cal I wanted to go to the toilet and he said upstairs, second floor. I went into the bathroom and was good and sick. I felt better then. Last time I went on the road it hadn't taken me so long to get used to the greasy food. On my way back downstairs I passed a hallway on the ground floor at the far end of which was a glassed-in door. Through the glass I saw Cal's wife taking a man in suntans and T-shirt through the high scrub grass in the back of the house. When I came back into the kitchen Cal asked me if I was going to stay long. I said no, I was just passing through, as I said.

We sat and talked about his union, the Mine-Mill-Smelter Workers of America (Ind.). Cal said Mine-Mill had just signed, down in Denver, a three-year agreement with the copper management. I was thunderstruck. I knew that the other unions, led by auto and steel, were going in for these long term industrial-peace contracts. But Mine-Mill was the direct descendant of the old Western Federation of Miners, the union of Haywood and Pettibone and Moyer. In the late 1930's and 40's, the copper miners, seeking a leadership that could be counted upon to stand up with its fists doubled, chose the Communists, and made Maurice Travis the secretary. Travis was a rough character who had lost an eye last year, or the year before, when a bunch of Steelworker Union goons broke into a radio station from which he was broadcasting in Alabama. The Communist leadership had almost gotten thrown out for living up to the *one*-year agreements. Now three years. I said, What's going on, Cal? He said, You know, the miners want a rest. The whole union does. The bosses are tight. And we've had to fight the rest of the union movement ("right wing bastards" is how Cal put it) and the government which had practically the entire union executive board under indictment either on Smith Act or Taft-Hartley violation. "The boys truly want a rest," said Cal. "All they talk about is baseball, sex and fishing. Sure, I know what you're thinking. But they need a rest. They're human. This year when they vote it will be Democratic." What about the party? Cal shook his head. "We're badly discredited, it's as simple as that. Travis was hated. I didn't know that until I came up here. I always thought he was a miner's Lenin. There's no socialist talk at all." It was interesting for Cal to use the word socialist.

I said, Cal, who was that guy your wife was hiding from me out back?

Cal got up and shut the kitchen door. "Jesus," he said, "why do you *always* have to be such an asymptote?" He grimaced and slapped his hands together and said, "Damn, damn."

Look, I said, a lot of things have changed, but I guess my basic loyalty is still to the Corpuscle Quartet.

That just about stopped old Cal in his tracks. He went to the kitchen range and stirred some cocoa. He had his back to me. He said, "Could you go after you have a meal?" I said, Hell, Cal, I can go now.

He was really troubled. I didn't know what to say to him. We hadn't even talked over old times. He turned around and sat down at the table and began to stick the kitchen knife into the table. He said, "Listen. Things have happened. I'm not young. No, listen. This isn't self-drama. I went up the wrong road and what makes me old is knowing I can't go back to the place I started from, I can't do any of it over again. I can't keep going either. So I'm here. Waiting for everything to stop spinning so I can figure it out. I told you I worked in Butte for two years. It's true. What I didn't tell you was that the party sent me there. Every place I've been to since Midge and I came out of the Army the party has sent me to. Including the university. I went there from Chicago because the party wanted me to build up the group there. When I told them I was fed up with college life they asked me to go into a foundry. I'd never done heavy work before, except in the Army. I didn't have to do what the party asked and go where they said. But I went. And then I got sick. Ill. I went up for a time into the mountains. And when I got better the party asked me to go to work in a smelter in Butte because the union needed the votes, and organizers. The trouble was, I got into the worst anti-Communist local in the entire international. I ran for union office. One day, while I was washing up for lunch, the boys threw me out of a first-story window."

I asked Cal how he felt, and he said almost healed. I told him I was sorry. He said there was nothing I could do except go quickly. I said I would go because I knew what was happening up here.

He got up and said, "You don't know a God damned thing. You always thought you knew things when you didn't. There's nothing to know. Look, just get out of here."

I made a mistake then. I wanted to get across to Cal that I was still what I had been, that the central idea which we had shared still animated me. So I told him that two or three years ago I had to report for the wire service the Smith Act trials in L.A. They were frame-ups. The people on trial were blind-willys, bureaucrats or fanatics who had done more harm to the cause of socialism in America than a hundred FBI's. But we, our Group in Chicago, we had once put our hands on a dream: to once and for all wipe out the contradiction in the two lives we all of us lead, between the way we preach in church and the way we act in life, the way we are with our families — where primitive Communism has always been practiced; from each according to his ability, to each according to his need — and the way we are with people not of our families. This was what to us the Soviet had meant; this is what the Labor Party and Swedish welfare payments and the TVA ultimately should mean. Men care for one another, Cal. It was the essence of what we believed that Communism was men standing up on their own two feet and, for the first time in history, ordering their lives in imperfect consultation but in perfect awareness. This, Cal, this was our dream and we would do combat for it. Won't we?

Cal made a fist. He was terribly angry. He asked me just what gave me the right to call anyone a stupid bureaucrat. I sighed. Oh Jesus, let's not get into an argument. How did this start?

He was red in the face. I could see that he was balding. He went out of the kitchen, and the house was quiet. I waited a few minutes, feeling awful. I wanted to go after Cal and have a talk with him. The house, with the quiet sun beating down on it, was hot. I went into the shabbily furnished front room. It was just about the saddest front room I'd ever seen. There were hardly any books in it, in Cal's front room. And the books that were there were by Irving Stone and Howard Fast and Carl Marzani. I sat down in a soft chair and switched on the radio. I waited for the news. In about ten minutes, the news commentator came on and with an Idaho twang at first related some bargains that could, he said, be had at the local bicycle center. Then he reported, reading plainly and with difficulty the names, like a child reciting a poem in a foreign language, or a child reciting an adult poem, that Nagy had accepted the demands of the workers who had called the general strike, the workers of the county of Borsod-Gomor. What these demands had been the local radio announcer did not say. It is not clear, he said, whether fighting still continues. The situation remains urgent. The news announcer turned into a disc jockey and put on Patti Page's "Tennessee Waltz." I sat and listened to the warm, quiet hum of Cal's house. I really had a hunger to go and find Cal and talk with him. I had some sort of idea that if I started out the conversation thus: "Cal, this unanticipated shift in the relation of forces . . ." he would talk to me. But as I waited no one came. And then I saw that no one would. I went out into the hallway and looked through the glassed-in door. Out back I could see nothing but the scrub grass. I thought of calling for Cal, or leaving a note. And then I thought, the hell with it.

I went outside and got into my car and drove away. I didn't even look back. I had no emotions about it. Well maybe I did. I was angry. I didn't feel it was my fault, or Nick's fault or Stu's. It was Cal's.

Near the city limits of Coeur d'Alene, I parked the car and walked into a good-looking (chrome inside and potted plants outside) restaurant. It was about three in the afternoon and although the restaurant was large I was the only customer. There weren't even any waitresses around. I sat down at the counter and waited. I tinkled the empty water glass with the fork. A waitress in a green, starched uniform came through the swinging doors of the kitchen. I ordered a hatful of food, and when she brought it I wolfed it down. I was hungry. Then I ordered a hamburger and a milk shake, and a piece of cherry pie with chocolate ice cream. The waitress grinned. She was pretty. A small, trim blonde and damn well made up considering this was Coeur d'Alene. She asked me if I was sure that was chocolate ice cream I wanted, and I said it was my favorite dessert. She said there was no accounting for tastes. An elderly couple came in and sat in one of the booths and she went to serve them. She had a long-legged stride for a short girl. I looked at her moving around, and she knew I was looking. I felt the sex build up in me. Also, I wanted a reason, some excuse to stay in Coeur d'Alene for a day or two. I had a feeling that if I did Cal would somehow seek me out and we could have that talk. I felt that if only I could have this talk with Cal it would be the start of a renewed attachment to what was old and previous in me, and I could then follow the track to the present time. I think I needed Cal to help me put the years between Chicago and now into a perspective. Some people don't need to. I did. I wanted to shake Cal loose from his caul of vulgarities, to make him come through as the old purehearted dogmatist I hoped he still was. I wanted to make a friend of Cal again.

Also there was this waitress. When she got through serving the old couple she just stood at the end of the counter. Another waitress came through the swinging door and started a conversation, but went back inside after a few minutes. The tips of my fingers were cold.

I smiled and shrugged. I got up to pay my bill, and she came around the counter to the cash register at the front of the restaurant. Outside the entire space along the front window on the sidewalk was taken up with potted plants. I asked her if she wanted to go to a movie, and she gave me back my change and said she was off work in about thirty minutes. I went outside. The sun was going down behind some mountains behind the restaurant. I sat in the car and wondered if I should take the girl back to Cal's house. Now, there was a crazy idea. In less than half an hour the girl showed up and got into the car. I asked her where she lived, and she said across the lake but she didn't have to go home. She said she was married and that her husband was doing electrical maintenance work on a pipe line in Canada. He had been away in Canada for four months.

She was a nice girl. Very pretty and not at all nervous, dressed in a sweater and skirt and carrying a wicker basket. We talked about her job. During some of the months of the year she was a potter; other months she did waitress work. This was the longest her husband had been away from home. She expected they wouldn't stay together much longer. They had no children and had been married three years. She didn't complain, just stated facts. I told her I had come from Hollywood, as we drove around town because she had some things she said she wanted to shop for. She was interested and asked questions. I also told her about Cal, I mean about looking up an old friend and how difficult it was. She said it was worse being a woman when your friends started having babies. I asked her who she was going to vote for, and she said she never thought about things like that. Things were prosperous, she said, around Coeur d'Alene. Logging and fruit farming were having a boom. I asked her if she had ever heard of Big Bill Haywood and she said of course, he was the union leader. I was surprised at this. I drove along the street where Cal lived and pointed out his house. She said she didn't know him, partly because she worked at the resorts fringing the lake and didn't know too many people in the center of town these days even though she had lived in Coeur d'Alene all her life except for two months she had spent at a girls' reformatory for shoplifting. She had never done anything like that before, and never would again, and the only reason she was sent away was because she had become frightened and not shown up at the hearing and was punished more for contempt of court than anything else. It had happened several years before, but Coeur d'Alene was a nice town and they hardly counted it against her. Only her husband didn't like to be reminded. She said I should stop circling the block where Cal lived, and that everyone grows up. I flushed. She put her hand on my shoulder and said she didn't mean anything by it. We drove out of town, on the new highway, around the lake. She knew of a film, a comedy Western, playing over towards Kellogg, so that's where we went. A rural drive-in movie. We laughed a lot at the picture. She had a fine sense of humor and didn't laugh at everything, only the really comic parts. I liked her very much. After the movie we went to a roadhouse, for dinner and drinks. It was a cool night. We drove around some more, pleasantly, and then she took me to a cabin near the lake to which she had the key.

In the morning we drove back to Coeur d'Alene where she said she had some more shopping to do. I told her I had to go on, and we shook hands. I said that she had made me feel better and stronger for the road, and she smiled. I meant it. I drove out of Coeur d'Alene about ten that morning. Her name had been Kitty.

I cruised out of town on Highway 10, crossing over into Montana on the Bitterroot Range, and south towards Missoula, in Blackfoot Indian country, mountain and forest, past the 1806 camping site, suitably commemorated, of Lewis and Clark.

This was old Indian and craggy mountain country. It wasn't like down in Texas where it was so hard to think Indians had ever lived. Pressed down at seventy, I had the feeling Blackfeet or Crow were right behind those great big boulders of the Bitterroot Range. I crossed the Flathead River at night, the car tires rumbling and shaking the bridge and the water below unseen.

The trees were great clumps of black in blackness. I stopped on the other side of the river bridge and got out of the car to be sick on the side of the road. Missoula in the morning, a burnt charcoal feeling in the center of my head, dry and pointed, making clean black strokes up and down, back and forth. In and around the tall cold mountains, the deep dark gorges, Sacajawea country. I thought of the nice old lady who used to sit, day after day, in the foyer of my office, wanting someone to represent her to the Hollywood studios because she had once sold a story to Vitagraph about Sacajawea, the Indian girl guide of Lewis and Clark. A few miles outside Missoula, I stopped for a grilled liver sandwich and to look over the brown buttes near Traveler's Rest where Lewis and Clark had stopped on the way in and on the way out, 1805-6. I loved this country, which was so hard and soft. It's a word we don't use any more in America, noble. I knew that there were moose, elk and bear still unkilled just beyond those hills, and antelope farther down the heavily timbered foothills. Eating that liver sandwich in the trucker's café, and listening to the drivers talk about football and women, I thought of old Father de Smet, the Jesuit who had missionaried among the Indians back up near the Flathead River. I listened to those truck-drivers and thought about the fur traders, the fathers of the sons. I felt tired and squeezed out; I could just as well have asked those truck drivers to give me a lift somewhere. For the first time I regretted having the De Soto. I would have felt better walking along Number 10 with not a damn thing in my hands.

*

Deer Lodge at noon. Small farm towns. Cowboy hats. Cattle behind fences. Long-distance vans. Curving highway, sinewy highway. Work gangs. Road repairers in their roadside steam-rollers, descendants of the soldiers who had failed to find and kill Chief Joseph, the greatest and best of the Indian strategists. I thought of Howard's girl, Suzie, the small wild Cajun and her way of drunkenly shouting that people were anti-Indian. We all used to think it was a joke. I wondered now if maybe beneath it all Suzie hadn't been crying, impossibly, to go back. Howard and his burial ground at sea. Hell, why not.

Down through the Sapphire passage, driving all night, without brain music, slowing down in high, rugged, valley-slitted mountain country, until I came, to rest, in Butte. When I realized I knew nobody in Butte, I backtracked on Highway 10 to the Junction with 91. I was still in the gold-field mountains of Montana. I pointed down old Highway 91, straight south, and let out. I went fast around those mountain roads, driving all day, not passing any towns for fifty miles at a stretch, up to ninety on the straightaways, not a highway cop in sight. I crossed the river ahead of Dillon, stopped to eat a sandwich in a hurry, and swept on south with the hard bright Montana sun in my eyes. Early in the afternoon I passed herds of cattle staring at me behind wire fences, and on the uplands fat gray sheep showing their tufted asses indifferently to me rocketing below them, and I stopped that afternoon, a few miles south of Dillon, in the rickety ghost town of Bannack, which looked to be, from the weathered remains of the capitol building, the rotting jail and hotel, and the wind-split log cabins, the oldest town in the world. There weren't many people around in Bannack; it was getting late for tourist season. I drove behind the decayed edifice that used to be the state capitol a hundred years ago and parked in a small grassy yard, and sat back and stared up at the cloud-filled sky. I started the motor and pressed the button which let the top down, then I switched on the radio. I waited through a daytime tribulation of "Young Widder Brown," whose little boy was being accused of contributing to the accidental death of one of his Brownie buddies, and then, inevitably, the five-minute news came on. I settled back to listen to it. But it was all about other things. I fiddled with the selector, but it was another hour before I could get a news broadcast. All that time I kept trying to find the news on the car radio and having to listen to disc jockeys playing "Heartbreak Hotel." Imperceptibly, the gray shadows lengthened and dimmed across the ghostly barracks of the town, and what few people were around disappeared to their homes I suppose.

The news commentator said that Nagy, who was the new premier of Hungary, had secured the promise of the Soviet commander-in-chief to withdraw the Russian troops from Budapest. Negotiations for a new order in Hungary were under way. The AVO secret police were to be dissolved, and the Kossuth Emblem restored. I stared out of the car window at the wide dusty abandoned street in front of the dilapidated state capitol, at the shadowed timbers of this decomposing town, and I thought of the gold miners. The newscaster ended by saying that fighting, between whom it was uncertain, was still going on in Budapest. I kept the radio going, and I reached into the glove compartment and broke open a bottle of White Horse and took it until it burned, screwed the cap back on, crunched into first gear and swung out into the main street of the oldest town in Montana. By the time I was past the cemetery I was up to seventy. I rammed my foot down on the pedal and climbed up into the brown rocky mountains of Highway 91, going south. But going.

As the sun sank behind the rocks I climbed higher and higher, 8000, 9000, 10,000 feet up, winding and changing gears between the cliffs and ledges, following the swaying rushing course of the Red Rock River, past Armstead, past Lima, without stopping in the suddenly descended night, leaving behind Coeur d'Alene with Cal in it, and Kitty who would never meet him, and the long straight ghost of the Western Federation of Miners, and the two routes of Lewis and Clark, up and up into the cold hard air of the black mountains, having to go into first gear for a mile at a time, the De Soto coughing around the turns, and then a flat stretch of darkened highway and a sign picked out by my headlights, *You are now leaving the State of Montana. Thank You. Welcome to Idaho.*

Amidst the gigantic black boulders on this level stretch of night-strewn tableland I turned and rumbled off the highway. I hadn't seen more than a truck or two in several hours. The wind, which had been strong a few thousand feet below, seemed to be such a condition of life up here that you didn't hear it; it was the thing upon which you rested. My headlights dripped up a hill and came up against an overhanging rock; I shut them off and stopped the motor. I kept the radio off, but switched on the inside light, which glowed torpidly from under the dash. I could see my reflection in the windshield. I don't know how long I stared at myself, drinking from the bottle of White Horse. Between each drink I put the bottle back into the glove compartment. For some reason I could not stop rubbing the stubble on my jaw. I was doing it in a peculiar rhythm, and then I couldn't stop. It was in time to the music in my head. Whoo-OOoom. Whoo-UUuum. Lli-IInng. Ri-llll. This time I sat back and enjoyed it. I didn't try to drown it. I thought about Cal and then I thought about Nick. Nick and I had met in a funny way. After I left home, I had slept in the basement clubhouse of the Knights Athletic Club of Greater West Side Chicago, hanging around, waiting to go into the Army. One night the Knights jumped a street-corner meeting of Young Communists, and I punched this wiry little bastard, Nick Melly, in the nose. Somehow in the scramble my own nose began to bleed. Then I didn't see Nick for six months, during which many things happened to me, chiefly leaving the gang. It was in the summer, down at Oak Street beach, chest-high in water, that I bumped into him again. Neither of us knew whether to begin fighting again. We didn't. We exchanged guarded insults and walked out of the water friends. He introduced me to his mob, lying around on the beach, some of whom were unfriendly; they remembered that I had been with the Knights when we knocked over their street-corner meeting. But Nick bawled them out in a language I did not yet know but was to learn. He said I was not a "class enemy." At first I thought he was joking. This was when my only ambition was to understudy the Chicago Cubs centerfielder, KiKi Cuyler. Nick's pals were in an organization called The League of Anti-Fascist Youth. That was the beginning.

I sat in the car, in the night, on the other side of the Montana border, and nursed the bottle and thought about Nick and the League and wondered where they all were. I knew I'd never run across some of them. I reared my head back the better to listen to the hum, and when it disappeared I went to sleep. When I woke up I put on the car radio, waiting for the news. Fighting was still going on in Budapest. I started the car, swung down off the saddle of ground back onto the highway and hit it up to 80 in the dark. I felt weighed down, but the less so the faster I went. The road was straight, the night was dark and I was singing, or shouting, at the top of my lungs. I suppose that for the next two or three hours I was half singing or growling up in those old mountains. I found that I had slowed down a bit though. You can't sing loud and drive fast, I don't care how much you have read to the contrary. The sky outside the car was black with bright stars. The still air rushed past the open window, and it was cold inside the car. I had to stop a couple of times and be sick at the side of the road. Once I fainted after I was sick and I hit my nose on the ground. But otherwise I didn't feel too bad. A few miles south of the Idaho border I felt the car sinking. I saw a clear path of highway in the headlights pointing down and I didn't feel like passing out again, so to remove the muzz from my head, and the fear from my stomach, I went. But went. Zow. One hundred on the straightaway down. And this time I could feel it in my back and under my ass and through my feet. Man, I was *alive.* I made the bends in seventy. That old De Soto never let me down once.

And then the sun came up. It seemed to rise smash into my face one minute without any dawn to close the night. The wind in the car was colder now, an early morning wind. Some cars passed. I went down to 90. It was down, down all the way. The boulders turned from black to gray, the grass became sparser and less green, the mountains began to swing away from the highway, and my eyes began to close. For a moment I almost fell asleep at the wheel. I took a slug of White Horse, replaced the bottle in the glove compartment, and went on.

And then there it was. Around a hairpin curve in the highway, I plunged the De Soto down into the vast monotonous panorama of the Snake River Plain. It was thousands of feet below, spread out like part of a topographic map, millions of acres of yellow scrub brush and grazing land and thin gullies and neat little patches of darkness which I knew in the full light of day were verdant green fields irrigated by water from the Snake River. The sun opened up from a kind of autumn haze spread out over the semi-arid grazing lands and I dropped down from the mountains, feeling tired and grizzled. My eyelids were heavy and I suppose that, in one way or another, I had been talking to myself most of the way from the Montana border.

And then I was down on the flat level highway. It was a bright clear morning but my head did not feel bright and clear. One thing, the sun had burned away all the music, well maybe not all but at least enough of it so that if I rolled the windows down I could be sure of what was inside my head and what was under the tires. I promised myself I wouldn't put on the radio until I got to Idaho Falls, where sure enough I didn't know a soul. I made Idaho Falls by midday, stopped for a hamburger and bought another bottle of White Horse and went back out to the car to listen to the radio.

It was lonely as hell in that old town of Idaho Falls. Or maybe I just naturally found myself, in all those towns, in the loneliest and seediest parts. I swear, every time I drive into one of those western towns somehow I find myself eating at some greasy spoon next to a liquor store and talking to the most embittered cluck this side of the Continental Divide. I had tried talking to people all along Highway 91, from the border to Idaho Falls and after, and most of them said they didn't know who they were voting for. Again I was surprised by the absence of boomers and hitchhikers. Maybe, who knows, this was the best of all possible worlds? I couldn't find any news, and I hit the road again, still south, into the sun, following the gorge-cut Snake River, in and out of Blackfoot, past the honeybee farms, up to one hundred again (when the hum started again, to die away) into Fort Hall on the Oregon Trail, away now from the river.

I knew Fort Hall. Back when E. J. Birdsong and I were hiking out west he had taken me to Fort Hall. It was town. Clean, full of sorrel-skinned farmers and cattlemen. I think it was the center of a reservation, Shoshone and Bannock Indians. E.J. had a girl cousin, a Shoshone schoolteacher whom he had wanted me to meet, but when we got there we discovered she was down in Salt Lake City, so we took out two other Indian girls, real Indians, brown as swamp clay and not half so hard to handle, and we went right into the reservation itself, to what E.J. said the Indians still called a lodge, which was a cross between a Navaho hogan and a log cabin, both rotting away. E.J. apologized, saying that these were poor Shoshone. It was summertime and we took the girls out to the meadow and played tag and football, the touch kind, of course, not tackle. We were all pretty embarrassed with each other, not having very much in common; even E.J., though he was Indian himself, didn't quite know how to talk to these girls. Well, after a while we began to play tackle football. Those girls were fast and strong as hell. About nighttime we naturally paired off. E.J.'s took him back to town, and I and mine went off to a little stream behind some cottonwoods. She just about gave me the shock of my life, by slipping down one bank of the stream and before she hit bottom most of her clothes were off and she was in position. I was young and wasn't used to that kind of behavior. I would have minded her laughing at my bashfulness, but she just lay back on the dry clay bank and didn't even look at me and said, in a calm way, that the football game had excited the very dickens out of her. That was how she said it. "The game. It excited the dickens out of me." I felt, I think the word is, diffident. I wanted to walk along the stream, or just sit on a rock while we swished our bare feet in the water, something like that. But not Nan. That was her name. So, suddenly feeling scared, I took off my clothes. It was a dark moonless night full of warm breezes, and I put myself into Nan without any trouble at all and we made love real slowly for a long time, at a kind of 45-degree angle on that dry clay bank. You could hear the water going past all the time. At the end of the long time, Nan suddenly gripped me and I had a pretty fantastic experience. I have always thought that that night with Nan was an important part of my education; after that I began to look at girls and women, no matter how fancy their clothes and quick their speech, in a different way, with the greatest friendliness but also steadily, if you know my meaning. Towards morning it began to get cold and Nan and I put on our clothes and walked back to the lodge. Crossing the meadow she tackled me to the ground and just lay on her back laughing to beat hell. When E. J. Birdsong and I said goodbye to the girls (he gave them some money, but it wasn't the way it looks in print) and hit the road, I felt fine. But all the way out west, to Washington, he kept worrying about whether he was going to get a clap. He wanted to stop off and get himself fixed up in an Army pro station. I had to keep telling him that for him that was okay, he was out of the Army, but I was an AWOL. Well, old E.J. listened to reason, temporarily, but then he couldn't stand worrying about it and in a little town called Redmond, Oregon, we went to a civilian doctor who said it was too late for a normal prophylaxis but he would give us a shot of penicillin. I wanted to wait in the doctor's waiting room while E.J. got his, but E.J. insisted that I would have deformed children. We talked about this for quite a while. In a way

I thought it was an insult to Nan, and the Shoshone. E.J. said, "For chrissake, man, you been seeing too many western movies, those girls were *dirty*." Well, we argued about it, and then I went in to the doctor with him and we got fixed up. But I felt bad about it.

Once into Fort Hall this afternoon naturally I didn't try to look up either of those two Indian girls. I just drove slowly around the town, feeling tired but better, and looking at the people. The town somehow looked less crowded and more prosperous than I remembered it. I went into a nice little restaurant which had a radio on and ordered steak and potatoes. Most of the people at the counter were not Indians. Some of them had farmers' and western Stetsons on, and we talked. They declared the potato crop was very good. One cattleman said market prices were firm and high, and he was glad he had stopped raising, experimentally, hogs because hog farmers were getting a bad deal from the government. Two farmers, a cattleman and the waitress behind the counter said they were voting for Eisenhower because he kept us out of war, and what was the point, they wanted to know, in changing horses in midstream. I said we weren't dealing with horses and everyone smiled so good-naturedly that I knew they weren't taking their politics seriously here, either. The one thing they were interested in was the local contest for sheriff. This they were anxious to talk about at length. I asked them if I might excuse myself to the small white radio sitting on top of a high shelf near us. Fighting, the announcer said, in Budapest still continued but appeared to be slackening. Premier Nagy had declared that one-party rule was to be discontinued. I went back to talking to the farmers and their suspicion that both candidates for county sheriff were crooks. Suddenly I felt depressed as hell. I thought of going out to the car for some of the White Horse but I knew it would only make me feel worse. I looked down at my hands and then I put my hands under the counter because the fingernails were bleeding. I guess I must have been biting them pretty hard all the time I was talking to the farmers. Now they stung and ached. The clock inside my head was wound up, and after a while I just wasn't too interested in what those farmers were saying . . .

About five that afternoon I slid the De Soto into a side road just off 91 and went to sleep. I slept an hour, dreamlessly, until a farmer, or farm hand, knocked on the side of the door and woke me up staring at the largest damn herd of cows I'd ever seen outside the movies. He was suspicious without wanting to be, but he smiled, and I smiled, and got out of there, and took the road down to Pocatello where I found the home road, good Highway 30. And then it was east, east to God alone knew where, New York certainly, and Chicago if I could take it, and maybe Boston where they were interested, they said, in publishing what I had to write.

There are two highways which in America are home to me. Well, no, not home. But when I am on them I don't feel so much a stranger. They run through the same kinds of fields and towns other highways do, and the same kind of people glance at you without really being interested; and there are the same hot-dog joints, and all-nite cafés, and gas stations and motels and oak-shaded houses where families live without ever walking out to the pavement to see you go by. But Highways 30 and 66, usually I don't feel too bad, walking or riding or sleeping alongside them. No, not 30 or 66. I think this is so not because these two highways possess any unique, endearing qualities but because I have always felt they belonged to me, like houses you rent. The rent I paid for the highways was the time I spent on them. You see, I never really *enjoyed* traveling. It was always something I had to do. Some people grow up where they are. I always grew up somewhere else. If I lived in one city, when that city got used up, in order to step up in the world, to achieve vantage, I had to go to another city, sometimes near, sometimes across to the far coast, and to do that I had to use the highway. And it was the highway, the road that was the education.

A while ago, a boy wrote a book in which he says The Road Is Life, all in capital letters. Well, that's right. The road *is* life. This particular young author was wrong, I think, in how he meant it, that the rhythm and texture and substance of the road were what makes up life; anybody who's lived on it knows better. It's a lousy life. If you're on the bum, you're always at the mercy of the weather, standing half a chance of getting either frozen to death or sunstroke on a patch of clear deserted highway halfway to nowhere, at the mercy of car drivers who you know have seen you and pretend not to; and if you don't have much money you spend most of your time being hungry and lightheaded which means you can't even enjoy the sights and scenery and have always to be on the watch for the policemen who will pick you up for vag and play games with you in the interrogation room if they happen to be bored. (In Jackson Corners, Kansas, I was slapped on the head just for standing on the side of the road on a hot summer afternoon, and that was when I *had* money with me to prove I was no vagrant. In Venice, Missouri, I received my second worst handling from cops who took me in on a suspected child-rape charge because some truck driver wearing the same kind of field jacket I had on did some little girl a hundred miles away. When the information came over the station ticker type that the Missouri state police had captured the right man, these local beavers knocked me around all the way to the edge of town, because I *wasn't* who they were looking for. On that one I wrote a letter to the Governor of the State of Missouri and the American Civil Liberties Union. The Governor never replied and the Civil Liberties Union wrote back, in essence saying they would have to have more particulars but even if I sent them it would cost me about three zillion dollars just for the minor delight of seeing some hick-town judge spit in my eye. I could tell you a few more stories of how cops treat suspected vags on the road but one story would be like another. What worries me is the way the same expression is always on their faces: I've been slugged by London police and Paris police but American police habitually look as though they had it in for you personally; they always end up hitting and kicking you as if you were hitting and kicking them, and that can be a frightening experience.) It didn't take me long to learn how to dress for the highway: shave every morning, crease in trousers, and a clean white sweater with some college letter on it and a suitcase with labels and a dumb earnest smile on my face. Once or twice I have even gone on the road like the college kids with a great big sign, LOS ANGELES OR BUST or some such stupid item. The thing is, it pays off. Car owners take a look at you and if you are enough of what they would like in their son they figure you won't put a gun behind their ear. Sure, I know it sounds nauseating. But if you want to get from Indianapolis to San Diego, man, you *compromise*.

And believe it or not, it's not that much better when you go driving. I've driven on those two highways, crossing back and forth across the country, probably more than I've bummed, mainly by hiring myself out to companies that need cars transported for them, although what you really always look for is a fat rich New York garment center *macher* who doesn't want the strain of taking his own car across the country to Palm Springs or Los Angeles and is willing to pay gas and oil which the transport companies are not. But in a car it can be as depressing as hitchhiking, because all the time you are tire-whining past fellow citizens who live walled up in their own old fears. That's not my phrase. A long time ago, in the twenties, John Dos Passos wrote a lousy play called *Airways Inc.* in which he says something about the multitude of Americans who scurry from store to subway to church to home, America that he's never known, where he's lived without knowing. Well, that's what driving through America is like. If only you had the assurance that in those darkened small towns of Moline and Decatur, Davenport and Pocatello there were just a few people who knew and cared. But hell, you never do have that assurance, do you?

So there I was, back on old Highway 30, heading east. I remembered that there was something else in that Dos Passos play that described how I felt, and I took the trouble to look it up. It wasn't as nearly what I meant as I thought all these years, as is often the case when you look up old quotes, but here it is. A spinster has just lost her strike-leading lover: "The house I lived in wrecked, the people I loved wrecked, around me there's nothing but words stinging like wasps. Where can I go down the dark street, where can I find a lover in the sleeping city? At what speed of the wind can I fly away to escape these words that burn and sting, to escape the lack that is in me like a stone?" That's the way I felt, leaving the coast, feeling every time I turned on the car radio that a wasp was going to sting. As I say, this quote from Dos Passos was fairly wet; still, it was more or less the way I felt.

The wasp stung again. Somewhere between Soda Springs and Montpelier, Idaho, a few miles north of Bear Lake, astride the Bear River, and back up in the mountains again somewhere near old Joe Walker's walking route through the Rockies to the West, I turned on the radio to hear that Israel had attacked Egyptian positions in the Sinai peninsula.

*

On a flat stretch of tableland I crossed over at seventy into Wyoming. This was the real mountain country, rugged and with a lovely harshness, Jim Bridger country, the land of western fables when fables could still be believed. It was almost night now, and I hadn't really slept for two days but I didn't feel particularly fatigued. I thought to (but didn't) turn north and try to find some road that would take me through the Sublette cutoff in the mountains to South Pass and up to the Sweetwater River, the most important part of the Oregon Trail. I don't know. Maybe I had some idea about sitting down somewhere in the Pass, as I had done in the Sierra, and having a long talk with Mr. Donner and his party again. Somewhere in the back of my mind I think I must have had this notion that if I could just catch the Donners further back and earlier on I could warn them not to split up at Salt Lake. In fact, I did a lot of talking to myself up in those mountains past the border into Wyoming, and I suppose some of it was with the Donner children. I think I advised them on what route to take. Also I think I started crying again, loudly. Not out of fear, or anxiety, but for no reason. It wasn't because I didn't like Wyoming.

Actually I love Wyoming. I love almost everything about it. I've never had a really bad experience in Wyoming. It's a high clean windy state. I even liked its state motto: *Cedant Arma Togae* — Let Arms Yield to the Gown. Also it was the first state to grant women suffrage. But even though it had granted female suffrage I couldn't seem to stop that damn crying. What the radio had said about the Israelis jumping the Arabs I knew was important, and worked in with the mood I was in that the whole starlit world was caving in. I think I really did expect by the time I came to New York to find out we were all in the war. As soon as I stopped crying it was the middle of the night. I braked the car between some rocks and got the blankets out of the rear trunk and covered myself and locked the door from the inside and went to sleep.

I got into Kemmerer early the next morning. Few people seem to know it, but there is a fair amount of workable coal in Wyoming, and Kemmerer, smack in the middle of Indian country, and just a few miles northwest of where the traders and trappers of the Rocky Mountain Fur Company used to rendezvous, is a coal-mining town. I didn't know anyone in Kemmerer but I had a letter of introduction to the union at the big phosphate mine just outside the town.

I had breakfast, cleaned up in an Esso station washroom and drove out to the mine. There I was directed to a house about half a mile away, and I found, waiting to go on shift, the union secretary and the president, the first a small, the second a big man, in their work clothes.

We talked over cocoa in the back kitchen. There was an old-fashioned, hand-crank mimeograph in the corner and stacks of blank leaflet paper. I asked them about the three-year contract their union, Mine-Mill, had signed. The president, a fairly rough old cob, said just a little angrily, "Look, don't be so surprised. The guys are tired. They've a right to be. Since 1950 and before, we've fought for survival, simply to keep our heads above water. And now we — they — want a rest. They don't want to strike, they don't want any trouble. They want to take long uninterrupted fishing trips." The secretary, who was a Mexican, said, "It's not a radical union any more. It's a good union. But none of the boys talk Red any more. All they talk about is sex, baseball, cars and the lousy Company." I said that was, in almost exactly the same words, what I had heard nine hundred miles away, and they shrugged. Then they excused themselves, saying that if I wanted to find out anything more I ought to talk to Logan Moore, the grand old man of the local union, who lived in Kemmerer.

I went back to Kemmerer and found Moore, after asking around, in the lobby of the hotel. He was about the tallest, or longest, man I'd ever seen, and I couldn't understand how he ever worked in a mine. Later, he told me he had never worked in a mine itself, only in the smelting plants and once or twice on open-cast in Minnesota. I introduced myself and we had a long talk in the lobby. He excused himself for not getting up, he had a broken leg, which was encased in plaster at the moment. He was waiting for his daughter, who was the accountant at the hotel, to take him home. There is not much to say about that lobby. It was furnished in drab, mildly righteous woods and was gloomy and dusty.

Moore was a very old man. His shoulders were wide, his head looked to be made of granite and he had a bass voice. He said that the national union office had sent him to recuperate in Kemmerer and that he was a kind of unofficial legal adviser to the local union, assisting them in negotiations, that sort of thing. He spoke about the three-year contract too. He said, "You can sometimes, if you work at it, persuade a steelworker or an auto worker that the boss is a human being. But a miner who belongs to Mine-Mill comes into the world absolutely convinced the boss is a no-good sonofabitch and he dies thinking the same thing. So when you see these guys voting in a three-year contract you know they've had it."

He said that because Mine-Mill had fewer competitors it was in a better position, say, than United Electrical or Fur and Leather. There was some talk, he said, of merging with other unions but not much. He said that when he last visited the union headquarters in Denver he was told that most of the boys would go Democratic this year. The Communists, he said, were badly discredited. Considerably friendlier feelings now existed between Mine-Mill and other unions, which he said was bound to lead to tacit or open no-raiding agreements. "But a firm crust of anti-Communism formed by party mistakes remains." I smiled. It sounded so awkward.

I made some sort of crack. He leaned forward and put his hand on my shoulder. He said, "Son, don't shoot your mouth off if you don't know what you're talking about. America changed, and the Reds were trapped in that change. They weren't born for our time. Maybe not for our country either. You can disagree all you want with them. If you want you can even kick them out of the country. But I'll be go to goddam if I'll let you laugh at them." I apologized. I didn't mean to hurt Mr. Moore's feelings. You see, in a way he was something of a labor hero. He had been the directing intelligence behind the first great auto worker sit-down in Flint, Michigan, in 1936, the strike that had cracked the biggest of them all, General Motors, the strike where they not only had to bring in Governor Murphy and old John L. Lewis but also the President and just about every spare state trooper in Michigan. Moore left the union, had had to leave, when the Reds bargained with the right-wing for the leadership of the AVB-CIO; his going away was part of the price, and ever since he had been shifted from one union to another, but had never regained anything like his former eminence. I wish I could say that after 1940 he had shot his bolt, but he hadn't. Even now, sitting in that moth-eaten old hotel, his leg in a cast and waiting for his daughter to take him home to have his dinner in this old one-horse coal town, you could just see the talent in him. Logan Moore was something of a great man. It was like talking to a retired general who had fought in an important war.

We continued to discuss union matters. He declared that Mine-Mill was still the most militant union in the country, but had almost completely divested itself of its Communist leadership. There was talk, he said, of merger with the newly amalgamated AFL-CIO but most of the cooperation was on a lower level, in terms of regional and local no-raiding agreements. The union still had a good position inside the industry: it could afford not to merge. I thanked Mr. Moore for his time and left Kemmerer that afternoon.

It has been written that one cannot have Socialism. One is a socialist.

It is true.

On the highway it suddenly came to me that things were changing in the part of America I'd seen, and I wondered what lay to the east. Five years ago there had still been important differences in the national character, from one state to the next, between the way people lived and felt in various sections of the country. Now I wasn't so sure. It all seemed to be simmering down to something very like a national conformity we had all written about but also reserved judgment about. It wasn't so much what people said—though true enough that was the same wherever I went, indicating a fair degree of prosperity, high consumer debt, heavy mortgages, more appliances than they knew what to do with, and a ferocious cultivating of their own gardens—as the kind of feeling behind what they said. I don't think it's only, or even primarily because the "mass media" (the liberal's perpetual out) have imposed the same closely similar superficial reflexes and forms of speech; no, it was something else, if related. Nobody, for example, was really interested in the national elections. They held "Keef" in affection and were suspicious of Nixon for being too "radical"—and Washington was a long way away. All the people I talked to felt "out of it." I think that was the feeling. And feeling out of it, believing that they could exercise no real influence over the important decisions in their lives, they were now busily brewing up a blend of wisecracking apathy in which you could hear the crackle of hostility if you listened hard. The accuracies of passion were concentrating locally. The nation, and the nation in the world, was fast becoming a deep, private mystery. We were going private. But as a people we weren't prepared to go private. It would be the killing of us.

I crossed the Green River and just outside the town picked up a boomer, my first in a couple of days. We talked a while and he turned out to be a Wobbly. When I told him about my mother and father he said he apologized for putting the touch on me for money. He was heading away from Idaho where he had helped harvest the russet potato crop and was going to Nebraska for alfalfa time. We passed some herds of sheep on the scrub-covered hills and I let him off just before Rock Springs. It's a fast stretch from Rock Springs to Rawlins and I did it at ninety. Just once I stopped, to talk to a farmer who was helping his eldest son dig a fence hole. They were sheep farmers. They said they were voting for Eisenhower. The father said his wife might vote for Stevenson for some dang reason. He was sorry, he stated, that Ike had ever asked the housewives to go to the polls. Now look at what happened. Things weren't too bad around those parts, he said, except that the farms seemed to be getting bigger. Eastern capital, he said. I helped them dig two fence holes and then went on towards Rawlins. It was like having an earache. I kept shaking my head but it didn't do any good. I felt mean and lonely out on those plains. I was in the middle of myself and concerned only with it. I mean mean enough not to pick up hitchhikers, two of them, a middle-aged man with two suitcases and dressed in an overcoat, and a young boy, spaced twenty miles apart. Man, it had come to quite a pass when I didn't pick up someone on the bum.

I pulled into Rawlins, which is a wide western town thirty miles due north of Bridger's pass, some time in the afternoon, having picked up nobody in the De Soto. First thing I did was check into the hotel, near the railroad yards, which was full of farmers and railroad men. I like railroad hotels, but this one made me feel a stranger, an immigrant's son. I decided to go out and talk to people but after I washed up I found myself trembling so hard in the bathroom I had to go and lie down in my room. It was one of those big friendly old-fashioned hotels. Pale green halls, large windows and brass knobs. I'd never stayed there before, and on my way to and back from the washroom some of the cattlemen and one of the room maids gave me curious looks. I guessed it must have been because I was in a sweat shirt and jeans, and I just didn't look like one of them. That depressed me. I didn't want those cattlemen and railroad men to think I was trying to dress like them. So, after I had a little nap in my room, I put on some decent clothes and went downstairs for a walk.

Just outside the hotel I ran into a mob of kids coming out of school. There were several Negro boys with them. The feeling among them was good; I mean they were mixing a lot, and punching each other around. Now I know that sounds sentimental as hell, to put it like that. But every time I see a Negro kid and a white kid together in certain parts of the country it makes me feel good. You have to know a little about America to understand exactly what I mean.

I walked down the sun-shaded part of the street to the railroad marshaling yards and climbed up on a fence to watch the shunting. Rawlins is a curious sort of town, but you find several like it all over the Old West. It is this combination of Cheyenne Indian-and-buffalo-hunter nostalgia (ten-gallon hats, and neon-commercial emphasis on the Wild, Wild West, rodeos and all that) plus a good old-fashioned streak of straight unionism. I'll tell you what I mean. A few yards down from me, on the inside of the marshaling grounds, a bunch of railroad men, a bit above the gandy-dancer class (they were engine drivers and coal heavers and points men) were sitting around on boxes whittling and talking. I jumped down from the fence and went over to them and said I was a reporter doing a coast-to-coast survey. There were about eight of them and five allowed as how they were voting Democratic this year. They were all members of the Railroad Brotherhood. One of them, a rangy man wearing a version of sailor hat and missing three fingers off one hand, offered me a chaw of tobacco; I hate the stuff but I wanted to talk so I stuck it in my mouth. God, how I hate chewing tobacco.

Those railroad boys were the only ones I had met in years who knew who Eugene Victor Debs was. Maybe it was because none of them was young. I told them my mother and father had known Debs; quite excitedly I told them that Clarence Darrow had defended my mother on a criminal syndicalist charge in Massachusetts and that my father once served time, in Atlanta with Debs, on grounds of conscientious objection in the first war.

Only one of the men was really interested in this. They were all very strong union men. "This here is a union town, and we aim to keep it that way," said the man who gave me the tobacco. Everywhere you go, if you follow a railroad route, you find these small western towns, bowleggedly independent and solidly union because of the presence of Brotherhood men. We all sat around and talked to a degree about politics. A couple of them said they had once been interested but what the hell was the use any more, television was ruining people. I said I was getting hungry and was going on up to the coffee shop of the hotel and did any of them want to come with me. They all grinned, and one of them laughed, and they said no, they'd had their coffee. I asked them if they minded if I climbed up over the fence rather than go through the gate and have to explain to the watchman, and they said it was all right with them. As I climbed down on the other side I saw that old Wobbly boomer hiking along the highway street that runs parallel to the main street of Rawlins. I called out and he recognized me right off. I asked him if he wanted to eat with me, and he said no, he wanted to make Medicine Bow by nightfall. We walked up the street together, and I noticed that the old fedora hat he had on had its brim almost clean ripped off. I went into a store and bought a Stetson and came out and gave it to him. We didn't make much of a fuss over it, and he accepted it. I asked him if he knew of another old Wobbly called Swede Hammeros, and he said the name sounded familiar but he couldn't recall. I said I was going to try and look up Swede somewhere on the road, and he said I was the first person he had met in several years who had talked with him about the IWW. He thought, he said, that the men had been good but the idea a bad one, he didn't like the idea of One Big Union now. "Son, if we'd made families we'd never of gotten into the IWW, and that's the truth so help me God." I said I thought it might be the other way around, but he said no, now he regretted being alone in the world and not being married. He didn't say it as though he pitied himself, just was weighing it up and decided it was all sad. He asked me if I was married, and I said no, and he said, "Son, you ought to be. Ain't no room in this country any longer for a man who ain't married. It's the most married country in the universe. When I was young it didn't make too much difference if you was married or not, there was a sort of cheerfulness on the road that made a floor for all the loneliness. But now there don't seem to be either ceiling or floor to it." Then he said something in Italian, which he said meant it was the way of the world. I agreed with him, and said that was how I felt more frequently than not. He said I was too young to be feeling that sort of thing. He asked me to leave him on the street corner where he would try getting a lift off one of the oil trucks. It was against company rules, but a lot of the drivers knew him, he said. I wished he hadn't wanted to go on, I would have liked to talk with him. But I said so long, and crossed the street. Last I saw of him he was standing on the street with his thumb lifted to the sky and wearing a brand-new Stetson, his suitcase at his feet. For no reason at all, certainly this old guy didn't resemble him, I thought of my father and wondered whether he was alive and where.

Inside the coffee shop of the hotel, which was just about the most efficient, intelligently air-conditioned place of its kind I'd run across in the West, I sat down and ordered a lot of breakfast food, ham and waffles, that sort of thing. It is a habit I have on the road, a habit I got into, of ordering breakfast menus in the afternoon, steak or hamburgers in the morning, and anything I felt like at night.

(I suppose I should break off at this point and explain to anybody who is listening that this narrative has not been written with an eye to anyone who does not know the American highway. You will simply have to imagine for yourself a good deal of the atmosphere, the billboard posters and low gully banks and details of motel architecture; if you can't, then read Dos Passos or Algren or Mrs. Maritta Wolff.)

A bunch of ranchers were sitting to my right hand, and we began talking. They had the local newspaper spread out on the counter in front of them and were talking about the Suez fighting. In a few minutes, we talked ranching. They were voting Eisenhower. The ranchers said that in their area there was a real antagonism between the big and small ranches. The smaller farmers, they said, and this included mainly the young ones and the ex-servicemen, were definitely feeling the pinch. They had to maintain thousands of dollars worth of equipment in order to compete, machinery costing anywhere from $20,000 to twice that figure. The market, as they knew it, was shaky. They said many of the smaller ranchers and farmers around Rawlins were selling out to foreign, eastern or local money which was busily engaged in buying up slipping or marginal places. None of the ranchers wanted to talk about co-ops.

I was the last one to clear out. I talked to the cashier, a pretty woman in her forties who was also the manageress. She complained that Rawlins was a union town, and that she was being forced to join the waitresses' union. A committee of railroad men had come by yesterday morning to tell her they would boycott the hotel unless she joined. She asked if I had read the right-to-work article in that week's *U.S. News & World Report*, and she said that ranchers around Rawlins were too proud to take subsidies and she was too proud to join the union. Then I knew why the railroad men down by the shunting yards had smiled; it was probably they who had come by. I told the woman that unless it was against her religious scruples she ought to join the union. "What are you," she said, "a union organizer?" I said no ma'am, I just thought she ought to join. She said she'd be damned if she would, unions were getting too big as it was. I said in a way I agreed with her, that I knew more about it than she did if she didn't mind me saying so. Well, it turned out that she did mind. She said she had heard there were some union organizers in disguise in Rawlins and she could tell from my accent I was one of them. "You're probably from Denver or New York," she said, as though that put the kibosh on me forever. I figured there was no point just standing there and arguing and I went on up to my room. I looked out the window to see if I could catch a glimpse of the old Wobbly but he was already gone. I lay down on the bed and became sick. It took me about an hour and several towels to clean up the mess and air out the room. I left a note for the chambermaid, apologizing, saying I was carsick, and then I went downstairs looking for those white and Negro school kids who had been playing so easily together. When I started out from Los Angeles I had told my friends Harold and Essie, who run the *Pacific Liberal*, that I would be stopping off in Fulton, Tennessee, where they'd been having all the trouble with integrating the schools, but as soon as I went on the highway I knew I wouldn't be able to do it. If you have a New York or California license plate on your car you need a handful of guts to drive into a small southern town when they're having trouble with the Negroes, or to put it more accurately when the Negroes are having more trouble with them. I had done that twice, once in Georgia, near Rome, and once in North Carolina, and you could just feel everyone freezing you with their eyes because you must be a reporter or a representative for the NAACP; I'd been shoved off the sidewalk a couple of times, and denied hotel rooms and in that place in Georgia had my rear window splintered by a stone. The thing is, I'd been in both towns by accident, before coming I hadn't even known of their troubles. Well, I knew if I went into Fulton, this time looking for the trouble to write it up, I'd have to be pretty tough, because nobody in Fulton would feel like seeing California license plates, even if I told them I had taken my first education in Chattanooga, which I had. I just didn't feel that tough, that's all.

It was dusk, and a cool wind settled on Rawlins. I walked around the center of town, which contains no skyscrapers or even very tall buildings, looking for those kids. The curious thing, I found them. A whole passel of them, in front of a house, on a street of big squat trees, elms, about a quarter of a mile from the hotel and the railroad yard. There they were, white and black, just messing around under the trees. They were comparing rock samples. They weren't much more than shadows, in that dark quiet street; they were all in jeans and shirts, usually T. I felt like asking if I could play with them, but I knew they would have thought that was queer. So I walked up to them, boldly, and said I was a reporter investigating racial tensions. They weren't at all put off by that, so I figured they were bored, and wanted to talk.

We went up the street to an abandoned old house and went into the unkempt yard and sat around in a circle. They were a sober bunch of kids and we talked about many things. They were the sons of oil refinery workers and small businessmen. What I really wanted to know was why the feeling between the three Negro kids and the others was so good, but I didn't ask. The closest I came to it was asking if they had lived in the town a long time, but they hadn't, not the three Negroes. Two of them were brothers, named Ernest and Edgar. They didn't ask too many questions about me, but were interested in telling me about their school. Several of the kids had a teacher named Mr. McGinnis who, they argued, was a pansy. I defended Mr. McGinnis and said they shouldn't make accusations like that without proof. Then I remembered that was an illiberal thing to say, and argued that even if he was a queer they shouldn't hold it against him. That did it. Some of the kids, including the Negro ones, started to move away. I got up and brushed off my trousers and tried to change the subject, but I had broken the mysterious link. I walked away down the dark street and knew the kids were looking after me. When I got to the hotel there was practically nobody in the lobby. I asked the clerk, a woman, if she would switch on the radio which she kept in a back office, and she brought it out (a portable) and put it on the desk and let me listen to it. Soon the news came. It didn't say anything about Hungary at all. It did say that the British and the French had sent an ultimatum demanding the right to post troops to separate the belligerents in the Suez peninsula, and that the British and French governments had vetoed a Soviet cease-fire proposal in the UN. I thanked the lady and went and sat in a deep chair. I called across to her demanding to know if she knew how close to war we might all be. She said, sweetly, smiling, she didn't think so, and went on adding her figures, bent over them. A rancher sitting on the other side of the lobby came over and asked if I really thought there was going to be a war. We had a few drinks together in the hotel bar, and he invited me up to his room where three of his friends were playing poker. They were all about fifty and had big bellies and wore work shirts and Stetson hats. I knew they were all ranchers; they must have been well off as hell because they were playing about $100 a pot which was spread out on the blanket of the bed they were playing on. My friend, whose name was Olaf Jackson, asked his friends if I could join in. They didn't much care for the idea, but they said all right if I understood the limit. I went to my room and came back and put down $1000 in traveler's checks on the blanket very casually. They were fairly impressed by this; well, maybe less impressed than worried that I might turn out a tin-horn. Perhaps I should explain about that thousand dollars. You see, in all the time I've spent on the road I usually haven't had more than a few dollars on me at any time, and sometimes less than the twenty-five necessary to show you're not a vag. Lots of times I've gone without shelter or food until I reached the next town because I didn't have a red cent. Well, this time it was different. I was going in style. So I had taken out $1000 of the money I had saved on the Strip and put it in my pocket because I had wanted to feel good about being on the road. What I had really hoped was that on some lonely and deserted stretch of highway I would get a flat tire and have to hitch a ride into the nearest town, and while my thumb was in the air the cops would come by and take me in to the station because I looked like a hobo and at the station just before I was booked, or maybe just after, I would pull out this thousand dollars in traveler's checks and plunk it right down in front of them all, the bastards. Of course it was a silly dream, but I had it. The thing is, I have never revenged myself against the cops of the several states where I was treated with less than courtesy. I couldn't hit them the way they had me. I think one of the most pleasurable experiences known to an American is to win a suit for false arrest. I still have this dream.

(The only cop I've ever really liked was one named Werner Seitz, who was in the Dearborn, Michigan, police force. He was a good old boy. He was in my first outfit, the —th Infantry, at a time when a few of us were involved in a textile strike in the nearby town of Durham, North Carolina. We were soldiers then, replacements sent into the —th just after it came back from Germany at the end of the war in Europe. We weren't in a line company, but in something called a service company, because most of us worked for a headquarters unit. There were about seven or eight of us who were a sort of unsecret society on the second floor of the barracks. The father of us all, but young for the role, was Dan Henry, whom we all knew as Big Dan, a rangy farmer who had gone out west from Illinois to work in the aircraft factories and became elected president of AVB-CIO local 819 in Santa Monica, California, where to the best of my knowledge he still is. Dan came into the —th along with a large-muscled fellow named Preacher who had a regular daily sermon over some radio station in Bakersfield, California. Then there were Sonny, a Tulane University-educated failure from Officer Candidate School (failures, also, were Big Dan and Preacher), myself, Victor, a refugee from Germany and a huge handsome night-club singer named Max. Max was quite a card; one night he slipped a rubberized poncho over my sleeping form and poured lighter fluid on the poncho and told everyone to gather around while he set fire to it. I awoke to find myself burning. I pushed Max down the stairs, still laughing. Everyone in that barracks was nervous; the war was over, they wanted out; most were married. Anyway, a textile strike started in Durham. Dan Henry and I went out there on our free nights, and on the weekends, to help the union; we attended meetings of the union — they began with a prayer and a Salute to the Flag — almost every week. Gradually, we brought Victor into the strike, and Preacher — who didn't like unions — and then even Sonny, who was a real go-down southern boy but very bright if a trifle effeminate — which was why, he told us, he had been flunked out of OCS: woman's voice. Max never did want to come along; months after he moved out of the barracks we learned that he had once been an FBI agent, though whether he was on duty with us or not we never did find out. Max was a sort of barracks scandal anyway. One night Joe Keeble, who also was in the barracks, went to visit his wife staying at the Washington Duke Hotel in Durham and found Max in bed with her. As Max told it, they all sat around and smoked cigarettes, and Keeble walked out of the room. The thing was, Max and Keeble had cots next to each other, but as far as we could see there never was any difficulty between them. Anyway, the last one we brought into the strike was this Werner Seitz, a stubby sunburned guy who had been hanging around with us for months even though he knew how Dan Henry and I were about unions. Seitz himself hated them. In Dearborn, the police all hated unions. For years the Dearborn police were little better than the personal retainers of Henry Ford Senior who used them to bust the heads of union organizers, and this was the atmosphere Werner became a cop in. But he had good instincts, and we worked on him, mainly by not, if you know what I mean. And then one day, without warning anyone, he showed up at the union's food distribution headquarters in Durham, a convert. From then on he ate, drank and slept union. Dan Henry secured some leaflets and books for him and Dan and I shared with Werner everything we knew. The upshot was, as soon as Werner went back to Dearborn from the Army he tried to organize the motorcycle cops and was promptly fired from his job. I wrote him a letter telling him to go to work in the Ford Dearborn plant, but he said no, he was going to buy a farm, which he did, and that's where he is now, with his wife and three kids, on a farm near Alpena, Michigan, up near the Canadian border. I don't know whether that's a good thing or not. I was in Detroit, coincidentally, at the time he was trying to organize the motorcycle cops, and for a month we lived in the same rooming house. What happened to the others I'm not sure. Dan Henry is still president of his union local, and the Preach still has a program every day in Bakersfield, Victor I'm told went to East Germany, and Sonny, well therein lies a tale. Dan and I didn't work on Sonny, or anything like that, but we all used to go on long walks in the North Carolina countryside, talking about this and that, and when Sonny went back to college his first semester he started a "Stop Bilbo" campaign, which was a nice thing for him to do. I lost touch with Sonny, and then about four years later I heard that Willie McGee, a Negro, was about to die in the Mississippi electric chair for the alleged rape of a white woman. Up in New York, all the newspapers had stories about how Willie and this woman had been making it for a long time, and a campaign was worked up around him. I wrote letters to several of my southern friends because I knew that letters from Southerners to the Governor of Mississippi were more likely to produce an effect. I also sent a letter to Sonny, apologizing for losing touch and asking him to look into the McGee case. I didn't even ask him to protest, just investigate. Well, I got back this letter telling me to mind my own business, the South could take care of its own, and enclosing a news clipping from a northern paper telling how some white men had raped a Negro girl, been caught, and sentenced to a year in jail apiece. I wasn't quite sure what point Sonny wanted to make, but we didn't exchange any more letters. Sonny turned out to be a big disappointment. Dan Henry always tells me, never mind, he was okay while we knew him. I suppose

Dan Henry is right. Even so, it makes you think how much influence you really do have on people in the long run. Well, the point is, the only cop I have ever liked was Werner Seitz, who is not a cop any more but a farmer near Alpena, Michigan. That's why I carried $1000 with me on this trip.)

So we just settled ourselves around that old bed and started to play poker. I wished I had a Stetson like those ranchers, and in fact was on the point of asking one of them if he would cut cards with me for his, but I knew whoever I asked would feel insulted, so I let it lay.

Those ranchers played a conservative brand of poker, it was all five-card draw. They said it was "dealer's choice" but I knew they wanted to keep on with five-card draw, so that was what I called too. You could tell from their conversation that they thought they were playing a brutal, masculine game; all they did was grunt and bet high and take swigs from the whiskey bottles. But you can't really get tough in five-card draw; the way they played it it might as well have been blackjack, since they only bet on receiving cards and at the end, with continual raising equal to being tough, and I didn't argue. Basically they played the way my mother's Dublin-Donegal Progressive Society played poker, a very slow game with everyone pondering their cards as if it were a chess game or something. Well, maybe seven-card high-low Mexican baseball, an extra card to a face-up four, threes and nines wild, double the pot to bet on an open wild card, is like chess but not this five-card draw stuff. They played like my maiden aunts. So I just sat there, grimly, pretending I was a big he-man by saying nothing except to declare: but to tell you the truth I was bored. I've played better poker elsewhere. The one serious thing about this game was the stakes. Sometimes there was $100 or $150, once $210 in the kitty; that may not sound much to you but I had to travel on my money, and anyway I always did play poker for money; or rather for the money plus the company, but I could never forget we weren't playing for matchsticks. That was the way I had been taught poker by One-Eye Gold and Reggie Lupo, the two AVB-CIO union organizers in Detroit with whom I used to travel in the area between Rochester and Detroit canvassing local unions for the Incentive Rates Department of the International Union, me providing cover for these trips by lecturing the local shop stewards on the various techniques for assessing incentive (piecework) wage rates and One-Eye and Reggie spending their time caucusing in favor of the then president of the union, big fat bumbling K. T. Tolliver as against Victor Hauser, the labor statesman. As it happened, Hauser beat us all hollow at the next convention and we found ourselves without jobs; I went to college, One-Eye went back into the factory, and Reggie Lupo, I suppose, back to the rackets whence he had emerged. One-Eye and Reggie Lupo were inseparable even though I think they despised each other a little. They always did organizing tours together, just the two of them; One-Eye a gargantuan Trotskyist, and Reggie Lupo basically a middle-income racketeer, very short and slim and dapper, a less excitable George Raft. They were called Mutt and Jeff by the other union organizers. I think what they liked in each other was the quality of physical ruthlessness, never displayed but for the occasion. One-Eye was always spouting but he could fight like a crazy bear; Lupo was very quiet except when complaining about his ulcers, but he had been a union goon for many years, which means he had come close to killing guys and maybe even had. I remember one night, after a truck workers' conference at the Hotel Schroeder in Milwaukee, Lupo and One-Eye and I were sharing a hotel room when we were awakened by a bunch of riprousing characters from the American Bowling League convention downstairs. These middle-aged adolescents thought it was funny to pound on our door and squirt water through the transom at two o'clock in the morning. Finally, Lupo couldn't take it any more and got out of bed. Aw, let them be, said One-Eye sleepily. Fuck them, said Lupo. He opened the door, and you should have seen those bowlers scatter for their lives. Because Lupo was pointing two .45 automatics at them. Lupo went out into the hallway, and one of the bowlers fell down on his knees and begged Lupo not to kill him. Lupo said, promise you won't make any noise on this floor. This bowler said he promised, and Lupo just stood in the hallway while the bowler got on his feet and walked away, so frightened I thought he would faint. What made it all a little humorous was that the bowler was wearing a woman's hat. I padded, sleepy, out of the room and took Lupo's hand and said, Reggie, come on. He said, How do you like those effin characters, waking up people, some of them with ulcers. It was only then that I had a good look at the guns. They were the biggest .45's I had ever seen in my life, and even though I had been traveling with Reggie for the better part of two months I never knew he carried tools like that with him. It gave me quite a feeling to watch him carefully put the automatics back into his satchel. The thing was, those guns were loaded and cocked. In the coffee shop of the Schroeder the next morning, while Reggie was having the car greased, I asked One-Eye if Reggie always carried guns with him. One-Eye became very angry and said, What guns? I never saw any guns! I felt like a dumb kid and never mentioned it after that. It so happened that coming back to Detroit from Milwaukee we were stopped by a traffic cop for speeding. Reggie got out of the car and walked up the highway and gave the cop a ten-spot, and all the way to Detroit Reggie and One-Eye argued, I mean vehemently, about whether we could have gotten away with only a fiver. Man, said Lupo, I hate cops. It sounded different from a man who habitually carried two .45 automatics with him in his suitcase. But it was one thing we all agreed on, particularly in Detroit, particularly in those days. That was when the Allis-Chalmers strike was still on. But I run ahead of myself.

The best thing about the poker game with these ranchers was that, after ups and downs, I came out about $100 winners. I told them I had to drive in the morning, but I would stay in to lose my hundred dollars if they wanted me to. They weren't bad guys and said no, none of that old poker courtesy was necessary, they understood. Which was nice of them, even considering any of them could have bought or sold me ten times over, and considering how profoundly they took their poker. I agreed to stay in for five more hands, and the dealer said, just as if we hadn't been playing it all night, "Ante up a buck apiece, five-card draw, nothing wild." He could say that again. One thing I had to hand to those old boys, they could tuck in liquor. All four of them had been on one or more of the bottles of booze since I'd come in the room, and they didn't even look sleepy. It must be this outdoor living. I asked permission to turn on the radio, and switched on to an all-night station coming from Denver. After a while, the news announcer came on with a summary, but all he said was that Nagy had discontinued one-party rule in Hungary. There was no further news out of Egypt. I turned the radio off and asked the ranchers if they didn't think that was good news, about the discontinuance of one-party government in Hungary. They looked at me. I explained to them this theory of mine, about how perhaps Hungary might leapfrog past Yugoslavia and pioneer new democratic institutional forms in the context of socialized industry, agriculture variously collectivized. One of those old ranchers put down his cards long enough to say, quietly, "You want a drink, son?" I said no, thanks, and went out of the room.

Then I did another foolish thing. I went downstairs to the lobby which was deserted and dark except for the lamp near the night clerk, this time a tubby little man with red hair. I asked him if he would help me make a long-distance call to Los Angeles. He told me I could take it from the phone on the register desk, but I wanted to talk in one of the booths. I got into a booth and sat down and waited. Outside I could hear him contacting the Denver operator who was getting to the Los Angeles operator. After a while he said there was no answer, was I sure my friend was at home?

That's when I became confused. I started to stammer and thanked the man apologetically for trying to make my call and gave him a dollar. He didn't think anything was queer until I gave him that dollar. Of course I had been calling my number in Los Angeles. My old flat. Myself. As soon as I realized that, a great big whoop of fright caught hold of me, like a silent circumspect tornado, and just about lifted me off the floor. I sneaked upstairs and went into my room and packed my bag, went downstairs, paid my bill and got to hell out of that hotel. I wasn't trembling or crying or even shivering; what this was was an intellectual fear, almost a philosophic insight. I suppose it was what you would call a *realization.* Man, I was scared. I walked down the street until I found the De Soto. It was a cold dark night, without any moon now, and damp. The De Soto was almost dripping wet. I opened the door and threw in my G.I. bag, then got in and started the motor. It sparked on the first go. I ran the motor for about fifteen minutes, at five miles an hour in neutral and not just idling because I didn't want to wake anybody, and I thought just one thing: I was up my own pole. All of a sudden I felt like doing something for somebody. I thought of going back to the hotel to give the desk clerk the $100 to give back to the ranchers, but I knew they would not appreciate any gesture, that no number of good deeds would bring me down from that pole, and so I put the car into first and got out of Rawlins.

Goodbye, Rawlins, Wyoming. God *damn;* why didn't I have a friend in it?

It was black as pitch and I was going on high plateau country, dipping down and then steadily rising, crossing the North Platte River about five in the morning. This was hill country, and I was going up into the Medicine Bow range of mountains. I knew about those mountains. Shoshone and Cheyenne used to hunt in their flatlands, and the early Comanche. It was on the other side of the mountains, on the Laramie side, that in 1876 gathered most of the Indian nations between the Mississippi and the Rockies, to meet with the government agents to conclude a peace treaty. E.J. had told me about this conclave, and I had read about it myself in the historical section of the New York Public Library where they keep the books locked up in air-conditioned vaults. Thousands and thousands of Indians — Arapaho, Cheyenne, Comanche, Sioux, even Cherokee — had come to make a peace treaty. The American government, which was then presided over by U. S. Grant, whose ear on Indian affairs was had by Quakers, sent a passel of men and wagons and some troops of soldiers who, under orders, paraded armed in front of the assembled Indians. The day before the conference was officially to begin, the Indians, about half of them, headed up by Comanches of the Sun-shade clan (said E.J.), roared down on the American encampment and rode around and around the American tents in concentric circles going in alternate directions, whooping it up to beat hell. The Americans, frightened, fearing a massacre, almost went for their guns. But it turned out to be only an Indian joke. After that, the Americans got down to business and didn't parade with guns in front of the Indians. E.J. said the legend was that his great-grandfather, Old Tonto, who was a young brave then, had ridden alone to Medicine Bow and interrupted a council of the Comanche wisemen to make a speech pleading not to make peace with the white man. But, aside from its being a serious breach of protocol for a young brave to muscle into the elders' deliberations, they said no, the Americans had guaranteed them hunting lands. And so they signed a treaty there, in Medicine Bow, in 1876. E. J. Birdsong said that he didn't really know whether or not his great-grandfather had been at Medicine Bow or just got the story around. He had done a lot in his time, E.J. conceded, but towards his end he was proclaiming his participation in every battle from Adobe Walls to Little Big Horn. I told E.J. that according to the books I'd read in the New York Public Library his great-grandfather had actually been at Adobe Walls and E.J. said, Well that sure does surprise me, I'd heard the story so much I more or less thought it was one of great-grandpop's lies.

Dawn, I was in the middle of the mountains. Not much traffic, considering. I felt a little better. I was still mildly chilled by that experience in the telephone booth, but I figured, what the hell, I had been nipping it a little up in the room playing poker. Also, I felt pretty good about coming away with that $100. For some reason, even though I was carrying a thousand in traveler's checks on me, I was beginning to fret about money matters. I was a regular little old spinster on whole stretches of the highway, buying non-super gas and the cheapest dishes on the menu and checking into motels without neon signs, that sort of thing.

It was morning by the time I came down out of the mountains. I stopped in Medicine Bow at an Eagle station for some gas and talked to the attendant. "Yeah," he said, "people are living better than ever," he agreed. "I'm sure doing so, better than in my whole life. Got a '55 Pontiac, a new television, a deep freeze," and here he laughed, "and fourteen bucks in the bank." I told him that was the story all along the line. He didn't give a damn for national politics, he said; it was all a racket. Anyway, that Nixon very likely was a Red. Didn't he just come on the television arguing for a four-day week? He'd like to see Richard Nixon running a filling station on four days a week.

I explained to this garage man that he was one of a vanishing breed, and he surprised me by not disagreeing. He said the filling station was now to America what the one-family forty-acre farm used to be, the outpost of independence. I asked him how much independence he could have when he was mortgaged to the Eagle Petroleum Company, and he said plenty, everyone these days was mortgaged to somebody, it was just a case of how much and to whom. Well, I couldn't argue with that. I asked him to crawl under the De Soto and tell me about my right rear spring. He did and came out and said it was cracked and I should get it fixed. I said I didn't have the time. His name was Larry, he said, and he had a wife and five kids. He grinned when he said that. I asked him where they all lived and he pointed to a disattached trailer in a field near the gas station. I wanted to talk about the war — he had landed in one of the early waves at Tarawa — but he didn't, so I showed him my credit card and got in and drove away. I marked him down in this little book I was keeping, of how people were voting. Larry had said he was voting for Eisenhower. He thought the name of the Democratic candidate was Stevens. But he knew all about Estes Kefauver whom he described as a publicity hound.

It was about seven in the morning and the highway was fairly clear of traffic. I could see about a mile down in the gray cold haze of morning that there was someone on the road, waiting for me. I started slowing down about half a mile off because I wanted to think if I felt like picking up anybody, which in my heart I didn't at all. But then, up close, I saw it was a man and a baby. I mean, what the *hell.*

I stopped. They got in. It was funny about him, he didn't thank me or start talking, just said, "I hope you're going a long way."

Morning and seventy m.p.h. Now bright and clear. Highway full of trucks. I asked him where he was from and he said, "Kentucky."

His clothes were dirty jeans, a T-shirt like mine and army shoes. He was about twenty-two and had long Elvis sideburns. The satchel he had been carrying was roped together, and had a box of baby Farina tied to it. I asked how old the baby was, and he said, "Four months."

I didn't ask him what happened, but as the morning wore on, and we got further away from Medicine Bow he told me the story. He was on his way back to Kentucky after two years in California working in an aircraft plant near Oakland. His story came out in snatches. He wasn't especially reluctant to tell it, he seemed to be thinking as he did. He had lost his job in Oakland and could find no other. Then the baby came. He didn't say whether he and the girl were married, all he would say was, "She ain't *no* damn good," and that she had run off with another man. She had been from Kentucky too, come out to join him in Oakland when the living was easy. Was he going back to his folks? No, he said, he was going back to some of her kin, they were friends of his. They had a nice piece of land, a cabin, running water, a few miles outside Bowling Green, and he was taking the baby with him.

We stayed silent for a few miles. Then I said, You know, you better watch out, traveling on the road with little baba, the cops'll pull you in for sure. I half suspected there was a restraining court order mixed up in all of this that he wasn't telling me about. You could tell he was a man on the run by the way he kept turning his head to stare uneasily at the police cars I occasionally passed on the highway. He said, "I ain't worried about the cops. It's Welfare I'm worried about." They might be able to help you, I said. He said, "Me and this li'l old boy traveled out all the way from Oakland in my car, which broke down just this side of Salt Lake City, and I got here this far, and I'll get to Kentucky, you going to Chicago?" I said yeah, I was going to Chicago. Eventually. I was careful to add that eventually.

He said, "It sure would help us a lot if you could take us all the way to Chicago."

I looked over at this sweaty guy with the dirty face and jeans and that baby, they smelled up the car and he felt like talking and I felt like a dog because I just didn't want any company. I wasn't in the mood. So I said I had to stop in Laramie for the night, maybe two nights, and he said that was too bad, he sure was worried about getting picked up by Welfare. He said he had no money, just about $1.40. "Welfare," he said, "you say they may be able to help me, but I know they'll want to take Tikie away from me. Well, I'll have to be six feet under if they want to take Tikie away from me." Then he said he had another kid, a little girl, with his mother who had custody. He kept using the phrase, "in plain words." "In plain words, I'm tired." "In plain words, it is a nice day." He was tired too. You could see that.

He said there was a good woman waiting for him in Kentucky, who would take both him and Tikie. "But I'll kill me and this here kid before we give over to Welfare." I thought about how long he had to go on this highway, and I said, Well you might think about it. He was very stubborn. "In plain words," he said, "there's nothing to think about. He's mine." And launched into a diatribe against his first woman, accusing her of all sorts of things, mainly contradictory. He asked me how far I was going. Well, what could I say? He kept making my flesh crawl by asking if I would take him to Chicago. Now, I knew, if I wanted, I could have taken him to Chicago. It would have meant him and the baby staying in the car for two days and nights, maybe me shelling out for a couple of nights' motels, which I could afford. I kept telling myself it would give me company. And also how much I would esteem myself once I got rid of them somewhere in the Loop, how I had put myself out for my fellow man and all that jive. But, you know, I just didn't *feel* like having anyone in the car with me. Well, maybe that isn't too honest. One or two of my special pals, like Henry Carleton or Chuck Podolny, or any of several young women I could think of. But not the Kentucky boy and his little baby. The more I thought about it the more of a panic I got into, because, I couldn't think of a valid reason not to keep them in the car with me. So I just pressed my lips tight and then said I would like to, except that I would be having to stop off in Laramie, I didn't know how long, on business. He knew all right that I was lying my head off, but he didn't seem to mind too much. All he did was ask to be let off outside the city limits of Laramie so the cops couldn't catch him inside. We drove on, just making conversation, stopping once for sandwiches which I bought.

It was a bright clear day, and by the time we got to the edge of Laramie it was not quite noon. I let them out, and reached in the back seat and gave the satchel with the box of Farina cereal tied to it to the Kentucky boy. All the time he had been in the car he had showered, I mean literally showered love, on that baby, calling him all sorts of nicknames, making faces and giving him mock punches and taking the kid's tiny paws to punch himself in the face. I got out of the car too, it was near a clump of trees with a motel in back, and I gave him $10. To have given him more would have been like buying my conscience. No, that isn't true either. That was probably what I told myself at the time. Because, you see, there was no earthly reason why I couldn't have given him bus fare to Bowling Green, I had one thousand one hundred dollars with me. Everything inside me was tight and ice cold as I gave him the ten bucks and wished him luck and told him not to put up a fight if the Welfare people got hold of him because I was sure they would listen to reason, which of course I was by no means sure of. I was so busy making excuses for myself that my mind felt fractured. I said goodbye to the Kentucky boy and got into the De Soto and roared away. I didn't look back in the rear view. Then about a quarter of a mile down the highway I made a U-turn and went back until just before the spot I left him. I turned off into a side road and then quietly, in first gear, crept the De Soto in behind a small mountain of chopping wood beside a lumber dealers. I stopped the car and opened up another bottle of White Horse and slugged some of it and sat back to wait. From where I was I could see the Kentucky boy (I didn't know his name, except Lester) holding the baby in his arms, standing on the dusty edge of the highway and waiting. He didn't stick up his thumb. Only waited. I was plenty angry. Well, god damn *him*, if he didn't feel like putting himself out to the extent of pushing his thumb out in front of him, it would take him that much longer, that was all; I could wait here as long as he could. A man came out of the lumberyard and looked over at me. I put the bottle of White Horse away. He came over and asked if I wanted anything. He was an old, bent Negro, with white hair, he looked like an illustration out of Brer Rabbit. I said, Grandpa, I'm just resting my weary bones. He turned away and went back into the lumberyard. The only thing I was afraid of now was that Lester would see me, but he didn't. I rolled up the window and watched. None of the time did Lester talk to the baby, who looked to be asleep in his arms. They just stood under the coolish sun and waited. So did I. I switched on the car radio and waited for the news. When it came the announcer came right on with news from Hungary. I turned it on full blast and it echoed like holy hell in that closed-up De Soto. According to the news bulletin, Soviet forces were withdrawing from Hungary, that was one story. The other was that Soviet troops were going into Budapest but only, Moscow said, to safeguard their positions. They were willing to negotiate the complete pulling out of troops. Also, Hungary was withdrawing from the Warsaw Pact. Also, and finally, Nagy had released Cardinal Mindzenty. What in Christ's good name all that meant, as I watched carefully Lester and his little baby, I didn't know. All I hoped was that old Mindzenty would keep his yap shut for seven straight days. Which I doubted he would, he being what he was. You had to hand it to the old bastard, in a way. He was probably the least tactical reactionary in the world. I began to grow very bitter towards that Kentucky boy, Lester, and his baby, as they remained out there, in the cool sunny wind, waiting for a car to take them to Bowling Green. Everything in me told me to get out of the car and yell over at Lester and tell him that I would take him to Chicago, or even Bowling Green. But I just didn't *feel* like it. If someone didn't pick him up soon very likely I'd get out of the car and slam his head with the bottle of White Horse. But someone did. A long-distance van came rocketing down the road and slammed down hard on the brakes. Man, I can tell you it wasn't soon enough. The stopped truck obstructed my view, but when it pulled away Lester and his baby weren't there any more. Fair and away!

I slumped back in the seat and rolled the windows down. The old Negro man and I guess the owner of the lumberyard, a chunky little bulldog wearing a straw boater, came out, and the bulldog wanted to know what I was doing around there. I said, seeing a friend off, started the car and rolled onto the highway.

I didn't much like the idea of following the truck with Lester in it so I stopped for gas about a mile down. I got to talking with the man pumping gas. He was an ordinary-looking American which meant that his features defied description. I hung around outside the De Soto, and when he said I had enough gas as it was, I asked him to give it a lube job while I waited. I wanted to put a lot of distance between that truck and me. So this pump-monkey put the car on the rack and started to gun-squirt grease into the joints. I could tell, that even with me watching, he wasn't doing too terrific a job because he didn't say anything about the cracked rear spring. He said that he had been born black-haired but now had corn-colored hair, that his whole family was like that. He had been a rancher, had run a cattle spread outside Medicine Bow, but gave it up about five years ago during a price drought and because he was being given the squeeze by the bigger farms. He said the town around Laramie was roughly split, between farmers and workers, and that the farmers were better organized, in the Farm Bureau. Some day I will tell you all about the Farm Bureau, it is a very powerful organization with a peculiar semi-official status. Sociologists and political "scientists" just love the Farm Bureau. It is the archetypical unit in our so-called pluralistic society. If it weren't for the Farm Bureau people like D. W. Brogan and Max Lerner would just pine away with underwork. While greasing my car, this fellow said that the farm owners were Republican, the railroad workers Democratic. I told him this confirmed what I had found out. He said he had more confidence in Kefauver than Nixon, which also began to confirm what I thought, that because of the personalities involved, most everyone I was speaking to was more interested in the Vice-presidents than the Presidents. Everyone had three quarters a thought that old Ike was going to kick off, and that would leave the country to Nixon. You would be surprised how many of these hard-earth Republican types were unhappy about that.

It was a slow morning for my friend and we jawed around. He said that a lot of Mexicans were coming into the state, and what he was worried about was the Mexican birth rate. He said there wasn't too much migrant labor or "boomer" traffic on the road these days. A burning issue in Laramie, he said, though most people didn't talk about it officially, was the way people thought their wage rates hereabouts were being lowered because college kids were on hand to take jobs. Also he said he was worried about "motionation." I told him that in Wyoming he didn't have too much to worry about in that department, but he said I shouldn't be so sure. I got a sudden stomach griping and had to go out in back of his garage, and he came and asked if anything was wrong. I said no, but I knew it was time to get out of there. He lowered the De Soto off the rack, I paid him and went tearing down Highway 30 towards Laramie, going through town like a knife, stopping at the two stop lights I actually had to, and then out of it like a shot, which was a shame because Laramie is one of the towns I like. It's a college town, for one thing, and I always like them, they usually have trees and shade and quietness and lots of post-teenagers carrying books and looking their best in saddle shoes and with that false, edgy contemplativeness I, personally, happen to like in students. Then Laramie is a wide and open town, not wide open, as in gambling, but wide to the sky and open to the air and very, very clean if a bit dusty. Except when there are rodeos and centennials, it's a quiet town, a lot quieter than Cheyenne, the state capital, and which is too damn conscious of its frontier heritage and "Wild West Days" for my taste. I mean, in Laramie when you see a character walking around in a ten-gallon hat, or even in chaps, you have a feeling he may really be a rancher, or if a town dweller he has some damn intelligent reason for wearing what he does, even if only for tradition's sake, which isn't so obnoxious if you really do believe in it. But in Cheyenne I always have this feeling that a dressed-up dude is a businessman drumming up trade for the annual Frontier Days celebration. That's the difference between the two towns. I hate Cheyenne. It's a lousy, phony town. Well, from the way I zinged through Laramie you would think I didn't like it, either. But I did.

About ten miles outside Laramie, through the yellow high rock walls of Cheyenne Pass, I turned off a side road and rumbled along until I came to a high brick wall and cruised along the wall to a sweet, lawny-looking place, a complex of government buildings. The entranceway was unguarded except by a man in overalls mowing the grass. It really was nice-looking, the clean-cut three-story buildings of red brick a relaxed contrast to the yellowish gray of the hills. The sign outside said it was the Cheyenne Veterans' Administration Hospital. What it was, a mental home, for G.I.'s, mainly of World War II, some from Korea and a few left over from the first war. It looked to be a considerably more pleasant place than Sawtelle VA, in West Los Angeles, with all those toothless old men wandering around under the eucalyptus trees waiting for the wineshops to open.

I knew where I was, not because I'd ever been here before, but because it was contained in a footnote of my Triple-A road book. I had come in by a side entrance, a dirt road, and soon I was on an asphalt one, nearer the buildings. Near a shed on a small grassy verge a group of guys were playing croquet. They were wearing the maroon bathrobes and G.I. shoes you always see in Army hospitals. I stopped the car to watch. They stopped their game, a few of them, to watch me. There was nothing embarrassing about any of this. I mean, it wasn't like in a short story, where the pause meant a sudden cessation of wind or anything like that. I was just looking at them, and they were waiting for me. They looked healthy enough, maybe just a little bent-over, the way everyone gets once they put on that maroon bathrobe, and not at all worried to be in the nuthouse. I told myself it couldn't be too bad a life, waking up not too early, making your bed, maybe a little physiotherapy and group psychoanalysis (this, I admit, didn't appeal to me), playing croquet and if you weren't violent or anything (I was a thousand miles from feeling anything like that) probably getting out to town on weekend passes. But no sooner had I decided it mightn't be a bad life than I put the car into reverse, waved to the G.I.'s and rolled back down to the road. Nope, not this year.

Near Cheyenne I stopped to talk to a sheep rancher who was standing by his car on the highway, it looked to me counting his sheep. He said, "Subsidies will never solve our problems. We're too proud." I thanked him and went on.

In the town of Cheyenne itself I talked to some local businessmen, the kind I hate. They said everyone was interested in who was going to be mayor, nobody talked much about the national elections. All the businessmen resented Kefauver because of his coonskin hat. They said he was trying to cash in on America's past. One of the businessmen who told me that was wearing a ten-gallon Stetson. And there wasn't much of a sun out this day. Do you see what I mean? It's not just that I don't like businessmen. Actually, I don't have strong feelings one way or the other, if they'd just go about their business quietly and make money and cut corners on each other, or even wear Stetsons in the *legitimate* way they do in Laramie. But what I really loathe is an *ideological* businessman. Out in the west one who tells the world he is a descendant of frontiersmen, or what is worse, thinks of himself in that way, or in the east a manufacturer who makes speeches to graduating classes of high schools telling them that not only is his factory the foundation of American society, which is all right if a little *hubris*-y by me, but that his values are too. That's what I hate. If you just think for a while you'll see what I mean.

I tried telling some of this to a jeweler on Capitol Avenue, which is one of the main streets of Cheyenne, as I was questioning him about his family voting patterns. He had already told me that his wife and her sister had come out of the kitchen in '52 to vote for Ike but weren't voting this year. But then he brought up the subject of the yearly centennial celebration of the Frontier Days which just near to sickened me, because he didn't even say it was a cheap way of making money, he actually said that it was "a fitting commemoration." To tell you the truth, I had thought that men who talked that way you found only in early Sinclair Lewis novels. I knew they made *speeches* saying these things but in private conversation, no. Well, I didn't lose patience with this jeweler, I tried to reason with him. I tried to explain that I was leaving the western country and how I felt about it, hoping to shame him, telling him how tired, ragged and hungry men had pushed aside the Indians and Mexicans to take the incredibly vast land for themselves. I told him all about the trip I had made through the mountains, how I had crossed the trails of Jim Bridger, Jim Clyman and Applegate, the soldiers Kearny and Doniphan, even that great big heroic phony Frémont chasing his own destiny like a boss his secretary around the desk without ever really getting his hands on her; I didn't tell him about the Donner party because that was a little personal. I told him about Francis Parkman, the first of our academic anthropologists never to see the forest for the trees and so in love with the Indians it made him a brave man. I tried to instill in him a little patriotism by telling him about some junior officers named Meade, Grant, Lee, Jefferson Davis and Beauregard who had tramped the western deserts and mountains in amity rehearsing for the blood bath of the 1860's. I told him all of that, and I've got to hand it to this jeweler, he leaned on his counter, that afternoon, and listened. But just when he was about to say something a customer came in, a tourist probably from Elmira, New York, asking for a snakeskin belt, and the jeweler had to wait on him. I didn't feel like hanging around, so I just yelled out for the jeweler to remember what I said, and he yelled back thanks a lot, as though I was there to give him a free lecture, or had submitted myself the way Seventh-Day Adventists do when they knock at your door and you have to stand there politely listening to it all and wondering whatever in the world possesses them to come around trying to persuade you. So I got back in the car and hightailed it out of Cheyenne, thinking about (I think with my tongue and mouth) what I'd told the jeweler, and I concluded that I really did believe all that, that all they should do in Cheyenne, if they have to do anything, is get together quietly somewhere and make a silent march through the center of the town and lay a wreath at the statue of Jim Bridger annually. But that's all. America's past in the West was never romantic, but that's no reason to spit on it.

It was already late afternoon when I crossed the border into Nebraska. As far as I'm concerned, it meant I was leaving the West. Strictly speaking, of course, I wasn't. In some ways Nebraska has more of a western heritage than some of the states on the other side of the Rockies. It is especially rich in Indian history, because there were about ten big tribes that regularly trampled and foraged all over it. But somehow, and I admit it's an idiosyncrasy, I always have the feeling that I'm leaving the West when I cross over the Wyoming border. I say it's historically inaccurate, but it's my feeling. For another thing, I stop *talking* to various people once I'm over the border, once I'm in the Dakotas, Nebraska, Kansas, Oklahoma and Texas, I just cease, usually at night, to converse with some of my favorite historical personages. I must emphasize that I am not mystical, in fact anti-mystical, it is just a habit I've gotten into bumming on the road, here and there. It's usually the same people I talk to. As I explained before, in Nevada it's usually the Donners. What I haven't explained is that I sometimes do more of this than I let on. So that, if I were to tell you the complete truth, I have talked in a few more places than I've already allowed. It's a little difficult to tell you why exactly I picked on these particular people. (Some you would have difficulty finding more than a footnote about in the standard history texts.) For example, I talked a couple of nights ago to Jim Bridger and to Clyman, but not to Frémont, who simply is not my class of people. All along the route I've been making remarks to Lewis and Clark, whom I actually know a great deal about. The only Indian I *ever* talk to is Chief Joseph, the Nez Percé, who is, for my money, the most peaceable and tragic and intelligent Indian America ever produced, including even the

Indian Bird's great-grandfather, who when all is said and done did do (subjectively or otherwise we needn't argue) his bit to sell out the Comanche nation and did ride up Pennsylvania Avenue in Washington like any store-bought chief and even tried to run for U. S. Senate which puts the real kibosh on him as far as I (and the Bird) are concerned. Once, in Colorado, I had a terrific wordless argument with Nathaniel Meeker, the agricultural editor of the New York *Tribune* who was killed by Indians in 1879. Well, anyway, that's what I mean, but I don't expect you to completely understand, because if you did it I promise I wouldn't understand.

About four in the afternoon, between Kimball and Sidney, I put the car radio on. In Hungary, it was reported, the situation was tense but quiet. Nobody knew if the Russian troops were going in or coming out. In Egypt, British and French air forces had begun operations. That's all the announcer said, "begun operations." Bombing, I guess. I switched the radio off. I wasn't too worried about Suez, because it was so unreal. Nothing would happen there, I felt sure. The French and English were so dependent on us for loans and supplies and we had nothing to gain and a lot to lose by a war with Nasser. But what was happening in Hungary, that wasn't unreal at all. I drove at 80 into the dusk thinking about things in general and looking at the Nebraska countryside, which around here is all sandhilly. I was feeling not very well. I couldn't get that kid from Kentucky, Lester, out of my mind, nor Hungary, nor those guys in maroon bathrobes playing croquet. I careened off into a ditch, which fortunately was shallow and all I got was a bumping around. But just as soon as I got the car back on the highway I slowed down and then I stopped. I didn't *like* going into ditches at 70 or 80. So I just pulled into a side road, emptied the White Horse and went to sleep. I had a really nice dream.

I dreamed an extraordinary scene. A school for deaf adolescent girls. We see, by a tree, a girl weeping. Another girl on the stairs sobbing. Several crying unashamedly. We don't know why. What misfortune had befallen the institution? Suddenly the school director (me) comes staggering down marble-veined stairs shrouded by Versailles-type trees and shrubbery, very misty, you know. He is tall, blond, rugged, a good face (not me). He is crying too. A number of girls, in gauzy saris, laughing and crying, are on his neck. His wife has had a baby!

When I woke up I almost wept, it was such a goddam *nice* dream. It was dusk, in Nebraska, over the state line. I wasn't sleepy, and I had a long highway in front of me. I was going to drive all night, I felt like it, that was all. I started up the motor, and I climbed out of the side road and hit 30 again, in this part of the state a good and new highway. You look at the highway and it is straight for miles, coming at you, with the white line of the center on the dark gray asphalt coming at you, and on sunny days the glaze at the far end making it look like a lake at the end of your highway, but it's seldom a lake only another damn hamburger joint or motel. That's a thing about that line, if you stare at it too long it hypnotizes you and you wind up in a ditch as I did just back there. On the other hand, I have spent many a night, in fact a few back there, after San Francisco especially, where my headlights glued to the cat's eyes or the white line in the center of the highway was all that was keeping me on this old earth of ours, and I have fallen in several minor states of mind wondering what would happen if that old white stripe should ever give out, for instance if the men painting it had gone off to lunch and some supervisor had put them to work half a mile up the road. Whenever I got glued to the line that way, I was pretty much convinced that if it gave out I would too. It never happened this way in the daytime, just at night, when the darkness closes in on you, and comes right into the car, bringing with it a kind of rushing, infinite silence that makes you think any minute you're going to become permanently unhinged. You *sail.* My own advice is when you start sailing through the night air, like Ichabod Crane or the Cotter's Saturday Night, you'd better slow down or stop altogether. That may seem gratuitous. But it's not all that easy to climb off the white stripe down the middle of the night-packed highway as you may think.

It wasn't night yet, and I was already east of Sidney, Nebraska, and going towards Ogallala. The highway here winds around fairly steep gullies but it's easy driving because the road has been engineered well. That's why it surprised me when these tears started streaming out of my eyes. I didn't think I was crying; in fact, when I lifted myself up to look in the visor mirror I could see that my face was calm, if a little dirty. But there was no doubt of it: I was crying. I wasn't even saddened; I was perplexed. So to while away the time cruising at 70 I rolled the windows down to dry my eyes and I thought about this and that, anything to get my mind off the things I didn't want to think about right now. I read Burma-Shave signs, then I made sounds every hundred yards when I passed telegraph poles, I played a numbers game with the license plates of automobiles coming my way, if the numbers averaged over five I won, under five *you* won. Then I relaxed into a stark little road game, which I have played off and on for years. It is about the most company-making game I know, even though put cold on paper some people are liable to disapprove. When night is coming on the Nebraska highway, you'd better put your value judgments away and just plain concentrate on how you are involved in life, if you have a night's driving ahead of you, through Ogallala and North Platte, Kearney and Grand Island and Central City. So I built them, one on top of another, and even though I've done it several times before, in times of lonely stress, it still made me feel better.

Jean, Irene, Chickey, Joyce, Jenny, Francie, Lisalette, Nancy, Natalie, Eleanor and Eleanor and the third Eleanor, Faith, Roberta, Roy, Betty, Stevie, Shelly, Gloria, Adele, Beverly, Marge, Ruth, Joan, and Joan II, Ann, Liane, Kaye, Margo, Sally, Marsha, Natasha . . . As I said, it looks bald and coldhearted, maybe even neurotic, stuck on a page like this. But each one of those was an experience in its own right, and without exception I liked those girls. By the time I got through remembering and counting the night had settled in and I was in Ogallala, stopping off at a restaurant for some corn flakes and milk, and to clear my head, a little, and buy some more White Horse. I fell to talking with the man on 11th Street who ran the liquor store, one of those hole-in-the-corner places. He disclosed he was a terminal cancer case, that he'd been in a hospital for about a year, and was waiting to die. I almost said to him, Why did I have to meet you now? He was a short, bad-looking shriveled-up man who was wrapped up in the idea of death. He couldn't get away from the subject. I suppose I didn't blame him much. We talked about a national health scheme. I told him about what the British did, and he thought that was a good idea. "It's a terrible thing," he said, "to die poor out of the sickness that made you poor." I think he took some solace out of saying that a lot of people were walking around Ogallala at this very minute with a cancer eating away at them and they didn't know it. I thought, at last, now I've got someone to listen to my troubles. But he didn't want to. Just as soon as I opened my mouth he looked uninterested. I wanted to tell him that it was my way of sympathizing, to tell him about me, but you could see he wasn't very interested. I bade him a fond goodnight and told him the end was in sight for us all. (I forgot to say that we were both drinking out of my new bottle of White Horse.) He said, "That's a hell of a thing to say to a dying man." I got kind of sore, and said, Well, what you've been telling me is a hell of a thing to say to a living man. He got uppish and peeved, and that's when we parted company. My conscience didn't hurt me; I was pretty stewed by this time. I walked back to the car and stuck the White Horse down behind the struts of the canvas top. You get found with an open bottle of hootch in Nebraska, while driving, and juridically speaking, it's your ass.

I knew where I was heading for, all right. And I wanted to get there. Norfolk. Norfolk, Nebraska. I'd never been there before. The Triple-A booklet said it had a pop. of 11,335, alt. 1526, over on the eastern part of the state. Norfolk was where one of the finest men who ever lived on this earth came from, Swede Hammeros. I was hoping to catch him in.

I got to hell out of Ogallala. I never stay long in Ogallala, though I've used it plenty of times, in Hollywood, as the place where the cattle trek ends, but, off paper, I've never found much in it to keep me. Just a collection of low buildings and cattle corrals in one end of the town. But even on the outskirts of Ogallala they were building those damn suburban housing developments. Now, I don't mean by that that I disapprove of the houses. By and large, I don't. Actually I like them. I think they're fit for people to live in, these phony split-level hutches with large modern kitchens and two bathrooms and all the rest. I don't consider anything about them evil at all. I wish more working people lived in them. Cathedrals are all well and good, and art galleries, but for restful, *profound* thinking, give me good old central heating and shiny bathrooms every time. And ungrainy toilet paper. What I hate is the way everyone who lives in them is mortgaged to them, they seem to accept these damn houses as some sort of gift, as though they had not worked for them, when they have, and plenty hard, and instead of saying, Isn't this *terrific*, now we can go ahead and grow up and raise some civic hell (which is just two ways of saying the same thing) they manicure the lawn and *worry*. Sure, I know what you're thinking. That it's sour grapes, because once they have that kind of house, in that kind of development, they'll never cut loose from Dollar Values long enough to listen. Granted. But just to make myself plain, I am not one of those who say, clutching the hair on their fat chests, Eight-y-y years ago the cowmen strode and now look at what there is, junior executives instead of Arapaho. Junior executives, as far as I'm concerned, have got to live somewhere, and it might as well be Ogallala, Nebraska as anywhere else. It's just their damn humbleness about it. And then, of course, need I add, Ogallala has an Annual Roundup.

It seems to me that when you are in the kind of mood I was, you only bump into one kind of person, and that is someone who has the same kind of mood, as though you carried an aroma of weltschmerz around with you that they can scent a hundred miles away. Just outside Ogallala, on Highway 30, I suppose partly to make up for the Kentucky boy, about nine in the evening, I saw this man standing by the side of the road with his thumb lifted. Really, he was nothing but a boy. I stopped and told him to get in. He was obviously a college kid, wearing a clean white woolen sweater with a large letter C in blue on the stomach. He was carrying a small satchel and was wearing a sailor hat. He said he was trying to make Omaha by twelve o'clock noon. I told him I'd be driving all night and would let him off in Central City which was about two hundred miles up the road on the highway. He breathed a big dramatic sigh of relief and said, "Mister, that's swell." It makes me feel quite old when some twenty-year-old calls me Mister.

The De Soto was following the Platte River which 30 does all the way to Columbus, Nebraska, and I settled down in the near-night to a steady seventy. I knew that as soon as it became really night I would be down to fifty, and to forty and sometimes twenty-five. It's funny about driving lonely at night. The lonelier you get the brighter the lights of the oncoming cars and trucks, until sometimes they become so dazzling you're creeping along at ten miles an hour. But I didn't want, for reasons of pride, for this college kid to see me behind the wheel of a virtually new car and doing twenty-five right off the bat just because it was growing dark. Later, if he asked questions, I'd make up some excuse or other. It's happened to me before. Only once has it led to trouble. A merchant sailor and I took a rented car from New York to L.A., taking turns driving, and I had to make a detour from Chicago to Minneapolis to see whether I wanted to enroll at the University of Minnesota for my degree in American Studies, and to see my friends, the Sverdlovs who taught there. After about fifty miles, it became pretty obvious to this sailor and me that we were going to hate each other like poison before the end of the trip. So we began to be superpolite, compromising on all sorts of small points that people who really like each other fight over. He would let me stop the car more often than he wanted, and I let him play the car radio which drove me crazy because that week of that year all the disc jockeys were playing a single disc, Kay Starr singing "Wheel of Fortune." I bear Miss Starr no ill will (she's Indian). But if you want to visualize what a state of mutual detestation and tension we drove in, do "Wheel of Fortune" over and over in your mind five times. I must have heard it two hundred times on that drive.

After Chicago, with him keeping a stiff lip, I made the detour to the Twin Cities, decided that this was not my year for the Ph.D. and in order to come to the sun as soon as possible dropped like a plumb line towards Texas. For the first four hundred miles there was a blizzard and icy roads. I'd never before driven on ice and I had to crawl along at about forty, and even so I skidded off the road twice. My nerves were not too good, having just had some bad experiences in New York. Somewhere in the middle of Missouri, for the first time, this sailor, who never called a woman a woman if he could call her a cunt, and a Negro a nigger (I'd advertised for him in the *New York Times*), finally boiled over. He said, *Well your best isn't good enough.* And that was how it was for the rest of the trip. You see, he had something on me. He could drive longer and better than I could; I wasn't pulling my weight, relative to his, and when we stopped off one night in an Amarillo garage we got into an argument and I said if he didn't shut up I'd leave him in Texas and take the car by myself to L.A. He just turned and looked at me and said, We're going on together or I'll whip you right now. And you know, I backed right down. I was so tired, and dejected, that I just grumbled and lay back on the seat and pretended to sleep. But he had me, all right. He stayed with me all the way to L.A., and in a better temper too, because, you see, I hadn't jumped out of the car and tangled with him. One reason I didn't was that I was afraid of him. After four hundred miles of skidding on icy roads, and not sleeping for two days and nights, and keeping myself up on dexedrine (he had a horse's stamina), maybe my judgment was clouded. But I just knew that all he had to do was stick out his right arm and I would go down. Also, I had a small obsession he might murder me. As the Lomaxes had when they drove Leadbelly across the country after securing his release from that Texas prison farm. So that was it. Counting all the experiences I've had, this particular one, in a garage in Amarillo, Texas, was approximately the most humiliating. A thousand times since then I've wanted to meet that sonofabitch on a street somewhere.

So even though I hadn't slept since Rawlins I kept up a steady seventy. This college boy I'd picked up and I started in to talk, and he turned out to be a phony. He said he didn't exactly go to college, the sweater didn't belong to him but to one of his buddies. I didn't press. Several times I have used this dodge myself in the past. As you grow older, people in their cars are less and less anxious to pick you up. A *young* hitchhiker they figure will be someone who will be too polite not to submit to their boasting, or listen to their troubles; at the very least he won't cut their throats. But as you grow older you can positively *see* the suspicion whip past on their faces as they don't pick you up. This is especially true when some damn maniac scabs on all of us by murdering some family for ten bucks. For months after that it's rough on the highway. It was my bad luck to hitchhike from L.A. to Denver about a month after RKO released a murder film, *The Hitchhiker*, about some one-eyed bastard who almost killed two hunters in a station wagon. It took me about six and a half days to make it to Denver that time; you could see the people driving cars and trucks just waiting for you to pull out a .45 automatic and hood one of your perpetually sleepless eyes. Most times hitchhiking, I was a fashion plate of the road; spotless, clean-shaven every day, baseball cap perched on the back of my head to make me look cute and like your little brother, obviously collegiate wool sweater with an (unearned) sports letter, scuffed saddle shoes, sometimes my best jacket, and a suitcase with varsity pennant decals stuck all over it which I kept for such occasions. Once I bummed from Detroit to Chicago carrying that sign, Los Angeles or Bust. My only excuse is that this was just after the cops in Venice, Missouri, had given me a shellacking for *not* having raped that little girl.

But I didn't press the point on this kid, even though I suspected why he had the get-up on. We rode on into the Nebraska night in silence. It turned out, from what he said, that his name was James McParlan, and that he was on his way to Omaha after a three-day pass. He was stationed at Offutt Air Base, headquarters of the Strategic Air Command. He said it as if he was a G.I. stationed at any ordinary air base. For all I knew that was how he thought about it. But *he* brought it up. He asked me if I was sure I couldn't go straight in to Omaha. I said no, I was going on up to Norfolk, and Omaha was too much out of my way. He went on a bit, how necessary it was for him to be back on base by noon tomorrow because a buddy was filling in for him in the orderly room, that it was a situation of a five-dollar bill passed between friends, and a moderately forged three-day pass. I thought how strange it was that this young man should engage in all the petty connivances of the enlisted soldier, as soldiers have done for thousands of years, as they do in Brecht's plays and in Schweik, at the same time that he was helping to staff the one place which more than any other has come to symbolize holocaust. I suppose, humanistically speaking, that should have made me feel good. Life goes on and all that. But it didn't. We got to talking about Offutt.

He was about twenty, and said he had joined the Air Force for four years to escape a two-year Army draft; most kids his age at Offutt had gone in for that reason. He came, he said, from Needles, Arizona, where he had a wife whose picture he showed me. I asked him if he ever thought about what the SAC headquarters was really there for, and he said no, not really. He said you got used to everything around there, including the security. He said he thought it was all a bit overdramatic; but I think he liked that part of it. He was especially fascinated by the huge bunker in which, presumably, all SAC operations would be conducted in event of war. He said that he had only been inside once, and that it was patrolled by an elite corps of MP's specially and personally trained by General Le May himself, young men who wore pearl-handled revolvers and blue berets. He himself worked in an orderly room topside. He had thought seriously at one time of staying in the Air Force, but after he failed to qualify as a cadet he had gotten bored, and now all he wanted to do was get out. But he said it wasn't too bad a life. Was he scared of having atom bombs all around him? "You get used to it," he said. Then I remembered that Offutt was only a kind of glorified communications center and that in all likelihood neither nuclear bombers nor bombs were kept there. That only made it worse, thinking that the kid was exaggerating in this way, he felt at such a distance from what the base was there for.

He said he wouldn't mind too much if we dropped a few bombs on the Russians. But he said it lackadaisically. He wasn't a bad kid, not terribly bright and you could see that one of the things bothering him was that he was not as smart as he would like to be. It had given him quite a jolt, he confided, to be turned down for a cadetship. I gave him a long speech about the H-bomb, and I must say he listened politely, then responded, "Well, what you say may be right, but we ain't gonna give up ours until they do, and they won't." I couldn't deny that. I slowed down to 60. It was dark night, and out in the open country. For a while we didn't say much. I think he figured I was some sort of crank, which on the H-bomb I probably could be classified in some such way.

For my part, I felt pretty cool towards this young character. Isn't there any place in America a kid from Needles, Arizona, can get a *moral* education? I guess not, really. The terrible thing about him was the way he kept saying how he and some of his buddies spent so much time surmising if there really was a hydrogen bomb somewhere around. "Man," he said, "if I could only just once *see* that thing!" He gave me the creeps, I say. Not so much because he failed to connect the bomb with what it could, and may some day, do, but the way in which the newest advances of technical science threw him right back to the days of the cave and sabertooth tiger, of totem-worshiping. That kid was straight out of *The Golden Bough;* thinking that he could sort of *absorb* by just seeing the damn bomb.

I switched on the car radio. No word out of either Port Said or Budapest. I turned it off. The kid sat there, wondering whether I'd lacerate his ears over Hungary, but that was one thing I *didn't* want to talk about just then. The worst thing to be is a prophet in another man's country.

It was a long night, and we thawed out. He put himself up in my eyes a fraction by saying that no, he didn't much care for the idea of a new war, and that he wouldn't, if he were in command, drop any bombs on the Russians unless they dropped one on us first. But even so I must say that I didn't find his conversation very entertaining, he was a pretty dull fellow, until slam bang in the middle of one of his sentences I said, What did you say your name was again? He looked surprised, as though he half expected me to get out of the car and phone up his C.O. to say he had a forged three-day pass, and said, "James McParlan." I did some computing and then asked him if he knew his grandfather's name. He said no, sorry he couldn't help out, he didn't know or couldn't remember his grandfather's first name. He himself was named after his father. James McParlan II. Junior. James McParlan. Holy cow. He said, "I beg your pardon sir." Slowly and very carefully, I asked him where he came from. He repeated, Arizona. Where did your father come from? His dad, he said, came from California, and he thought before that from Colorado. I got really excited then. But I tried to control it. Are you sure from Colorado? No, the kid said, he wasn't sure, just perhaps; somewhere around there; maybe Utah or Idaho.

It fitted. What did your grandfather do? "Do?" Yes, for a living? "Never knew him, sir. Why, do you think you know my family?" No, I told him, I've never met any of you. I asked him what his father did. His father, he said, was assistant chief guard of one of the Atomic Energy Establishments in Nevada, near White Sands proving grounds, and before that had been a store detective. Boy, that really got my flesh to crawling. I was sure of it — this was James McParlan's grandson! I know that as you read this you can't get excited as I was, and I don't care whether you're inhabiting Britain or America at the moment: nobody outside a few scattered labor scholars remembers who James McParlan was, though I'm told some very conservative citizens once put up a statue to him back in

Pennsylvania. I'm sure that statue isn't there now, and was either blown up or melted down by command of the old lion myself, John L. Lewis, president of the United Mineworkers of America, U.S.A.

The kid said, when I asked, that he really didn't know much about his grandfather. I asked him if public protection, being a cop, was a family tradition, and he said he didn't think so, it just worked out that way. No, it fitted too well. I said, Are you sure your grandfather wasn't an official of Pinkerton's detective agency? The boy shook his head and said he had never heard of Pinkerton's. Well, he had me there. He said that his father (his mother died when he was ten) never talked much about Grandfather, except to make him out a kind of pioneer up around Idaho or Colorado. He was a pioneer all right, I said. Then I told this kid who he was, or at least who I thought he was. The grandson of James McParlan. I wasn't diplomatic. I just told him straight, not sparing his feelings. Maybe I would have been more charitable if I'd been sober, but I wasn't. That White Horse was dead and gone. I was doing around 50, and steadily slowing down, but I didn't feel liquored up. To make a short story short, he didn't even blink. When I got through, the boy shook his head and said he didn't think that was *his* grandfather.

Except for the labor scholars, only a few Wobblies around L.A.'s Skid Row or over at the defunct IWW headquarters in Sheridan Square, New York, could right off the bat, and with a spit in the eye, tell you about James McParlan. To put it no worse, he was the rottenest sonofabitch America ever produced, not barring Judge Thayer or Joe McCarthy. James McParlan, twenty-nine, started his real career as a labor spy in the Pennsylvania coal fields. A real merry fellow, ginger-color hair, gift of gab, liked to fight or sing, definitely popular with the Irish miners who made up the quasi trade union, the Mollie Maguires, otherwise known as the Ancient Order of Hibernians. (Like the IRA.) The coal company boss, a man named Gowen, wanted the leading Mollie Maguires hung from a high gallows because they punched when he punched, blew up his shafts when he beat up their men, and shot his when he shot theirs. As you can see, not exactly candidates for a Labor Party selection board. Gowen hired McParlan to get the goods on the Mollies. Using the name of McKenna, McParlan traveled the coal fields and when he couldn't find any real evidence to link the Mollies with serious violence he provoked some himself. He wormed his way into friendships and families and then, at a mass trial, testified against the coal miners. Eight men, most of them McParlan's friends, were hung on his testimony. He left Pennsylvania in a hurry. You might think that having done a good lifetime's work he would just go off and buy a chicken farm for himself, like Harry Orchard, the perjured witness in the Steuenberg murder case and in which McParlan also later figured. But no. He went west, and for more than twenty years he worked for the Mine Owners' Association in Colorado, and the West generally, to break the Western Federation of Miners, forerunner of the present Mine-Mill-Smelters' Union. He was paid millions of dollars to provide strike-breakers and industrial police (goons), to infiltrate his spies into the young mining locals, to deliberately create sabotage so as to blame the unions (they were doing enough on their own without his planting the evidence), to cause factional strife, provoke stupid strikes and in every way play the bastard, except this time he was out in the open. For a quarter of a century he must have been the most hated man in America by American workers. Considering that he had been dealing with the Mollie Maguires and the pistol-wearing miners of the hard-rock gulches of Colorado it is one of the prime miracles of all time that he lived as long as he did. His final big job was to find some proto-Van de Lubbe to "confess" to the murder by latch-gate bombing of ex-Governor Steuenberg of Colorado, a very weird and obsessive character named Harry Orchard. Clarence Darrow defended Big Bill Haywood, Moyer and Pettibone in a classic trial and got them off. All told, James McParlan worked for Pinkerton's for twenty years, as a kind of Death Valley Genghis Khan. In the house I was brought up in, I was educated by my father to consider carefully the social circumstances surrounding Judas' action, but that a man like McParlan was simply outside the human pale. Even now, I really do believe that James McParlan was a case of almost pure *evil.*

Getting more and more excited, I told this kid, McParlan, all about his grandfather. I told him how his grandfather had spent two years of his life singing in miners' barrooms in Pennsylvania and working down in pit with them and dandling their children on his knee and telling them that violence was the only way out against Gowen, the mine superintendent, and all the time collecting and manufacturing on the spot the evidence that would hang eight men. I think my manner must have offended this boy, because in the reflected light of the dashboard he looked a little frightened. I was practically shrieking at him by the time we hit the outskirts of North Platte, Nebraska. I wasn't any longer interested in convincing him about the H-bomb; I wanted him to know about his blood line. I'm not sure I can remember all I said to him in the car that night, but I'm sure some of it must have had to do with exhorting him to get a discharge from the Air Force so that he could go to Detroit or Butte, Butte better, and take a job in a factory or a smelter and learn how to be a union organizer. Now, the plain fact is I wasn't even sure this kid was in any way related to the historical monster, James McParlan. But in the frame of mind I was in, I *wanted* him to be. And you can't say I was completely off, because after all he did have a grandfather who came from the area, and his father *was* a cop. The upshot of it all was that this kid told me that in my yelling I was weaving all over the road. I slowed down and stopped the car.

That was when he really looked scared. He said, "Now look, don't try anything funny." He had his hand on the door handle. I was practically crying with trying to get this message to him, of how he could *redeem* himself. But when he said don't try anything funny, I could see he really was worried I would try, and that brought me back to reality quite sharply. He had on this expression, an almost animal wariness, that those kids had back in Rawlins, Wyoming, in the dark front yard under the trees. So I just lay back and rested. I was suddenly tired. Not stewed or excited or lonely; just plain tired out. I didn't care a damn whether he jumped out of the car and ran away into the night or not. I was *spent*. He said, softly, "Mister, you been yelling at me more than an hour." I said I knew. I didn't apologize. I said we get our education in all manner of ways.

He asked me if I was sick. How could I tell him I was sick of a community where you couldn't contribute your share? How could I tell him what it does to be brought up to organize socialist trade unions and find yourself a Hollywood agent at the age of twenty-nine? You see, all the while I was shouting at the boy, I had this corny idea of making him *our* son, the one who would go on to do what we had not. For all I knew, this kid, McParlan, knew more about America than we. We. Who the hell was "we" anyway? Could we have been a "we" and folded up as easily as we did? So I just lay back and rested easy and let this kid off the hook of my imagination.

To change the subject, and make things a little more comfortable, I pointed out the sights as I started up the car again. Since it was dark and moonless I told him he had to use his fancy. I knew some of the old cow trails leading to Ogallala, and I told him about those, how the trailmen would trek up from Mexico and Texas, hitting the Platte River around Kearney and follow the river to fatten up the cattle until they came to Ogallala. I told him about Horse Creek, back near Highway 26, where more Indians assembled, in the 1850's, than at any other time in the entire history of Indians in America. I asked him if he wanted to make a little detour to Massacre Canyon, quite a way south, where the Pawnees and Sioux had their last big battle. It was one of the places I always liked to stop in. The kid said no, he'd just as lief keep on. I went on pointing out such sights to him, but I don't think he was much interested. He was, I think, thinking I was, well, odd. But it really was a shame the way that boy didn't know his own history.

It was about midnight when I hit North Platte. Most of the town was asleep, and I headed for the main hotel in town. McParlan and I didn't say much to each other, except to pass the time of night. I like North Platte. Contrary to what I've been saying about my feeling that once I crossed eastward over into Nebraska I was no longer in the West, North Platte was an exception. You can still feel the West in it, in the way it is laid out, small but proportional streets, a certain kind of self-respect which is most easily recognizable by the minimum amount of screaming used-car lot banners and neon in stores closed for the night. If there is one thing that drives me mad it is a neon advertising sign in a store closed for the night. You would think they might leave you alone while they went home to play with the family, or bed down with the wife, or count their money or whatever it is store merchants and salesmen do at night.

One of the nice things about North Platte, in fact, is that its main street is so dusty at any moment you expect some ghost rider in the sky to hitch his piebald to the post in front of the hotel. I parked. McParlan said that he saw an all-night hamburger joint down the street and asked if he could bring me back anything. I said no, and got out and went into the hotel, which was completely dark except for the lamp on the desk clerk's accounting table. The clerk was a middle-aged, hulking woman in a severe high-necked black dress. She looked up from her accounts, squinted into the half-light and said they were full-up, there was a stock-dealers' convention in town. I said I didn't want a room, just like to sit in the lounge and write a letter. She was okay about it. So I sat down at one of the tables, switched on the lamp and wrote a letter to my friend Essie Hardy.

Dear Essie,

I've had a question on my mind for some time now and I couldn't think of a better person to ask it of than you. You might consider this a postscript to that last conversation we had, before I went away, when we both were wondering what happened to writers who didn't want to sell out. As you know, I have been considering leaving the States, at least for a while. Something struck me right now, one of the things I wanted to know, and if I don't send this off I'll forget it. *What's it like in America these days?* That is the question. I think, at least tonight I think what I mean, really mean, is, is it possible to have a small circle of friends, friends of grace and purpose, not incestuously, but on a basis of mutual respect, work and a kind of humorous, informal dignity, in the United States? The reason I'm asking is that I haven't found it possible; not for me. I am too opposed to what practically everyone I know is doing to their lives. Not so much their jobs, but the way in which they are excusing away vacuousness and social irresponsibility, and the way they don't give a damn for anyone or anything except their mortgages and babies (okay, the babies, fair enough). As I say, it just struck me that this is what really makes me happy, to have that circle of friends. I've grown sufficiently old, now, to know that it is a very hard thing to achieve, and we find it mainly through luck. But there are times, it seems to me, in any country, any nation, when circumstances are such that it is easier or harder. On the Left, in 1956, it is hard. I'm not grousing, just thinking. D. H. Lawrence used to say how much we all of us are starved not so much of sex but of the societal instinct. By me, that does not mean everyone living in everyone else's lap; nothing is more certain to eventually mutz up the societal instinct than that. I've tried it and I could tell you stories.

I wonder if it is different in Paris or London. I will give it a try perhaps. Really, the only ones in America who it seems to me are able to make this particular scene are the fanaticals, who drive themselves as hard as they do, either in politics or business, because they cannot bear to ask the difficult, human questions, or the starved ones, the ones who don't care, or who have been conditioned since birth to accept a weak spindly paste on their plate, such as I have heard the English do. I am speaking here now, of course, of that loosely assorted cast of characters we call intellectuals, though not exclusively. America just isn't enough for me. None of us were made to live out our lives in the back lawn of a $10,000 split-level house. I'm not neurotic enough to enjoy being lonely, although I know anyone who wants to do original or valuable work must always be. I was pretty well known back in L.A. when I went away; I always thought I would like that. But it didn't seem to help. Strangers seem to be afraid of me. And, on the Left, where I have most of my friends, I think they too were afraid, or bored, which isn't so very different. The Lefties definitely disapprove of my way of living, which is pretty quiet, considering. They don't like the way I look at life, and the serious way I make fun of politics, of me and them, of life in general. Don't they know that the only respectable recreation left to a man whose back is to the wall is to kid himself? Don't they know that my kind stays in politics forever, while all around me their kind is falling off logs at the first sign of white water? They have no weltschmerz any more and no irony and not much of a sense of humor; also they are puritanical as hell. Now, several times, I have been offered *in,* but always on their conditions, if you know what I mean. Either by a woman, who says, Marry me (or something), and I will be your cloak of respectability (not in so many words, of course). Or by a political confrère, who says, Be Responsible! God, how I hate some of these Responsible geezers. Or by a perfectly nice man or woman who chews me out finally for never being *satisfied.* Well, hell, I'd *like* to be satisfied, and actually I am, halfway, a lot of the time.

So, the thing is, what *is* going on in America? In these terms? I mean, do you have to be *married,* to a woman or a corporation or some dead-ass ideology, to knock your brains out *completely* — be Responsible — to have friends? The more I lived in L.A. the less I knew about America, the more distant it became, even when I knew that L.A. was some sort of crazy portent and advance guard for the whole thing we call the United States of America, L.A. with its electronic factories, and shifting population, and minority groups rubbing up against one another, and the city center becoming a slum, and the housing developments and the utter, desolate, anomie-laden disguises of the community and all the kitsch the fragmented community stuffs up its arse-end in order to keep its guts from spilling out.

I know this is not an easy question to put to you. But I've been thinking about it. Maybe you should talk this over with the O'Neills, whom you don't know. Why don't you call them, they are living at 1372 North Beverly Glen, L.A. 24, phone in book, and tell them what I'm thinking, and can you all agree on some sort of rough answer. I suppose I'm not really depending on anyone for a reply, I just would like to know.

ever,

(I haven't mentioned the O'Neills yet, but I will.)

When I got through writing the letter, I sealed it up and asked the lady if I could buy a stamp. She sold me one, and I went to the corner of the lobby where there was an indoor postbox and dropped the letter in. Then I went to the desk and asked if there was any mail in my name. For years, whenever I have been on the road, bumming or by car, I have asked correspondents to send letters to this hotel in North Platte with the notation "Hold for Arrival." But this year the lady at the desk asked me in exasperation, "Ain't you ever going to *register* here?" She handed me a letter and I read it by the light of her lamp. It wasn't a letter but a postcard, from my friend Esmeralda, the one who had visited me while I was ill and told me how her passion for a fifteen-year-old boy was breaking up her engagement. I had sent Esmeralda a wire from San Francisco asking her to give me the address of Marshall and Ginny, an academic couple I knew were somewhere in southern Illinois. As I said, Esmeralda and I had been political friends, at sword-points, all through college but she had liked me and I respected her. On this postcard Esmeralda had written: "I won't give you addresses." And that was all. I felt the blood drain out of my head, I asked leave of this woman if I could just sit in one of her chairs. She nodded and went back to her accounts. I flopped into one of the deep chairs and stared. I felt as though someone had kicked me in the balls. Man, halfway through the country, feeling the way I was, isn't that a *message* to get? I knew what Esmeralda meant. She meant the works. All the time I have known Esmeralda she has been a stickler for a certain kind of propriety; maybe that is because she was well brought up by her folks, upper-class real estate people, in Georgia. So when she got down to writing postcards like that she meant it as a *condemnation.* And that was the way I took it. Right then, in that dark hotel lobby in North Platte, Nebraska, I felt I didn't have a friend in the world. To be frank, I felt just like going to a whorehouse.

I thanked the lady for holding my mail and went out to the car, feeling like a sad drunk. But I was sober. There was nobody in the car. I got in and drove up the street to this hamburger joint which was just closing down for the night. I asked if they had seen a kid in a college sweater. One of the countermen said that he had bought a bag of hamburgers and set off down the main street, which was Highway 30 in town. Good luck to him, I thought. I couldn't blame him much.

I wanted to stay in North Platte for the night, but I didn't feel like searching around for a hotel room, so I put my foot on the gas pedal and was outside the town in a minute flat. And going east on Highway 30, *shaworrr* the wind whipping through the rolled-down windows and ramming the canvas top of the De Soto. I stopped for a moment on the highway, put the top down and lit out. *This* was the way to go. On a dusty, moonless wind-filled night, I looked down at the speedometer — 95. Oh, it felt terrific. Slicing through walls of dark wind, it was almost *creative*.

A few miles down the highway my headlights picked out McParlan standing by the side of the road, thumb up, bag of hamburgers in the other hand. I slowed down, and yelled.

An hour later I was down to 70. I had to make Norfolk by morning. I ran into a bumpy stretch and skidded around a little in the dark but kept it pointed straight ahead. I seemed to have broken through some barrier; I didn't have to go 50, 40 and then 25: steady 70. In and out of Lexington and out towards Kearney. Even in the dark I could tell I was coming into the eastern alfalfa-growing part of the state. It was harvest time and the black night outside the car smelled like a gigantic *kasha* bowl. And this thought came to me: how long had we been operating out of our depth? We never had, never had lived, an alternative in America. The liberals did because they wanted, and want, the same mixture as before, only better. But we, we never touched that *source* of life which provides alternatives, meaningful, stark and immense.

But if there was one thing I didn't want to do tonight, after receiving Esmeralda's card, it was to have thoughts. I wondered what to think about. I had counted the women in my life, actually several times over. Ah, but there was another good old standby. With the top down and keeping to 70 as if I were crucified to it, I counted up all the jobs I'd ever had since I started working. I hadn't played it with myself in quite a while, and now I could add one or two more jobs to the list. I was always fair. I never included jobs I'd had for only a week or two, or else I would have been summing up all night long.

I couldn't remember ever having had so much difficulty going back to the first one, in Chicago, but I finally remembered. Bookie runner for Louie Kaplan's store-front cigar business on 12th Street and Pulaski. Then news vender. Soda jerk. Apprentice bartender. Filler of hair tonic bottles. Quarry laborer (borderline, for only a few weeks). Advertising executive, junior model. Comparison shopper. Department-store stock boy. Punch-press operator. Store salesman. Railroad clerk. Soldier. (That was a laugh but at least I had an MOS 745 rating.) Personnel executive. Military policeman.

Secretary, God help me. Architect's assistant. "Public relations" writer. Trade union administrator. Statistician. Newspaper editor (college). Wire service reporter and desk man (not college). Film cutter. Taxi driver. 16-mm film cleaner. Story editor. Film writer (muck-grade). Story analyst. Associate TV producer (formal title only). I think that was all. No, more. Candy mixer. Dock laborer. Hollywood agent (how could I forget). Journalist (too vague, cut). Spot welder in fan factory. I spent about an hour sorting them out and counting them up. Thirty-three. I wondered how they would look on the back of a book jacket. You can't write a novel in America without having thirty-three jobs, especially lumberjack, seaman and truck driver. Funny. I never was any of those. Well, the next time I meet a lumberjack at a literary cocktail party I'll put it to him, was *he* ever a candy mixer or runner for Louis Kaplan's bookie?

The time went by, and I fled my thoughts. The speedometer was down to sixty, and I knew it would keep slowing down. I wasn't tired, I was just getting drained. I'd known it would be harder driving east than the opposite direction. It always is. Everybody west of the Mississippi talks to you. But they are less and less welcoming east, until by the time you get to New England it's all some people can do to say good morning. The only unfriendly people I've ever met in the West live in or come from Salt Lake City. I don't know why.

The besetting national sin. Explicitness. What terrors does the implicit hold for us?

At fifty in and out of Kearney, town of alfalfa mills, at one point a stronghold against the Indians, now a few streets of dark windows in the night. I knew that the stretch between here and Columbus, particularly at night, was featureless. Not even enough damn neon signs, if you ask me. So I had no recourse but to plunge right back into my thoughts.

I no longer try to solve mysteries, I try to flee them. That is the dividing line between youth and age.

Hemingway, the Old Language Purifier. "The world breaks everyone. And afterwards many are strong at the broken places." I had a feeling I would find out soon enough.

The youths see the war approaching five to ten years before it does; they prepare themselves for it with their organized, vicarious bohemianism and illiterate weltschmerz and self-pity. The war won't come for a while yet. (I kept my hand off the radio switch.)

Perhaps I won't begin to write well until I stop being wishy-washy about people. Are they this way or that? I keep learning too many things about them. Are villains villainous?

Then I thought of a script for a movie comedy, concerning a ballet dancer who goes in for football at Oregon State. I laughed, plotting that script all the way to Grand Island, which is a very large town in the daytime. Going through Grand Island, I thought about why I never really enjoy listening to jazz with girls. I have yet to meet a girl truly interested in jazz or political theory. There are some. But I don't know any. Grand Island, Nebraska. Every time I think of an "average" American town, it's always Grand Island. The cops neither tough nor soft, the food neither bad nor good, halfway to a city but you can still smell the farm life in it. Goodbye, Grand Island, Nebraska. I didn't know anyone in it, and I kept on thinking:

A strange thing to remember, at two in the morning. Strolling, at midnight, down Hollywood Boulevard after putting the college newspaper to bed and Carol, my night editor, the young girl off the farm with sturdy body and strong breasts and *vrai naïf* mentality, slipping her hand into mine when we had hardly spoken to each other before. There is an essay by R. L. Stevenson entitled, or in which he uses the words, "point of honour, touch of pity." Good title for a novel, I thought.

And, racing back up to 60 (higher the speedometer, higher the morale; simple) through a couple of villages, I wasn't thinking of a novel but of a short story which, off and on, I'd been working on for the past few years. I was having plot trouble, very unusual for me when you consider I have made my living in Hollywood for some years as a "story" man. The basic plot is very simple. (Goodbye, Oak Hill, Nebraska . . .) You see, there is this thin middle-aged Negro man standing out on the ledge of a hotel in the center of Los Angeles, threatening in a very quiet way to jump. Now, it is obvious that he is threatening because he wants someone to say to him, Look, don't jump, I'll help you with whatever it is. First the hotel manager says it. Then a policeman. A priest. A newspaper reporter. A woman social worker. A doctor. An ordinary worker down in the street. These seven people all exhort him not to jump, that life is worth living, that no problem can be that bad. So finally this old Negro man edges back into the room. And that's where the story really starts. Because when the man has told them his story they realize with horror that he was quite right to want to jump, that they could not solve his problem in a million years. But what can they do? After all, they promised. So this timid little Negro man starts to haunt their lives, not aggressively, just *there*, asking to be helped as they promised; he is all innocence. They stopped him from putting an end to his problem so they must help him. But they can't. He dogs their footsteps all of them, until eventually they go mad or kill themselves, or otherwise ruin their lives.

Two things bother me about this story. One, what problem is so enormous, so insoluble that seven people could not solve it? And two, how to end the story after all seven people are wrecked. Off and on, all the way from San Francisco I had thought about alternative problems, rejecting each in turn. Start thinking about it yourself and you'll see what a teaser it can be. No fair with "incurable illness." That's too easy.

So I barreled along, trying to figure out what problem to saddle this old Negro man with, and how to adjust the plot so that at the end we don't get *too* damn symbolist, I mean like the Negro suddenly turning into Jesus Christ or John the Baptist or somebody, and naturally when you are in this frame of mind a lot of thoughts come out at you from the dark and smack into your catcher's mitt like revealed truth itself. Let me tell you, a cross-country trip in your own car, at your own speed, is the cheapest psychoanalysis I know.

For example, it suddenly struck me that all these years when I have thought of going into teaching what I really visualized was a sort of martyred retirement from the world and then taking it out on those poor young students with an air of deep personal injury which I would express with erudition, patience and urbanity. Pardon me while I puke. I mean, that is a hell of a reason to want to go into teaching.

I skidded three times and zinged off into what I guess must have been a field; it was too dark to know. It had started to rain and the highway was slick. I must have knocked down some of the crops because in the morning I found oats all over the front end of the De Soto. Back on the road, I cut it down to 50 but not because I was jumpy. I wasn't. I was thoughtful. You see, I think I went off the road when I had the thought that all my life I have been looking for a woman. The woman. Now, that's enough to upset anyone. I have put in a good solid ten years what the old-timers used to call wenching, and I hated to have to admit to myself that a lot of it might have been due to searching for that one good woman everyone else also and always searches for. Not all of it, mind you. It's a fairly surprising thought, at the age of twenty-nine when you think you know something of the world, it comes at you that maybe you, like a lot of other guys you have lectured to against just this sort of weemy-dreamy childishness, may be looking for Miss She. I said wenching above. I wish people would begin to understand what a combination of squalidness, exaltation, missed signals and unexpected surprises it all is, instead of picturing it as a seventeenth century English lord with an ale-house girl on his knee. I bet he was a pretty lonely guy too. No, I wonder. Was he? That was one of the terrible parts about bumming around, in a car or on the thumb. You start to get all sorts of domesticated fantasies. I doubt whether there was a single time, since I first hit the road, when I have not made up my mind to get married at the end of the road. Not settle down, not buy a nice little cottage — I don't go *mad* when I have this fantasy — but just get married, find this tough, honest, beautiful perfect woman and go hand in hand through life with her like Clarence Darrow and his wife Ruby (his second wife, that is). I remember when my side got beat at the union convention and I left Detroit to hitchhike towards Los Angeles and the university, I became so convinced I would marry that I used my last eleven dollars to board a train at Kingman, Arizona, to get to the big city faster so I could propose.

I concluded it was all very sad, this business of being single. The other business, marrying, was equally sad if not more savage. Single people often accuse married people of becoming vegetables, which is true enough. But eventually single people make a vegetable out of their singleness; they have to; only it takes longer. You just can't beat the game. It can get pretty sordid. For example, I thought, keeping to 50 on the wet Nebraska road, I am not exactly what you call a creative courter. I mean, if I like a woman, and want her, I just naturally find myself making the same pitch to her that I made to the last woman. Not that I'm lying, or insincere. I mean what I say. And it doesn't have anything to do with flattery or sex innuendoes or anything crude as that. It is just a line of conversation, about me, her, the world, men and women, that assumes the same pattern every time. The relationships are different, the women are different, but not that first big conversation. Even to me it sounds phony, that I should find myself saying the same things, approximately, to different women, but *what* I'm saying I believe. I have this awful nightmare that some day two or more women I have known or loved or been friendly with will accidentally meet at a party and will find out what I talked about that day or night. You just can't explain a thing like that.

It is a small aspect of life I think novelists should deal with more often. In books, you read dialogue between hero and woman and that's all there is to it. But whenever I run into this sort of thing in literature I keep having this nagging question: has he ever talked like that to any woman before? I mean *exactly* like that.

The De Soto hit Columbus at four in the morning. I finished the last of the White Horse and tossed the bottle out of the window. I could hear it smash against concrete and that's when I realized I was in a town. I'm no damn juvenile delinquent; so I circled around and went back to where I had dropped the bottle, got out and used my flashlight to pick up the shards from the road. It so happened that where I had stopped was where the highway narrowed, just after entering Columbus, between two garages, whose shadowy outlines could just be made out. As I was bent down in the middle of the road — there was no traffic that time of the morning — in the light drizzle someone appeared. I think he had come out of one of the garages. He stood at the side of the road and didn't say anything, just stood there. I hunted around a couple of minutes to pick up the pieces of glass on the dark wet highway and then I heard him speak. "There's not much that a one-armed fella can do to help, is there?" I pointed my flashlight up through the drizzle.

He was a slender round-headed youth with buck teeth and he was wearing an old-style army poncho. You couldn't tell whether he had lost an arm or not. I didn't say very much. I knew if I got into the De Soto and drove away that would be the end of that. I mumbled something polite, that I didn't need any help and then he *smiled*. I suddenly had a picture of this youth coming up to people on the beach, or at parties, or in lovers' lanes and saying straight out, just like that: There's not much that a one-armed fella can do to help, is there? And getting his kicks from the panic he put into people. I got into the car, and stuck the pieces of glass into the glove compartment because right just then I didn't want to start hunting up and down the highway for somewhere to throw them. I went into gear and hurried into and out of Columbus. I really was in a hurry to get to Norfolk.

Mainly by using side roads after leaving the Platte River, I got to the Elkhorn River about five in the morning, and was in Norfolk a few minutes after that. It was a farm town, Norfolk, but still asleep under a gray, lowering sky. Nothing was open. The farms were still, the houses sleeping, the stores shut. I took the De Soto into the quiet main street and parked it on the corner in front of a parking meter next to a drugstore and went to sleep. Half an hour later I was awakened by the rumble of a truck through the town. A block down a guy in a white uniform was toting dairy cases from a small milk truck. I got out of the car and went over to him and asked if he knew a family named Hammeros living anywhere around. The milkman, a young and tanned boy, said the name sounded familiar but he wasn't sure. He suggested I go into the dairy and ask, which I did. Inside three or four guys were hustling cases of milk and cream, and I asked them if they knew a family named Hammeros. None of them did, but two of them had only recently come to live in Norfolk, one from another town, one from off the farm. The oldest of them suggested I wait around until the drugstore opened. It was owned, he said, by a man who knew everyone in town because he had lived in Norfolk all his life. I thanked him and asked if I could buy a bottle of milk. They gave me a bottle of milk and a carton of orange juice but didn't take any money because there was no cash register around. I was thirsty. Then I went back to the car and sat in it. But I was too restless. So I got out, and walked around the town in a light, cold rain. It was just a farm town. I kept trying to see what role Swede would have played in the town, but it was a pretty modern little place — parking meters, some ranch-house type dwellings on hills above the town, a couple of movie houses, television aerials everywhere. I got something to eat in the coffee shop of the single hotel in town, the first customer, and spoke with the chef-waiter. He turned out to be a Greek from Omaha who had been in Norfolk six months and didn't like it but was staying because of, he said, one of the waitresses he wanted to marry. He winked when he said marry. I asked him if he wanted a ranch-type house and a car, and he said no, to tell the absolute truth, he would like to take the car he had, an almost new Ford, and a beautiful American woman back to his town in Greece, Piraeus. I wished him luck and he gave me an extra cup of coffee for that. An hour later the owner of the coffee shop and the hotel came in, and I asked him if he knew where a family named Hammeros might live. He said he had lived in town a long time and the name sounded familiar; I should try the old man who owned the drugstore. It wasn't open yet, though, he said, so I might as well hang around and drink coffee. The owner and the Greek chef and I sat at the counter and drank coffee and I stuffed myself with doughnuts because I was hungry, and I hoped I didn't look too bad after all that driving. I couldn't have needed a shave too badly, and my jeans and T-shirt couldn't have been too dirty, because they were being polite, and if there's one thing you learn it's that if you need a shave nobody is polite to you on the road in certain states, and Nebraska is one of them. New York isn't, and upstate Illinois isn't, and California isn't; Massachusetts is. I suppose it has to do with how hysterical and unsettled a state is. Even so, I asked if I could use their washroom to clean up a bit, and the Greek chef reached under the counter and gave me his electric shaver. Man, that really touched me. I don't know, maybe he was just lonely there in Norfolk, Nebraska, thinking of taking a beautiful girl back home to Piraeus, Greece.

When I came out of the washroom I looked considerably better, even if my face was wind-burned to a crisp. The hotel owner, a stocky character who wore a farmer's hat, asked me why I was looking for the Hammeros family. I bought another coffee and told them. When I was about seventeen, just before I went into the Army, Swede Hammeros was one of my best friends. He wasn't exactly a father to me; more like an older brother, even though he must have been in his late fifties then. This was while the war was still on. For a kid I had had something of a checkered history up till then. My folks had a split-up, and my dad and I had been living together in a flat on the corner of Grenshaw and Pulaski in Chicago above a bar. I'd gotten into a little trouble car-stripping and through intervention of a social service bureau I was sent not to a reformatory but a business school, McCormick Commercial, which was down in the burleyque and whorehouse district of The Loop, Wabash and Harrison. The night I graduated this place I came home late from a party and my dad walloped me. Maybe I would have taken it any other time, but no kid ought to get licked on his graduation night, so I just ran down those stairs and went to live in a little clubhouse we'd fixed up a couple of blocks away.

By we I mean the Knights Athletic Club of Greater West Side Chicago, my gang. About twenty guys, twelve or thirteen active. My gang. I slept down in the clubhouse in the months after graduation. Nobody objected. I was president of the club. I had all sorts of odd jobs, but mainly wandered around Chicago, looking at life and wondering often. It became a little sticky when Avrum moved in. Avrum was a stateless refugee who was a member of the club. He was much older than any of us, how much he would never say, but he might have been twenty. He had gone to elementary school with us. We all felt sorry for Av. He wasn't a bad guy, really. Except around women. Moon-eyed. In order to stop Av hanging around, the class sweetheart once stood up in classroom and read aloud a note he had just slipped her, about how much he loved her and would die for her and how he dreamt about her night and day. That just about finished Avrum in the school: it took guts to stay on and graduate like the rest of us. I remember our club spending about two weeks in earnest meetings deciding whether or not we wanted to beat up on this girl, but we decided not to because Jackie, the vice-president of the club, was going around with her and he put up an objection. Somewhere along we lost touch with Av, except when he sent us all a letter saying he had joined the Army and was in the South. The next I knew he had moved into the clubhouse. I asked him, What's up, Avrum? He said he had broken his eardrum in artillery practice and was on leave from the hospital. We lived together for about two or three weeks down there, eating hot dogs and beans or beans-and-ketchup sandwiches. It was during this period that my drunken father came pounding on the door, begging me to come back. Well, the truth was I'd been missing him, so I took him back home, early on a warm summer evening, with all the neighbors on their front brick porches staring. I can tell you, I held my head *up*. But when I got Dad upstairs there was a woman there; I remembered having seen her around the neighborhood, a sad-faced Viennese. So I just left him with her and went back to the clubhouse. It wasn't that I had anything against her; it was mainly that I was *surprised*, or at least so I thought then. Well, about a week after this, the police showed up for Avrum and took me down to the station too. Av had lied. He hadn't been in the Army at all. He had been arrested for child-molesting and sent up for six months at Joliet; and on release he had gone out and tried to lure another little girl into a basement, and the neighbors had almost lynched him before he escaped. That was when and how he came down into the clubhouse to live with me. The cops tried scaring me with an accessory-after-fact charge, but any West Side kid knows his law better than that, and finally when I stuck to my story (which was true) that I hadn't known Av was a fugitive from the law and that if I had known I would have turned him in (which, of course, was not true), they had to let me go. It was a little bit of a near thing though, because the station house was the one nearest Manley High School and I was down on their blotter twice already, once, as I said, for car-stripping, and once for mayhem, which in Chicago means rioting, this time Jews versus Italians. A year later, at Fort Meade, Maryland, I was washing in the company latrine and whistling a left-wing tune — which I always used to do in a strange place in order to find any other left-wingers — when Avrum's brother came up and introduced himself to me, a shoe salesman recently drafted and now an infantry soldier. We talked about a lot of things, even went into Baltimore once together, but the one thing we didn't talk about was Avrum.

It was also in this period I met Swede Hammeros, when I took a job at a biscuit factory on Division Street, the place Nelson Algren writes so well about. I got involved with trying to organize this factory, full of Catholic women, and met Swede, who had drifted in and now was trying to do the same thing. We wanted to try to get the women to sign union pledge cards and then present the cards to the District Bakery Workers' union, which was not too interested in organizing the production workers, having recently concluded a sweetheart agreement with management to leave the "inside" people alone in return for jurisdiction over the truck drivers. It wasn't the easiest job in the world organizing that place. The women were mainly Catholic and married. Ask any union organizer about that combination. Also, conditions weren't bad, even if wages were. The company had a phony profit-sharing scheme which looked good once you were in about your fifteenth year with them. Anyway, I took to going up to Swede's small, mean, one-bulb room after work, and after a while I got to love him. He knew I was palling around with a bunch of Reds, but he never said a word. I liked Swede because even though he knew more about life than I, he treated me as an equal.

He was born on a prosperous farm a few miles outside Norfolk, Nebraska, in 1890. He wanted to go to sea, and left the farm, and his family, as soon as he could and without any formal schooling, although by the time I met him it seemed there wasn't anything he hadn't read at least once. For a while he worked in San Francisco as an ironmonger, and out of curiosity joined in the campaign to free the McNamara brothers which fizzled when Darrow entered a plea of guilty for them because Jim McNamara had really planted the dynamite in the ink alley behind the Los Angeles *Times* building. After a spell of lumberjacking in Canada, he went back to the farm in Nebraska. His mother and father were still alive, but one of his three brothers had been killed in a field accident. He resumed his place on the farm but he was like a firebrand in the peaceful neighborhood. He took out a subscription to *Appeal to Reason* and talked socialism, retreating into the status of village crank. Some time before 1916 he got married and lived a farmer's formal life. In 1917 he was drafted into the war and became a first sergeant with an infantry company which fought in the last engagements in France and then was sent as part of the Expeditionary Force to Siberia when the Soviet Revolution broke out. He went AWOL from the Army and beat his way across Siberia, finally joining up with the Reds to fight against Kolchak. After twelve months of riding with a small band of pro-Bolshevik Cossacks (the only ones in Russia at the time), Swede found himself in the Caucasus. He left Russia via Persia, after being wounded, and shipped aboard a Death Ship which he rode to Dakar. From Dakar he sailed to Brazil, where he took up with a German girl in São Paulo and had a son by her. But he began to grow homesick. So he took her home to Norfolk, which by now was almost a city. He remembered it as a village. His first wife had divorced him when he was in France and had moved out of the neighborhood. As time went by, Swede discovered he wasn't cut out for farming any more, although he gave it a good long try. Finally he took a train for a long talk with Big Bill Haywood, then president of the International Workers of the World — the Wobblies. By this time it was 1921, and the only one left on the farm was his youngest brother, married and with his family. After the visionary excitement of Russia, Swede was disappointed with most of the American radical groups and that was why he wanted to talk to Haywood. The upshot was his hiring on as a "general organizer" for the IWW, roaming the country, preaching the gospel of syndicalism and One Big Union. The German girl, disgusted, took herself and the child back to Germany. When Swede told me about it, he said he was really hurt by that, especially no longer having his kid around. He plunged into IWW work because now he was like most Wobblies: married to the organization, an itinerant fruit-picker, hobo and street-corner lecturer, participating in most of the famous IWW battles. In the twenties he spent two years in prison on a charge of attempted murder. By 1930 the IWW was a ghost, Haywood was in Moscow, and Swede found himself one of the army of unemployed. He was in on the Hooverville march, and in the famous news photograph of the Washington, D.C., trooper-police, directed by General MacArthur, breaking up the veterans' march with bayonets, you can see Swede up there in the front rank with a brick in his hand. He had a copy of that photograph in his satchel in his room when we worked in the biscuit factory. By 1933, Swede was a habitué of soup kitchens. His radicalism took on a gaunt, bitter tinge. Most industries wouldn't hire him; he was blacklisted. He hoboed all over the country. One morning, he stopped off in Lorain, Ohio, and knocked on a back door to ask for food in exchange for chopping wood and stayed to marry the kindly, buxom widow who lived in the house. By 1935, he was forty-five years old. At this point, the authorities caught up with him for deserting in 1919. His neighbors in Lorain, having grown to like Swede, circulated a round-robin petition, and after serving a few months — it was a gubernatorial election year — Swede was let out on pardon and parole. In 1938 it almost killed him to learn, from his second wife, that his son had joined the Nazi Party. It was the one subject Swede talked too much about, when I knew him; it *haunted* him, that he should spend his entire life fighting for certain things only to have his only son become *that*. Everything began happening too fast for Swede, especially when the war broke out in Europe again. It was hard to think of it as a "bosses'" war. He started to settle down to a peaceful old age. He and his wife took the money out of their cherry orchard business and traveled the country in a car and trailer, just relaxing and viewing the scenery. Every now and then Swede would go out of his way to point out some special place where he had fought or been jailed, but his wife was a good-humored, totally unpolitical woman. Swede was surprised he didn't mind. He told me afterwards that he didn't love her, not the way he had the German girl, but he liked his wife better than any other human being he had ever met. In 1941, after Pearl Harbor, Swede and his wife hurried back to Lorain, which had become transformed by the war plants. Both he and his wife went to work, he in a munitions factory, his wife in a department store. In the middle of the war Swede was elected to the Lorain (Ohio) City Council, a fact of which he was very proud despite himself. Sometimes Old Comrades from the IWW used to drop by the house. In 1943 his wife suffered a stroke and was taken to a Chicago hospital. Swede stayed by her bedside for months. She was paralyzed. Then she died. Swede decided there was nothing much left for him; he stayed on in Chicago. She had left him some money in her will, but her relatives started making a legal fuss, threatening to drag it out in probate court, so Swede wrote them a letter, telling them to shove it, he didn't want the money, and took a job in this biscuit factory where I met him.

After I went into the Army I lost touch with Swede and when I came back to Chicago he was gone. I heard nothing for years. Then one day, in New York, when I was working for a recording company and coming back from dubbing, about eleven o'clock one night I saw him on a subway train way out near the Bronx Parkway. He was asleep, unshaven, ragged, smelling of whiskey. A bowery bum. I went over and woke him up. He could hardly talk. He said he remembered me, but I don't think he did. I took him back to his rooming house and gave him all my money and spent the day and the night with him. It was pretty awful. He was just hopeless, and would spend hours just sitting on a curbstone or his cot saying nothing. I had to go away to Florida for a few days, and when I got back Swede was gone. Again I didn't hear anything. Then last year, the year before I left Los Angeles, at the agency where I worked I received a Christmas card. All it said was: "Good luck from Swede Hammeros." Somehow, Swede had pulled himself out of it, probably with his last stretch of good energy. Because, you see, whatever else he was, Swede was not a bum. He was a man of probity.

The hotel owner and the Greek chef heard me out, and then customers began coming in. The owner had to go front and check with his room clerk, the chef had to go out back and start making breakfasts. A waitress came in tying her apron, but the chef poked his head through the partition slit and shook his head at me to tell me that wasn't his girl. I paid the bill, and then went out to the drugstore.

The old man, the proprietor, wasn't there; he was away on a trip to Lincoln. His son, fat and thirtyish, said definitely there was a man called Hammeros who had come into town, he knew because he filled prescriptions for him. No, he didn't know where he was, hadn't made out a prescription for him for a while. I could, however, go on out to a certain address on the outskirts of town where Hammeros had been sharing a house with another old man. I took down the directions.

On a dirt road near an unrepaired wire fence stood this hulk of a house, peeling gray paint, high grass, dirty windows. I drove up into the front yard and knocked on the door. Someone out back called to me, and I found a very old, very bent man at something like a small drop forge in a shanty in the back. He didn't tell me his name. I asked him about Swede Hammeros. He said yes, he and Swede had lived in the house together for two years. Nice fella, Swede. He had died at the beginning of the year. If I wanted to, I could drive out and see his marker. I talked for a while with the old man, who looked about one hundred and ten but was all right. He said Swede was bright and chipper to his last. We didn't talk about what he had died of. He knew all about Swede's Nazi son, so I knew that *that* had never left him, but at least it told me he was alive and thinking up till the end. I thanked the old man and asked him if there was anything I could do for him, and he said I could drive him into town if I was of a mind. So I did.

After I dropped the old man off, I went out, according to his instructions, to the local graveyard which was shared by several towns around there. It was in an open space, just off the road, fronted by a red brick fence and a fancy gateway and surrounded by a fringe of trees. Those were the only trees, it seemed, for miles around, the prairie stretching away in all four directions. It was like an Indian encampment. I parked by the side of the road and went in. There wasn't an attendant around, so I just walked around searching. The day had turned warmer and the sun was out. Every now and then a car rumbled past on the road, but otherwise it was quiet. Those gravestones were a history book, some of them going back to the Indian wars. There was even one small marker for a baby which gave his name, age 11 months, and "Killed by Indians." That was all. "Killed by Indians." The wind was rushing through the trees like some sort of quiet locomotive and I walked around looking for the newer gravestones. On a fresh plot of land, I saw Swede's marker. It was a surprisingly large one, a purple-vein marble slab which said: "Charles Augustus Hammeros. B. Dec. 2, 1890. D. January 18, 1955. He Fought for the Liberation of the Working Class. R.I.P." I sat down on the gravestone and studied the marker, trying to figure out what he had been like before he died. I didn't cry. Just felt *heavy*. And then, of course, I found myself talking to him. Not giving him a eulogy, or anything like that. Just telling him what he had meant to me, and how all these years I had carried with me a picture of him in my mind because I had wanted to be something like him when I grew up. He was the unphoniest man I have ever known. I tried explaining why it hadn't worked out the way I had planned. I told him what had happened to the union movement in the past ten years, but I suppose he knew all about that. I definitely did not make apologies, because you did not apologize to such as Swede. I mean, he never took anyone's guilt for his own: it was in him to make you shoulder your own burden.

I got up and wandered out back of the graveyard, climbed a small wooden fence and went into the field to pick some cleome and goldenrod. It took me about an hour, but I was patient. When I had an armful I went back into the graveyard and put the flowers down next to Swede's marker. Then I went out to the De Soto, started it up and turned right at the next road, heading east.

Noon, and I was back onto some kind of main road, going to the border. Farm country. I stopped to talk to nobody. Steady 60. I switched the car radio on. The new Hungarian government orders its troops to take up approaches to the Danube bridges. Anna Kethely becomes a member of the government. Soviet intentions are uncertain. By the afternoon I was across the border into Iowa. I cut south, on Highway 75.

Corn country. But even here, billboards. Billboards, mile after mile of them. Blaring, glaring, staring. Suddenly I began to hate — personally — those billboards. You just don't know what it's like, when you're on the road, once you start really *seeing* those damn things. You might think they give you company. But they don't. They make you lonelier than ever. They don't even go off at night but smile hostilely out at you under floodlights. They never change. The same ads in the country, in Iowa, as in the city, New York. And they're always so *breezy*. If only one of them contained a figure that wasn't smiling, or happy, or content. In the States, if you've been in the businesses I've earned my money in, you're supposed to adopt a tolerant or analytical or professionally cool eye towards billboards and television (and radio, you ought to hear *that* these days). But I've never been able to. All I ever could remember, working at these jobs, was the hostile, deceiving *lying* of those billboards when I, or I and say Birdsong, or I and anyone else bummed on the road, to have to hitchhike a gauntlet of those gorgeous, tight-assed ladies in bathing suits who we *knew* were never built like that, and confidential garage mechanics admonishing us to buy Mobiloil for our *new* Buick, or *doctors* warning that our stomachs might cause us to divorce our wives unless we drank Pepto-Gizmo every morning; compared to these the political billboards were positively *honest*.

Well, suddenly, I began again to be revolted at the sight of those billboards, and almost puke every time I turned on the radio to hear those unctuous voices *lying*. And don't tell me that I didn't have to listen or look. Everywhere you go, if you're alive, you've *got* to notice. Even if you ignore the billboards and refuse to turn on the radio, you can't ignore the television aerials, dragging all that miserable Pepto-Gizmo out of the air. Those aerials were what was worse. Because you could only *imagine* what was coming through those sets. I know it's supposed to be a naïve attitude, especially from someone who knows about politics, the way I'm supposed to. Advertising is only a part of the superstructure; our prime target is the economic base, the structure of economic power, who owns what and how it is used, and all that. But when all is said and done, you don't have to live every waking moment of your life with the fact of economic oligopoly, in the sense that it's a razor on your eyeballs and hot needles in your ears. But you've got to *live* with advertising, smell it and taste it. You can't get away from it. And especially when you know what advertising is all about — how much of a confession of *failure* it is in America — all you want to do is run away. But there's nowhere to run; everywhere you go there are those billboard mechanics, doctors, waitresses, retired couples, bread-eating children smiling and running after you, breathless to confess their part of the national failure. One of the reasons I like Iowa is that the roads are a state disgrace, very narrow with small cement wings on both sides, and you have to concentrate on your driving and have less time for the billboards. In some place like Texas or New Mexico or Nebraska, on a wide open straight road, you can see that white-smocked doctor with his warning finger and grim smile coming at you a mile away. One of these days I'm going to point my hood ornament at that bastard and at 100 m.p.h. let him have it right in the bellybutton. I wish I could justify this by saying that our people don't even need half of those advertised things (they don't) while all over the world people are still starving. But I never think about that when under attack by the billboards. All I can think of is, how *craven*.

I got into Kansas City in the early morning, and went to see the only two people I knew. The first was a woman, Mildred, a housewife whose husband I had worked the San Pedro banana boats with. For six months, after the job petered out, we had visited back and forth, and then they had moved to Kansas City where he worked as a lineman for the Bell Telephone Company. About a year ago he, the husband Clive, had died in a fall from a pole, and I hadn't seen Mildred since before that. I found her address and knocked on one of the doors in a six-flat brownstone house on Cleveland Avenue. Mildred was up, so was her kid, five-year-old Tony, the radio in the kitchen was on full blast. Mildred and I sat in the kitchen and drank coffee. She was on her way to drop Tony at the local private kindergarten and then to her job. She was a secretary in an insurance office now. We sat and sipped coffee and listened to the radio. Mildred did not mention much about Clive, nor did I. He had been a large, sandy-haired man, easygoing and religious, a Catholic. Mildred had pursued a political life completely outside her marriage, saying, I'd give my right arm if Clive wasn't a Catholic, but he's the best man I know. And Clive would always say, Aw but honey, I'm a lousy Catholic, don't that help any?

The radio reported continued fighting in the center of Budapest. I went and turned it off. Mildred twisted her coffee cup in her hands. "All my life," she said, "I've been a Communist. What they call a lifelong Communist. What was it for, what was it all for?" I couldn't answer that question. When it was time to go I took Mildred downstairs, dropped Tony off at his school and Mildred off in the business section. Mildred's expression, even as she said goodbye to me, was still dry, torn, bitter. Then I drove over a few blocks to a slummy section of town and looked up Herman Weaver in the telephone book of a drugstore. I phoned, and he said for me to come over to his room, which was almost around the corner from where I was.

Originally, I met Herman when I was flying high on Sunset Strip. I was his agent. I brought him out to Hollywood after my agency had sold one of his novels — about lonely firemen — to Otto Diedrich, the Vienna-born film producer whose existence is sacred testimony to the proposition that no matter how bad your taste is God will not strike you down, even to protect the populace from your talents. It was Otto who nicknamed Herman, for publicity purposes, "The Gorki of Kansas City." Herman detested Diedrich with a pure, virginal, native-born loathing. Their week of story conferences together was low comedy, the jokes not too funny. Diedrich's idea had been to bring Herman in for a few days, just long enough to discharge a contractual responsibility and establish ownership of the story, and then send him back to Kansas City in time for a Hollywood hack screenwriter to come in and tart up the story. It happened just this way, too, and the film has cleaned up. Herman sued. He didn't have a chance. I knew all along that he was being taken by Diedrich but couldn't rat on the organization, and now I wondered if Herman held it against me. You see, I think that Herman is one of the few men writing in America to whom attention should be paid. But, in Hollywood, he was in over his head. I was in charge of giving him the red-plush treatment, booking him into a large suite at the Beverly Hills Hotel, but he fled after he saw, he swore, a red ribbon tied across the open commode, fled to a Fifth Street fleabag. Herman was an original. His only friends in K.C., the ones he wrote about, were the pimps, clochards, whores, dope pushers, cattle stunners, pickpockets, and he saw no reasonable motive for changing his style just because he was temporarily à Hollywood. After the Beverly Hills hotel episode, Laura Collins, my boss, took pity on Herman and seriously suggested to me that I induce him to see her psychiatrist. During Herman's two weeks in Hollywood he was fawned on and laughed at behind his back, wined and cheated (I connived at the cheating), flattered and lied to. His final story conference with Diedrich was a one-punch affair, Diedrich being on the receiving end. Much later, I learned that the agency and Diedrich had connived in this too. But the contracts had already been signed. Herman went back to Kansas City, more than ever convinced that only the dispossessed had integrity. Before leaving, he and I spent one sunny afternoon pouring liquor into the tea glasses of an Italian sidewalk café a few doors down from the Benedict Agency. I told Herman that I had long admired his woman who was British and a part-time philosopher. I said that some day if I went to London I would like to meet her. Naw, said Herman, well maybe. But, you know, she's not our speed, no, not our speed at all. You and me, we be just two country boys.

That last day of Herman's in Hollywood we just sat out there on the sunny sidewalk, dark glasses shielding out the smog, drinking whiskey in tea glasses and laughing over the few experiences we had had together. For instance the two producers I had escorted him to.

The first had been Hilton Durling over at Alarm Pictures.

As soon as we were ushered in by Hilton's *two* secretaries, Hilton sprang up and advanced on Herman saying, "You know, you are the greatest living American writer." Herman looked at him dead-pan and said, "Next to Homer I am, next to Homer." "And a dry sense of humor too," cried Hilton. We sat down, Hilton talked literature for an hour and finally brought out the story he wanted Herman to do. He said, "This is a story I have been saving for you, because some day I knew you would come to Hollywood, probably when you couldn't pay your gas bills." This nettled Herman who said, "I can pay my gas bill." Hilton said, lowering his voice and tensing it up the way he did in a story conference, "This American tennis champion, an amateur, fought his way up from the slums, now he walks and talks like a sun-bronzed god, he goes to France for a tennis tournament and this nun falls in love with him." "This what?" said Herman. "She's thirty-three," said Hilton. "How old's he?" asked Herman. "Nineteen," said Hilton. "That is a very interesting story you got there, Mr. Durling," said Herman.

"Yes," said Hilton, "I thought you would say so. The nun goes along on the tour with the boy, this screwed-up American kid, holding his rackets, sitting quietly in the grandstands, just watching." "And chasing his balls," said Herman. "What?" asked Hilton. "I take it you have a problem with this story, Mr. Durling," said Herman. "Yes, that's right," said Hilton, glancing proudly over at me. "It's all wrong for her to be a nun and so we thought she might be transmuted — transmuted, you understand — into an American society girl, the daughter of the nation's largest car dealer, but a deb with a difference, she's crippled mentally, just come out of a mental hospital and . . ." Herman said, "Mr. Durling, isn't that a classic French story you have?" "Yes, yes," said Hilton, shoving the manuscript into Herman's hand. I took it out of Herman's hand and looked at it. "Hilton," I said, "this is a screenplay." "Yes, that's right," he said, "but it's all wrong. Completely wrong. Hack work. Too many cooks." He said, "Please give the play back to Mr. Weaver, Mr. Weaver please take that story home with you and study it and I would be honored, deeply honored, if you would have lunch with me any time this or next week. If you don't feel like discussing the story, fair enough, but see if you don't" (here Hilton paused to search for a word appropriate to Herman's background, or what Hilton thought it was) "swing with the story, if it doesn't enter your bloodstream." "Yes, all right," said Herman politely, "I'll see if it enters my bloodstream."

As we left the Alarm lot, Herman said to me, "Nice man, seems more intelligent than most." He meant it too. The next day, in response to a phone call, I took Herman over to meet Bobby Burroughs at Worldwide Pictures in San Fernando Valley. Bobby was more businesslike. As soon as the formalities were over he said, "Everyone, the whole world, Mr. Weaver, honors you for your atmospheres, but I'm probably the only man in Hollywood who knows what kind of plots you can write. If it is your pleasure I would like for you to go back to your hotel room — or if you wish, use my own home — and give me a one-page synopsis of the best story you know. Don't worry about whether it would make a movie, that's my department."

So that afternoon Herman left me and went to his Fifth Street hotel and worked on a one-page synopsis. Next afternoon, at the appointed time, I took Herman back to Burrough's office. Eight men were seated in the office plus one secretary, pad on knee. It fazed me but not Herman. Among the eight men was the Executive Vice-President in charge of Production, No. 2 man on the lot. Bobby looked as though he had had a baby. Herman started to read at two o'clock, at two-fifteen he finished. Everyone in the room was polite, relaxed and suffering from fallen faces. Bobby grinned uncertainly at No. 2 and said, "That's a very interesting story, Weaver, but you see it does present certain problems. As it stands it does possess an undeniable and if I may say so powerful inner logic, a man named Bronco Bucolski who sleeps in the coalbin of a church, argues religion with the acolytes, makes love to his own married daughter and spends his days at the race track snooping through the grandstands after the races for winning tickets carelessly thrown away." "I like that last part," spoke up one of the seated men. No. 2 belched, like a slow-thinking geyser, and finally said, "Musical, the last part." "Well, obviously," said Bobby. Herman looked over at me and I motioned him imperceptibly to say nothing. No. 2 got up and said, "Looking for tickets, I like that." All the others got up and filed out after No. 2. "Mr. Weaver," said Bobby, "could you go home and do me a ten-page synopsis of your story, concentrating on the part at the race track?" I said, "How much, his price is a thousand a week." Bobby said, "Only a synopsis, you heard the story." I said, "No spec." Bobby went around behind his desk and said, "Let me discuss it with my story editor, you'll hear from either him or me." Of course we didn't . . .

I drove over to Greely Avenue. Herman's place was above a laundromat, one large room, small kitchen, toilet up on the roof. The room was decorated mainly with Mexican Indian blankets, trinkets and statuettes from the tourist highways near the border, and on the old brown horsehair sofa were two artificial satin cushions, marked in fringe, one saying "Remember Pearl Harbor" and the other "2174th A.F. Wing Supply Section — Go 'Em Tigers." I had to go through the laundromat, which had just opened and had no customers yet, to get to Herman's door, and he met me at the bottom of his stairs. We went upstairs and drank some coffee. He looked tired and worn. "Poker," he said. "You play?" I said I played. "Stick around, it's a six-day affair," he said. I said I didn't know if I could but thanked him anyway. That was how Herman kept himself alive, by acting as dealer in a revolving, permanent poker game. Recently, he had written me, he had run into trouble. A reporter for *Collier's* Magazine had gotten him stewed on martinis and Herman had told him about the poker game, *Collier's* had printed the information in an article on how famous authors make a living, and Herman's poker partners had forthwith departed the game on the assumption that Kansas City policemen know how to read. But all was well now, he said. The heat had died down, the poker players had bawled him out and then had returned to the game, which was usually held in a tavern basement. As dealer, Herman sometimes made as high as thirty dollars a night.

After coffee Herman said he had to go meet a man. I went along. We hung out in a Thompson's cafeteria and waited. A procession of gentlemen and ladies came by to say hello. Sometimes Herman introduced me. Little by little, our table filled up. A fat, made-up old lady, two short and cadaverous brothers in the rag business, a Chinese in a business suit and a Negro on crutches. Herman sat talking with them in a language, and about affairs, I did not understand. The Negro on crutches asked me if I wanted to go with whores, and I politely declined. He took no offense. Slowly, I began to catch the rhythm of their social converse, which was a deeply bitterly grooved run of gossip. Herman didn't do much talking. Around noon a cross-eyed man in suntans and T-shirt like mine came in, and Herman went outside to talk to him. He came back holding two packages by their string. "Bread," Herman said, "he bakes it specially for me, I like his bread." After a while, I said to Herman, I'm getting to feel comfortable around here, I'd better shove off. "Your deal," Herman said. He walked me outside. "Good to see you," he said. I like your friends, I said. Herman shrugged, "They scare me. I'm a peaceful man." Good to see you, I replied, and walked to the car and left Kansas City and Herman Weaver.

North again. Highway 69.

I didn't know this part of Iowa too well. All afternoon I went through a succession of small towns — Carroll, Boone, Ames, Marshaltown — going like hell in order to make Cedar City by nightfall. I was feeling bad again. There was nothing I could do to shut out the brain music, so I didn't try, just rode with it. But you can't ride too fast on those Iowa roads. It was all hog or corn country.

I thought of cutting up to Albert Lea, over the line into Minnesota, but it was getting late. I wanted to see my friend Bruce, who had gone out of his way to be involved with me in the trouble on the campus paper. Bruce came from Albert Lea. He was one of those boys with white tight souls, a very cautious and systematic character. We had a strange relationship in college. Everybody thought we were best friends, because we always presented a united front. But we never really spoke the same language, Bruce and I. Every time I made an overture, he would freeze up. Matters weren't helped much when I made a pass at his girl at a party; that was the thing about him, he was so controlled: instead of walking up to me and taking a swing he just looked furious and flipped an empty cigarette package at me and stalked off. By trade, Bruce was an ex-farm boy turned steeplejack. Whatever else he didn't have he had principles. The problem with Bruce, as far as I was concerned, was that he was too *old* at twenty-two; it was as though he had spent those twenty-two years entirely in practice to be editor of the *Christian Science Monitor*. Come to think of it, it was a good thing I didn't go up to Albert Lea, I remember he wasn't there any more. He was in New York, working for a passive-resistance organization. Maybe I'd meet up with him again. Maybe this time we could break through. We spent all our university years trying.

I got into Cedar City about six that evening, tired and wound up and frightened. Several hours before I'd stopped drinking White Horse — whatever else I am I am not a lush, and I knew just how much of that stuff I could take without *having* to have more. As I say, I love college towns. Quiet cobbled streets overarched by ancient elms; a sense of repose, the sunlight speckled on the lazy sidewalks. In Cedar City there is a small, sluggish river, like the Cam, where students can go rowing. At the moment I didn't have much of an eye for the scenery, I just wanted to get to Axel and lie down for about a year of peaceful Sundays. The music in my head was something approximately like a roar and was dividing out into *tunes*, which was an entirely new development.

Using the address he had sent me, I found Axel's house. It was a large comfortable-looking place set back from one of the small, autumn-shaded streets. I parked the car and just lay back. Then I saw Axel walking down the street, carrying a bag of groceries crooked in one arm and his briefcase hanging from the other hand. He looked as young as ever (he was about five years older than I), his clean, square face reddish with the evening sun. But there was, I could study him as he came down the street, a new expression to him that I could not remember. He swung in at his path and went around back, without seeing me. I sat back in the seat and thought about Axel. It was twelve years.

When I was sent to Germany as an occupation trooper at first I didn't mind. I had a platoon sergeant's rank, largely unearned, and nothing much better to do with my time. In fact, I thought about staying in the Army for another two years and possibly as a Regular. The first time I got drunk I banged up the billet a little — it was an old SS barracks — and after three days on the local rock pile I was taken before the regimental adjutant who offered me blackmail. He would, he said, order a summary court-martial which would deprive me of my stripes for disgraceful and unbecoming behavior (or some such thing) *or* I could sign on for another two years as a "battlefield" second lieutenant. I said no, and as it happened there was such a shortage of NCO's in our zone that I kept my stripes. It was shortly after this incident that one morning I woke up and decided, like any civilized person, I detested the Army. Until then I hadn't. Too young, or something. But that morning, and I don't know what triggered it off, I woke up and wanted *out*. Of the Army, of Germany, the works. Well, I didn't have enough discharge points.

All this time I had not let Germany get to me, I had kept it away from me. I didn't even sleep with the German women, on principle, at first. So Germany eluded me. What did not elude me was the sure knowledge that back home nobody understood either. Between the pie-in-the-sky Madison Avenue boys with oak leaves on their shoulders and the AMG Babbitts whose personal lives belied the slogans they fluently spun, the Germans were being missed by a mile. The average German (and there *was* an average German) was a hard nut to crack, the hardest. Now hardly distinguishable from the rubble around him because (he grovelingly complained) he had listened to too many slogans, this German now resisted all slogans equally, even our best-intentioned ones. Having performed phased surgery on his conscience since 1933 (and how long before that, hein?), and suffering dazed, genuine befuddlement when the waiter brought the bill of indiscriminate bombings and defeat, this average German hungered, yes hungered, more than anything else, for *examples* — examples of democratic, disinterested behavior. Had this German been able to see with his own eyes Americans, or the French, or the British, or the Russians actually practicing what they preached . . .

But he was not able to. To instruct him, no such behavior, no such action, existed. We were more like shrewd young businessmen than soldiers. Like co-conspirators. All we ever talked about was black market, currency rates and nooky. No, not co-conspirators, we didn't cooperate enough for that. Each man went off on his own separate deal.

The two hard forms of currency were cigarettes and sex. Cigarettes were harder to find. (There was no passion to it at all. A vulgar, careless carnality at worst, a discreet lasciviousness at its best, a normalized domestic obscenity at its usual.)

Instead, the Americans distributed baseball bats to the Hitler Jugend (warning them, of course, that these were to be used on baseballs and not Jewish skulls) who secretly laughed at them, and distributed poster paper to the (correct) political parties, and set up Amerika Hauses and . . . preached, everlastingly preached; at the same time, also, and without batting an eyelash or changing the pace of our pitch, we just kept innocently rolling along right out there in front of the Germans, the eight-point veterans of Camp Kilmer knocking aged civilians off the sidewalks to show how brave we would have been, laying eleven-year-olds for a bar of soap and then not paying off, black-marketing ourselves blue in the face, pawing the women and puking on the streets. And when there occurred, one cool April morning, a pitched firefight between a Negro truck company and a Texas infantry team in Würzburg, my marvelous boss in SHAEF G–1 solved the problem in true *democratische* fashion by recommending shipping home the Negroes: at a time when the least (and most) common denominator for all Germans was a deep revulsion against *anything* military, of anything smelling of it, SHAEF Hq. decreed splendid new uniforms, shiny boots and silk scarves and blitzed buttons, for all garrison troops. No wonder that as time went by, and the Germans saw that apparently whatever we said about collective responsibility we were only going to hang those dumkopfs at Nuremberg, they began to walk a little more erect, keep their hats on their heads, thank you, and argue back.

So all the time I was there I feared them; I had thought how easy it would be to hate the beasts. But there weren't any around. All the Germans left alive said the beasts had been killed, or were in the Russian zone.

Where in hell had all the villains gone?

I even made a pilgrimage to watch the War Crimes trial. I must have sat in the multiple-translation rows for two or three days, in a kind of deadly hypnotic trance, just looking at Goering and Hess and Speer and Streicher and the others. But they weren't villains either. It had all become something dry and foreordained and legalistic. I even began to feel sorry for the men in the box. It gave me the shivers. I lined up for a billet tag, on an open street corner in Nuremberg, and when the NCO behind the improvised desk began to argue with me, because I'd come down from Frankfurt with a pass and not furlough papers, I hit him so hard he fell against a G.I. radio on a stand which broke. I hit him as hard as I could. And then I ran, all through those hulking ruins, hitching a short ride with an education officer who said he taught at Pomona college in California.

But the MP's got me, about half an hour later, as I was walking down the street. There was a young MP and an MP about ten years older than I. They had the goods on me, all right, and there was nothing I could do about it. The young bastard was all for taking me in on the spot. But I took this older MP aside and talked to him. I lied my head off. I said that I had enough points to go home, which was almost true, and that I had a sick wife. It just so happened that I struck oil. He really *did* have a sick wife in the States whom he could not get back home to because his MOS (occupation number) had been "frozen." I asked him if he would give me a chance to get back to my unit in Frankfurt, and he said yes, but that he really would have to send the MP report to Frankfurt within twenty-four hours. The charge, he said, was assault and battery, and that I had hurt the NCO, very likely broken his jaw. I thanked the MP, and asked if I could deliver any messages for him, and he said no, he didn't want me even knowing his name. I got out of there in a hurry and instead of waiting for the regular military train hitchhiked by truck to Frankfurt. To this day I remember everything about that MP, how he looked, how he talked. If it weren't for him I probably would have been thrown in a military pokey for three or six months, and in all sincerity I don't think I could have stood it.

As soon as I got back to Frankfurt I decided to lay my cards on the table to my superior officer in the I. G. Farben building where I worked. His name was Major Presley, and he had been a tax collector in peacetime, a big tan lantern-jawed character with whom I got along fairly well. He was all right, the Major. (Until a couple of years ago we exchanged Christmas cards regularly.) He understood right away that I was in trouble. He said that he could arrange certain things, mainly my not having to wait for a normal complement of home-bound soldiers but receiving an assignment as a "courier." What he could not do, he said, was arrange for orders putting me on the ship. I said that I could arrange. I know this sounds unconventional, but you have to remember that this was 1946, and the Moms of America were raising holy to get their little boys back home in a hurry. The Army personnel setup was in chaos. I knew because I worked in SHAEF G-1.

It all happened within twenty-four hours. I went back to the barracks, turned in my equipment and arms without notifying too many people, and then returned to the Farben building where I persuaded one of my platoon kids to hold up for a day and a night a Military Police report which would soon be coming from Nuremberg. Then I went downstairs to the basement, where the communications and duplicating apparatus was kept, and I bribed another boy in my platoon to come in fifteen minutes late in the morning tomorrow. He had an idea what I wanted, and he held out until I promised all my cigarettes, which were more valuable than currency then, and my camera. Also, for some strange reason of his own, he wanted any of my staff sergeant's (T-3) stripes I had not sewed on my uniform. God knows what kind of jig he was dreaming up for himself. His name was Timmy Thames and he was a nasty, rich boy from Rhode Island. He was one of the few people in this world it would be true to say I detested. The only thing that worried me then was whether he would go through with his end of the bargain.

But he did. Early the next morning I slipped into Timmy's office and cut myself a set of orders moving me from Bremerhaven military compound to the next boat leaving for the Z.I. (Zone of Interior). The mimeographed orders were stenciled beforehand; all that was necessary was to insert my name, rank and serial number. I did it, and then went upstairs to my office where Major Presley gave me my courier orders. I didn't hang around to say any goodbyes, except to Presley, who asked me to send him a Christmas card. As I said, until recently, we exchanged them faithfully every year. I hadn't really made any good friends in the Army in Germany. I wasn't sorry to leave. At Frankfurt Station, Am Banhof, I rendezvoused with the two officers who were officer escort; they gave me a .45 to wear and we went out back of the station and got into a caboose car linked up with three freightcars on their way to Bremerhaven. The captain who was lead escort said the orders specified the freight as captured enemy documents from the Wehrmacht Engineer Office. Maybe so. But one of the G.I. guards up front, at a stopover in Kassel, came and told me that at least a section of the first car was filled with champagne, destination some general officer in the Pentagon, Washington.

We "escorted" that train to Bremerhaven, with the G.I. guards, all southern boys, jumping off every time we stopped to fire their burp guns in the air to scare away the German civilians who ran up the cinder banks to retrieve the coal our engine dropped. You have to remember the way I was feeling about Germany then, I *hated* those G.I.'s. Just by being ourselves like that, Americans, we were making real democracy impossible in the occupied zones. That's one of the reasons Germany confused and sickened me, and most of all eluded me. I had expected anything except what I found, that hard winter: a cringing lickspittle population dispossessed morally and materially, which contained not a single Nazi. I made pilgrimages to the concentration camps but still I didn't understand it. What the Nazis, the Germans, had done was beyond my powers not only of comprehension but also of feeling. I could hate the murderers of a few individuals. But how do you hate, actively, morally, the murderers of millions of them? Where murder, mass murder, is organized like a Ford assembly line, where do you begin assessing the blame? And who among this now docile people were the murderers? There wasn't anybody around who seemed especially eager to come forward and say, Yes, take me, I am the evil one. If you didn't watch it, soon after you came to Germany you began to think of the years between 1933 and 1945 as a time when the country had been occupied by a bunch of people not quite so popular as the Americans. That was the impression the Germans gave you.

I wanted someone to blame it on. Sometimes I would walk along the streets, and out of sheer frustration think, You are the Enemy, Every Single One of You. Away with You. But that scared me even more because then I was thinking like *them.* The one thing I knew was that slogans and baseball mitts and AMGOT food boxes wouldn't do a thing for the Germans. What they hungered for, I say, after all those years, was *examples.* If we had acted *nobly* I think perhaps we might have gotten through. Instead, black market. Gimme. Those G.I. guards with their burp guns on the train. It just about drove me crazy. After a while you couldn't argue with the Germans. Their logic was ironclad. They had an answer for everything by the time I left, an answer that had more to do with our actions as troops and governors than anything else. Rotterdam? What about Cologne! Military atrocities? Katyn! The Jews? What about the U.S. Negroes? Occupied Europe? The British colonies! Concentration camps? *What* concentration camps! You couldn't win. Not the way we were acting. In 1946, it was too late already. We had our chance and botched it. That was when, and probably why, I hit that NCO. (If it's of any interest, I broke his jaw, and when I got to Chicago eventually and wrote in for my back Army pay they said they wouldn't give it to me because I had an assault-and-battery charge outstanding. But a lawyer got me the money, about $400.)

MARCH 1946

Scene: an office in the SPD headquarters (Socialist Partei Deutschland), Frankfurt-am-Main branch. The speaker is the editor of the local SPD newspaper, a former concentration camp inhabitant. He is talking to the Technician, Third Grade.

EDITOR: "*The questions you ask, sergeant, they are not easy to answer, for it is always the same question you ask in different forms: how did it happen here? But, you see, we do not know either. You ask a Socialist and he will tell you it was the Communists who made the Nazis. You ask a Communist and he will curse the Socialists for talking too much and doing too little. Ask a Centrist and he will tell you Hitler was conjured up as a counterpoise to the threat of the proletarians. Ask a Nazi — if you can find one — and he will tell you it did not happen at all. (Angrily) Communists, Socialists, Catholics, we have all been in the camps. You think we made a United Front even in there? Ah no! We argued inside the camps and we still argue. (Standing up, ending interview with the Tech/3.) Now you, young soldier, what do you expect? A booklet on how it happened.* WE DO NOT KNOW OURSELVES! *You think that by asking me questions about the election of 1932 you will find the answer. I laugh! As well inquire into the causes of a plague by a review of the incidents of the day before it struck. You want to know about the Nazis, about Hitler, about the 'German problem'?* Tell us!"

MAY 1946

After putting together the weekend guard roster, the Tech/3 left the caserne and walked up Rotlinstrasse around in front of the 97th General Hospital and along the bomb-pitted streetcar tracks to an intact, almost Georgian solid house on Rex-allee which overlooked a cratered-out field of potatoes and a small grove of splintered trees. On the second floor of the house he was admitted into an apartment by a little bull of a man, with apple cheeks, a hard cherubic face and a pleasantly neutral smile.

"Herr Feldwebel," said the little man, bowing and stepping back into the apartment. He was, as usual, dressed in morning coat and knife-creased trousers.

"Professor Bunch."

The Tech/3 followed the Professor through a foyer to a large, sparsely furnished music room done in old, polished walnut. The room overlooked a garden. Tree foliage filtered patchy daylight into the ordered and otherwise darkened room. Four anonymous straight-backed chairs faced a polished, grand walnut piano occupying the major corner of the room. In the center of the room was a folding camp cot made up with sheets and blankets. High bookcases were fitted into the two free sides of the room. Inside the bookcases lay hundreds of assorted pawn shop objects.

"You have done the new finger exercises as I explained?"

"Yes, Professor Bunch. Five minutes in the morning just after I wake up, five minutes before lunch and ten minutes in the evening. It is sometimes hard for me to make a fist too early in the morning."

"Good," said the Professor. "That means you need my exercises. Now please select the music you wish to play from and we will prozceed." The Tech/3 riffled through various sheets from the compartment under the long bench that ran the length of the piano keyboard, propped up some music and began, hunched over in labor, to play. Professor Bunch lay down on the cot, his hands folded over his stomach and listened, nodding with closed eyes. "Yes, that is good . . . You are more relaxed than last week. But you still go too fast, your fingers run to catch up with your eyes. You must examine for the correct notes. Ja. Ja. No. No. Do not do that when you come to a zeries of same notes, do not make common noises because they are zuddenly easy. Evenly. Evenly, Herr Feldwebel."

Ten minutes and the Tech/3 was tired. "You rezt for fife minutez and zen we rezume," the Professor said, and left the room. The Tech/3 got up from the piano and walked to the bay window and wondered why anyone would plant a tree so that its leafiest part would spread the light out of the room. It was warm, and he pushed open the window and went back to study the music. The Professor advised against this during rest periods.

Professor Bunch was writing a book which he expected would revolutionize the technique of music teaching and undoubtedly become classic. But recognition, he warned himself and well-wishers, would not come overnight. His book, the unfinished manuscript of which included a thousand-page history of German music by way of introduction, was to be a triumphant, detailed and comprehensive exposition of his Method. The Bunch Method, as it applied to the Tech/3, involved a system of syncopated finger exercises three times a day done with a stick of balsa wood in one hand and a small rubber ball in the other, no metronome (which the Professor declared *destroyed the brain cells progressively with its monotonous beat), urging students to choose their own practice music sheets and before each practice period a ten-minute session given over to preparing the pupil's brain to "aggzept the labor" by lightly psychoanalyzing away potential distractions. The Tech/3 had declined further debris-clearing upon the Professor beginning the first session by a solemn inquiry as to the method and regularity of his abusing himself.*

An integral part of the Method, the Professor calmly explained, was the regulation and coordination, at a distance he hastened to add, of the teacher's and pupil's "zeggshual patterns." Though himself avowedly ascetic in these matters, the Professor enthusiastically pronounced that the best piano teachers were homosexuals and the best pupils eunuchoid with strong but properly repressed sado-masochistic drives. The Tech/3 did not know whether the Professor had been a soldier or civilian before 1945; the Professor never mentioned the war years. He made his living teaching music to the occupation troops, by developing G.I.-taken photographs and by repairing cameras. He also dealt in the black market in an industrious but minor way.

"Nein, nein, Sehrehrter Schuler, *you muzz give zuh brain zells a relagzashun." The Professor shut the door behind him. "Now do me anozzer fifteen minutes of your eggserzise and zen I shall instruct you in how you damage your camera." Again he lay down on the cot, a cased Leica in his hand, and closed his eyes, letting his other hand dangle on the floor. His indeterminate German accent usually thickened noticeably from start to finish of the practice session.*

A quarter of an hour later the Tech/3 sat back, exhausted. Today his timing was sharper and the score had begun to make a little sense. He had come to Professor Bunch without knowing how to read notes and had learned to read complicated chromatics within five days with the aid of a kazoo-type instrument and a simple mathematical table, all part of the Method.

"Sehr gut, Herr Feldwebel. *In siggs months you will be playing Wagner. Ah, but I forget. Wagner is undemocratic."*

The Tech/3 spent four hours every week at Professor Bunch's apartment, Tuesday evenings and Saturday late mornings. The Professor was quite willing to talk about anything if the point of origin was demonstrably musical so that, if he made an indiscretion, he could easily retire into technical innocuousness. The Tech/3 was sure Professor Bunch had been a Nazi. He said, "I did not say Wagner was undemocratic. I said the German ruling class had made him so."

Professor Bunch laid the camera down on the uncarpeted, neatly swept floor and folded his hands over his eyes, smiling slightly. The Tech/3 started to play again, soft-pedaling, thinking, what angle will I be hit from today?

"Tell me, Herr Feldwebel, you continually refer to the ruling clazz when you talk about the Nazis. Most Americans just say Nazis. Granting your thesis of last week that the Nazi leaders were the produzing group, so to speak, of Nazi theory, thiz week you will perhaps admit there was alzo a conzuming group which very frequently dictated to the so-called ruling clazz what its preferences were. Just as, I am told, your American conzumer exercises a veto of your capitalists by purchazing or refusing to purchaze zertain products. Perhaps even, Herr Feldwebel, if I make so bold an analogy, ze German people were as rezponzible for the Nazism of their leaders as the American people for the trade practizes of their capitalist clazz."

The Tech/3 ceased playing. "The American people," he said categorically, "are responsible for their ruling class only negatively in that they have thus far not gotten rid of it."

"And perhapz," the Professor smiled up towards the ceiling, "they have not done zo because the ruling clazz, how you say, fits in perfectly with their own plans."

"They have not done so because the capitalists control the machinery of the state, the law courts and Congress and police."

"And perhaps alzo the conzsiousness of the people."

"Yes," said the Tech/3, "that too, through their ownership and control of radio, newspapers and motion pictures."

"Ah yezz, the virgin zeduced. Just like our own great German

mazzes." He smiled idly, ironically. The smile died on his lips. Suddenly he did what he had never done before, shouted.

"Yes, what *conzentration camps! No, don't open your mouth and tell me about Auschwitz and Buchenwald and all the rest."*

The Tech/3 tried to shout down the confused roaring in his ears. As with the time on the mountain near Heidelberg, this was what he had been waiting for, and now that it had happened he did not, as at Heidelberg, know how to deal with it.

"I have seen *them!"*

"You have seen nozzing, *nozzing but wooden buildings and barbed wire and propaganda plaques. All else is your imagination. Have you found a zingle German who zaw zuch thingz, who was a gward or a clerk in one of the campz, who will zo much as hint he ever knew about them."*

"The DP's —"

"Ah, yez, the victims. For them the campz are real enough. But for the German people they do not exist, they are not eefen a bat dream, just zome more of your American good intentions. You think you will make democratz of the German people by telling them that what did not exist existed. If you do, we will zimply tell you, if we zay anyzing at all, that for us *they do not exist and nothing you do can make us believe they did. If you do force us to say 'Yez, I knew about them' you will be doing a stupid and dangerous thing, for you will then be forcing us to lizzen to you as we lizzened to our former leaders, those you choose to call the spokesmen for the ruling clazz, but then you zhould zimply have zsheep with democratische wool instead of zsheep with Nazi wool going 'baaa-a!' at your commands. You promized to democratize us, not make us zsheep,* hein? *So I suggest you let us find our own way to a discovery of evil."*

The Tech/3 said, "What you are saying is that we should leave the German mentality alone."

"Eggzactly. It is much more real to the German nation that they have been bombed by their enemies and led into hunger and foolishness by their leaders, more real than the conzentration camps you zo

much like to talk about. Therefore, if you continue to talk about zem, the Germans can come only to the concluzion that you are far more interezted in your own righteousness than their welfare, and once they are convinzed of thiz you zshall never rehabilitate them." Bunch sneered. "Rehabilitate. Who are you to rehabilitate. *Homesick provinczials who vomit in the streets and make whores of the German nation."*

The Tech/3 stood up. He wanted to smash the Professor.

"My God, how can you dare speak like that. There is not a German walking the streets who is not a criminal, who does not share the guilt —"

"Guilt, my young friend," said the Professor, "is a relative thing —"

"— either for what he did or refused to stop."

Professor Bunch ignored the Tech/3, his words coming faster, as though he were a fencing master, lunging, parrying, his movements becoming less subtle as his pupil revealed less and less skill until what he was doing bordered on the easy brutality of the teacher who has lost respect for his charge.

"— a relative thing of time, plaze and zircumztance. Now take your Negroes in zouthern Oo-ess-ay, it is a relativity of plaze perhapz."

"The rest of America is against that sort of thing."

Bunch smiled thinly. "Are they? And the loyal Japanese citisens zent to conzentrati — my pardon — relocation *campz."*

"The result of temporary hysteria."

"Yez, of course. So you agree. Wizz your Japanese it is a matter of time relativity. Temporarily. A matter of a year or two. Here in Germany it was alzo temporary. A matter of twelve or thirteen years. Poof."

"Are you really saying that there is no difference in . . . in —"

"The moral outlook," suggested Bunch.

"All right, the moral outlook of us Americans and you Germans."

Professor Bunch spread his hands deprecatingly. "I am but a humble instructor of the piano and am not competent to judge." And in the next breath, rising to his feet: "You have had your opportunity and you have — how do your comrades zay, fouled it up. You dezerve to lose the next war. You deserve whatever happens to you. Now please go. I am tired from all this zenzeless talk. And you must find anozzer teacher. It is no longer possible . . ."

The Professor held out the Leica to the Tech/3. "Auf wiedersehen, Herr Feldwebel. *I am tired.*"

The Tech/3 took the camera, saying, "Tell me, Professor Bunch, were you a Nazi from the earliest days?"

The eyes of the Professor stared blankly at the young American soldier. Then he seemed to collapse on the cot. He sat on it, his head to one side and looking up mirthlessly at the Tech/3, his mouth barking with laughter. He laughed until the tears came to his eyes, and as the tears rolled down his seamed, rubbery cheeks, he poked out his hand and drew back the sleeve of his coat. The Tech/3 knew what would be there before he saw it.

"Ja," *said Professor Bunch. "You see. The number is political." The arm dropped to his side. His head rested slightly askew, the pouched, veined eyes almost sightless.*

The Tech/3, clutching the Leica in both hands, gave a small gesture, like an involuntary shrug.

The wind moved the branches of the tree outside the window, which scratched. Finally, he left the room.

The Professor sat like a defiantly, somnolent, paunchy bird. The window began to rattle softly again, and he rose from the cot and circled the room, as though to assure himself that everything was in its proper place, and then he went to the piano and played the simple melody of the practice sheet with one finger. He breathed heavily through an open mouth. The next pupil, due in ten minutes, was to be stopped at the threshold of the music room by the look of utter, despairing fear on the face of Professor Bunch.

APRIL 1946

The jeep sped quietly through the tiny German town, its canvas top stuttering in the wind. Only a few inhabitants paused in their Sunday stroll to stare at the two soldiers in their ugly little vehicle with

U.S. ARMY stenciled in white paint on the side below the driver's seat. After the village the cobbled road narrowed up into hard-packed dirt between two small hills and wound around, up and up, in short quick spirals, until the crest of hills became a mountain with solid masses of trees surging to the road: gaunt black trees with thin branches which met high overhead and suddenly made everything quite dark. There was no light in the forest, only a silent brightness flashing through the branches.

At the wheel of the jeep the Technical Sergeant, third grade, felt each bump of the road. He had been driving fast since morning and felt nothing under his sleepy pinprickled feet when he let up on the gas pedal. The jeep slowed in a gloomy wooded well where the road split into a V and became two wide and dusty paths running on ahead through tall trees and thick wild grass glinting under the intermittent sunlight. He braked, keeping his hands on the steering wheel and felt slightly dizzy: the silence of the forest pressed strangely into his ears. The tops of the trees were shrouded in a delicate inert mist.

"Let's go back home," said Ralph Stevens, a Texan, and a corporal.

The Tech/3 lifted himself out of the jeep and walked off the road into the dark trees and turned his back. The forest smelled damp and warm. Ralph swung his beefy legs over the side of the jeep and jumped out. He marched up and down the middle of the road, snapping his knees high, sniffing in the air moistly, then went back to the jeep where he opened a pack of cigarettes and listened to the running motor. He studied the fuel gauge, then got in.

A muffled cheer sounded off through the trees where long slender beams of bright dusty light pinned dry and deadening leaves to the forest floor. Then another cheer, less loud, followed by a low heaving of dim voices.

The Tech/3 slid back into the driver's seat and released the hand brake. Ralph looked straight ahead. "We're too far out. Must be ten miles back to those signal boys in Heidelberg." He turned to the Tech/3, then away, shrugging. "Okay, it's your jeep. But we ain't got that much gas."

The Tech/3 gunned the engine. He smiled. "You had me worried there for a minute, Ralph. I thought maybe you were nervous, or something." Ralph, who shared his billet, had without warning pistol-whipped an old German man in a black-market transaction a few weeks ago. The Tech/3, surprised, had looked on. That was when he began taking Ralph on these weekend jeep rides of his, probing further and further out each time they went. Ralph had once been a master sergeant. His hobby in the city was to walk up behind German civilians and tread on their heels and make no pretense of it being an accident.

"Just lay off," complained Ralph. "Sometimes I don't even know why I come with you."

The Tech/3 rolled the jeep off the road and slowed abruptly as the path in the dense sheeny grass veered up off to the right into a cluster of slim white trees.

Ralph pondered his cigarette. "It's gonna rain. Sure as God made little apples, it's gonna rain."

The sounds were growing into a steady wave of shouts in German. The Tech/3 maneuvered the jeep in the trees so that it pointed down to the main road. He switched off the motor, putting the key in his trouser pocket, and climbed out. Ralph slowly crushed his cigarette against the dash and reached under the front seat for the .45 automatic in the holster of stiff black leather. The Tech/3 was the platoon sergeant, and Ralph was the supply sergeant. It was against regulations to carry unauthorized firearms, but it always made them feel easier. The laughter of many men died down in the treetops.

Ralph hurried through the grass after the Tech/3, fitting the automatic to his waist by slipping a few notches in the fiber belt. Catching up, he noisily pulled out the clip of seven bullets and shoved it back in the butt chamber.

They walked out of the forest, the two of them, and were in an open field. A big and noisy crowd of Germans, all men, was watching a soccer match being played in a clearing which had been hacked out of the tall white trees of the mountaintop.

The Germans noticed them at once; two American soldiers had come onto the field where a goal had just been kicked between two upright poles bearing pennants. The players were running towards the center of the field to place the ball in play. A loud cheer went up.

The boundaries of the game area were marked off by a knotted rope looped taut through small holes in waist-high wooden boards which had been hammered into the earth at precisely spaced intervals. The ground on which the players ran was rough with tufts of grass and tiny water holes and inside the earth clods was mud. The air was different here, it was cold, and smelled of the wet sweet tang of the underside of pine strippings. The Tech/3 watched the players scramble for the ball. Ralph started walking after him.

The Tech/3 stopped where he could see the game better. Ralph looked around him. On both sides of them, and all about the field, were Germans. There were not many young men in the crowd, but the soccer players were young and their hair slipped over their wet red young faces when they ran. They wore shorts and short, not long, socks showing chunky muscled legs with hair, and most of the players had on heavy woolen sweaters. They were brawny and well fed.

The Tech/3 said, "They look good."

"Like the old SSers," Ralph muttered quietly.

They knew the Germans were talking about them. Spectators on both sides of them deliberately moved a distance away. Ralph leaned on the rope, alongside the Tech/3 and close to him, then stood up and surveyed the crowd. His hand rested on the holster strapped to his hip. He never could forget he had once been a master sergeant.

The Tech/3 said, "Stop it."

Ralph looked at him and returned his hands to the rope but did not lean on it. The crowd fell quiet. Ralph said, "Hey . . ." but nothing else.

Suddenly a player kicked the soccer ball high into the air and it shot far and free downfield. The Germans cheered the men thundering after the bouncing ball and two of the center forwards collided in midair. They tumbled to the ground and the play rushed past them. Watching, the Tech/3 lit a cigarette. The crowd was becoming excited again.

A very fat burgher, a round head and slit eyes and a round porcine belly, in a black overcoat and dark glasses, stood in front of him.

"Haben Sie ein cigarette, bitte?" *He wasn't saying it the way they asked in the streets of Frankfurt. Ralph glowered over at the hoglike German with the hidden eyes.*

The Tech/3 nodded slowly, reaching into the pocket of his Ike jacket. He placed the pack in the German's hand. "Hier."

The fat man inclined his head politely, took the pack and counted out nine cigarettes in loud English, "One, two, three . . ." He gave the pack back to the Tech/3 and walked away.

Ralph protested, "The silly bastard."

The Tech/3 moved down the sideline of rope after the man in dark glasses who had taken his nine cigarettes, and some of the spectators turned to stare.

The Tech/3 stopped and pretended to watch the field.

Play whipped about in spasmodic little whirlpools of arms and legs, with the healthy young men in sweaters badgering the other team near the goal sticks where the two Americans had first come on the field.

Another man stepped up to them. He was one of the few young ones and had a lean washed face, a pursed mouth and a prewar suit of good tweed. He grinned. "Hahve yue ai tsigarette, Joe?" his voice rising pleasantly.

The Tech/3 said, "Raus!" *not looking at him.*

The young German in the fashionable clothes smiled indulgently and returned to his group. He said something. The Germans laughed quietly and turned to contemplate the two soldiers.

Ralph asked, "You think maybe now, ass-hole sergeant, maybe now we should try and get outta here?" speaking low and rapidly and bitterly.

"No. Now we can't go."

Upfield, one of the players, tried to "head" the ball but it glanced off his skull and bounced away. The official scorer was poised expectantly at his blackboard across the field.

From the other side of them a small old man with an imbecilic glaze limped over, saying something which the Tech/3 could not understand except "cigaretten."

Tiny senile eyes sought those of the Tech/3's.

"Give him one, damn it," he said. "Just one."

Ralph reached in and fumbled awkwardly as he unbuttoned his shirt pocket. He handed over a cigarette. The aged and emaciated German bowed deeply. Both his legs beneath dirty knickers were crippled. "Bitte. *Thank you. Thank you oh so much," he croaked, touching the lustrous round* Hakenkreuz *at the peak of his cap. He shuffled back to his friends. Swiveling to face the two soldiers on one of his bad legs, he held the cigarette between his two forefingers and carefully, almost lovingly fieldstripped it without touching it to his lips. All the Germans laughed very loud. The sky was roiling with massed rain clouds, and the sun was going.*

"Please let's go." Ralph sounded out of breath.

"All right. But wait a couple of minutes first. And please take your goddam hand off the goddam gun. Fine?"

Play sped near them. The men in sweaters ran swiftly past several times.

The ball was kicked upfield and retrieved by the tall slender goalkeeper in a bright green sweater who stopped the ball and started fast, nursing it down the near sideline, abandoning the goal completely; he kicked the ball a little way out and there was nobody, absolutely nobody, to interfere and then he kicked again, arching his leg back and shooting it forward expertly, and the hard round ball sailed high into the cold sunless air and struck Ralph in the face as he was thinking he would go now, and then the ball bounced away.

The lanky goalie in the green sweater vaulted the rope. The Tech/3 knelt down and snapped open Ralph's holster. The .45 service automatic with the clip of seven bullets felt much heavier in his hand than it did during pistol practice on the range inside the Hamburg Landstrasse kaserne.

Ralph had sunk to the ground, looking sick and frozen and holding tight to a knot in the rope. His eyes were wide open. He said, "Hey . . ."

The soccer player stopped before the Tech/3 and laughed. "What? You would shoot me? Oh, no." He ran after the ball in a few long graceful strides, almost like a young girl, and then he walked back with the ball under his arm.

"Raus!" *he said quite loudly the way Americans do, making it nasal and imperious. Then he ducked under the rope barrier and tossed the ball into play. All the Germans yelled victoriously. Nobody paid any more attention to the American soldier on the wet ground and the one standing over him with a pistol in his hand aimed at nobody.*

"Can you walk? Hey, Ralph, dammit — can you get up?" The Tech/3 was frightened and disgusted. He offered Ralph his hand.

The game had not resumed. Across the field on the blackboard a score was chalked up for the goalkeeper's team. The German crowd roared with applause and hearty laughter.

Together, Ralph and the Tech/3 stumbled away from the soccer field through the tall forest grass, and all the way Ralph tried alternately to talk and pull a handkerchief from his back pocket but couldn't.

The Tech/3 glanced back. Five or six Germans were clustered around the spot where Ralph had gone down. They were bent over. "You must've dropped your cigarettes," the Tech/3 said.

The jeep was still there, among the white trees.

The Tech/3 helped Ralph into the back seat and went around to the front and climbed in, jamming the key in and hastily shoving his foot on the starter. The engine coughed. Then, after a moment, it revved and ran. The cold white mist of the treetops was closing in, slowly and without a sound.

It was much darker now and a few raindrops splatted on the windshield.

As he steered off the footpath in the woods towards the main road to Heidelberg, the Tech/3 listened to a loud cheer skimming the treetops. "Game must be over," he said.

Ralph wiped his face with his sleeve and saw blood on it.

The Tech/3 reached into the back seat and tugged at Ralph's belt.

Ralph looked straight ahead at him, oddly, dully triumphant through the blunt blind pain rolling over his head. He shifted slightly away from the Tech/3's grasp, unbuckled his holster and laid it on the empty seat beside him. He took the automatic out of the holster and flicked the safety. Then, with it in his hand, he sat back and waited.

They didn't say a word to each other.

And the Tech/3 knew, at last, why it was he had been taking out the jeep on these weekends. He had met his Germans.

At Bremerhaven I boarded a ship using my forged papers. Twelve hours after arrival at Camp Kilmer, New Jersey, I walked out the front gate, not fancying a ten-day troop train ride to California, where I had asked the Army to discharge me. I made my way to Cache, Oklahoma, and stayed a couple of weeks with the Indian Bird, and a whole mess of Comanche men, women and children in one big house on a dusty side road, and then we cut out together . . .

Had Enough? the Republican Party billboards sneered down from sun-baked rooftops on the street of drunkies, crips, punch drunks, loonies, plain bums, plain and fancy bums, junkies, smallest-time thieves and drifters of no trades. But the men did not sneer back. They weren't even noticing.

Skid Row, City of Angels, 1946.

It was one of those hot, dry days when the smog sits and strangles Los Angeles a little.

It was one of the many streets which could have been laid down in any midwest city; no palm trees here, no sun-tanned girls in halters and shorts, a boomerang of an avenue from Sixth Street to Second Street, lined with small handbag factories, loft machine shops, wholesale leather goods stores, four city blocks no different from any other in America, except that the secretaries and women workers avoided entrances opening onto the street, preferring alley exits, side doors, anything except a route which might take them down Los Angeles Street midday.

A small melon-breasted Mexican woman, new to the neighborhood but not the country, got off a bus and walked up the street, past the empty store fronts, the empty lofts, the empty men. She chose the shady side of the street, unaware until too late that the shade side was the Biarritz, the Riviera, the club of Skid Row after two o'clock and before sundown.

This was Los Angeles Street, one of the two main thoroughfares of Skid Row. Sixth Street, east and west between Los Angeles Street and San Pedro Street, cheap bars, fleabag hotels, the rialto of broken men. Los Angeles Street, running north-south between Second and Sixth, rest haven. The sun beat mercilessly on Sixth all day long; it required no brains at all to take the shade on Los Angeles Street, just drop on your haunches on the east side before one, shamble across the street after two.

The Mexican woman clutched her handbag tighter when she realized what she was walking through. Men in work clothes, men in tattered clothes, men in G.I. suntans, and not a single woman on the stretch of hopelessness from Second to Sixth on Los Angeles.

The tubby little Mexican woman shuddered. *Qué mal!* She was used to being whistled at. She did not like being whistled at but, *Madre Dios*, this, these men with dead eyes and sagging shoulders, these no-men, better they should whistle than be dead standing up. She passed a store-front mission. A dozen or so men lounged idly in front, not talking much, not moving much, not caring much. A few heads were brought up, then the heads dropped again.

Madre Dios, she said to herself again, and walked around a corner and was out of sight.

Among many there were four hunched listlessly on the curb.

One was a brown-skinned boy, E. J. Birdsong, known as the Indian Bird. He was thinking, vaguely, of going home.

The second was me.

The third was Adolph Tucci, pronounced Touchy. He had a narrow bony face and bee-stung, trembling lips which smiled often and without the need of stimuli, eyes of a melancholy sweetness. He was also growing bald. His only known boast was that he had gone up in an airplane fifty-seven times and never once landed. Perhaps because he had gone unwounded through four campaigns his general had taken the habit of insisting that Adolph jump from his personal plane and in his personal "stick." Jumping over Falaise Adolph had broken his arm and was in a base hospital when his general came around.

— How do you feel, Tucci?

— They got me fixed up fine, sir, as you can see.

— We're going over again in three days.

— Gee, sir, I thought they was to give you all a rest.

— It's somewhere in Belgium, Tucci. It would please me if you came along.

(Adolph did not want to make the jump into Belgium, but he did not say this. He had joined the war because he was an Italian and loathed Mussolini; he was, in the literal sense, an anti-Fascist. He felt sorry for the general, who must be suffering from nerves if he needed a communications sergeant to make the jump alongside him. He did not want to be disloyal.)

— I've got a busted wing, sir.

— The doctor tells me it's only a simple fracture. It's healing.

— Gee, sir, you need men that bad?

— I need you in my plane. We have made a lot of jumps together. If we're lucky this will be our last.

— I don't know, sir. This arm.

— You're my good luck charm, Tucci.

— Would the doctors let me go?

— I've talked to them.

Under the general's supervision, a layer of new plaster was poured on the cast on Adolph's arm, and a machine-pistol embedded in the plaster. He could not wave his arm without pointing the weapon. The jump, into Belgium, behind German lines, was a success. Casualties were less than average. Adolph landed softly near the small town of Maldegem and joined the attack. He went into a small *tabac* at the edge of town and opened fire with the plaster-of-parised machine pistol, killing half a dozen rural Belgians who were in the place drinking peacefully at a few old tables. Shipped back to the United States for treatment, he had walked off the grounds of the Army hospital and panhandled his way south to spend most of his day in Pershing Square listening to the old men fight over ancient politics. Adolph was a registered summer student at the University.

Beside Adolph, humming a tune to himself, his short chunky arms supporting a broad blond face, still wearing the pink pants and epauletted shirt of an Army officer, was Axel. Axel had been a

Graves Registration officer in the Pacific "steppingstone" campaign, and *his* problem was that he had seen too many dead young men and that his wife, a student doctor, had committed suicide a week before he came back to San Francisco. After which Axel stumbled dazedly on to the internal belt line for drifters, Highway 66, and kept getting on and off buses until the Greyhound passenger agent in Los Angeles advised him to take a boat if he wanted to keep going. But keeping going was the one thing Axel did not feel like; so, like thousands before him, he just let go to see what would happen, slipping easily down the walls of the funnel into that four-square block area reserved, almost exclusively, for the ones who couldn't keep hanging on. Adolph and Axel were inseparable. Axel knew Adolph was taking care of him down to the details of dressing and undressing him and going with him every Wednesday out to the VA hospital where Axel was receiving treatment for malarial after-effects.

A slight shuffling of logy feet, and E.J. raised his head; he got up. Adolph nudged Axel who touched me, and we all rose to our feet and retreated into the shelter of the string of men in front of the store-front mission. Adolph had to help Axel.

Inside the mission house a warm air of lassitude hung over the unoccupied wooden benches. The rector sat in a corner of the raised platform and with half-closed eyes stared gloomily out of the front window at the backs of his parishioners silhouetted against the dazzling sunlight of the baking street, and listened to the slow, unurgent sound of his wife and volunteers preparing the dinner of surplus C-rations and split-pea soup in the back room, knowing that at six o'clock sharp the men on the street would be sharply smitten by the pangs of redemption.

On the street the men watched in various postures of passive sullenness a police van slowly cruise them, its back door hanging lazily open and revealing three or four bedraggled sleeping drunks. Several times each morning and afternoon an LAPD paddy wagon patrolled, squared and bisected Skid Row at three m.p.h., three police officers moving along the sidewalk scaling the dead, dying or inert scabs from the living desiccated corpse of the Row. It was a mechanical agricultural operation, performed with efficiency and without rancor by the police upon indifferent subjects.

The driver of the wagon always looked as asleep as his passengers, he had been doing this for a long time. The motorized patrol was usually made twice a day, cop teams making constant saunters along the border streets to check ID's, roll up sleeve and trouser legs for junkie spot checks and generally to make themselves known. The younger cops regarded this assignment as easy and unpleasant and did their jobs with crisp contemptuousness. The older cops knew better, and did their jobs with a slow, thorough cautiousness, knowing that the wrecks they walked among were the most dangerous when provoked: the hopeless who lived so deeply in the dark of what was left of themselves that their sense of proportion and consequences was as personalized as that of ultimate lunatics, where a caustic remark or unpaid 35¢ debt was carelessly avenged by a knife in the belly. These older cops knew what the rookies did not, that it was useless to acquire friends on the beat, to learn first names, to try to do anything but smell out, the first five minutes of the start of any patrol, any changes in the air of the Row which might be preliminary to an unpredictable, sometimes comic, sometimes fatal, often both, outburst of obscure violence. Being a cop on the Row was like working in the bowels of a nineteenth century coal mine, hammering away at the seams, loosening the rock to be hauled away, never knowing when the timbers will split to seal you off from the world of sanity and sunlight, constantly bedeviled by the gnawing sense that the creaks and groans and grinding moans of the raw material you work in presage a cave-in. The experienced policemen on Skid Row were frightened men.

But the habitués of the Row had themselves been scared once too often. The group of them in front of the store-front mission, with the disappointed preacher and his hardworking wife inside, communicated, if that is the word, to each other in the low hoarse murmur which, had all other noises on the street been temporarily stilled, had the traffic's rumble and juke-box tinkling miraculously stopped for only a few seconds, would have supplied the Row with a sound not unlike the low, uncommitted bawl of cello basses tuning up.

The mission bums watched the policemen, two rookies, and a more experienced partner, pass them by, neither furtively drawing away nor ceasing their cello-bass sounds nor yet defiantly half turning to present a front view. These men had nothing to prove which hadn't already been disproved. A quick frisk, a deft lifting of a pants leg, the mental imprint of a new face, all on unresisting subjects, and the cops and their motor escort were gone, leaving no trace of resentment or even of interest behind.

Axel was drunk, so gone on alcohol he would sometimes roam the edges of the Row with the other chronic alcoholics looking for parked automobiles likely to have anti-freeze in the radiator. But this was California.

We had been together on the Row for six weeks, along with scores of other ex- and presently serving servicemen, AWOLS, deserters or ducks who were too ruptured to try on civilian life for size. Not that we kept good track of time. Had any of us been questioned individually, the estimates of how long we had known each other would have wildly conflicted. Axel, the furthest gone, would have said a year or so; Indian E.J. would have said a week because he didn't like to think he had been down here longer than that. It was assumed by the Row that because we ganged together so closely the four of us were confirmed, comradely queens.

After the cops had gone, Adolph looked around and said, "Where's everybody today?" Usually there were fifty or sixty men congregated around the mission between meals, today only half or less that number. Not that there was any particular reason to congregate there; it was not a social center; you did not find yourself there in the hope of being with your friends. It was just a place in the shade outside where, for the price of having to listen to a tired exhortation to come to Christ (delivered in approximately the style, which could be heard several times daily on local broadcast stations, of a worn-out salesman urging, in the tones of one too long at his trade, a visit to some declining resort town), you could get a free lunch and supper a few times a week. The preacher did not allow regulars, less because it was a rule than because it would shake his self-esteem. Also, next door was a blood bank where, three days a week, it was possible, if you did not show up too often, to sell a pint from your veins for five dollars. Adolph and I regularly took turns. Axel still had malaria, and E.J. would not.

I took a few steps out and looked up and down the street. The ranks of dirty, resigned characters did indeed seem thinned. A man in an expensive Florida suit approached. I blocked the man's path. He had the ruddy, glowing complexion of a retired businessman, a not difficult touch if he was an out-of-towner. I held out my hand. The man hurried away, gathering speed as he went, as the melon-breasted Mexican girl had, as though fearing that the men strung out along the street had the capacity or the will to do anything except what they were doing.

Adolph, sitting on the sidewalk, shook his head. "You *know* you got to tell them a story." I hunched down beside Adolph, ignoring E.J.'s stern look of disapproval. E.J. did not like for me to panhandle. He said it was undignified, and that you wouldn't catch an Indian doing it. I smiled up at the Indian Bird. Earlier in the day I and Adolph and Axel had found a drunk lying in the alley behind the Greyhound bus station, with three cans of Sterno on the ground beside him. Adolph had carried away the drunkie's Sterno, replying to my feeble protest, "What in hell, he's lucky, we ain't rolling him."

Adolph never wore the two rows of ribbons to which he was entitled unless it was to procure on the streets. He carried the double row of plastic ribbons around loosely in the pocket of his faded suntans, ready to whip them out and pin them on whenever we needed money. To someone like E.J., who never had the chance to collect more than his Good Conduct and American Theater ribbons, this exploitation of his country's honors was something close to desecration. But Adolph was not squeamish. "Look," he explained without heat, "all over the city are pictures of guys in uniform asking to be elected to public office because there was the war. I bear them no grudge. And they shouldn't bear me any." Adolph did the panhandling for both Axel and himself, because Axel was, for days at a stretch, incapable of helping himself out of his wine fog, and thus Adolph felt doubly justified and reassured.

Adolph had been the one to teach me how. Watching him do it, slouching against a bank building on the corner of Spring and Fourth, or placidly but purposefully breasting the crowds on Broadway to tackle a prospect, it seemed neither difficult nor degrading. Adolph had seniority by virtue of his seven months' residence on the Row (Axel had three months, I and the Indian Bird only a few weeks apiece), and claimed to have learned his begging technique from the pros. "But," he insisted, "I got my own unorthodox style." Where most panhandlers baited a hook with pleaful eyes and a generally whining mien, Adolph, when he roused himself to the task, carried it off with a brisk, menacing formality, lurching directly in the path of the "clients," as he called them, and declaiming "I'm *hungry*" . . .

I didn't mind so much. I was tired for a young man. But E.J., the Indian Bird, never could get used to it. He said the filthy, sunny streets and the bums were unbefitting. He had already been honorably discharged, and I don't think he much enjoyed himself. But I didn't mind. The one thing about the Row was that it was filled with okies, weary old Wobblies, drunkies and dopies far gone, whores on their last legs — they never *judged* you. The cops today patrol the Row in teams of two; then it was three.

Axel was the only one of us who could genuinely be called a wino. He drank quarts of it a day. Any kind. Gallo, sneaky pete, the distillation of canned heat. We got to know him about a month after he came home and learned his wife had killed herself. He said the most terrible thing about it was the way his mother, whom he despised, had let him know about it. First a telegram to New Guinea, saying the wife was ill. Next, a telegram to Hawaii that the wife was gravely ill. Finally, in San Francisco, a letter explaining that his wife had died peacefully in her sleep. Axel said what had happened was that his wife had turned the gas on in an oven into which she had inserted her head when she learned he was coming home. He was, like me, an AWOL.

Every few days E.J. or I would stand on a street corner at Pico and West Boulevard — popularly known as the "slave market" — and wait for shyster employers to come by and pick us up in their trucks for a day's work in the gravel pits in Eagle Rock or knocking down walnuts in Van Nuys, at cut-rate wages. In the middle of the second month we attended a wedding of an old whore and a crip on the abandoned stage of a Main Street theater closed for repairs. Half the Row showed up. The ceremony was conducted by a lanky preacher who also was an ex-G.I., a former Marine chaplain gone apeshit. We were sitting, more or less peaceably, in the frontish rows of the darkened theater when the cops broke in, pouring in from all exits. Adolph with his paratrooper's instincts got us out by diving through a small doorway in the orchestra pit.

We were almost caught because Axel was slow to catch up with us; by this time he was walking around in a perpetual fog. When we saw that Axel could not lift his leg more than a foot off the ground, we decided to deposit him at the Veterans' Hospital in West Los Angeles. That was about when we all split up. Adolph went up north, and after the Indian Bird and I had an argument he went and joined a rodeo in Riverside and then returned to Oklahoma.

Two years later, by coincidence, Adolph and Axel and I found ourselves at the same university. We were friendly with each other but sometimes months would go by before we would get around to visiting with one another, and then it was hardly what you would call a reunion. It wasn't exactly that we were ashamed of our days on the Row, but it was simply, I think, a function of our recognition that it hadn't been part of life, that life, for a month or so, for us, had stopped back then. Axel had married again. Just before we met again at college, he picked up a girl in Exhibition Park and married her, his second marriage and her third. She was, then, seventeen, having run away to marry a sailor, and then a soldier. Afterwards, with us, Marie would laugh about her Victory-girl days.

I liked Marie enormously. The half literate, shrewd, tough and foul-mouthed daughter of a back-country Alabama dirt farmer, she had gotten out the only way she knew, by learning to use her considerable charms somewhat prematurely. I also thought she was beautiful, in a full-hipped, round-faced freckled way. So did Axel. He adored her. But he was also a little afraid of her. He knew she had saved him from a breakdown and worse, and that she was twice the woman of any we knew. But he was repelled by her lack of education. I don't think it was a question of contempt. It was that he feared from this gap might arise a whole spectrum of complications in their relationship. When Axel was promoted to an instructorship in his department, he took Marie to her first faculty tea, and in the middle of what I suppose must have been a tiresome conversation, Marie suddenly blurted to a professor's wife, "Aw, for criminy sakes, fuck off will you!" Needless to add, Axel took Marie to no more faculty teas. That was the big problem in their marriage. Not so much that Marie didn't understand Axel's work, which she didn't. But that, sensing what her own ceiling was, she determined very early on never, not even for Axel, to pretend to an erudition which would never come naturally for her. Marie, pre-eminently, was the Natural Woman. When Axel's mother, whom he hated and feared, came for the first of her marital inspection trips, she pecked so mercilessly at Marie for two weeks that Marie, bearing it no longer, took her out for a long drive in the country and, parking in an orange grove, gave the mother a terrific, and no doubt vulgar tongue-lashing, concluding by saying that if the mother argued back she, Marie, would open the door and make the mother walk back to town. The mother did argue back and Marie did push her out, and the mother did have to make her own way back.

I tapped on the radio in the De Soto, sitting back, and the news out of Hungary was the same. A new government waiting to find out if the Russians found them acceptable. I turned off the radio, and got out of the car and went around back of the house. Axel and Marie were playing with the three kids. Axel started for a moment; he hated surprises ever since the war. Then he gave that characteristic duck of his blond oversized head and said, "Well look who's here."

"Hello stranger," said Marie and came over and kissed me. "Sorry I can't kiss you," said Axel, "I haven't gone that way yet." "Give yourself time," said Marie. The kids went on playing. Only one, the oldest, Corny, seven, remembered me anyway. Marie said for us to sit out in the yard and she would bring the drinks. I was still feeling pretty awful, though I didn't show it, and didn't tell them. But I knew that in a few moments it was going to feel just perfect being there.

As I sat there, in the tree-shaded yard, listening to Axel talk and Marie make cracks, I thought of how unfair it was that I could listen with only half an ear, the rest of me attuned to fears and internal musics. If only they knew! And I suppose I wanted them to guess. But they didn't. No, I would not receive great help here, only a night's refuge. So . . . all right.

Axel was telling me that he was now an assistant professor of sociology. He grew quite cheerless describing his work, and also malign. Marie came over and sat in his lap. Corny called over and said it was undignified. Marie said, "Go fry a fish, Corny." Corny came over to have his head rubbed, and then I had to rub the heads of the two smaller ones, a boy four and a girl five. I asked Marie how she was, and she said she'd just had a hysterectomy, now for the first time she could, in her words, just lie back and enjoy it. I didn't guess Axel was taking her to too many interdepartmental teas.

That afternoon, we just sat around, drinking gin, and being with one another in no particular way. I was glad they had missed me. They asked me all the gossip from Hollywood and I told them. Marie kept saying I was making it all up, but I swore that was how I had actually lived these past few years. Corny wanted to know if I had met Jimmy Dean, and I said yes, once in a director's office.

When it was time for dinner Marie went inside, and just before she went she said, "There's someone inside I think you'd like to meet." Axel gave me a curious look. I knew it would be a girl. I prayed to God she would not be attractive.

After Marie went, Axel clammed up a little. We used to be able to talk, but now in the form of grumbling and musing he was avoiding me. I didn't know why. I wondered if it had to do with the someone they wanted me to meet inside and decided it didn't. I am used to my friends having this reaction. They are living settled lives and I come in off the road and they get nervous.

Axel and I went into the living room and started in drinking again. Although it was an old and somewhat rickety house, someone had furnished it with style, and inexpensively. Everything seemed to fit. It was one of the few American homes I'd been into where most of the furniture was low Swedish *manqué* without making you feel you were in a midget's house. I doubted if Marie had done the furnishing: it was not one of her talents. As if reading my thoughts, Axel remarked that their friend, Gerda, who was staying with them, had, while she had been married to one of Axel's friends, a professor colleague, done up the house when they first moved to Iowa. Gerda hadn't shown up yet and I told myself several times no matter *what* she looked like I was going to be on my best and aloof manners.

Marie came in and we all sat around drinking. The two of them seemed to recede into some sort of distance as we talked, about the university here, and personal things, and politics. Axel had made himself a real American home, at God alone knew what expense, and

I was feeling as though I were in a foreign country. It was the way I had been feeling all year, whenever I looked in *Life* Magazine or heard television or stared at the billboards. It just wasn't my country any more. Even here, with Axel and Marie, in these relatively conservative surroundings, I was sensible only to how rapaciously, lifelessly "modern" everything had become. The strange thing was, I didn't feel out of it as a radical but as something very like its opposite. More than anything else, *Life* Magazine and TV and billboards and everyone I knew mortgaging his soul to a car-port house, was making me feel I was not the son of immigrants but an eighth-generation American, that I was sitting in a hard-constructed rocking chair on the porch of my house somewhere in Vermont and feeling terribly *old* American, as though I were some obscure but stern-souled Van Rensselaer or Cabot or Stevenson. When I had first started out from Los Angeles I had felt less of this; I mean, I didn't like what I saw and kept thinking how much better and more human, now and in the future, things could be, given a different style of life. The dissent was contemporary, if you want to put it that way. But as I kept going in the De Soto I think I slipped back into the past. I began, without being aware of it, to compare what I was passing through with what *had been.* I didn't any longer feel outvoted. I felt left behind. Let me tell you, it is quite a jolt to realize that, at twenty-nine, you are *crotchety.*

When supper was ready we had it in the kitchen, which was when their friend Gerda came in. She was a very good-looking woman, a little younger than I, almost as tall, broad-shouldered, with one of those dark ovaloid Jewish faces that always break my heart. I knew Axel and Marie were watching me, so I was just one inch extra charming to Gerda. Had I not been they would have thought I was planning something, which I damn well was but wasn't going to do anything about. Gerda was an amateur painter, it turned out as the evening went along, an amateur dancer, and was living in Axel's and Marie's house with her five-year-old daughter by the broken marriage. The little girl came down later and was a real problem case, hostile to everyone not excluding Gerda. Gerda was currently attending a "creative writing" workshop at the university. Later in the evening she admitted to wanting to be a writer, was afraid she had no talent and asked my advice about breaking into television. She had gone into psychoanalysis shortly before her divorce. Around the suppertable it turned out that Axel was going to a psychoanalyst also, but it was all right. He just shrugged and made a lot of obscene jokes about it. I think it would just about have killed me for Axel to be in psychoanalysis solemnly.

We talked for a long time into the night. Axel said the situation at his university was causing him to think of leaving. He, too, asked my advice about how to break into television. He said, *break into the Establishment,* and that he was three quarters inclined to try it. He loved teaching, he said, but he had lost faith in most methods and practically all of the goals. He quoted a lot of statistics at me to prove the reactionary character of the American working class and how fundamentally natural to the American personality and political system was McCarthyism. He aggressively felt that intellectuals no longer had a role to play. I told him I was a little discouraged to hear him talking like that, and he suddenly became very angry and said, "You'd lose that goddam holier-than-thou attitude if you had to stand up six times a week in front of a sea of irretrievably ignorant Iowa faces." I said yes, I probably would. But that no matter what, intellectuals would always have a role to play, and that one of their roles, if they had to, was to stand anywhere, but *stand* and shout bloody murder, and then I became hot under the collar and said that the second job was not to break into any kind of Establishment and that it smelled no nicer to me that he should want to break into the smelliest one of them all, that I didn't see any particular virtue in that. "Balls," he said, and I admit he was a little drunk by this time, "the only thing to do is make money." For about thirty minutes straight he talked of nothing but making money; Axel was ferocious about it. He got up and pointed a finger at me and shouted, "Facts and figures, you sainted sonofabitch, give me facts and figures about your damn progressive working class. Give me facts and figures just to hope on." He ran over to his bookcase and threw some heavy books on me. "Those," he cried, "they're studies of voting patterns. Facts and figures, my ass, facts and figures my ass. Those well-fed bastards will vote us into fascism yet, wait and see if they don't." After a while he calmed down, and then, the way he used to do it, sobered up on the spot and said, "It's just that I can't stand your goddam innocence." Marie said something about my not being innocent, and Axel turned fiercely on her and told her to go and boil some coffee. "And not interfere with men-talk, huh? Intellectual!" said Marie, and stalked off into the kitchen. Axel stared at me, and said, "Political libido has got to go some placc, kid."

Gerda sat in a dark corner and watched us. There was a terrific current of electricity running between us; I was practically floating across the room to her. The terrible thing for me was that she was *waiting*, in a kind of passive, misery-approaching way. I have seen this in women before. They like you, and they sense you are used to having your own way with them, and they attain a facial expression as though they were going beneath the waves for the third time, and that they are at your mercy. It always seems a little *premature*. No sooner do I look at a woman I like than she gets an expression on her face which has seemed to go through forty years of *relationship* and is already accusing me of things more in sorrow than anger. That was the way Gerda looked now. What she didn't know was that, no matter what, I was absolutely determined not to do anything. I wasn't even sure why. I just had a feeling that if I messed around on this trip it would be the wrong thing to do. I really wanted, while I was on the road, to look at America and try to figure out why it wasn't my country any more. If I used the highway the way I used Sunset Strip there would be no point.

About eight in the evening, after supper. Axel said some of the other academics were dropping by. Once a week, he said, a very few of the other people employed by the university dropped in at one another's houses for a bull session. They were, he said, the "good" people at the university. When the bell rang he went to the door. At the door he turned to me and said, with a sudden angry irony, "Hungary, facts and figures, that's what I like." I didn't do it, I said. "The hell you didn't," he retorted.

The house filled up in the next hour with four instructors or associate professors, who were male, and an English department research worker who was a woman. They sat around, in Marie's low chairs or on the floor, and started to talk. It was all strangely formal. The talk was slow, studious, relaxed, but you had the impression that they did not talk like this one minute before they rang the bell of Axel's house, nor would they talk like it after they left. One of the young men sitting on the floor — a tall, lean handsome man smoking professorially on a pipe — was Gerda's husband. Gerda was in the room, and she cast furtive glances his way which he answered with modest, reassuring smiles. She was very nervous at having him around but he seemed to take a sort of pleasure from it. She had terrific legs. Her husband saw me looking at her and grinned over at me. I cannot say I liked him. When your wife is so obviously miserable in your presence you ought to at least salute her by wiping that patronizing grin off your face. He looked like a kind of Dorian Gray of the campus to me, the appearance of a boy of twenty-one when Axel told me he was in his early forties.

Axel slipped into a mild and good-humored mood, and said I was going to deliver a short report on the state of the Union. We all laughed, and then I did. I told them, roughly, what I had seen, wishing only that I could be honest enough to explain that my angle of vision had been somewhat foreshortened by circumstances not entirely under my control. I told them I had been traveling across a morally apathetic country determined to indulge in no experiments and bent on a personalized, not to say privatized existence. The passion for trivia had overleapt itself; a considerable amount of colloquial conversation, sometimes the bulk of it, was connected with last night's television show. The unions were depoliticalized. America, I thought, for the first time in my experience appeared to be going "mass." Several of those present demurred. Axel said nothing. Gerda's husband said, smiling, "Maybe we'd better have some definition of terms around here." He really was a patronizing bastard. Okay, I said, aiming between the eyes.

Here is what I mean. A mass society is where the top dogs and the bottom dogs, I beg your pardon, "the people," subscribe to the same bottom-dog (or possibly middle-dog) values. But above all, the same ones. Where the top dogs have lost the capacity for independent leadership, and the bottom dogs, I beg your pardon, "the people," have lost the capacity to do anything more than riot, metaphorically and eventually maybe not so metaphorically. No conversation exists between the two through tongues; that is, I said, in what your language is called "intermediate institutions."

In the puremass society, I said, which thank Christ exists nowhere on this earth, nor could it I think, it being a law of social physics (I hope) that the human, individual spirit is not *that* malleable — in the puremass society, no cushioning composed of intermediate institutions, such as trade unions, women's organizations, etc., exists to insulate top from bottom dogs. They communicate directly, again, I suppose ideally, through television. Each becomes much *too* available to the other. The top dogs become too easily frightened, and the bottom dogs too easily set in motion. In such a society, the individual is characterized by easy stimulation by far-off events and also apathy about these events. He swings back and forth between energy and apathy but above all lives surrounded by a sense of unreality.

The languages instructor cut in. He was skeptical but interested, you could see. "My friend," he said, "you're defining us right into hell. But look around you, here or anywhere else: we're not exactly what you call an unorganized people. Decidedly not."

The woman English researcher said, "My God, we're strangling on organizations."

But are we? I said. Look again. Just how significant, or invigorating, is this group life? Not very damn much, is my answer. As far as I can see, mass-ification is happening, and fast. And the interesting thing, I said, is that it is happening to the Great Middle Class, you all, more, and faster, than to the workers. The fact is, I think it perfectly possible that the middle class will become "massified" before the working class. That it should thus fall victim to its own instruments of manipulation is an irony which I do not personally regard as very sweet, but because, so help me, I was trying to deliver an objective report I did not say this.

I could see Axel looking at me as though to say, I get off here, Buster, you're romanticizing the workers *again*. So, in response to no particular question, I put it to them: Next time, I said, a big steel or auto or meat strike occurs, think. Is there any institution to which the middle class owes loyalty in the same way a wage worker owes loyalty to his union? The company? Don't make me laugh. The whole idea, as I have learned it, is that you *ought* to move on if the money is better. To the church? Cut it out. To his community, the suburb? *Look around you.*

They sat silent as dormice. So did I. I wasn't even sure I agreed with my own theory. If it was correct, we were in a hell of a shape. If it was wrong, I didn't know what to think.

"Meanwhile, back at the ranch," said Axel. Snickering.

Meanwhile, I said, back at the ranch, generally speaking, things were prosperous; people were living better than ever and were in hock up to the eyeballs. Passion was out; littleness was in. The preoccupation was to cultivate one's garden, metaphorically and literally. But nobody was happy. When I finished, Gerda's husband took the pipe out of his mouth long enough to say, "That's about the picture here." And was immediately greeted with scorn by the others, who declared I was generalizing. We got into politics straight off. They were all, they said, voting for Stevenson, except the woman English researcher, a Christian pacifist who wasn't voting at all and who, in fact, was not going to pay her taxes this year. She sounded not at all brave when she said it.

I asked them if they thought there was any hope for the Left in America, and they replied, definitely and emphatically, not a hope. "The question," said a small barrel-chested teacher of political science, was, "Is there any hope for decency in America?" I said that I myself took the view, that there was a substratum of hard-rock conservatism that would always resist the final encroachments of indecency. Axel said, "It will come in through the back door of mindlessness. In the end, Justice Douglas, Edmund Wilson and Joe McCarthy will find themselves on the same couch watching I Love Lucy."

Whatever their views, and they all differed, they agreed that the culminating victory of the ruling class, power elite, Establishment or The Right, call it what you will, was in the process of achievement through the "mass media." "Against Fascists I would be brave unto death," said the instructor of Romance languages, "but I admit I am a coward in the face of television." They all laughed but you could see they agreed. As it also turned out, with the exception of the mousy little English researcher, they began avidly discussing "how to break into the Establishment," one way or another. There was a lot of loud and almost surly talk of making money.

I asked them what the dominant atmosphere on the campus was. Impotence, shouted the languages instructor. Withdrawal, said Axel. Confusion, said Gerda's husband. Gerda, I suspect more to say something than any other reason, declared, "How can you be so pessimistic, you're practically burying America in its grave; surely, you're generalizing." They all looked at Gerda as though each, in his own turn, had heard her own rosier version of events before. "Gerda," remarked her husband, "don't be an hysterical optimist." Ice settled over the room for a moment until Marie broke it by saying, "That's one hell of a lot better than being hysterical pessimists. Look at you guys, moaning in your juice, good jobs, money for clothes and kids, and you talk like it's the end of the world. You've still got students, haven't you?" Axel protested mildly, "Honey, have you seen those corn-fed faces?" Marie became angry: "I *am* one of those corn-fed faces." Axel blew a kiss over at her and said, "Not any more you ain't. Quit being such a snob." I thought Gerda looked at Axel and Marie enviously. You couldn't see her and her husband doing that sort of thing without a cutting edge. Suddenly I felt a wave of sadness for that big, fine-legged girl curled up in a dark corner of the room who was always trying to see the bright side of things. She was a born victim. But I pulled myself up short. The closer I grew to people on this trip the easier it would be to *victimize* them. Yet, I confess some slight disappointment when I realized she no longer had eyes for me but had them focused plaintively on her former husband. I was far out.

We talked on into the night. These teachers had lived together in the desert and they showed the signs. While decrying the trend among their colleagues towards loss of essential faith in the efforts of reason, towards anti-intellectualism, and emphasis on technique, almost automatically they found themselves, in the talk, sharing in our national repast of blandness. After bitterly criticizing the Democratic Party they stoutly and vehemently insisted they would vote for Stevenson. When I pointed out that the logic of their own arguments, particularly in the field of foreign affairs, was such as to suggest nonparticipation in electoral affairs, or even a vote for Eisenhower, they balked. In some obscure way voting for Stevenson was an act of faith. I had run across this thing, this abdication of thought to prayer, among critical liberals all over the country, as with Communists who yet refused to leave the party, despite all. The fascinating thing about the people in this room was that, although like Axel they had at their fingertips the drawn conclusions of voting studies and demographic tabulations — and were far more recondite on these points than I — none of them had read Stevenson's speeches. When I pointed out that what Stevenson had to say was mealymouthed and disingenuous in the extreme, even cowardly on some issues, they were unimpressed. The languages instructor said, approvingly, "The man's got an election to win, a party to keep together." The others murmured assent, and already I could see them thinking I was some sort of political vegetarian.

I put to them the question I had been asking all across the country, especially to intellectuals: if, as you say, you more or less accept C. Wright Mills's definition of a well-knit, irresponsible power elite moving us inexorably, if not always consciously, towards some sort of national disaster, do you not *therefore* see any necessity at all for making a clean break with this drift and, if necessary, laying down your jobs, your reputations and if need be your physical freedom? The next hour we spent picking holes in this formulation, and I winced. I knew where I had really last heard the echoes of this kind of moral dilatoriness. In Germany, just after the war, when the good burghers acknowledged the democratic argument by agreeing with the assumptions and the conclusions but were, literally and physically, incapable of drawing a line of action between the two. A failure of moral imagination. Finally, I asked them all if indeed they thought the stakes were absolute. Thirty minutes of conversation, and with varying degrees of reluctance all agreed except surprisingly, the timid little English researcher who said I was exaggerating the danger to the country. Something in our arguments had sent her off into a mood resembling a mousy patriotic binge. She felt, she said, that it was necessary not to show weakness to the Soviet Union. On the other hand, the men in the room were almost suspiciously eager, suddenly, to acknowledge the danger, from ourselves, to our institutions. Within the space of minutes they became Jeremiahs. I was finding it hard to keep up with their arguments which I soon saw were not heading us into logic but nihilism. Soon we would be discussing the best means for three of the five men to break into advertising or television, including Axel. The barrel-chested political science teacher declared, "We can go only as far and as fast as the uncommitted, and the merely liberal, will let us." I said if we held back for fear of alienating the liberals and the unaroused (they jeered at the use of this word and Axel said I was becoming a fanatic. Was I?) we would merely be helping preserve the illusion that the crisis was partial and could be met by partial measures. Precisely the point, said the languages instructor. I had insufficient knowledge of the American soul. The crisis, he said, was wholesale but the measures which would defeat it were partial. As in the McCarthy example. We scrambled about that. I said that McCarthy had won, that he and what he stood for had left a savage and enduring scar on America. Nonsense, said the anthropology professor, a seamed and aging grayhead, it was a fever which had passed. It was the turn of the others now to jeer at him.

The English researcher (she was, Axel said, writing a book about the affair between Dickens and Ellen Turner) said crisply, "But look at the facts instead of always listening to what you want to hear. The workers are well fed and well housed, our middle class is anything but disgruntled. McCarthy is dead and we're still able to gather here in Axel's house to say what we want. We won't go to war because we know the Russians can do us as much or more damage than we them. Europe is bound to go Left sooner or later, pulling us with them, and Russia is bound to democratize itself as standards of living rise. All we need do is sit tight and wait for partial measures. I'm frightened when anyone speaks of *un*partial measures, I really am."

Axel spoke up and said, "One, you're positing a permanently stable economy from what we have today; two, that we haven't been frightened by McCarthy into talking about the wrong issues; three, that everyone in SAC and the Red Army High Command is Marxist; and four, that the Pentagon won't become frightened when more and more revolutions break out in Asia and Africa — I can't accept any of those assumptions."

"Axel," said Gerda's husband, "every time some pipsqueak Burmese revolutionary makes a speech it scares hell out of me; our people just don't know how to deal with that sort of thing. You've heard the kids at school here; they think the way to adjust to social revolution is to drown it in Point Four dollars or drop the bomb on the Kremlin."

Then, suddenly, somehow, we found ourselves back to Mc-

Carthyism and the question of moral courage. Only we were talking about it in very personal terms. Or rather they were. Three of them had been teaching at the height of the scare and two had been graduate students. In a flash, they were squabbling over who had put on the least timid performance. The conversation was quite ugly. Each felt that he had to make a judgment of his own personal stand at the time. I thought they were using the adolescent ethic of the movie Western sheriff. I suddenly longed for Southern California where my few friends and I never had to indulge in this kind of thing, never had to prove our bravery in the face of what was, let us face it, a rather weak kind of fire when compared to what politicals of other countries have had to endure. I thought of Southern California in Axel's living room, but everything I had done or felt there seemed curiously unreal, as though it had happened to someone else. I could remember everything in California, but I couldn't *feel* it. Too many freeways, too much sun, too much abnormality taken normally, too many pink stucco houses and pink stucco consciences and pink stucco relationships. That was when I got into a frightful panic. The bottom dropped right out of my stomach with a straining, hoarse fear. Because it was just then, with the full force of my mind stimulated by the talk in the room, that I realized I was wrong, I was not leaving something. I was not leaving anything at all. I was leaving something which I could remember in distinct detail but not feel. I was leaving nothing. I almost fell off my chair in fright. I think the only one who noticed was Gerda. She looked as though she were going to say something. I tried very hard to focus on the conversation because all the teachers were trying to tell me something, it was about how the university was run. They were telling me how disgusted they were, teaching a quiescent student body. They were telling me how frustrated by the committee system and psuedo democracy they were.

It appeared that this particular university was governed by a president who insisted on democracy and harmony at the same time. Harmony, they told me, with the president. Bureaucratization of the faculty, they said, left an active teacher with very little leisure.

They sounded as though they hated their colleagues, their president and their students. Especially the students. To a man they said they refused, on principle, to involve themselves with the personal lives of the students. I remonstrated, naïvely as it turned out. You don't understand, I was told. Counseling is the curse of the academic. It means nothing to the student, who is so befuddled by quibbling and useless ricochetings from "required" to "choice" courses that he is more disoriented at the end of his four years than before. Counseling is the way the president—whom they all loathed as a turncoat scholar—humbles and shackles the gifted academics. Above all, they unanimously hated the "survey" courses, on a par with which they placed television for creating the condition of "facelessness."

I got up and excused myself and walked swiftly upstairs to the small attic bedroom which Marie had prepared for me. I lay down and sweated like a hog. I used all my strength to fight down the waves of nausea. Marie first came up and asked if anything was wrong, and I said, No, just a little tired, I'll be right down. Then Axel came up, very angry, and said, "Jesus, man, I brought those jokers over for you. The least you can do." Five minutes after he left, Gerda came in with a cup of hot tea. I couldn't help wondering whether she wasn't doing this to give her husband a fist in the eye, and decided it was uncharitable. She said the people downstairs were pretty miffed; I had walked out at the point where it looked as though I were disgusted with them. But how could I tell them? Any of them?

Gerda stood in a corner of the room, hunched against the low wooden rafters and said, "They are all troubled men." You mean, I said, men without alternatives. Spleen or adjustment. Yes, she said. She looked at me steadily and, for the first time I had the feeling, without searching; without flirting. As though she recognized something in me. Looking back on it I think that Gerda was probably the only person all across the country who knew I was ill. Including myself. I swear, the dark smile she gave me was almost *comradely*. Well, for one reason and another I wasn't feeling very comradely. But if she wanted to get in beside me and tell me everything was all right, that was just fine with me. Then Gerda did the goddamndest thing. She came over and kissed me on the *forehead*. After she went downstairs I got up and went down too.

Everyone was gone, including Gerda and Marie. Axel was waiting for me. He said, "You didn't have to show it that openly. They hate themselves more than you could." I don't hate them, I said. He sat morosely in one of Marie's deep canvas chairs and fondled his drink. "An ugly evening," he said. "A really ugly evening." I'm sorry, I said, and I was on the point of explaining it all to him. But all. Only, Axel was too involved with something that had happened this evening. He said something curious. "We haven't settled down yet." Settled down to what, Axel?

"The war," he said. "The long war of attrition between the embattled few and the mob at the mercy of the deafening system of communications. We're still licking our wounds. In a year or two, it will be straight trench warfare. None of this 'I refused to be a stoolpigeon, I stood up for academic freedom, I did this, I did that in the bad old days of McCarthy.' The real test will be in the trench warfare. No villains, no heroes. Only history to judge. Our enemy: mass communications, mobocracy."

I couldn't tell whether Axel was drunk or just morbid. He could get pretty drunk on his morbidity. He jerked his head up. "You sonofabitch," he said, "you don't know a goddam thing, you product of nineteenth century rationalism." He pointed a finger at me. "You know why kids go to college?" he demanded. Sure, I said. To get a degree to make money. He looked nonplussed. "Awright," he said, "so you know that. But one thing I *know* you don't know. By 1970 there'll be a seven million university population. Seven million." I said, Axel, democratic education. He said, "Fuck, mass education. It's all around us." What is? I said. "Homogenization," he said. I went into the kitchen and poured myself a drink and came back.

Axel and I sat up until about three in the morning, dozing off and talking, dozing off and talking. Axel kept muttering about homogenization. He said it meant that the values of the market place were becoming those of the university. He said it was now a sin for a professor to be different from anyone else, that it was undemocratic. He said he was going back to England, where there was no fucking pretense, where there was still an upper class to preserve certain fucking cultural values. I said, Axel, for Christ's sake, you're talking like a fool. "Oh yeah," he yelled, "well I was in *love* when I was in England." His mouth opened like a fish. He said, "Now *there* was a .45-caliber Freudian slip. I'm terrible about them." He got up and peeked into the kitchen. "Where's Marie?" I said, I think she's gone to bed. "Thank God," he said. "Man," he said, "when I make those slips and Marie is around I sweat. She doesn't know Freud from Liberace but she can read those goddam slips like they were recipes out of *Ladies' Home Journal*."

This psychoanalysis doing you any good, Axel? I asked. "No," he said, "but it's doing the psychoanalyst a lot of good." We laughed. I was relieved and glad he hadn't said "my" psychoanalyst; that's when they lose their sense of humor. I sat Axel down and urged him to keep reading the journals of the Left, and he came awake and cross-questioned me briskly, now all the social scientist. He quoted a flock of statistics at me, again, to prove the apathetic character of the working class. He said bluntly, repeating himself, that after giving it a great deal of thought he had concluded that not only the methods were wrong but also the goals. They were obsolete goals. Socialism, he said, is twentieth century Victorianism. He said though he and a few others subscribed to Left periodicals they felt that these periodicals were "behind the times." Then his attention wandered. He was thinking of something else. He got up and went upstairs and when he came down he showed me a format for a new television quiz show he said he and Marie had worked up. He asked me what I thought of it. I told him that no matter what I thought of it, and I preferred not to read it, I would see that it was pushed in New York. Then for about an hour he asked me questions about getting into television. "I hate teaching," he said. "I want to break into something else. Make money." I told him we'd talk about it in the morning. Satisfied, he sat back and relaxed and asked how Adolph was. It surprised me he hadn't heard for a few years. I said Adolph was doing all right now, he was a lawyer, except that his marriage was going badly. "Good," Axel said vehemently, "I always did hate that bitch." Axel, I said. "Axel nothing," he said. "Boy, if you want a goddam symbol of American womanhood, it's Adolph's wife. That's what I'm doing next," he said. "An investigation of the relationship between sexual activity and politics." I couldn't help it. I said, For Christ's sake, Axel! He jumped up and waved his arms around. "That's what I mean," he shouted, "twentieth century Victorianism. Do you know anything about it? Have you thought about it? Do you know what you're talking about?"

And so, of course, I had to get angry. I shouted back, that what I objected to was the way he was fitting into the whole trend, even though this or that particular piece of work might be valid. "Valid! Valid! Don't you use that word on me, you sonofabitch. I spent five years in graduate study so I could earn that word!" Just then Marie, in her bed clothes, appeared, and said, "Axel, you'll wake up the kids."

Axel pointed a finger at her, swaying drunkenly. "American goddam women, if you don't think they're the dotted lines on the goddam political graph you are so far out I can't even talk to you. It's a war to the finish. Thurber was a goddam prophet not a cartoonist. Take our money, our balls, our heritage. Waiting there in a corner for us to jump at you and then you eat us up.

"That's why," he shouted, "that's why I was smart enough to beat the system." "How did you beat the system, dear?" asked Marie with the deceptive sweetness she can put on just before she breaks a brick over your head. Axel went over and stuck his hands on her shoulders. He said, simpering exaggeratedly, "By marrying a barefoot Alabama gal who still got the cotton in her ears." Marie just looked at him grimly, then grabbed his hand and said, "C'mon to bed, drunk." Axel went without a backward glance. I went back into the living room and shut off all the lights except one and sat there and sipped Axel's liquor. I wondered if Axel hated teaching as much as he had said. I hoped not. His one book, about the mapping of social change in the region of the Tennessee Valley Authority, was a pioneer effort. And now — sex and politics. I don't know. Maybe he was on to something real. Maybe I *was* old-fashioned.

I tried to remember what the teachers had said in this room. Three words kept coming back. Impotence, confusion, withdrawal. Controversy is out, committee is in. I was beginning to feel sleepy. Also less bad. I wished I could stay at Axel's to rest up and figure out where I was going next. But I knew if I did stay I would start spieling like a madman. And I had the feeling that if I stayed it wouldn't go down well in this house right now, and that maybe Axel would kick me out. No, I would go tomorrow. I went over and snapped on the living-room radio. I had to fiddle around for about fifteen minutes, and then a news announcement said the Hungarians had taken up positions on the bridge approaches to Budapest and that Soviet intentions were not known. I didn't know, as I turned the radio off. Maybe Axel was right, to investigate sex and politics. I desperately fiddled again with the radio to find the news. Maybe something good was happening in the world, somewhere. Something which I could rush up to Axel with and say, no, *roar*, Get off your goddam ass with sex and politics and go back to why you were *born*. Axel, Axel would quietly sneer, And just exactly what would that be? And I would say, The common ownership of the means of production, distribution and exchange, *that's* why you were born.

The only thing I could catch on the radio was a short announcement that the Israeli army had entered the Sinai peninsula. Jesus, I didn't know *anything* any more. What a hell of a place to hear a thing like that. Cedar City, Iowa. I went over to the phone and asked for long distance, I wanted to make an emergency call to St. Louis, Missouri. I gave the operator the number. It finally answered and Kevin-John Sullivan came on, sleepily. Kevin-John, I shouted, this is me! "Yeah, yeah," he said, just as though he knew I would be calling. Kevin-John, I said, have you been listening to the radio. "As a matter of fact," he said coldly, "I have." That stopped me. The idea of Kevin listening to the radio just when I was shook me up. Kevin-John, I said, I'm coming to St. Louis. "Okay," he said. I said a few more words, and so did he, and I hung up.

I sat there in Axel's living room for a long time, I suppose. And I thought of Gerda upstairs. I didn't want to marry Gerda. But how can you marry the *world?* I wanted to marry it — *it* just didn't want to marry *me*.

I went into the kitchen and washed up for Marie because I knew it would please her. Then I shut off all the lights and started climbing the wooden stairs up to the attic. But from the living room I could see that the light was showing in the chink under Gerda's door which I had to pass. It was like a situation in a young man's novel. I sat down on those stairs and pondered for about five full minutes. Then I got up and went past Gerda's door and on up to my room. I closed the door, took off my clothes and lay down on the narrow camp cot they had fixed up for me. I had an erection so big I thought it would pick me up and throw me out the window. But it went away, and so did I, into sleep, finally.

As soon as Axel came upstairs in the morning with a cup of coffee to wake me I knew that we had not made contact in the night. He was breezy and friendly and you could see he had figured out how to deal with me, like an affectionate but eccentric friend, a Chekhov figure. Inwardly, I shrugged. What the hell was the use? Around the breakfast table everything was all right. Gerda was sleeping late. Axel and I went off to the university which is built right into the various hillocks of the small town. He spent all his time describing the various intra- and inter-departmental intrigues. He said the worst thing about it all was the anti-Semitism. I raised my eyebrows, and he said, "Don't argue with me, I know this thing when I see it." It had taken him a while to recognize it, just as long as it took them to figure out he was a Jew. Axel's name, Kane, is not Jewish and he is built like a half-back for Upsala University, rugged and blond. He said they let him know about it in all sorts of little ways.

We sat in his office and talked. Once again he began to talk ferociously of making money. A couple of times colleagues came into his office and Axel became nervous, I could see, about having me there. When it was time for him to go off for a class, I went back to the house where Marie was avidly flirting with one of Axel's graduate students, a bespectacled youth with whom I quarreled on the spot. When he said that freedom meant the right to go into any bar of his choosing I almost hit him. After he left, Marie and I gossiped, then I told her that I would have to be going. She asked why, and I said I don't know why now any more than the last time I had seen her and Axel, which had been after I brought Joan to their house near Chavez Ravine after our fiasco in the mountains.

Marie said something strange. She said, shaking her head bitterly, the way I lived just wasn't "proper." I laughed a little, and so did she. She helped me pack my bags. I asked where Gerda was, and she said Gerda had decided to go off and have a conference with her husband. Marie called it her "weekly masochism." Marie and I did not discuss Gerda. Instead, she asked if Axel and I had had a fight. I said that Axel and I always fought, but she said she meant a serious one. I said I thought not. But I sensed that perhaps she was right; that in some way Axel and I had had a real quarrel, without meaning to. Later, when I was living in England, Axel came through London, knowing my address, and made no effort to get in touch. It still rankles.

Marie helped me put the bags in the De Soto. It was a fine, brisk sunny day. I got into the car and she came and leaned her elbows on the window frame. "You know what?" she said. No, what? I asked. "Next time," she said, "stick around longer." I'll try, I said. "Another thing," she said. "I'm taking three night classes a week. In the Humanities. And you want to know a third thing? Axel is damn proud of me." Honey, I said, Axel was proud of you the first day he met you. Then I remembered that Axel had picked her up on a bench in Exhibition Park; she saw I remembered, and we both smiled. "You can say that again," Marie said militantly. She kissed me on the cheek and I drove down the shady street, watching Marie go back into the big ramshackle house in my rear-view mirror.

Axel met me at the university, on the steps. We stood around the De Soto and chewed the fat a while. We didn't have much to say to each other. Mechanically, he asked me where I was going, and I said I didn't know but would write. A lot of girls were included in the student crowds that kept passing in front of us. Axel's eyes were glued to the girls. He saw me noticing. "That's my Official Problem this week," he said. He laughed but I could see he didn't mean the laugh but did mean the remark. I got into the car. Axel came and leaned on the window. "Damn pretty, these corn-fed bitches, aren't they?" I agreed. "How'd you like to teach them?" he said. "Staring down at those round little heads and those farm-girl bosoms, all day long, six days a week. A man gets hungry." This was making me feel uncomfortable. I tried some sex banter with him but Axel was looking fierce. "I'd like to do some of them," he whispered, "I'd like to do some of them." Sure, I said. So would I. He stood up and looked at me. "Don't you patronize me," he said. Hey, Axel, take it easy, I said. His clean square blond face broke into a sudden, easy grin and he said, "Have a good trip. Let me know where you are." My heart sank. It was a hell of a way to say goodbye. I backed out. Halfway out in the street I noticed a parking summons stuck beneath my windshield. I let it alone, swerved into traffic and headed out of town. I felt pretty sad, all things considered.

I headed southeast, towards Burlington, doing eighty, which is speedy on those narrow, banked Iowa roads. I wanted to get to the Mississippi River. Ever since I learned how to drive, if I had to go north-south or south-north anywhere in the middle of the country I always liked to do it following the Mississippi, which has almost as many faces as it has bends between New Orleans and Cairo. I hit Burlington by late afternoon, stopping for lunch, and then struck out on a bunch of side and auxiliary roads all through the country of the Mississippi, which was just then beginning to turn a thick, muddy yellow-brown. I knew it took longer, moving off and on, jumping in and out of those tortuous side roads, but I liked to keep the river and its country in sight. The river is about the friendliest thing I know between the city of New York and the Continental Divide. I just like to *contemplate* it. I didn't feel a special kinship, or pass the time of day with Mark Twain, or anything like that. But just the sight, or the knowledge of the prospect of the sight, of that enormous wide slow-rolling river, powerful, was like a balm. For years I'd been promising myself a trip from its sources up in Minnesota where it is supposed to start as a tiny stream bubbling out of a few bushes down to Pilotown, Louisiana, which is about as far down in the Delta as you can go without drowning in a gulf of mud. Somehow I never seemed to do more than the stretch of river I was driving along now, from Burlington to St. Louis. Not that you can actually drive along it. All you can hope to do is hit patches of road which for a few miles parallel the river. But that's usually enough for me.

I sped through Keokuk and past Quincey and towards evening I stopped off in Hannibal, Missouri, which I sometimes do. Now Hannibal at dusk is one of the prettiest sights in America, but I won't even try to describe it. Go and read *Tom Sawyer* and *Huck Finn* for yourself. Right as you enter town by the river route you can see, on top of Cardiff Hill, the only lighthouse on the Mississippi River. I liked to sit in the car and watch the sun go down behind that lighthouse. Which I did just now. Then I went on into town. Now some people don't like Hannibal because the town tends to advertise its one and only resource, the fact that Mark Twain spent his boyhood there. If you've got enough money, you can visit the

Mark Twain Cave, where Becky Thatcher and Tom were supposed to have become lost; Mark Twain's early home; Riverview Park which has the official S. T. Clemens statue overlooking it; the Tom and Huck Monument and all sorts of minor plaques and notations. I myself prefer the life-size statues of Tom and Huck. Commercialization of this sort I don't mind, because it makes people use their imaginations. Anyway, Hannibal is still a quiet and comely town, with trees that look as though they were there before the Cherokee.

All the way down to St. Louis I thought about Mark Twain and the other man I regard as America's greatest, Clarence Darrow, and how they would have disliked the America of today. Both were philosophic pessimists, who insisted at the top of their voices that, to use Housman's phrase, man is "deceived alike in origins and expectations." But you never really believed them when they said it. They spoke and fought for life, for buoyancy, and you couldn't read either of them without feeling a terrific sense of exhilaration. Today's optimists, after you read them you feel like going out and slitting your gullet.

I rode the Missouri-Illinois border highways through the night, and I had plenty of time to think. I didn't stop to eat or especially drink, the latter mainly because I am down twice in the books of the Missouri State Police, once for vagrancy and once for, as I've explained, child rape. (Suspicion.) Even here, along the river in the night, the damn billboards had lights on them. It made me furious. Around a quiet bend in a fairly abandoned stretch of road I stopped the De Soto, and after taking a good look around picked up some rocks to heave at an illuminated sign for Calvert's Whiskey. It took me near on to five full minutes to knock the neon tubing all the way down from the outline of the aristocrat offering you a drink. Satisfied, I climbed back in and got going, having suddenly remembered it was Missouri. Samuel T. Clemens would have approved, but not, I fear, the State Cops.

It was a warm, cloudy night with occasional mists of rain which seemed more to pass you by than fall. This was all river country — you could *hear* it. The sluggish power of the water, the dark shapes of the bluffs, the illuminated bridges. Then into the outskirts of St. Louis and past the gas station, then run by a man named Redhead Neville, where I once worked ten days as a pump monkey, sleeping on a cot at the bottom of the grease pit until the day I was fired from the job. I felt no sentiment about passing the place. And on into St. Loo, the second or third ugliest city in America, after Indianapolis, Detroit and perhaps El Paso. I hadn't known I was going to point this way until the evening with Axel and his friends when suddenly, no matter how I felt, I wanted to see people who were *fighting*. So, reversing a previous decision, I was now heading towards Clinton, Tennessee. And St. Louis was the first stop on the way.

As soon as I got into town I phoned up Kevin-John and said I was coming over. He sounded a little surprised that I had actually made it; he was neither cool nor welcoming. Just factual. He might be drunk. It was close to midnight. He wouldn't, however, let me come to his place. We agreed to meet in a bar in the center of town.

It was a fancy "intimate" bar adjoining a muddy, well-policed parking lot, and I knew that inside would be indirect, magenta-tinted lighting, the kind of place Kevin-John liked to do his drinking in. I had hoped he might have grown out of such places. I hate them. About the only use they have is where men can rub knees with high-priced whores and consummate, if nothing else, business deals. To me they are the essence of sleaziness. As I drew up, so did Kevin — in a new yellow Oldsmobile, about ninety yards long. It looked like a custom job. For some reason this did not surprise me. After Kevin was kicked out of the party (he was the chieftain of the young Communists on our college campus) no telling *where* he would go. As he stepped out of the car and gave his keys to the parking attendant I could tell (1) that he knew I was watching and (2) that even so, he was used to handing his keys to parking attendants. He was dressed in a natty single-breasted brown suit, brown suede shoes and a sharp air of affluence. As soon as he saw me he came over and put his arm in mine and we walked towards the side entrance of the bar. *This* bar had two lousy commissionaires, one at the side and one out front. I said dryly, Okay, I'm impressed, Kevin-John. He didn't say anything. He was, however, sober. That was one thing.

He steered me into a large, gleaming room which contained a triple split-level bar. Somewhere in a crevice an organ was playing

"Nola." We climbed circular, purple-carpeted stairs with gilt balustrades, and when we got to the top and smallest bar the bartender, a couple of girls and their men said, "Hello, Kevin." Kevin-John looked genuinely pleased to see them and went over to chat. Everybody slapped everybody else on the back. It could have been the Pottstown, Pennsylvania, country club. I examined Kevin-John from the bar stool. Right now I had no idea what he was like. He still looked terrifically young, like a boy not yet out of his teens. America, I reflected, is a nation of Dorian Grays. Kevin-John was about thirty now, and he should have looked it. I thought, the sudden realization, in America, that you are no longer young must come as a shock. As a nation we are *committed* to youth. Middle age is the time for viewing honestly the realities: which is why we insist on remaining young.

Maybe I should say something here about Kevin-John, although I know I've mentioned him before. He, too, was from the university days, the days of the loyalty oath. He was the guiding light of the campus Reds, who were an odd, jinxed, warmheaded lot, reflecting in a bizarre and exaggerated way all the defects of heart and mind of adult Communists but lacking the compensating features, such as stature. (Still I would rather see any of them on my doorstep today than anyone else from the campus.) They were dogmatically well organized and gave the best parties on campus except for the co-op boys (when they could inveigle the Veterans' Hospital nurses over) and the Trotskyites. You could never tell with them. It was all either summer or winter, never in between. When I was editing the campus paper, they were usually on my back; once, waving a chair, I had to chase one of them out of the cafeteria annex after he called me a bourgeois opportunist. But after I broke with them they became more friendly. I suspect that was partly Kevin-John's doing. He could be hell on a comrade but sweet to an outsider. Upon the Cominform break with Tito it was more or less understood between Kevin-John and myself that we would confine our discussions purely to local matters, or else be constantly at each other's throats. Kevin-John had been sent by the party to take over the campus branch as a step up to the national executive, which he never made.

Kevin thoroughly enjoyed and exploited his role as junior Stalin.

He had once been a fraternity boy, and I don't think he ever completely lost his basic contempt for young Communists. Somewhere in his heart of hearts I suspect he thought of his comrades in much the same way that his commercial dairy-managing father did, as misfits. He was possessed, I think that is the word, of a quality of profound disinterestedness which was universally interpreted as evidence of the victory he had won, in a successful and epic inner struggle, over his bourgeois personal background. He was not only capable, but also luxuriated in using his quick mind as a whip to be employed with a fine and indiscriminate arrogance just this side of gratuitousness. Savage on his party comrades, he could be coyly, persistently diplomatic and "tactically friendly" with non-party people, especially wheels. His habitual tone was a helpless sneer, often disguised by an ineffective giggle of sorts. Very often we'd quietly slip out to a West L.A. bar after slanging each other at meetings. I had to admit, though, he was a strange boy; he drank too much; he denounced "the bourgeoisie" and yet was in transparent awe of them; emotionally dislocated, terrified of women and needing them, glib, charming, dandified. A Catholic, he foreswore all forms but Marxist theology; a collectivist, he believed in a dialectically evolved *Uebermensch;* dedicated to a classless society he kowtowed to snob value; kicked out by his Christian Front (fascist) family, he could never stop loving them. (And yet, I fear I am missing something central in Kevin-John, but I know as little of what it was now as then. Perhaps only to explain why I liked him, I would like to balance these lines. To say, for example, that he was decent and generous in nonpolitical matters; but I cannot. He had no life outside politics.)

Later, after college, he was to be dropped from the only home he had ever acknowledged — the party — to attempt suicide and finally to drop out of sight. About a year after he disappeared he showed up one rainy night at my flat on Pico Boulevard, fairly sober and saying that I was his only friend. He stayed half the night talking. My God, he needed to talk! The strain of one political defeat after another had accentuated what he called "private problems" and he had been arrested twice for drunken driving. The party, believing him, as they said, "a weak link in the security chain," had dropped him, and advised all party members to do the same.

Overnight, Kevin said, he had lost all his friends. He said he knew all about the incident where I had run down to the headquarters of the party to raise holy christmas over his expulsion and that he was grateful. He said that he didn't feel bitter about the party; the worst thing was, he would have done the same in their shoes. When he realized that, he said, he began to break — emotionally — with his past. He sat on my couch and said things about the party I'd never expected to hear from the lips of that pinched, Irish, alcohol-ruddied face; dry, dispassionate judgments, on himself and his comrades. I suppose, he said, they were right. I was a weak link. At first I thought of killing myself. But now I have a chance for a new life. He had come over, he said, in order that I should give him a reading list. (In the party since sixteen, he boasted of never having touched writers on the Index.) So, feeling a little foolish, I did make out a list for him. He knew the writers I liked and while I was writing out the list at my desk he praised some of them as a way of connecting with me. When he left that night he said, I've got a chance for a new life, and I'm going to take it. He shook my hand wanly. I walked him to where he boarded a streetcar, after shaking my hand again, and said, You know, you really are my only friend. That night was the last I had seen of Kevin-John. At the time, I had felt terrifically optimistic about him. He hadn't wanted to dwell on his past glories, or the past at all, but was full of what he could do in the future, and I was very pleased that some of my arguments and entreaties had at last come to fruition.

Now . . . as he approached me I knew he had become, in a worldly way, and in some measure, hard-bitten. I couldn't tell whether he was putting on this show for me. But I got his message. We sat over drinks, and he laughed and said, "Just like the old days." But he wasn't that all eager to talk. I asked him how he was and you could see him scheme what parts to tell and what to leave out. I must have been crazy to come to St. Louis with those words still ringing in my ears, that I was his only friend.

"I suppose," he said quietly, "we ought to catch up on each other." To make it easier for him, I started telling about myself, but Kevin-John broke in and said, "You can relax about one thing." I said, What's that? "I haven't turned stool-pigeon." Actually, although I pretended that it was the furthest thing from my thoughts, I was a little worried. There had been rumors of the FBI putting the pressure on him, and we all knew if Kevin-John cracked he could list a thousand names before pausing for breath.

"But another thing I'll tell you," he said. "The one thing I would hate to see in America is a Russian Soviet system." He said it with real meaning. I said, What the hell, Kevin, the both of us. "I know about me," he said meanly, "but you, you still call yourself 'Un Homme de la Gauche.' You're still toying around with ideas about maybe it would be a short course in socialism if the Soviets took over here." I told Kevin to stop talking like a fool, if he remembered aright I was the one who used to tell *him* this. He grumbled away the argument. "You know what?" he said. "I'm frightened of the Soviet Union. I've been frightened of it almost since I left the party. Have you ever," he demanded, "read Trotsky?" I wearily reminded him that it was I who years ago had told him to read Trotsky. He looked narrowly at me, almost as though he believed I was lying. I tried to take the temperature out of the air. What are you doing now, Kevin-John? I said.

"Why do you want to know?" he demanded. Oh hell, I thought. We had another drink, and the man at the organ announced he was playing a special request, "Candy." I said, I want to know so I can call up the shamuses, I want to know so I can blacklist you to the grave. "Okay," he said, "I just had to make sure." Fuck, I said, you're playing some goddam part, only it's to the wrong audience. Play it to Daisy but not to me. (Daisy was the woman — and Kevin's one-time closest friend — on whose proposal he had been expelled and who had then grimly enforced the no-fraternization order on him.) "Daisy," he said, without emotion. "I suppose she's beating her tits over the Twentieth Congress. She's probably looking for me to beg my forgiveness." I said, Something like that. He laughed shortly and called for a double. I said, Kevin, lay off that stuff, I want to talk to you. "I talk better this way," he said. "And you lay off me. I haven't taken anyone's orders in a long time."

Eventually, Kevin got around to telling me a little about how he had spent the past few years. For two years, he said, he hadn't known which end was up. He tried three psychoanalysts, two of whom refused to have anything more to do with him after a few interviews. (He sounded a little proud of this.) He stayed with the third eighteen months. Then he took a job as a stock-market teller. He kept it for a year. (Kevin-John as a market teller!) But he was found out. This Immigration Bureau detectives had come around, wanting him to testify for the prosecution in a deportation case against a Chinese student. Kevin said that when he kept refusing, the investment firm fired him. Then followed a year of both the FBI and Immigration Department on his heels, never demanding but invariably, just by showing up during working hours, managing to get him fired. Finally, he had found work as a salesman for a baseball equipment concern. He said, "I found myself selling balls and mitts." The company transferred him to the St. Louis office where, to quote Kevin-John, he had risen like a rocket. He was now chief salesman and assistant sales manager and expected, within five years, he said, to sit on the Board. "I like the work, the people, and the prospects," he said. "I like selling those goddam little things." He looked up to see how I was taking it, and then he said, "You know what your trouble is, you're a prig. Always were, always will be."

By this time he was good and stewed. He kept talking about how he had refused to let the Immigration Department browbeat him; he was proud of this. "They had a lot on me," he hinted darkly. I suddenly wondered whether my friend Kevin-John had turned homosexual. A few of my social-work graduate student friends in college had always tried to convince me of this. I used to have terrific fights with Kevin's local functionaries over his drinking, which I said was merely a sign of someone who liked life. I was wrong, and they were right. The trouble was, I never came near understanding Kevin-John's private situation, and he knew it, and wouldn't forgive me, like my friend Rafe Hawes. If only they'd *talk* about it, instead of clawing it to death.

Naturally, in about an hour, we found we didn't have much to talk about. Not that I didn't try. But he wouldn't speak of the past, and about what we were both doing now he was insufferable. He kept telling me to settle down, get a business job, learn to like people, relax, buy a car, put a down payment on a house. The thing with Kevin was, you could never tell when he was being cynical, coming you on or being straightforward. I expect it was always a combination of the three.

When I asked him if he was doing any political work at all it was my only question which seemed to spear him through the middle. He simply said no, and let it go at that. One thing I was glad about. He did not mention Hungary. Not once. Somehow we got around to talking about religion, and he said not to worry, even if he wanted to, the Catholic Church would not re-receive him. He had, he said, joined a Unitarian church in St. Louis. He saw the way I was looking at him and held his hand out, then turned it over quickly and said, smiling thinly, "Flip-flop." He asked me whether I had read *The God That Failed.* I almost screamed, What is this, a gag? He insisted strenuously it was no gag. I said, Next you'll be telling me you watch television. He banged his small, red fist on the bar. "Damn right I watch television," he said. "I watch it a lot." And then he fell clean off the bar stool, staring at me until he hit the floor.

A man in a tuxedo appeared out of nowhere and took my arm and said, "Charlie, we don't want no trouble here." I said, Take your fucking hand off my arm, he fell off. We helped Kevin to his feet. He clambered back up on the bar stool and said, "Another." Which he got. And started to drink. Then he smiled over at me. It was a thin, friendly, pleading old Kevin-John smile. I said, Can you put me up for the night? Still smiling, he shook his head, quietly. I snorted. Take it easy, I said. "Sure," he said lazily, "what other way?" I walked out of the bar, away from Kevin and the hidden organ and the triple-level bar, into the parking lot where it was dark and pouring cold rain.

I had another, slighter reason for stopping off in St. Louis. Bobby Burroughs was having a preview at the Ambassador Theater. His films, two of them, were called *The Man From Galaxy One* and *The Shipwreckers,* a pirate story with a Freudian moral for our times. The first was science fiction, Bobby's speciality. The preview was set for tomorrow, and I knew Bobby would be in town. He liked supervising his own publicity arrangements before a preview. He said it gave him a chance to get out and talk to people. After I left Kevin-John in the bar, I called up all the expensive hotels in town until I found the one Bobby was in. The first thing he said was, "Did you come all the way out from the Coast to see me?" I said no, hung up, and went over to Bobby's hotel.

Bobby Burroughs, I ought to tell you, is a very interesting specimen. He was one of the first producers I met when I started to "cover" Worldwide Pictures. I was new and virginal to the business. The first thing Bobby said to me when I paid my first courtesy call to his office was, "You know, of course, that I testified . . ." Podgy, homely, a vivacious, shrunken sly-Welsh face scarred by pockmarks, he was from a Chapel mining family out of the Rhondda Valley and had broken into pictures as an immigrant tea boy when his family had packed him off to live with relations in America during the long coal-pit depression of the thirties in South Wales.

A scatty, plunging, volatile man, very facile, Burroughs had been for many years a Communist and had also worked out a wry, unshakable psychoanalytical explanation for his membership and recantation. He had not, he told me, come forward to testify until he was found out, was "fingered" by someone else (his ex-wife), and then his guts spilled all over the Committee table. Altogether, he had fingered only a few less than Elia Kazan, who with a screenwriter named Martin Berkeley holds some sort of record in Hollywood for this sort of thing, although I take it it is not very tactful to mention such things these days. Part of Bobby's trouble was that he not only named people from the long-ago past but had included three of his present assistants on the Worldwide lot, including a friend of mine, Louis Shipley, who later found his way into Chino Reformatory for stealing cars. Bobby used to go to Louis' father and ask to see the boy, request refused. What made it touchy was that Louis' father was head music arranger at the same studio and sometimes toyed with the idea that it was Bobby who was principally responsible for Louis' breakdown. I had known Louis at the university, and I didn't think Bobby had had much to do with it. But the one time I tried to tell him this he grew almost surly and said, You think so? Well I think you may be wrong. I said, Bobby, that's perverted, to want to think you sent Louis into a tailspin, you're not that big a man. Bobby just grinned and said, I ought to hire you.

Bobby had a habit, a bad one if you ask me, of liking to talk politics with the few liberals still around in Hollywood, as if to prove to someone that he was neither afraid nor ashamed. He thought of himself as a true intellectual, and that was usually his artistic downfall. His mind was like a soft dart, very pointed, very swift. He could be a warm, sentimental man, easy to laugh, easy to cry. His pictures were low-budget science-fiction yarns, Westerns, and the things he liked to do best, horrors, all quite interesting in their way, models of craftsmanship, deploying techniques first exploited by the cinematic one-man band who had given him his first job in Hollywood and who incidentally sent Bobby a Christmas-wrapped gift box of human — possibly his own — excrement by Western Union the day after his testimony in Washington. Bobby was, in fact, a kind of B-Grade Orson Welles. Unlike any other producer on the Worldwide lot, he had complete command of the actual film-making process. Bobby possessed a minor genius for unearthing talent even as he misused it. His forte: taking a "social" theme and making junk of it. In this sense, he was a B-Grade, not Orson Welles but Kazan. The flaw, I think, in his creative make-up was a monstrous, tender ego, which, halfway through shooting a picture, prevented him from any kind of self-critical examination and then, later, in the projection room, caused him to curl up in agony. All his pictures were might-have-beens, artistically. All made money.

After his first wife divorced him, he got a shrewd little Beverly Hills harridan who prodded him into taking a tougher line with his studio bosses. Though constantly in training to contest the position of "Crash" Kirk, the No. 1 producer on the lot, he was also afraid of Kirk. What he could not see, although I tried to tell him, was that his power struggle with Kirk had been made irrelevant by television. But Bobby refused to see TV as anything except a passing public fancy. He had taken too many changes in his relatively short life, too many shocks to what he thought and believed; he was *for* motion pictures now, forever. He could not, would not, go on to television. Bobby was a cultural manic-depressive; one day blowing hot and enthusiastic, tomorrow fear-stricken and withdrawn. He was convinced, when I met him, that only he in Hollywood could spot the "Stalinoids." Because he feared, respected and loved and hated the Reds he saw them everywhere and inside everyone. He prided himself, especially since his testimony, on his honorable relationships man-to-man; and yet in my dealings with him I had gauged him an opportunist and on occasion a liar; a persistent and almost compulsive double-dealer of his close associates but not of those outside the Hollywood system with whom he had made friends, such as hillside neighbors; he took exorbitant pride in being a "good neighbor." He had a true comic inventiveness but not the courage to see it through. Working with even mediocre writers, he could take the dopiest story and come up with a superb comedy screenplay which was never realized on the screen. Though terrified of losing his job, he nevertheless dreamt dreams of becoming a kind of overlord of Hollywood. He was the only man I have ever known who was under double psychoanalysis. Four times a week he went to a Freudian, twice a week to an Adlerian, without telling one of the other's existence. When he told me this, long after I got to know him, he winked and said, "You can't be too careful these days, kid." Lade-ee-z and gem'men, I give you . . . Bobby Burroughs.

Bobby was, needless to say, staying at St. Louis' most expensive hotel. Not the plushiest but the most expensive, a small Georgian-house affair, with embossed miniature colonnades and painted in spotless white. It was located in an almost slum section of St. Louis, just off the Negro quarter. A doorman who looked like the old family retainer escaped off the *Gone With the Wind* set let me in and ushered me up to Bobby's suite, which was the entire top floor. I was surprised to see that when Bobby opened the door he was very drunk. He had had half his liver shot away at the Tarawa beachhead and rarely touched liquor. He said, turning away, "Come on in, I'm tired."

As I came in, I saw a girl in a gold lamé dress and purple hair slip into one of the other rooms. Purple. Bobby said, "Forget it, it's Jane." Jane was his wife. We went into the living room which was furnished like your rich old uncle's, the one who had collaborated with the damYankees and had been given half of Maryland in return for services rendered. The entire suite was littered with "24-sheets" and cardboard advertisements for Bobby's two films. I said, What's the drunk for, Bobby? He said, "I'm tired, that's all. I'm making money for everybody but myself." (He had a large house in Bel Air, a swimming pool, two new cars and a small oil well near San Pedro.)

I flopped down in an enormous overstuffed chintz-covered chair and said, Come to New York with me. Bobby said, dryly, "Sure, wait a moment while I cut my throat." I said, I mean it, Bobby, the trip would do you good. Take a boat to Europe with me, it'll make a man of you. Bobby snorted, "Redemption — fuck you." Thing was, I wasn't kidding. I felt like taking Bobby along with me. It looked like a perfectly sound idea to me. And he was right, I did see it as a way for him to redeem himself. He was always referring to his testimony, finding excuses to allude to it naturally, as though it were the denotive word "the" or a normal household article; it was his way of defusing the subject of any moral pejorativeness. I could not go along with him on this. I mean, I don't especially see a man's climactic act of moral catastrophe as very competent matter for social conversation; but somewhere along the line Bobby had, in truth, sucked me into a position where I could think about what he had done without inwardly wincing.

Soon, up in his suite, I began to horse around with Bobby. I thumbed my nose at him, for instance. He stuck out his tongue at me. This had a history. The very first day I stepped into his office, as I said, he stopped me at the beginning of my "pitch" to inform me, boldly and slyly, that he had been a "testifier" and that according to some people he was a rat, traitor and scoundrel. Without pausing he spent the next two hours telling me why and how he had come to testify (I found out later he left out some relevant details — such as trying to phone up people, as many as he could locate, to tell them to their faces, electronically speaking, that he was going to name them in front of the Committee — but this is of no matter here). Then he had sat back in his big red-plush leather chair (like the one I had at the Agency) and said, "Well, any comment?" Well, what can you comment when a man has just put on a performance like that? You can't call him names and you can't begin to bargain over ethics with him. So I thumbed my nose at him. And he knew I meant it. So he stuck out his tongue at me. And I knew he meant *that*. It may sound childish as hell, the way I'm writing it now, but such are the lubricants of human relations I am told. And so we got into this habit of thumbing our noses and sticking out our tongues instead of talking. I suppose if we had to, we could have carried on an entire conversation with gestures like this.

I finally said, after we had a few stiff drinks in silence, with not a peep out of his wife in the other room, Look Bobby. He said, "Don't make me a speech, I'm a very fatigued man. One of the pictures isn't even music-tracked in yet." I said, Look Bobby, what have you got to lose? You've got a wife you're afraid of, you make pictures you're not proud of, you've got low blood pressure and catarrh, and so? He said, quite angrily, "Who said I was ashamed of my pictures?" I sighed and slumped lower. He made a long, querulous speech about how his product might not be the biggest but for what it was it was the best. (In his way, he was right, too. The day they get around to giving Academy Awards in the category of For What It Is, Bobby will be a world beater.) And then he stood up and slammed his drink against the wall. It did some pretty horrifying things to the wallpaper. "I know," he shouted, "I know what you really mean. You're talking about my testimony."

I said, tiredly, I'm not either and tried thumbing my nose at him. Automatically, he stuck his tongue out, then began to shout again. "You think," he shouted, "I helped to ruin the lives of innocent people, huh?" I said, Something like that. He snarled, "Up your nostril I did. Innocent my ass. Sure, innocent, while we're at peace. In a war, and don't kid yourself that's what we're in, a long-term ideological war, how innocent do you think people would be?" (I think he meant to say *those* people, Mr. Freud.) Bobby rushed over to the radio. His wife came out one of the doors, still in her gold lamé dress. I couldn't take my eyes off that purple hair of hers. She looked at the wallpaper and then at me. "So?" she said. "Easy, easy," Bobby said, "I'm looking for the news." He kept twisting the dials on the old-fashioned console model but all he could get was squawking and "night music." He switched off the set viciously. "You been listening?" I nodded. "Innocent, hah?" he screeched. I started to get up. There was no point. I was tired, too. I said, Do you want to come with me? He said, with equal seriousness, "No." Then abruptly, he came over and poked me in the chest. "Big Chief Pure in the Heart," he said, "so all right, you didn't testify, I did. *Does that make you a better writer?*" He retreated to a wheeled tray full of bottles and waited, I suppose, for me to hit him. I got to go, Bobby, I said. "All right," he said. He stuck out his tongue but got no reply from me. His wife watched us. Man, how I didn't like that woman. The only nice thing about her was the purple hair. Bobby said, "We didn't have much of a talk." His wife came up to him, and they both walked me to the door. At the door, Bobby said, "*Sholem*, sucker." Peace, I said, and closed the door behind me.

I was twenty miles north of St. Louis, on Highway 61, when it came to me that I wasn't going south any more. I just didn't have it in me to cover the integration story in Clinton, Tennessee, or go on down to have that long talk with Reverend Martin Luther King in Montgomery. I wanted to get to wherever it was I was going in the quickest, shortest way. I tried to argue myself out of this, tell myself that of all the people back on the California campus Kevin-John was the one most likely to go to hell in a handbasket, that there were a score of men and women contemporary with Kevin-John and me who were now living settled, sane, unhysterical lives. But I had seen those, and they were one of the reasons I had to get out of California; every time I visited their houses it was like talking to people whom the earth had swallowed up. Political fear plus that peculiar, cathedral-like domestication in the "young married" is one of the genuine terrors of America: it is sluggishly bestial. It is banal, it permits no real release of energies and instead it substitutes *Eigentlichkeit* manqué if there exists such a phrase, it gives the illusion of being one's self while one is going in exactly the opposite direction; and yet we, of the road, envy this state with all our hearts and curse our insights, our embattled self-pity, our prickly isolation, our failure to find identification in either the present-day circumstance of America or its traditions. For we are neither aging bohemians (awaiting a lucky thunderbolt of discovery from Madison Avenue) nor fading revolutionaries. We are still young and strong, with many years left in us. We are the residual legatees of struggle, of cultural involvement, of personal meaning, of the search for justice and honesty. Why is there no place for us in America?

Slashing through the night rain, I turned on the radio. This time I didn't have to search. All you could get was war bulletins. Somewhere east of Macomb, an announcer came on from Washington and said that Soviet troops had launched a massive attack against the Hungarians. Battles were raging in various parts of the country.

Budapest was being contested. The revolutionary radio had just gone off the air, the announcer said.

Turning east on Highway Junction 24 I reached Peoria, Illinois, by early dawn. I could go no further. I knew that. Two days ago I might have tried to make Chicago in one no-stop burst. But not now. I parked at the side of the highway just outside Peoria and sat behind the wheel for what seemed hours. All this time the car radio was on, reporting various Soviet attacks on the Hungarian revolutionaries. Every five minutes there was a new report. Finally, I started the De Soto and crawled into Peoria. It was very early in the morning. I made my way out to the Caterpillar Tractor works on the east side of town and parked in the huge lot near the entrance gate. The first shift had not yet come to work. It was a gray cold wet morning and I sat in the car with the windows rolled up tight and the radio on alternating between chirpy g'mornin' records and news reports.

Soon the maintenance men began driving and walking in, trudging into the factory with that already weary, head-down feeling I knew so well, not even bothering to say hello to each other. Half an hour later the first shift began to stream in. In a few minutes the outside parking lot, where I was, was almost full. I had the car parked just next to the wide asphalted lane that led into the main plant. The men, and a few women, poured through the gate. Then I rolled down the window and yelled, "Johnny!" He heard me right away. I saw him jerk his head up and look around, with that slightly grinning, birdlike way he had, his mouth open in a kind of innocent, violent expectation. He was walking along, in the middle of the crowd of men, in overalls and an old battered fedora in the rolling, bowlegged way I remembered, smiling amiably at the few men around him in case they had called. When he saw me in the De Soto his expression didn't change, he just walked out of the stream of ingoing workers and reached through the window and rubbed my head with his fist. "Hello, theah," he said.

I guessed he was trying to remember my name. You could see him trying to figure out exactly who I was but sensing that I must have once been a friend. Johnny sometimes had lapses of memory. Though it had been some years since we had last seen each other, he was easygoing and conversational, as though we'd recently been on a fishing trip together. He called me by my name, and refreshed by the recollection he greeted me enthusiastically, stepped back and looked at the car and laughed, "You just sell your mother or something?" I asked Johnny when he would be free and he said lunch; no, right now. Wouldn't that make him late to work? "Work, there's always that," he said.

"Just wait," he said, "and Ah'll be raht back." He ran into the plant. I watched him disappear inside the building with that bow-leggedy style of his. Actually, it was against my better judgment to have stopped by; two years ago, coming back from an advertising conference in New York, I had sent Johnny a postcard from Chicago asking if he wanted me to drop into Peoria and see him. He had sent back the postcard, overstamped, with a neat and laborious pen scrawl: "Better not. I might not be here." Which was his way of saying that he'd just as soon not see any of the people connected with the last strike. So I had by-passed Peoria. In coming by the factory now, I had not meant to interfere with his life, or to stir embers he would prefer left alone. God knew Johnny deserved some peace.

After Camp Kilmer, I kept walking AWOL down east of the Alleghenies, doing odd jobs, until I came temporarily to light in Durham near where, before shipping to Germany, I had been stationed with Dan Henry and Werner Seitz in the —th Infantry, about half an hour's bus ride away. A strike called by the local textile union was in progress and already several weeks old. The mills, on the outskirts of Durham, were shut down. I hung around, and helped, and slept at union headquarters, a small office above a chocolate shop at back of the Washington Duke Hotel. At the office I met a man called Johnny Savoy, who kept inviting me out to his place . . .

The morning after a homemade bomb exploded in the loading yard of the central Taussig mill, causing twenty dollars worth of damage in splintered windows, the entire executive board of Local 118 was jailed on a criminal syndicalism statute and the union office padlocked. Deprived of my bedroom, I figured now was as good a time as any to meet Johnny Savoy and his friends.

The number was 12 Choctaw Road, on the highway outside

Chapel Hill. The approach to the house was nothing more elaborate than a pair of parallel ruts leading off the highway into a large field of untended scrub grass, weeds and wild flowers. About a hundred yards this way of the woods sat a small frame cottage. Even in the dark, as I strode towards it, I could smell the decayed wood slats under the paint. Lights were on behind drawn shades, otherwise the house would have been impossible to pick out at night, possibly even in the daytime. There was no path in the grass after the ruts stopped. I had to go in high-stepping, as over corpses or lovers. It was the kind of shrubbery that gave out a noise. I wondered if it was kept that way purposely. Even before I got to the porch the lights were snapped off. Now it was all night and silence but for the insects. The steps creaked audibly.

I knocked and waited. From inside I could hear a squeaking noise, I knew that sound — a portable mimeograph, on rollers, being pushed rapidly about. One of the window shades rustled a trifle.

Then the door slowly swung open. A flashlight beam was shone in my face.

"What do you want here?" The voice held a rich up-country accent, now sharp.

I said I had been asked to come here by Johnny Savoy.

"Who sent you here, boy — ?" Two more shadowy figures emerged from inside the house and stood on either side of me. One of them I thought was a woman.

A voice directly at my ear spun me around. "Didn't you hear him say he was a friend of mine? And so he is." There weren't two voices like that in the whole of North Carolina. I thought, they must have sent Johnny Savoy to circle around me when they heard noise.

Johnny and I shook hands warmly, and the first voice invited me inside the house.

We got a good look at one another when Johnny turned on the lights and locked the door. Even before I could adjust my eyes to the light I smelled oil and ink and paper dust. I saw that their faces were ink-smeared. A girl stood off in the corner shyly examining the visitor, me.

Everybody just stood around waiting for the honors to be done. Finally, the second man, tall and slightly sway-backed, with a narrow long bony face and close-cut hair, stuck out his hand. "I'm Tod North," he said.

"That's right," chimed in Johnny Savoy. "And that there is Matt Sylvester and his sister Libby." Hands were shaken all around.

The standing around began again. We were all uncomfortable.

The living room, in which we stood, was piled to the plastered-up ceiling with bulky packages of raw mimeograph paper. In the corner stood two rickety army cots with blankets. The walls were spattered, new stains added to old until the floral wallpaper pattern was completely obscured, from ceiling to floor, by sprays and configurations of various hues of ink. I could see through to a small bedroom where an ancient hand mimeograph was partially covered by a torn tarp.

"I heard your machine outside. I know how to work one," I said.

Half an hour later I was at work, and the small house on Choctaw Road had settled back to its routine. My principal job the first night was to separate sheets of mimeo paper by blowing down into them and then feeding the machine which was cranked by Tod North. At first we talked of nothing but the latest developments in the strike. That morning, old man Taussig had sent an angry telegram, released also to the newspapers, to his mill foremen authorizing the importation of as many strikebreakers "as may be deemed necessary by your circumstances." The first carload was expected the following morning. Also, out-of-state private detectives were beginning to show up all over Durham and Chapel Hill. It looked like the genesis of a showdown.

In the middle of work that night Johnny Savoy went out back and dragged in another army cot. I guessed I was being invited to stay the night. I did, and the nights that followed. Nobody asked me about why I was wearing a U.S. Army uniform.

The strike lasted on through the summer and into the first cool days of autumn. The union lawyers successfully litigated the reopening of the union office, but I remained at the house on Choctaw Road.

It was too early for anyone on the union side to admit officially the strike was dragging. When management announced that returning millworkers "would be financially aided with a view towards restoration of their pre-dispute position," only fifteen men applied. In that sense, the strike was solid. But with each passing day it became more and more obvious that something would have to give, and soon. The union treasury had been wiped out by bail demands, and the personal resources of the strikers were on the verge of exhaustion. The company having successfully subcontracted rush orders, finally came out and said it, under no circumstances would it negotiate with the union. Ever.

The people inside the house on Choctaw Road went on with their labors.

Matt Sylvester was the district Communist leader, coordinating the activities of, all told, thirteen men, women and children.

His sister, Libby age seventeen, a freckled southern goddess, cooked and cleaned up after the men and did the chores we were too busy or shiftless to do for ourselves.

Johnny Savoy was the official chauffeur, bodyguard for Matt Sylvester, mechanic and informal liaison between the house on Choctaw Road and the union.

Tod North wrote the leaflets and press releases.

I worked closest with Tod, typing and mimeoing and blowing into the paper, packaging the leaflets and cutting wood out in back. Tod North, The People's Poet; lank, cadaverous, in whose alert, glistening eyes there was a personal history lesson. Hardly anyone on the Left, in the late 1930's, wasn't aware of Tod North's name and work. His had been one of the most promising and important names in what was then called proletarian literature. Even my father, who never read poetry, sometimes declared aloud Tod's verses. He had been that kind of poet. Discovered (through an almost mystical accident) by a rich Long Island patron of the arts (who prided himself on traveling far distances for his catches) while he was plowing out a bare living around his share-hand's shack in west Georgia, and writing beauty with pain and clumsiness at nights, Tod at first had to be argued into showing his work. The Long Island man had to ask his permission to take the pencil-smudged lines up north with him, and then a month later, Tod was off his land, out of his shack and living in New York. His star burst with a tremendous, scintillating explosion. Every publication, from *New*

Masses to the *Saturday Review*, especially *New Masses*, printed him. He loved the big city and ran wild in it. For a year or more he functioned as the roman candle of literary Manhattan. His drinking partner was Thomas Wolfe, and he was regularly invited to dine at the Fifth Avenue home of his publisher. But, in the end, he became the Left's own very special poet. Another year of sitting on the platform at mass meetings in Madison Square Garden, of soirées in Greenwich Village and all-night talkathons at Sixth Avenue cafeterias, and Tod began to write about a very special vision for a very special audience, verses beginning "You Georgia Mother with hands of iron and heart of rushing waters/The land will be yours/When the Red bugles blow in the morning . . ." and he was not, when I met him, a good poet any longer. The fact was, Tod was a calmly terrified man. Sick at heart, he was trying to retrieve, by hand-cranking a mimeograph machine in an old house in North Carolina, what he had lost somewhere on East Fourteenth Street.

Tod lived on meager royalties plus money which a few northern friends sent him. The economics of the rest of the group were equally simple. Matt Sylvester and Johnny Savoy, as paid functionaries, pie-cards, monthly earned $28 and $17 respectively. When the money came.

A common commitment and shared work, but little else, bound Matt Sylvester to Johnny Savoy. Their relationship was awkward and formal; a strange and uneven comradeship. Johnny, the perpetual disciple, loved Matt Sylvester, worshiped him, looked upon him as the Dixie Lenin. Matt was never permitted to go on long trips away from the house without Johnny as bodyguard and batman, seldom walking abreast of Matt but slightly to the side and rear. Johnny aped Matt's speech and hand gestures and, as best he could, tried to copy Matt's long-legged, never-look-over-your-shoulder stride. To try to keep up with Matt, Johnny Savoy had developed a peculiar, unrhythmic half-jog which made it appear as if Matt were pulling him jerkily along on invisible wires. Johnny Savoy, the peewee, grimly bowling along on the heels of big Matt Sylvester, was a fine visual joke for a town which seldom laughed these days.

People did not so much snicker at Johnny's fabulous ugliness, his rodeo-rider stance, cauliflower ears, enormous arms and short stature. What was really comical, to some people, was the intense devotion with which the agile little man guarded Matt Sylvester, as if the task was for him indisputably the most vital and cherished aim of his existence. Wherever Matt Sylvester went, Johnny Savoy tagged inevitably along, grinning affably at passers-by, occasionally whistling at a girl, cutting up in general.

Outside the house, and most of the time inside, the two men rarely exchanged the normal pleasantries.

The contrast between Matt and Johnny could not have been more extreme if it had been planned that way.

For one thing, Matt stood a sizable head taller than Johnny, and in everything else he was, outwardly, what Johnny was not. Handsome as a statue, imposing, reserved, he was a local hero even though half the town would have clapped hands at his hanging. Twice, before the war, he had been ridden out of Durham on a two-by-four and somewhere in his past he had caught a load of buck-shot full in the face where it showed. It was rumored around the union that he had once been to Russia, though I never learned the truth of this. A lot of people would have liked Matt dead. He bore his scars quietly.

His response to Johnny's love was grudging and undauntable. He seemed to harbor a secret anger that his superiors should have foisted upon the small, disciplined colony which he led a man of such dark repute and frivolity. Most of the time he dealt with this by ignoring, or appearing to ignore, Johnny's presence. Johnny's adulation rested around Matt's neck like an iron garland; it was no secret that on several occasions past Matt had requested Johnny's transfer. But Johnny was not reassigned, and Matt remained the nervous object of those bright, preposterously worshipful eyes, provoking him to treat Johnny with a harshness all out of proportion to his aide's errors of judgment and breaks in discipline. The fact was, Matt's disinterested ferociousness rolled off Johnny's back. It was Johnny who made the excuses for Matt. "Don't make him no mind," he would tell me. "Sometimes he's a mite too busy to take the iron out of his tongue."

Matt was made implacably brusque not only by his knowledge that another human regarded him as infallible and was inspired to live by him, but there was also the question of political imperatives, in which Matt was a strict and fundamentalist disciplinarian. Johnny Savoy was simply not Matt Sylvester's kind of revolutionist. He was, by nature, fey, light of heart and not above engaging in a tavern brawl to prove his point. Despite the sincerity with which Johnny gave his heart and soul to his movement, he was, in that soul, an anarchist, than which there was no more violent epithet in Matt Sylvester's political lexicon. For Johnny Savoy, no task was too grubby, no assignment too humdrum or fearsome — and he slept loudly at meetings. His courage, tested ten times and ten times that, was unquestioned. But his spirit was simply not constructed in a way which might have fitted him for engagement in the brand of politics practiced by the Matt Sylvesters of the world. When all was said and done, Johnny attained inner peace only when crazily careening the old Ford over lonely country roads or skulking into fenced-in company towns at dawnlight to toss leaflets on workers' doorsteps, or singing on a picket line, or standing protection for Matt Sylvester at open-air meetings.

Matt carpeted Johnny only when the infractions were of too flagrant a nature to ignore. In my presence it happened three times: when Johnny made a round of Durham saloons in the company of a person he described as a "right sweet feller" and who revealed himself at evening's end as the local assistant Klan Kleagle; when Johnny arose in the middle of a class on rural sociology at the nearby University of North Carolina and spent the final fifteen minutes of class time haranguing the flabbergasted professor; and when, at a by-election rally, Johnny placed a lighted firecracker under the chair occupied by the senior senator from North Carolina. What Matt did not lecture Johnny about was any aspect of his private life, which could not have been easy for him since Johnny and Libby, Matt's sister, were lovers. This fact Matt simultaneously ignored and accepted.

Between Libby and her brother there had grown a strangely formal relationship. They did not know each other well. Upon the death of their father, a back-country preacher, Matt had brought her down from the village in the hills in which they had been born. Until the day he suddenly appeared at the burial, Matt had not been seen in those parts for over a decade, during which time he had been in Spain, become a Communist, been married and divorced. Libby was on her second year at the Choctaw Road house; she and Johnny Savoy had been together only a few months when I showed up.

"Wish I knew where they found the time to do courting," observed Tod to me. "Makes me feel old not knowing."

I soon learned that one of the few scrupulously observed rules of Number 12 Choctaw Road was that nobody was to comment, one way or the other, if both Johnny Savoy and Libby Sylvester were found to be missing together. It was to be assumed that they were out at chores, separately. That is, until the night they broke the bed, and we heard them.

The strike, now in its fourteenth week, refused to die, and in its way was well towards becoming a local institution like the Washington Duke Hotel and the Tarheel football squad. Some newspapers sent in special correspondents. *The Nation* and *New Republic* took to hailing the endurance and courage of the strikers, who could have used less good will and more funds.

On the first day of the fifteenth week, skulls were split at the mill gates when truckloads of imported and local scabs staged a lightning assault on depleted picket lines. The gates were forced, the scabs poured through and by that afternoon some of the smokestacks were showing activity. The tactic backfired, however. Strike morale, hitherto slipping off gradually into a morose apathy, suddenly surged. The next day saw a triple line of continuously moving, singing, cussing strikers at all the main gates. As soon as deputies began herding the scabs through, war broke out, fists and stones flew, heads bled. And the scabs were tossed back.

Next morning the entire contingent from Choctaw Road was on hand at the Durham city courthouse. Spectators overflowed onto the lawn to witness the arraignment — for "incitement to riot" — of the union's executive board (only recently out of jail on another charge) and most of the picket line captains. A fancy bail was named again. And again an emergency call was sent out for the union's chief legal counsel in Philadelphia.

After a day in the courthouse, the five of us piled into Johnny's 1935 Ford jalopy. Matt told Johnny to step on it. Taussig company police and out-of-town Pinks were lounging around the courthouse spoiling for blood.

The Ford sped away.

On the highway just outside Choctaw Forest, Matt said, "Can you see okay out of your rear mirror?"

"Sure thing," replied Johnny. "They been on ouah tail since the co'thouse. The ol' buggy won't run any faster, Matt."

We all looked back. Behind us, about a quarter of a mile down the road, drove a Packard. The Taussig company cars were all shiny black Packards. The distance between the two vehicles rapidly closed.

Johnny's free hand came up with a jack handle. Matt took it.

"Won't we be able to shake them?" Tod chewed at his lip. No other cars were visible on the road. The next police station, even if it had meant safety, lay on the other side of Chapel Hill. It was growing dark.

In the front seat, next to Johnny, Libby lowered herself to the floorboard and scrunched with a quiet and practiced air. Tod stopped biting to stare down at Libby. He said, "They wouldn't try anything like that this close to town."

"I dunno," said Johnny. "Don't think so. But you can't never tell with them sumbitches."

The Taussig car was much closer now. It was crammed with men.

Nobody spoke in the Ford which swerved around a curve in the road.

Then Johnny said simply, "Don't nobody fret. Jes' hol' on."

With that, he braked the Ford sharply, slowing down. Matt, intent on the back window, was flung against the front seat. He started to speak but changed his mind. In the car Johnny was boss.

We all sat low.

"Haw!" shot up Johnny's laugh.

Matt frowned anxiously. "What's on your mind?" He had heard that laugh before, and vowed that next time there would be plenty of "collective discussion" before it was put to use again.

"Y'all about to witness a very unfoahtunate acciden'," said Johnny. I thought, my God he's showing off in front of Libby.

The Taussig car was almost on top of us now. There were six or seven men inside, sitting impassively, all of them except the driver wearing raincoats. They closed in on the Ford as if it didn't exist on the road. I knew I wouldn't soon forget the face of the man who was driving. The man was smiling and his eyes were wide open and (it seemed) interested in me. When he was near enough to the Ford, he leaned out of his window and waved cheerily and called something.

"The bastard," murmured Tod.

Imperceptibly the Ford kept slowing down.

And then suddenly picked up speed. The Taussig car jumped forward with us. We got up to 70 along the forest road. The Packard, coming up on our left side, was obviously preparing to ram when Johnny Savoy began swerving violently. The Taussig detectives, fearing a trick, skillfully followed the movements of the Ford, turning when our vehicle turned, swerving when it did. Then, without warning, Johnny Savoy raised his right leg off the gas pedal and slammed it down on the brake, upsetting us and catching the Packard just as it was attempting to pass on the driver's side. The bumpers of both vehicles locked with a sharp crunch which we did not hear clearly because we were tangled up together. The Ford, easing over to the far side of the road, lost speed rapidly as Johnny applied his brakes in short, spaced jerks, dragging the Packard along. The detectives were all moving in their car, shouting at each other while the driver, no longer paying attention to me, tore frantically at his wheel. He failed to disengage. The Ford skirted the edge of the road, and the Packard, with its broader wheel base, rumbled along the shoulder, boiling up opaque clouds of dust in its wake. It was then that the Ford shot ahead with a burst of speed. The sound between the cars told of ripped-away bumpers.

"This is where I hope that sumbitch makes his mistake," shouted Johnny inside the Ford.

And the sumbitch obliged. Instead of accelerating to purchase traction, the detective driver tried braking back up the road. But he had been forced too low on the shoulder; the Packard lost momentum, wobbled for fifty yards along the soft shoulder and then went nosing obliquely into the ditch where it almost turned over, rocked a couple of times and remained there, at a wonderful angle, trapped. The Ford, we, sped forward into the darkening forest.

For a few moments none of us spoke.

Johnny surveyed his handiwork in the mirror. "Y'all watched like I tol' you? 'Cause I ain' gonna do it again today!"

Libby, on the floor, began sobbing. That was when I and the others were almost killed. Instinctively, Johnny took his hand off the wheel to comfort the girl. "For sweet Christ sake, Johnny!" Matt shouted. Startled, Johnny turned his head to see what was wrong. At that instant the Ford zoomed onto the soft shoulder. Johnny rammed down on the gas pedal as the car boiled down the shoulder. We shot down the road, unable to climb up, and then, leaning at a sharp angle, Johnny shouted, "Ever'body get oveh on the lef' side!" and the Ford gradually eased up to the road proper. We were safe. Libby hunched over by the door and bawled like an infant.

In the back seat Tod was breathing heavily, and Matt was glaring at Johnny. Johnny cleared his throat uncomfortably. "Well, I mean, Matt . . . You oughtnt've scared me like that. It was all right. I had my knees on the steerin' wheel all the time."

Tod began to laugh, halfway to crying, as if he would never stop, even if asked. He leaned over and grabbed Johnny's head and kissed him with a loud smack. Matt patted Johnny's shoulder. "That's all right, Johnny. Thank you."

"Any ol' time," replied Johnny Savoy.

It was night when the Ford was parked in the woods behind the house on Choctaw Road. Tenderly, Johnny helped Libby out of the car and together they slowly walked away into the trees. Matt went into the house.

I asked, "How old is Johnny?"

Tod shook his head. "None of us know,"

Tod and I sat on the front stoop. The night was cool. "What do you think will happen to them?" I asked. Tod thought about it. He shrugged. "Marry, maybe. Johnny wants to, but the girl don't know. She's not used to makin' up her own mind."

"Libby got any other beaux?"

"Not now. Once she did." We exchanged glances. Tod grinned and leaned back on the stoop. He looked up at the stars in the night sky. "That's right, boy. Me."

When we came into the house Matt was feeling around in the dust and rubbage under his cot, and then came up with a bottle. Silently, Tod broke out the glasses, and silently Matt poured. Tod and Matt and I drank, slowly and in communion. Then Matt left for town.

An hour later, at the mimeograph machine, I asked Tod where Johnny Savoy learned to drive the way he did.

Tod said, "He drove a truck in prison." Then he changed the subject. But later that night, when we were both feeling groggy from the whiskey and the machine, and when I least expected it because Tod usually kept his own silent counsel, he shut down the mimeograph and sat down on the bed to light a cigarette. "There's no reason for you not to know, really," he said. I stacked the paper while he talked.

"You see," Tod explained, "except for Libby, we all been in the pokey one time or another. I even got throwed into a New York can once. Only Johnny, he served more time. All through the war, in fact."

He lay back on the bed.

"The thing you got to understand about Johnny Savoy is first, that ain't his name. He's breaking parole by bein' here. And the second thing you should know is that he comes from I reckon three generations of coal diggers in Harlan County. Johnny, that's his real first name, grew up smelling coal dust and listenin' to mine talk and watchin' Mr. Lewis' union men and the company men fight it out in the streets. If you ever been to the County, boy, then you know that a miner's prime item of equipment there used to be, and maybe still is, his shootin' piece.

"Well, Johnny's ma and sisters kept him from the street fights about as long as they could. But then one day Johnny comes up from the shaft and they tell him his father is lyin' at home with his head split wide open and his wits pourin' out by the minute. At that time there weren't no open union local in the town, only a secret one, and Johnny's pa was secretary. The day and in the bar he got hurt the union president got killed with a bullet.

"I guess Johnny made up his mind in about the only way he knew how. Before, he'd always been a high liver, didn't have much to do with the union, it weren't exactly what you call his style. But when this thing happened to his father he just jumped into the family car, without tellin' anyone, and made it down to Louisville. I don' know how he did it, either, because he wasn' much of an auto driver in those days. In town, the way I piece it together, he spent a few hours walkin' around to see the sights, sat through a picture show, and in the evening he broke into the National Guard armory, sawed a hole down into the basement and ripped two machine guns out from a padlocked gun rack. On his way back to Harlan state troopers got him for speedin', and then they spotted two black muzzles in the rear seat. Johnny hadn't even tried to hide the guns.

"For stealin' federal property he was sentenced to a few years in Leavenworth. That part was cut down when his ma and sisters, his pa had died by then, got a Congressman to speak up and write a letter. It was just after D-Day that Johnny got out. He visited his ma and kin, and then went on up to Chicago and marched into the offices of the party lawyers who had defended him. After movin' around a bit, he was assigned to us down here."

Tod finished the story. "He came to us out of Leavenworth." He lit another cigarette and said, "Tonight's entertainment, boy. Let's go back to work."

That night, after Matt had returned from town, and Libby and Johnny were asleep in the woods somewhere, I could not sleep, thinking about what Tod had told me. Towards morning, shivering with cold and huddled in my blanket, I started to write a poem. Through the open window I could see it was a cold sharp North Carolina dawn with the moon, small and white, still visible away off through the tall pines at the end of the damp dusty road which ran past the house and off through the woods at the edge of town.

Suddenly Tod North was standing next to me. He had come in from the mimeo-bedroom. Matt was asleep. Tod whispered. "What you composin' there, boy?"

I was embarrassed to be caught at it by a real poet. Secretly, I hoped Tod would ask to see it. I told him it was a poem.

For the first time in the house I heard Tod raise his voice. Fury forced his face into rigidity. "Goddamit!" The words came squeezed and stifled. "Haven't we got enough work here for you? You want more, is that it? Is that it?" He stalked to the front door, and turned around. Tears of rage corroded his young farmer's face. "The mill hands starvin' out an' you sit on yo' ass in the moonlight an' . . ." He choked off. Blindly, he banged out the door, striding with heavy jerky steps down the rut towards the highway in the misty morning.

My face was hot with shame.

Matt moved under his blanket. "Don't make Tod no mind," he said softly. "Sometimes, at night, he goes into that other room when he thinks none of us is watchin'. He ain't actually writ nothing for two years."

On the Monday of the seventeenth week of its duration the strike collapsed. Disguising their humbled pride with a show of gray-faced impassivity, the hands lined up at the gates of the mills and waited to be asked in. On Tuesday, a selected 10 per cent of the work force was discharged "for economy reasons." All were members of the union executive board or strike committee. On Friday a squad of clean-cut, genial young industrial engineers came over from the university, strolled about the mills making time/motion studies, and then fifty hands in all departments were laid off. Those who remained worked the empty looms; no extras were hired.

At the house on Choctaw Road five people waited for signs of revolt from within the mills. Johnny and I took the car to the union headquarters in Durham. The office was cold, empty, desolate. A fortnight passed. Nothing happened. The strike was dead, over, kaput.

That Saturday weekend Matt spread out on his cot, for squaring up, all the accounts on the money left in the strike relief fund collected by his group. Saturday night, after sweating over the ledgers all day, he announced that there was $31 short. Tod and I worked over the accounts with him. We looked all over the house for vouchers or receipts that might have been missed. Finally, Johnny came into the house, covered with grease and oil from the Ford. Libby was in the kitchen. Johnny asked us what we were all doing.

Matt said, "Johnny, would you know where $31 of the relief money went to?"

A pause while Johnny carefully laid down a wrench. His face was without expression when he said, "Yeah, I know. Don't look no more. I took it."

Three nights later half a dozen white men, two white women and a tall, scrawny Negro woman of antiquity dressed in a Mother

Hubbard trooped into the house. They arrived within ten minutes of each other, from different parts of the woods out back of the house. Matt asked me to stand guard outside the house. I was not to be allowed at this meeting since it was officially called by the organization.

Libby had been sent away to Winston-Salem to relatives. Since Johnny's confession she had refused to be alone with him.

Matt and Tod and the strangers remained in the locked living room more than three hours. I could hear only murmurs through the front door. Johnny Savoy was inside the living room, too, but I did not hear him say anything at all.

Just once, when the old Negro woman came outside to attend her needs, the front room door was left ajar. I, who was sitting on the porch, heard Matt's angry exclamation, "God damn it, Tod, how can you sit there and speak up for a comrade who goes off to spend party funds on a woman . . ."

"It wasn't no woman. It was your sister and he loves her . . . !" I recognized Tod's anger-charged voice. I glanced inside. Johnny was sitting on a broken chair in the middle of the room, his head sunk miserably in his hands. Then the old woman, careful not to look at me a second time, returned and closed the door firmly. The voices inside subsided.

About two that morning the meeting broke up. The strangers trooped by me on their way into the woods. Nobody shook hands.

Johnny Savoy had been expelled.

I walked through to the empty bedroom and sat down. After a few minutes Tod came in and immediately began working the mimeograph machine. I said there wasn't any use making up more leaflets, the strike was over.

Tod kept turning the crank like a man in anesthesia, his eyes half shut. "We'll make up some more, I said. God damn it." Then he left off and lay down on the bed next to the machine, chainsmoking and nibbling on his fingernail. He said nothing to me. Matt had taken a couple of the strangers home in the Ford, and Johnny, whose province, the car, had been usurped, was nowhere to be found. I went to sleep.

About five in the morning I was awakened by Matt. He was sitting on my cot. He told me about the meeting, and then he said,

"You see now why, don't you? To keep him in means I or someone else always will have to watch him, no matter how loyal he is or how many times he wants to throw away his life for us. Because some day he might get careless, not only with himself but with all of us . . . You see that, don't you?"

But even way back then I knew better than to answer a man asking himself a question.

Johnny Savoy left very early in the morning, after Matt had gone to bed. He didn't say goodbye to anyone except me. Just before sunup he came into the house carrying a cardboard suitcase and stopped by my cot, lowering himself to it so as not to awaken Tod and Matt in the far corner of the room. He shook me.

"You know what happened, don't you, kid," he whispered. I nodded. "Jes' remember. They had to do what they did. I didn't leave them no choice." He was apologizing for them.

Johnny Savoy stood up, reached down to shake my hand and then was gone, out the open door, walking swiftly with Matt Sylvester's stride down towards the dewy road. I looked around the room into which was coming, grayly, the first light of day. Matt had a blanket over his face, but he moved. Tod was awake, too, his eyes bright on the door Johnny had gone through.

Then Tod North, the People's Poet, arose from his cot and walked into the bedroom. And this time he locked the door behind him.

Johnny came running back out of the plant against the stream of incomers, cracking jokes all the way. Here, too, he was popular. He jumped into the De Soto and laughed, "Le's go to my place and drink up a storm." I felt like telling Johnny that I didn't feel so good, but it wouldn't have made much difference if I had, he would only have slapped my back and said, Li'l ol' drink fix that up fine, or Boy, how come you takin' yawsef so seriously nowadays. And then he would break up into that beautiful, melodious unexpected laughter of his, that I could remember even after all these years.

We drove out to where he lived, an old and rather handsome south Illinois house with gables. A Caterpillar factory family owned the house, and Johnny had a room on the ground floor at the back. I parked the car and we went in. Johnny went through to his room without introducing me to the woman in the kitchen or her teen-age son. They seemed to accept Johnny as one of the family. He shut the door and said, "Waal, boy, le's see if you c'n still drink." He pulled a bottle of bourbon out of an old battered suitcase under his bed, brought out two glasses and we sat around with it. I really wasn't very sure he did remember me, clearly. Memory worked in a funny way with Johnny, striking him about three weeks after every one else. Abstractions always had been beyond him; but when he did remember it was the color of your hat, how you felt on a particular day, that kind of thing.

"Waal," he said, "passing through?" I said yes. He said, "As usual not knowin' where." I laughed and said yes. "Hell, boy," he said, "when *are* you goin' to settle down?" I said, When you do. He said, "I'm as settled now as I'll ever be." He drank off a slug of whiskey. After some silence he said, "Le's find out what happened to every-one. How long you been out of touch?"

I said, A long time. He asked quietly, "Ever see any of 'em?" I said that by accident I had run into Tod, a few years ago, working in a G.E. plant in Schenectady, New York; he was writing off and on and had a woman somewhere in town. Johnny said he had lost complete touch with Tod. Matt, he said, was in prison, on a Smith Act charge. I said I had later news, that Matt's lawyer had sprung him on an appeal. "No," said Johnny, "I been keepin' pretty good track. They tried to get him out on appeal, but the gov'mint lawyeh says Matt is dangerous to American institutions, so's he's theah all right. Alma may-ter. Leavenworth.

"I go to visit him," Johnny said, "every month or so." He opened his bureau drawer and took out a stack of letters. "We write." I asked Johnny if they weren't out for him too, and he smiled and said, "Who? Me? Ah'm too small fry. Allus was, allus will be. Best news Ah ever did hear though, old man Taussig got kicked in the haid by his prize bull on his experimental farm and died last year." I know it sounds inhuman, but we laughed to beat hell over that one.

Neither of us brought up Libby. It just lay there. Johnny said, "You bring a woman into town with you?" I said no. He said,

"We'll get us fixed up." Anything you say, Johnny. We sat around talking about the old days. He said that eventually the union went back into Taussig's mills and organized them. But, he added, the leadership locally was conservative to the hairline. "Sometimes," he said, "you ask yourself, what's the point?" But you could tell he wasn't being too sincere. To Johnny there always would be a point. (I didn't tell him what I knew, that the local union president in Durham was also the chairman of the White Citizens' Council.)

I asked him what he was doing in Peoria, and he shrugged and said, "Aw, you know, jes' helpin' out." He had been in the factory four years now, but he wasn't a shop steward or anything, just a rank-and-filer. "Ah got a good setup heah," he said; "ain't nothin' to complain of." He looked at me and said, "Boy, are you sure you're *well?*" I said no, as a matter of fact I wasn't, I'd been sick in L.A. He said, "You want to lie down." Then he went out the door saying he had to "make arrangements." I lay down on his bed, in that nearly bare room, with only a small portable radio, some picture magazines and a nude calendar to grace it, and dropped off to sleep, in my clothes. I had a dream, which generated the moment I lay full out. In this dream, I was called outside the house whose street had been transformed into a kind of parade ground. Marshal Josef Stalin flanked by Soviet aides was mounted on a gray charger coldly surveying the ranks of Hungarian satellite troops drawn up in regimental formation. I rode on my horse across the parade ground and Stalin said, "Murder them." One of his aides unslung a tommy gun. I took it, wheeled my horse around and sprayed the Hungarians with a never-ending spray of bullets. Then I walked my horse into the soldiers killing them. I smelled and touched death as never before. And then, in the dream, I began to cry as I slaughtered the Hungarians. I woke up weeping and exhausted. About half an hour later Johnny came back and said, "Get up, boy, we got a party on." It was then that I sensed that so long as I was going to stay in Peoria Johnny would keep me busy, I guessed so that we wouldn't have too much chance to talk.

He said we would use my car, and we went out to it. I thought as he passed the woman of the house in the hallway he looked a little shamefaced. He didn't introduce me. We got into the De Soto and, guided by him, I drove into the center of town and parked down the street just behind the freight station depot. Johnny looked around carefully and we walked quickly down the street and let ourselves in the side door of a three-story building which housed a woman's apparel shop on the ground floor. We went up two flights of stairs and walked into a comfortable, old-fashioned apartment with large overstuffed chairs and tasseled lampshades and antimacassars. It looked as though your grandmother lived there, including an enormous television set in the corner. Johnny threw himself into a chair and told me to make myself comfortable.

Two men, one in work clothes, the other in a suit, came in. Johnny introduced me as a friend from Chicago just passing through. They sat down and we started a friendly conversation, about this and that. One of the men got up and switched the television set on, the way we used to turn on the radio, low, for background music, and we talked against a housewives' quiz conducted locally, which we all gazed at from time to time. So we just sat around. We talked about pro football, reminiscing about the Chicago Bears when Halas was coaching and they had Bronco Nagurski and Danny Fortman in the line, and then we started talking about the elections. The man in the work clothes said most of the union boys were voting Democratic. He didn't say for Stevenson: he said Democratic. "Or to be more accurate," put in Johnny, "anti-Republican." The other two from Caterpillar didn't argue with him. A woman came in then, obviously from a shopping tour. Her arms were filled with packages. She was small and thin and looked like an unprepossessing Peoria housewife. The men didn't get up to help her and she went into another room and came out with some new bottles of bourbon, gin and scotch. The men took her for granted with slight overcasualness. She sat down at a card table and we joined her for some drinking. Nobody introduced me, nor her to me. We went on talking about the elections. Neither of the Caterpillar workers was much interested in Taft-Hartley. The man in the business suit was on the union executive board, and he said that Taft-Hartley they had learned to live with. The other man, however, did grumble about "all those Wall Street people in Washington." I did not make much of an impression when I pointed out that the process of introducing big businessmen into high government office had begun well before 1952, in fact during the Democratic administrations. Johnny said, "Ah hail, all they're lookin' for is a good excuse to vote Democratic, these boys." The union executive member said the membership of his union was not interested in politics, although he was. He was suspicious, he said, of the long-term wage contract, but he said it was bound to come sooner or later. "My people," he said, "smell the money in today's air. We've succeeded in educating them to the fact that the corporations are too damn fat, but instead of wanting to fight the company most of them are hoping for a long period, a kind of truce, so they can store up some cash of their own to pay off those houses and TV." They all agreed Stevenson was a pretty colorless personality and chortled at the idea of Kefauver and his coonskin hat. "He makes things a little more interesting," said the man in work clothes. "Yeah," said Johnny, "jes' lahk Hitler and his mustache." "Ah well," said the union executive, "nobody gives a damn who wins on top. It's all the same anyway." The other man grew restless and the woman poured us some more drinks. She then got up and turned on a record player and there we were, sitting around that card table, drinking with the television *and* the record player on. Then, the man in work clothes said quietly, almost muttering, "Where's Della?" The woman, "Out back." He got up, hitched up his trousers and without a word of goodbye disappeared into a long corridor off the living room. Nobody remarked his absence. The woman said, "All that really matters is how long Caterpillar can keep going. I'll vote for anyone who promises a year steady work." The union official seemed to find this amusing. I said, rather more loudly than was warranted, *Arbeit macht Frei.* Johnny and the union executive turned steady gazes on me. The woman said, amiably, "What are you, a Communist?" Johnny, who was mildly stewed, said, "And what if he is? The boy's got a right to his opinions." Then Johnny and the union official began to talk about fishing, in the middle of which the latter simply got up and disappeared down that same corridor.

I asked Johnny how long he expected to stay in Peoria. He said, "I might make my life here. At least for a while. Matt and me, we got some idea about openin' up a fishing lodge in Vermont. When he's out, that is." I said, Then you're waiting for Matt. "Why, sure, boy," he said smiling. Then he got up and, in an exaggerated duplication of the gesture of the first man, hitched up his trousers and said, "Geronimo!" And, doing a silent sailor's hornpipe, went into one of the side rooms off the corridor. Eventually, I too arose. The first door I tried was locked. The woman at the table just looked at me. I opened another door. There was a girl in it, sitting in an overstuffed chair next to a well-made bed, reading a movie-star magazine and chewing gum. She could not have been more than sixteen. She was pretty. She looked up. I shut the door and went back to the big room where I took a chair and sprawled in it. The woman at the card table looked at me coldly and then got up and disappeared into what probably was a kitchen. She shut the door behind her. There wasn't a sound in the place. I sat a while, and then one of the doors opened and the sixteen-year-old girl, perhaps she was seventeen, came out and went into the kitchen. She gave me a full look. She, too, closed the door behind her, and I could hear the sound of women's voices. Then the girl came out carrying two Coca-Cola bottles, did not look at me and went into her room, shutting the door softly behind her. I sat there a while, and then turned the record player (the musical score of *South Pacific*) off and switched the television channels until I found a news telecast. The man in the picture tube said that fighting was raging in Budapest. According to Moscow Radio, Kadar, the man Rakosi put in prison, had formed a "revolutionary workers and peasants government" and it was this government which had requested Soviet intervention. I turned the television set off and went back to my big soft chair. I kept remembering a phrase from an essay on Emerson by John Jay Chapman in which he described how Emerson had let loose something within him which made him in his own eyes as good as anyone else. It was Emerson, Chapman said, who had first made it possible for him to say to himself: "After all, it is just as well that there should be *one* person like *me* in the world." All through my travels it was this phrase from Chapman which used to reinvigorate and refresh me. But I couldn't point to any single writer or teacher who had ever given me this exultance; it seemed to me that when this first happened to me (I think it was probably some time at the university) it was the result and culmination of virtually all my experience. Thinking on it, it seemed that I had lived half my life according to the terms of literary wills drawn up by the unattainable, or unemulatable, or dead and desiccated. I liked Chapman because he spoke so much truth about America and yet was incapable of being adored, or totemized. He, too, scored the lack of passion which in America is one effect of that almost total absence of concentration except on making money. He, too, saw that "when you see cruelty going on before you, you are put to the alternative of interposing to stop it, or of losing your sensibility." And what, after all, was television, billboards, the whole way of life that America had advanced and fallen into, but a vast and pervasive cruelty to the human spirit all the more sinister because everyone protests honorable intentions. The bleaching-out of the bones of the spirit is an atrocity compared to which Hiroshima and Belsen are positively *understandable*. Chapman was ultimately broken by his fight against what he termed "atmospheric pressure" in America, this intellectual dishonesty, moral evasion, congenital and amiable and diabolic blandness. Nobody reads John Jay Chapman any more. If you doubt it, ask any university student or graduate in America today who John Jay Chapman was and you will probably receive the reply, "Um, wasn't he a Supreme Court Justice or something?" (Sure, I know about the reissue. Which raises a question: in our circumstance in America, does a paperback reissue revive, or bury deeper in the disguise of rehabilitation? We have never lacked for books. We are choking on them [cf. "paperback revolution"]. What we lack are men who can be excited by books.)

So I sat in that old whorehouse in Peoria, Illinois, and I could not *move*. The motor had gone dead. If the whole place had been on fire I could not have fled. I was beyond dead; felt nothing, saw little, heard everything. I don't know how long I was there, sitting like that, with that whey-faced little woman peeking out the kitchen door occasionally to see if I was still round. I wasn't even waiting for Johnny to come out. Finally, I knew that if I didn't do something, I'd just lie down on the floor and someone would have to come and carry me somewhere. I called to the woman for a coke, which she brought me, in ill-concealed bad temper, and then went and hid herself behind the kitchen door some more. I do declare she was afraid of me. I took out from my jeans pocket a small container. For the past six months I had not been without this particular celluloid container. Inside were a number of spansules, capsules, pills and tablets. I used this special container mainly for purposes of reassurance. This time, however, I swallowed two dexedrines, and then sat back for it to hit. When it does it is swell. Fifteen minutes later the jolt came. I went downstairs to the car and wrote out a note, telling Johnny that I had to leave town, that I wished him luck and that I would see him next time I was through. I went back upstairs and into the kitchen where the woman was sitting drinking a cup of coffee and slicing pieces off a jelly roll. I asked her to give the note to Johnny. Still sitting, she took it and read it, then folded it up and went right on eating. I said goodbye and went out the way I came.

By the time I got to the De Soto I was feeling terrific. There is nothing quite like a kick on dexedrine. It dries the mouth, flattens the belly, and even in Peoria, Illinois, you stride with seven-league boots. I swung into the driver's seat and almost knocked my head off against the roof. I sat with my head in my hands for a few moments, swearing, hoping the collision had done nothing to reduce the potency of the spansules. After the ringing went away, I started up the car, and cruised the afternoon streets, looking for a hitchhiker or someone who might be needing a ride. Nobody seemed to, so I headed out of town on Highway 24, going east, and just as soon as I was in a no-speed-limit area I cracked my foot down on the pedal. I could feel sap rising up in me like oil in an engine. It was a cold thinly sunny day after the rain but I had put the top down and waves of wind made me sit up straighter. I kept a sharp eye out for speed traps. I wanted to keep going this way. Between Peoria and the junction with Highway 66, I hit 100 for minutes at a time, a not inconsiderable achievement, as they say, on Highway 24 which is fairly narrow. I stopped off at one small town to eat, gas up, crawl under the car to check the rear spring and send off five cheerful telegrams to various people around the country. Old Man Chapman, when he retired to Dutchess County, like Tolstoy at Yasnaya Polyana, had written, "There's only one real joy in life . . . the joy of casting at the world the stone of an unknown world." Man, that's what I was, at 100 m.p.h. skidding past the stop sign at the junction to Highway 66 and heading due north, north to Chicago, a 100-mile-an-hour stone from another world hurling myself at the first real world I had ever known.

Chicago was my home town.

*

After I put down the phone, in that dirty old YMCA room on Wabash Avenue above the railroad tracks going towards the La Salle Street Station, I sat down on the bed and looked out into the Chicago night. I thought about the nature of self-pity. And I began to entertain a sorrow — no longer for myself; I think the past eighteen hundred miles had burned most of that out of me — for all my friends and brothers in Chicago, that the world of which we had talked and attempted for had not come to pass, and I wondered whether they felt as misfit as I. This was, I think, the basic failure of the Left in America, that it failed to prepare us for defeat, to train us in the arts of custodianship. But what was it in us which led us for too long to accept the stewardship of the incompetent and blind? I have never held with the widely prevailing view that adherence to an idea is to be explained, merely, by unbalances of the soul. And yet . . . and yet, what was it we all shared in common, aside from the vision?

I checked out of the Y and drove straight out to Rogers Park, where I had arranged, by telegram back in Los Angeles, to stay with Paul and Helen Wooster. I didn't know what my reception would be. But when I got to their flat, on a nice, prosperous tree-shaded street, Helen flung open the door and kissed me terrifically. I was really surprised, because when I had lived at her house Helen and I had often been not exactly what you call friends. Behind Helen, in the doorway, was Paul, graying, handsome, a little paunchy, beaming. They were, it struck me, *glad* to see me. At that moment I think I felt nothing more than deep abiding relief.

Helen was as I remembered her; deep-voiced, self-assured, deceptively willowy. She and Paul and I, we immediately went into the kitchen to talk. They hadn't known anything of my activities since I left Detroit, and it was with the usual difficulty I tried to explain. I had expected them to judge; but they did not. They seemed to find it delightful that I should have spent the past two years hobnobbing with movie royalty, and we laughed and laughed over my store of Hollywood jokes. I knew that at least Helen had changed and softened when, during a lull in the conversation which I wished to avoid, she said, re politics. "Oh, that old stuff. There's plenty of time for *that*." Even so, soon and inevitably we found ourselves talking of our union friends who had been ejected from the movement. Paul said most of them — former regional directors, trade union chairmen, labor executives, research personnel — were now making their livelihoods in the nooks and crannies of the industrial relations scene. Helen was doing part-time work for DePauw University and Paul was doing off-hours private consulting to a firm of timber merchants. I blinked at Paul, and he said, grinning ruefully, and somewhat shamefacedly, "If you can't lick 'em, join 'em." "Oh, Paul," said Helen, "don't be so pompous." It made me very happy to see these two. As lightly as I knew how, I asked them how they were. Helen smiled, because she knew what I was asking, and without any reserve, although Paul looked a little embarrassed in the background, told me the important parts of their history over the past years.

"The first thing," Helen said, "is that Paul and I are legal as hell now." Paul blushed and said nothing. "Oh, Paul," said Helen, "you *are* a puritan." "It's my upbringing," said Paul. It was too, I thought. Paul's father, a capitalist of the old, calvinistic stripe, had been a lay preacher and Church Moderator in the company town which he had built for "his" workers outside Pittsburgh. A long time ago we had stopped making jokes about Paul's father twirling in his grave.

Helen said that after I left Detroit the whole shebang collapsed like a house of cards. Victor Hauser had won such a decisive victory at the convention that he was able to clean out from union headquarters on Woodrow Wilson Avenue everybody left of center. Which meant us. Paul and Helen were fired together. John Alston, my best friend, had abandoned the union and gone on to New York. I knew about that part, I said, because I had worked with John in sound recording. I was surprised at my tone when referring to John, and it was obvious neither Paul nor Helen felt any of this. They had made their peace with John, I had not. I found, as I talked with them, that I kept intruding the subject of John into the conversation, as though I wanted them to speak ill of him. But they wouldn't. This surprised me, because in the old days Paul and to a lesser degree Helen had been censorious, within the Detroit Left, of John. I had to admit to myself I still bore a grudge. Do you ever forgive your teacher?

Helen explained, with considerable humor, that in the middle of the convention explosion Paul had gone to his wife, Cora, a newspaperwoman, to ask for a divorce so he could marry Helen. Cora had become hysterical, as was her wont, and had gone to the union to demand they fire both Paul and Helen, which Hauser did, all right, but not because of any of Paul's domestic difficulties. Then Cora ran to the party leadership and demanded that they intervene to "save our marriage." It was characteristic of the Detroit Reds that they should have consented, and Paul found himself in the slightly grotesque situation of attending a political meeting, called by the top leaders of the state organization, to discuss his marriage. It must have strained his loyalties to the limit. When it was suggested that he return to Cora, Paul did not stalk out of the meeting, he tried to *argue* with them — and all this with Cora weeping histrionically in the corner. At the time I worked with Paul he was about the most henpecked man in creation; it was as inevitable as these things ever are that he would wind up with Helen, who admired, loved and wanted him, and who had worked at his side, day and often night, for five solid years. I know I should feel some sort of sympathy for Cora, but as Freud is supposed to have said when a group of colleagues were discussing, in psychoanalytical terminology, a certain patient, "But gentlemen, when all is said and done, Herr X is a sonofabitch." That is the way I feel about Cora.

Things became so hot legally, said Paul and Helen, that they had to flee Michigan, leaving fortunately no children behind to Cora, to wander the country for a few years, doing litigation and publicity for various shrinking Left unions until, finally, they wound up in Chicago where their luck was changing for the better. Paul was now a part-time legal consultant to the regional office of our old union, the Amalgamated Vehicle Builders. The hows and whys he had achieved this minor position in the union of which he had once been the legal brains, he would explain later. Helen insisted she was now a homebody, but I doubted it. What I did not doubt was that Helen was more at repose with herself than I had ever seen her.

Now, all this may sound a little squalid, domestic difficulties and all, but all the time I had known Paul in Detroit, he had been a dried-up calculating machine, with the courage of a fish when the chips were down; the party and Cora and his father had scared all the male sex clean out of him. He had been a total intellect (and pretty good at that), deeply uncomfortable in anything except purely cerebral relationships. I doubt whether he and Helen would have made it had they not first softened the ground between them by years of consulting over trade union statistics. What made the whole thing poignant, it seemed to me, was that Helen was a Negro. Maybe I should explain.

In 1946, after going AWOL from the Army, bumming the western highways in the company of E. J. Birdsong and establishing temporary residence on Skid Row, I found my way back to Chicago. It didn't take long for me to realize that I had outgrown Chicago, the local radical movement and my friends. Most of my short time there was taken up with hacking, frustrating quarrels, sometimes pointless, occasionally violent, with people whom I had dreamed of returning to. I tried to make contact; I tried to tell them what I had seen and learned, but they were strangely unreceptive, even wary. You've grown away from us, their eyes seemed to say, come back before it's too late. But I knew I could never come back. I was ready to eat the country, and they were not. I just didn't belong in Chicago any longer, it seemed. An abyss of experience separated me from my friends and comrades. All questions about the Army and Germany I evaded; yet I tried to *tell* them. I had been a thousand light-years away, and I could not come all the way back. Where for me the League of Anti-Fascist Youth was a stop on the way, for the others — even my Corpuscle Quartet — the League, or its parent organization, was *the* stop, a home. It was a question of what I suppose I'd best call occupational aptitude. Since childhood, I had taken it for granted that, one way or another, I would be a changer. It was my *job*, in the same way that you may be a shoe salesman and another man a sign painter.

But the Army, and then Germany, made me realize that I had been seeing life not through my own eyes but by means of leaflets, texts and the eyes of those who shared my dreams. I also realized that by transferring my allegiance to a group such as the League, I had relinquished, in exchange for the benefits of warmth, comradeship and the keys to the doors of my youth, some of my few natural instincts for observation. Dad, with Darrow, used to try to teach me that "knowledge was the product of doubt" and that to the degree a man gave up voluntarily his right to doubt he was also giving up his right to think. I saw that that was what I had done, as a member of the League and even more so as one of its leaders. But I could now try to assess, with a degree of objectivity, the razor-edged blessings of the League.

One of the things I had most admired about the League of Anti-Fascist Youth, and the William Lloyd Garrison School, was that they both subscribed to an international ideology which somewhere on earth seemed to be *working*. Even Dad could not deny Steffens had said so. At League meetings you had the feeling that you were actually helping Chinese and Africans and Russians liberate themselves; you had a feeling, implicit in the ritualistic, byzantinized language which was spoken at these meetings, that there were people all over the world who thought as you did. Best of all, admit it, you felt as if you were *winning*.

I could not but compare this sensible emotion that I was riding the wave of the future with the lugubrious state of mind of the labor people, my mother's and father's friends and co-workers, who belonged to the anti-Communist "democratic socialist" branch of the working-class movement. Though, by ideal, equally internationalist, *they* didn't have a single spot on this earth they could point to and say the future was working. Deprived of a mecca, of a superfunctioning Vatican, of a source of inspiration and a proof that somewhere the working class was exercising power (and the Garrison School was very competent at furnishing this type of proof), they had, my father's friends in particular, over the years steadily narrowed their horizons until the union local, the shop-floor grievance, the collective bargaining agreement had become ends in themselves rather than steps towards the New Jerusalem whose vision had made splendid and uplifted their younger years. I had seen my father's breed change and decay, diminishing until they became either fat-cat AFL business agents or Old Home--type left-wingers, Kiwanis of the Red mythos: even as I honored and loved them I felt betrayed and bored by their everlasting smoke-filled meetings, their card playing and cigar chewing, their Chico Marx problems with the language, their unshaven passionate wrangles over long-dead points, their marvelous, doomed attempt to dress up a European ethic in American clothes: their lack of shame at any of this. At the first opportunity I allied myself with a group which seemed to synthesize the humanism of early childhood associations with *success*.

But I knew it was time, now, to see the League of Anti-Fascist Youth for what it was and what it was not. And the first thing I saw was that the many "struggles" (as people in it called each campaign) of the League were conducted on such a low level of pragmatism that even the infrequent victories held little meaning. Ostensibly devoted to the cause of speaking to "The People" at their own level and in their own language (the other way had been tried and failed), the League had become fatally implicated in the *way* to say it rather than the thing that needed saying. It had forgotten, if indeed it ever knew, that leadership requires the habitual, systematic telling of complex and compromising truths, of hammering away at *what could be true out of what was true*. And this it did not do, I was coming to suspect, because it no longer knew what the truth was. There was always at hand an excuse not to generalize, not to (dirty American word) theorize: there was too much practical work to do. It was a good excuse because it made sense. Getting wage increases, day nurseries and justice for the Negro was not only right in itself but captured the trust and loyalty of "The People." It made converts. True enough. But converts to *what?* Campaigns were waged without any real ultimate goal. And about converts: I knew that whenever participation "in struggle" succeeded in bringing in a new member this person forthwith was pushed into a second campaign, and on and on, so that it was entirely possible to be a dyed-in-the-wool, paid-up member of organized leftism and know nothing more of the real issues of American radicalism than the joyful ennui of stamp-licking. It was a good, and fulfilling, way to chase your tail, but it should not have been confused with Building a New World Fast.

Nor was it enough to dismiss the whole thing, Moscow took snuff, Chicago sneezed. What *was* the attractiveness of this message, both apocalyptic and passionately empirical, which went straight to the heart? *Why?* Why did some of the best Americans I have ever known, Americans readier than most to sacrifice life, liberty and property in the name of irreproachable ideals, why did they so persistently sabotage their hearts and minds? Was it the highest secret price you paid for knowing that your philosophy, and certainly your party, hadn't the slightest chance of achieving power? Was it, in fact, the easy way out? When the muck is rising to nose level, how *do* you keep a clear head?

And, sooner or later, I had to begin thinking about myself too. Why, before I went into service, had I clung to the League for dear life, and now spend my afternoons avoiding old friends and sitting in the bleachers of Wrigley Field? The more vaguely alienated from them I felt the more open I saw it all. There had been many strong, valid reasons for going to the League. But didn't some of it have to do with a desire to escape the rat-race which had killed my mother and ruined my father? As much as I loved my days at the Acme Screw Factory and all the other machine shops I'd worked in, was the subworld of industry the one I wanted to inhabit until I died? Wasn't there, despite all protestations to myself, a good part of me which hated that subworld, hated not the machines and noise and dirt (young, I liked these) but the way it narrowed and pressed down a man and fatigued him before his time? Did not, in a word, the tradition in which I had grown up, and which as a matter of course expected me to take my place somewhere among the machines and grease-lidded workers, repel me? Closer yet, was not the League a way of escaping entrapment — did I perhaps not sense that ideas were my only means of escaping entrapment and climbing out of it even before I had a chance to enter it as a man — joining the first group that recognized ideas as a special mark of distinction? I wondered if I would not have jumped aboard *any* train which seemed to be traveling *out*. Interesting questions. It was a truism I had always accepted that a man could not achieve personal satisfaction if he cut himself off from the struggle. And that, friend, is without quotes. Day after day I sat in the bleachers and thought: maybe yes, maybe no.

My life in my home town (which I choose to call it) ran to the same irregular pattern as the months on the road. I drank away most of my separation pay and had a bruising fight with an old friend on the sidewalk outside the Rialto Theater on State Street because he accused me of insulting his girl, which in fact I had done. I won the fight, but this only made me gloomier than ever, and the word soon got around that I was, if still trustworthy, "unstable" and very likely suffering from combat fatigue (although I had, of course, not seen a front line). My closest friends, the old Corpuscle Quartet, had not yet come home from the service. Only the girls were around, which would not at all have been bad had I been able to address myself to them individually. But their idea of welcoming a returned soldier was to surround him with a kind of group, motherly warmth. The one time I tried to kiss one of the girls, in her darkened hallway, she recoiled as though with the horror of incest. I'm sure I stalked away muttering which only, of course, contributed to the general impression that I had been radically corrupted by Army life. I deeply missed the boys of the Corpuscle Quartet. But Cal was still somewhere in the Philippines, Nick was at an army hospital recuperating from an amputated arm and refusing to see anyone from Chicago, and Stu, of whom I have yet to speak at length, was languishing in a jail in Dutch Guinea. I did not feel lonely, but I did feel alone.

Once, during this period, I took a train to Ann Arbor to see Maureen Langer, the North Shore girl who had won my heart so many (it seemed) years ago, but our interview was strained, and all I could take away from it was the slightly farcical memory of Maureen and her groom-to-be, a tall lanky law student, showing me around their new small apartment. It did not make me feel better to realize that I had on several occasions written Maureen to explain that under no circumstances was I ready for marriage. (The idea, indeed, was laughable.) Still, this did nothing to revive flagging spirits, especially when to it was added the humiliation of a lesser incident which had occurred when I had pressed the bell of Maureen's sorority house. The girl who had answered the door asked me who I was, and I had told her, and she had fallen back with an astonished giggle, hand over mouth, and said, Oh, so *you're* him. I realized then that Maureen had very likely been reading my love letters (the most embarrassing of them written from the deck of a troopship going to Europe) to her sorority sisters.

On returning to Chicago from Ann Arbor, I began making nightly raids on the Garrison School to interrupt the class lecturers and engage them in direct, not to say what I then felt was eloquent polemic. The school did not renew its offer to take me on its staff. I spoke several times in Grant Park, became involved in a few more fights, and waited impatiently for one of the Corpuscle Quartet to return. In the event, it was Nick, minus his arm, who came back to Chicago first. I was terrifically happy to see him and full of foreboding, which was fully borne out when I met him at Dearborn Street Station, and put out my hand to shake his, reflexively. I could have struck myself dead. Nick drew back and said, through his teeth, "Don't you have any tact, you sonofabitch?" Later, we tried to laugh it away, but I knew I had hurt him. During the first two days we spent together, mostly walking along Michigan Boulevard and in Grant Park, Nick hectored and nagged and resented me unmercifully. He had heard stories of my "behavior" and was entirely on the other side; his emotional needs were now to be with the movement and its adherents, and he would not jeopardize that to defend me. Perhaps in this I am misreading Nick's motives, which were in any case understandable. But it came as a real blow to me, for after he came back I knew that I should find no real support in Chicago. Cal's strictures, when he returned, would be harsher still. At the close of those two days with Nick when I tried to talk politics with him, he froze up and then burst out that I was heading for a betrayal of all we had promised to do together. I lost my temper and said that that was what I was thinking about him, Cal and all the others. We parted on openly hostile terms. I remember the very last thing Nick said was, And don't go around pretending you're an artist, because you'll *never* make one. A week later occurred an ugly little anticlimactic incident between Nick and myself which finished us.

Paul Robeson was giving a concert in Grant Park which thousands of Chicago-area trade unionists and left-wingers were due to attend. I went too, partly I think to see Maureen, who came down from Ann Arbor to be one of the money-collecting hostesses. I was then in a pipe-smoking, Stendhal-quoting (and misunderstanding) phase, and I wanted to impress Maureen with not only my maturity but also my indifference to her. Alas, Maureen who had been *born* mature saw through me instantly, and grinned fondly all day long. During Robeson's speech the loudspeaker cables were cut. The crowd stirred. Someone cried out, There he is, that's the one! And parts of the crowd went after a boy in a red sweater, with Nick out in front, screaming, Lynch him! A large proportion of the running crowd was composed of Negroes who took up the cry, Lynch him! The police intervened, and several of them sheltered the suspected saboteur in a doorway of a fur shop on Michigan Boulevard while police reinforcements poured in from neighboring streets. There was a near riot, with Nick in the middle of it. The notables on the speakers' platform appealed for order but since the cables had been cut their voices carried no further than the first few rows of audience on the park side of the boulevard. I saw a policeman advancing on Nick with a billy, and I dashed across the boulevard and grabbed Nick, pushing him away from the police and over towards the park. He didn't scream or abuse me, he just put his shoulder grimly against mine, and pushed back, breathing hard and on the verge of stubborn, bitter tears. Finally, he cursed, "Let me go-o-o!" in a kind of wail, glaring at me with such unalloyed loathing that I did let go. He was swallowed up in the swirling, milling crowd, and I walked down one of the side streets without looking back. To this day I will never forget that look of hatred on Nick's face. Today, Nick, after an unhappy career as a steelworker, student, and an abortive marriage, is a social worker, but I doubt if he has forgotten, either.

A few days later I was in Detroit, with no money or friends, except John Alston. Sometimes I think John Alston was my destiny, and that is not a word that rolls easily off my tongue. By way of union contacts I had met him at an army camp in Maryland while I was in transit overseas. The Army bored him beyond words, and he could never disguise his contempt that I was not as he in this attitude. We spent a few weekends together in Washington, he had advised me not to go overseas, I had refused his advice, and then we lost touch. All I knew about John was that he was married, had a family, was a young trade union functionary and had a power of influence over me which to this day I do not completely understand. It had been John who introduced me, casually and condescendingly, to a side of wartime Washington which I, a dog-faced corporal, might otherwise never have seen.

John Alston was not like anyone I had ever known before. Though still in his early thirties he affected the mannerisms of someone many years older; ferociously ambitious, of nimble soul, he nursed a power to conceal his humble origins as the son of a lower East Side cigar maker. John was on the make, and he was gambling on the red. Somewhere in his history — on tours for the government into tenant farmer territory, on tear-gas and picket lines, somewhere in the midst of his premature participation in the echelons of authority — his youthful idealism had cracked against the face of reality, causing him to shift over to an applied, detached, even fanatic study of the techniques of power, of manipulation and maneuver. When he had a chance to go to a university, he did not, as most New York radical boys did, choose a local, familiar school, but a small one in the Ivy League. From the school, and from government service beyond the Rockies, he emerged with an anonymous accent to cover over his brisk Delancey Street nasality, a fund of folk jokes for any occasion, an almost embarrassing pride in his ability to blend with natural sons of soil and toil, and an Ivy League bride. Drive and luck and a small genius for thinking — and charming — on his feet had pushed John to the top of the strongest and most strategic of industrial trade unions, the Amalgamated Vehicle Builders, from which he had been drafted into the Army, he claimed, by a cabal of opposition union leaders. A subscriber to the Hemingway code, he liked to prove his ability to take punishment and thus was constantly nursing fantasies of revenge. You were either for John or against him. In private moments he liked to talk, with a kind of genuine self-drama, about living, working and dying "with grace." He was a man of great fear and therefore an opportunist; of vast personal charm and quick generosities. There was very little of the spontaneous in John; always he calculated, even his remotest facial expressions. His frown was theatrical and his smile was bestowed. It was his fate to use his ideals to force those of higher station to accept him, to doff their hats and call him John.

The few weeks I spent in Maryland and Washington with John, the object of his vanity and kindness and bored observations on life, I think changed my life. He knew how to prick my pride, how to humble a young man and make him stupid. But also to teach. He had to have protégés. I was only one of the several, but this I did not learn until I was well into Detroit. One of the ways that Alston made me feel stupid was precisely in the similarity of our backgrounds. For me, being dirt-poor was something which gave me a kinship with other poor people at the same time it was something to *get over;* being poor for Alston was a genetic crime which his parents had committed against him — but he was determined to *use* it, like a thin cold spring inside him. Not for a moment, by the time I knew him, did he believe in the outer face of the world; he said I was a fool because I did. Look behind the face, he ordered. Take even your best friends apart to see what makes them tick, he ordered. Above all, never think of dying for a cause; it is the indelible mark of the slob.

For the few weeks I was with Alston I absorbed the glimmerings of a whole new way of looking at life, with a kind of unreal superrealism, even with a curious, stoical *tendresse.* He taught me the outlines of a system of skepticism and tactical maneuver, the remnants of which I carry with me to this day; a sense of combat and tactic whose tensileness lay at the very heart of the basic defense mechanism of that plebeian class we were committed to serve, and which, while still in the service of those whom we regarded as exploited and downtrodden, should also be applicable to all times and places and situations. From Alston, additionally, I learned to want to be fashionable, to play the game, in and among that curious déclassé elite in which he moved and to which I aspired. The trick was to be studiedly simple, even primitive if necessary. I started to read Hemingway and Forster and W. H. Hudson because these were John Alston's favorite authors. The first phase of our relationship was climaxed by a glorious, groggy two-day-and-night drinking levee in the Mayflower Hotel suite of the Texas judge who was then chief political adviser to Henry Wallace, the Vice-president of the United States. It was V-J Day, and Washington was bedlam, except in those rooms up at the Mayflower where, spontaneously, a group of soldiers and a few civilians had come to talk, seriously, and drunkenly, about the future. I will never forget those two days during which I could not have uttered more than ten words; Alston wouldn't let me. This was his world, and I was goggle-eyed. OSS agents with central European accents, young New Deal brain-trusters, a couple of propaganda experts from the Pentagon, a Congressman from Minnesota and a factory magnate's son from Indiana, a Ranger brigadier general, two men in civilian clothes who had just come out of Yugoslavia, a corporation attorney who quoted Bukharin and a trade union official who quoted Durkheim, a grizzled merchant seaman and a radical clergyman, and a number of young majors, captains and lieutenants (I was, as I say, a corporal), the whole assemblage sprawling around on the floor and drinking from an inexhaustible earthenware crock of whiskey which was passed around by the Judge, who sat stiffly in a wooden chair in the middle of his living room. The one time I tried to speak, everyone looked at me as though I were something the cat dragged in, and I shut up. For three nights and two days during the Victory celebrations, while Washington boiled and went roaring crazy under the Judge's windows, they sat around in those rooms and drank and talked as though they would never stop. They talked of the war, how it started, how it was fought, whether we would fight with Russia. I shut up and listened and learned things I had not known. I found out that the week before, an association of the largest industrial manufacturers in the United States had convened to launch an ambitious campaign for cracking the unions, for a counteroffensive against those new institutions which they had been forced to tolerate during the war but now believed threatened managerial prerogatives; what amounted to an industrial *putsch*. This bit of intelligence, so stunning to me, was discussed with equanimity and even phlegm by the others, who seemed to accept, calmly, as their starting point, that the end of hostilities would see the beginning of a real class struggle in America.

I think it worth more than passing interest, which is to say I believe it exceedingly important, to note the fundamental assumptions which seemed deeply worked into the fog and smoke of the Judge's rooms, assumptions on which many thousands of men and women in the coming years were to base, and often to break, their personal lives:

that the essentially defensive military victory over Fascism was in itself a smashing blow for social progress and had already more than secured our foot in the door of the future; and that a world-wide Popular Front was on the utmost verge of pushing civilization as we know it over the hump of "pre-history"; and

that this would not be achieved without some convulsive confrontation with the domestic Right in America, most probably during a forthcoming depression; and

that this millennium, our strictly rendered version of the Second Coming, was to be interpreted and hoped for in as many ways as there were socio-political doctrines represented up at the room in the Mayflower; and that this was a cause of no anxiety to anybody; and

that the principal architecture of this City of God for which we were working and meant to continue working could be represented by something as mild as an indigenous Labor Party headed by Phil Murray, or yet by the sovietization of the Youngstown Sheet and Tube Co.; that it was the fact and not the form of change that was decisive, and

that the war had made us good.

I had heard, and half believed such talk from my own comrades, but to hear it from these men of such obviously disparate roots and convictions jarred me.

Of one thing only, of what had happened to those two Japanese cities, nobody talked much, avoided it in fact. Well, *they* might feel guilty but I didn't. I was a member, in good standing, of the Double Feature Generation: nothing new was startling to me. This was what most separated me, perhaps, from the others in that room up in the Mayflower. They were from a generation which still counted in single lives; I had grown up when you worked your way through to the value for a single life by starting the other way around, from the millions of dead, and from the engines of war which the others, the ones Alston had brought me to listen to, had made but were afraid of (and which I hadn't made but felt completely at home with). Roughly speaking, the others valued each single human being because theirs was still a traditional America, where the link had not been broken, at least in their minds, to the ol' swimming hole and the rurally based verities; while I, and those of my age group who cared, if we made the effort at all, could achieve this respectful contact with life, as composed of individual human beings, only by struggling back over the logistical coldness of what we knew to be true in contemporary America, only by deliberately discarding certain assumptions of modern behavior which we had grown up believing as natural and ordained, assumptions from which the older generation (sometimes as little as five years older — generations succeed each other quickly in my native land) turned their faces away in horror and guilt. (When the Judge was told of Hiroshima he suddenly felt old, tired and worn out, and very very afraid. When I read about it on the tickertape in the War College I felt exhilarated, rather interested and not in the slightest guilty; in fact, I wished I had been there to see it . . .)

But this was not enough to keep me in Washington. I had to see for myself. Against John Alston's advice I volunteered for occupation duty in Germany; duty anywhere. John was hurt by that and we didn't send each other letters all the time I was overseas. Then, just before I left Frankfurt, I wrote a postcard to a union friend of mine and said to give my best regards to Alston, who had by this time gone back to Detroit. I received a postcard back, at the bottom of which my friend wrote, "Alston says drop around when you get out of the Army." All the time I have known John Alston that is the way we have done things, obliquely and never directly.

So one rainy night in 1946 I banged on the door of a tract house in a working-class zoning development on Telegraph Road in Detroit, and the door was answered by Rhea, Alston's wife. I was surprised. I had expected someone different looking. Rhea was a tiny, whippersnap of a woman, a faded Scott Fitzgerald belle. (Some years later I chanced upon her marriage photograph: she had been marvelously piquant then. The scandal had been first-rate when Alston took away the daughter of his college provost, John, the cigar maker's son.) She invited me in, said John had told her about me. I was pleased and flattered, and we stayed up for several hours talking about Alston, more frankly and deeply than we ever would again. I was ingenuous in a way I now recognize as brutal, because I did not know how it was to be married, and I remember asking Rhea what she would do if Alston were unfaithful and she said, like a shot, Leave him. I remember feeling proud of the way Rhea had snapped off that answer. But when it came to the point, a few years later, she was tired and couldn't and didn't.

John himself came in out of the rain, from a late meeting, and seemed genuinely happy to see me, if not especially surprised. Rhea went upstairs to bed, and John and I stayed up talking. He told me that he had been unable to get back his old top job with the union; he was now Fringe Benefits Administrator. It was a step down which he blamed, correctly, on the machinations of factional enemies. His demotion was the first of a long series of defeats which was eventually to demoralize and splinter the Left of the union. Alston talked, I listened. I didn't understand most of what he told me that first night; it mainly concerned intra-union quarrels and gossip, but as I was soon to learn, factional disputes took precedence over all other issues inside the AVB-CIO. Towards dawn, Alston asked me about Germany, and briefly I told him. When I finished he nodded, just once, and said, Well, maybe you did have to go and see for yourself. For weeks afterwards as I began to live in Detroit, I walked about in a small aura of personal triumph because Alston had, as much as he ever would, allowed he might have been wrong.

I wanted to go to work in a shop — an auto factory — immediately. But about a week after I arrived, while I was watching him shaving, he said, I want you to keep to an agreement. What's that? I asked. He said, lathering his face casually, Keep your mouth shut and your ears open. Don't make any speeches, don't try to think too much at first. Do what I tell you, without questioning, even if at first it seems silly or pointless to you. Don't argue. I don't have time to waste. Six months of living here, and learning from me, will answer most of your questions. What I want from you, in return for getting you in, is for you not to do silly and pointless things. Listen to me and keep your mouth shut.

I was offended, but also very flattered that he should want to be my teacher and guide in Detroit. I thought it over and then eagerly agreed. As soon as I declared myself in he said, If you really want to learn, you shouldn't work on the floor. That's for the jerks. You should be with me, near the top, so you can watch how policy is made.

Within another week I had been hired, through Alston's influence, as his administrative assistant at union headquarters on Woodrow Wilson Avenue. As I found out later, this took some doing, because the AVB had a tradition of hiring staff members out of factories. But Alston had gone to bat for me, with the Left, his comrades, as well as the Right.

I didn't realize how much of a marked man I was, coming in as Alston's protégé. For one thing, it meant the instant hostility of people like Paul and Helen. The Left inside the union was never to forgive Alston for bringing in an outsider without prior consultation with them, and it marked the first major, open quarrel he was to have with them.

Observing and participating in the life of the union convinced me that all my prior experience had been bush league. That was how my mentor, John Alston, wanted it and that was how he treated me. I remember once barging into a private conference on wage tactics between Alston and Paul Wooster and sitting down, by instinct, with them to join in. Paul was slightly affronted, but Alston grew red in the face. He didn't have to say anything, and I got out, my face flaming. Later, he came into my cubbyhole and said, Let me make things clearer. You're here to learn. Keep your mouth shut and watch until you know enough to shoot it off, and don't even do that without checking with me first. Don't argue with me; save your first doubts until you know how to have intelligent ones. In return for which I'll tell you everything I think you're ready to know.

I knew what he was saying by repeating himself. So that was the deal. Plus another condition. I was, Alston said, to stay away from the Detroit section of the League of Anti-Fascist Youth. Alston's faction, which included the Communists, was under a heavy barrage from the opposition, led by Victor Hauser, and Alston didn't want me used as a pawn.

It wasn't easy at first to stay away from the youth movement. But I accepted Alston's conditions. I kept my mouth shut and my eyes open, and gradually I came to be accepted, even by the toughened, union-wise veterans, the Old Guard, the Flying Squads who had marched on Ford in '32 and knocked Harry Bennett keel over ass, who had been in the Flint local when the majority of members were Pinkertons and stoolies, who had fought at the Battle of the Viaduct and sat down the first historic time at Kelsey-Hayes. But I was not so easily accepted by my own comrades. For one thing they were of a different class, middle-class professionals, a heavy sprinkling of ex-professors and a surprising few from America's First Families. They thought I was crude and obscenely young. (I hadn't learned to change some of my Army habits, such as wearing the same shirt for a week. It took Alston to sit me down and tell me about this.) I would have been a lot lonelier had it not been for a Finnish-American girl, a shop steward at Dodge Local 3, a lean pretty girl who introduced me to the Finnish community of Detroit and the mixed pleasures of all-night summer picnic drinking. I hope I have enough time to tell you about Sylvie Torvald.

Like those around me my entire life was tied up with the union. Working for the union was an around-the-clock proposition, seven days a week; it pleased me. I thought that I knew how to work but had to admit I could take lessons from the people around me. Soon I was indulging in "chop chop," union jargon for factionalism. You couldn't avoid it in those days in Detroit. My circle of friends was drawn entirely from the union, or Left unions in Detroit. (I used to hang around the Office Workers Union but stopped when they asked me during an insurance agents' strike to telephone scabs at three in the morning and hiss, "We'll get you, scab!" Not that I decline this tactic always; but *office* workers!)

This factionalism of which I speak was conducted like a war, the terms of which were often squalid — and yet in retrospect I think that the rivalry of Victor Hauser and K. T. Tolliver for presidency of the union was the expressed essence of all the conflicting drives in the American working class immediately after the war. I joined the union when Hauser had just unseated Tolliver for the presidency at the annual convention but had failed to acquire a majority of the national executive board, which was still in the "Tolliver camp." The real business of union staffers that year was to prepare for the next convention at which Hauser and Tolliver were to try to smash each other's faction. It was more or less understood in the labor movement that the AVB convention would be critical, and Left and Right unions from all over the country (and Canada) poured money and staffers into what should have been a purely domestic do. From the United Automobile Workers, our sister union across the town, both factions freely drew men and material. We saw as much of the UAW's president, R. J. Thomas, in Tolliver's office as I'm sure the other side saw Walter Reuther in Vic Hauser's office. Sometimes it seemed everybody's quarrel but ours.

Left and Right in the AVB-CIO were not too easy to define. Though the union's vice-president and one-time president, fat bumbling K. T. Tolliver, drew some of his support from the Left, he was anti-communist, anti-ideological, anti-theory. His motto was, "I'm for higher wages, decent conditions and only enough political action to protect ourselves, and I hate Victor Hauser's guts." Hauser, and his two brothers, Dominick and Jess ("From border to border and coast to coast/The bosses are saying who they love most/With candor and frankness and joy, they confess — /Victor and Dom and Jess" — Our Faction verse), were determined to oust Tolliver and along with him his Communist allies. It was our tactic, usually, to deny Communist influence, but nobody believed this. Political plots, cabals, nightly caucuses, intrigue, festered. I was having the time of my life. I took it as an article of faith that most of my time should be spent factionalizing for my side. It was an open secret, or at least regarded as such in the labor movement, that Victor Hauser's principal ambition was to be the first Labor President of America. Those of us who opposed business trade unionism believed this would be an unmitigated disaster, as we felt Hauser to be an unprincipled Social-Democrat whose "objective" function was to clothe Reaction in socialist garments. That was the kind of terminology we used in those days — and without a smile. Granted hindsight, I believe we were more than half right.

No two men on this earth were more unalike than Tolliver and Hauser. Tolliver, former coal miner and belt-line welder at Ford River Rouge, was a hard-rock American unionist with no use for abstractions and a loathing for "fancy" talk. His talents lay in the direction of table-pounding and roaring imprecations across the bargaining board. He was in the John L. Lewis tradition. If need be, Tolliver would walk into a plant and personally pull the power switch if wage negotiations stalled. He was extremely bluff and uneasy in handling the complicated statistics and labor sociologese at which Hauser was so adept. We did not know it then, but Tolliver had outgrown his time, which was that of the early sit-down strikes and when the union movement was still rooted in small-town America.

Tolliver was very popular in the union, despite and probably because of his frailties; he knew how to have a good time and, never known to refuse a drink, often made a fool of himself and when he made a mistake admitted it with disconcerting gusto. Even The Other Side couldn't help but think of him as "fat old K.T." He was tough, warm and human. He was loved.

Victor Hauser was not loved. Admired, held in awe even, respected, but not loved. Shrewd, capable, brilliantly opportunistic, he had once been (and we rumored him still to be) a member of the Socialist Party. He could be a formidable ideologue. His position during the war had been bitterly anti-Soviet, when he had pulled the rug out from under the Communists, and prepared the ground for his own accession to power in later years, by waspishly denouncing the no-strike pledge, a pledge which the Communist leaders pursued with a blind vigor that they were later to rue. Tolliver, on the other hand, while in no sense a Communist, or even a convinced left-winger, got on notoriously well with the various delegations of workers and trade unionists which the Soviets sent over during the war.

Hauser had none of K.T.'s vices, major or minor. And this is why he was not loved. His efforts to be one of the boys, efforts we felt sure had been urged on him by his redheaded brainy wife—were painful to witness. It is difficult to describe the attitude of union rank-and-filers to the man; a kind of respectful, contemptuous marvel. Like Tolliver, his union record, in terms of courage, was impeccable; he had been at the center of the Battle of the Viaduct (and in the AVB until recently no one could aspire to a high union post unless he had participated personally and preferably bloodily in the early eruptions of violence). The plain fact, however, was that the ordinary worker did not feel comfortable in Hauser's presence. Hauser didn't drink, he didn't smoke, he chewed gum and it was rumored (by Our Side mainly) that he didn't even do that other thing. Friendly biographers (and he had them already; he was a genius, among other things, at public relations, the rules of which K.T. never did get quite straight in his mind) interpreted Hauser's startlingly upright character as the natural result of a strict upbringing. Assisting Hauser were his two brothers, Dominick and Jess: all three boys had been trained for union leadership by a father who had them practice-orating in the front parlor from age five, and had worked their way through the Soviet Union in the thirties. It was a point of considerable ironic humor, which Our Side never did know how to use, that Victor Hauser had once sent a letter out of Russia, when he had been employed by the Kiev Tractor Works, which ended, "Yours for a Soviet America." Though Hauser's faction included the most conservative union elements, his brain trust was heavily weighted with socialist-minded experts; this at a time when the House and Senate in Washington had been captured by the Republicans in the landslide of '46.

Unlike most of the unions with which I had had previous connection, the AVB-CIO was extravagantly *American.* It had been organized principally by the American-born. My own tradition was completely different. My mother and father had spent their lives organizing a labor movement whose membership was almost exclusively foreign-born. Until the day he left the movement my father had never learned more than a crude, broken English; both he and my mother had been successes at union organization. My faction in the AVB did not have much time for the foreign-born organizer; it was, in fact, Hauser who was most friendly to these, and in ordinary circumstances it almost certainly would be his faction in which I would have naturally found myself. What prevented it was that I had thrown in my lot with the Communists.

It is surprising, now, how little area of disagreement there was between our faction and Victor Hauser's, objectively, to use a word we were fond of then. And yet we hated them, and they us, with almost stupefying venom. In Europe or Asia or Africa we most certainly would not have hesitated to do physical harm to one another (and, in fact, we sometimes did). The real point of this antagonism, I think now, although it was not that clear then, was also the motive behind most of the terrible factionalism which debilitated postwar America's labor and liberal organizations and which did so much to pave the way for that political vulture, Joe McCarthy, who made his career and left his stamp and scar, more than anything else, by feasting off the bare bones of a progressive movement already exhausted by internecine battles. That is, the Soviet Union. Most often, this took the form of forcing a stance vis-à-vis the American Communist Party, whose existence counted for far less than its symbolic value. In retrospect, what I think we were all fighting about was conflicting assessments of the durability of the capitalist system in the United States: it was this which lay behind the question of Russia which lay behind the various factional issues. The fighting was strong and pitiless while it lasted which historically speaking, wasn't long. The Cold War settled our hash.

It was my luck to join the AVB when the first symptoms of arteriosclerosis were setting in. The second round of postwar strikes was on. The industrial scene, as they say, was turbulent. The auto companies and the union had thrown off the kid gloves, wage restraints and Production Board etiquette and were going at it bare-knuckle to settle whether the union was to preserve, and if possible extend, its gains won during the war. If there had been a twenty-fifth hour in the day, the union staff would have tried to use it; headquarters was a beehive. My first regional convention was a revelation. A mixture of old soldier's get-together, primitive soviet, clubhouse whingding, the French Assembly in a financial scandal and a World Series baseball game; it was in almost constant uproar from the opening gavel as delegates argued, shouted, shoved for the "mike" and occasionally settled it out in the corridor. What bothered me was that in the AVB there was a tendency, only slight at this date but terrifying to anyone brought up in the labor movement, not to close ranks when threatened by anyone from the outside. "He may be a sonofabitch," was the official motto, "but he's *our* sonofabitch." However, it didn't always work out this way. Already there were symptoms of a malaise deeper than mere factionalism. Union brothers knocking each other senseless, going to management with tales, cooperating with the FBI, on both sides fabricating known lies. Union headquarters resembling Tammany Hall. On both sides the main interest had become not shop issues but tallying up convention votes. We told ourselves that this had to be so that, when the other side was decisively beaten, we could devote ourselves unsparingly to factory-floor problems (and beyond) without having to be diverted by unionists playing the bosses' game. I should have known better, but I did not. Because I really did believe, as most of us did, that Victor Hauser *was* playing — objectively — the bosses' game.

So there it was, the AVB-CIO. It was not subtle but it was democracy.

During this period, I was living in an enormous apartment out on Seven Mile Road which was governed by Hiram Sverdlov, a professor-turned-unionist, and his author-wife, Nancy. The Sverdlovs were upper class, and in their hearts thought of me as a grub, and I disliked their delicate malice, their academic passions, and yet they were my confidantes for over a year. (Both Hiram and Nancy were of old southern stock; I am vulnerable to any interpretation of their place in the labor movement as a displacement of liberal emotions once imposed on Rastus and Beulah in the shack out back of the big house. Still, better with us than against us.) Among the other inhabitants of the Seven Mile Road apartment were Roy Adams, who had become spastic after a strike battle in Toledo; Horace Hibbins, the gray-haired "dean" of American union journalists and one of the original muckrakers; Viola Willard, a Negro stenographer for the union and part-time mistress of an executive board member; Tony Turk, an itinerant folk singer; and for a while Werner Seitz, the former motorcycle cop of whom I have already spoken. Also, there was a fat Negro named Joe Moon who was an FBI stoolpigeon, of whom as little as possible best be said. All things considered, it was a fairly quiet place to live; nobody intruded on anybody else; I felt at home in my tiny, dark room. About the only violent thing that ever happened in the Seven Mile Road apartment, once or twice a month, was that Hiram Sverdlov, who was working on a massive biography of the poet Thomas Hood (he'd been writing it for seven years, after hours of editing the union newspaper, *Belt Line*), liked to get stinky-drunk and play the parlor organ at 4 A.M., loud Bach.

After Viola and I became involved with each other, I decided to pull up stakes and move to another part of town. The atmosphere between the Sverdlovs and myself was not growing any more relaxed. They were part of the faction-within-a-faction which deeply resented John Alston and, by extension, me. They were also the most rigid left-wingers in Detroit; the upper middle class making common cause with the slum-bred comrades in cracking down on anyone who seriously questioned the Line. John and I were becoming increasingly critical of Left strategy within the Tolliver caucus, though not of the caucus itself, and this did not endear us to our colleagues. As though he could not help himself John was to make his criticisms in personal, crude, black and white terms, and more and more, as he grew unhappy in his union job, begin to chop away mercilessly at his own comrades for their stuffiness and puritanism. He was, at this early date, preparing his road out of the union movement, but I misinterpreted, believing that he could enjoy character assassination only because he had so successfully mastered the tactics of the situation. In a sense, he had. Right up to the end his political instincts were outrageously insightful. It was all very mixed up in my head. John and I frequently went on the road together on union business, staying at hotels and eating at expensive restaurants, and we were very close during these times. At first, I used to book the cheapest rooms and eat at the greasiest spoons, on principle that it was workers' money I was spending. This made Alston furious. He repeatedly told me to grow up, to remember I was "in the big time." His most persistent argument was that if I was to overcome my most grievous natural fault — youth — I would have to artificially stimulate stature by learning to be at ease in the world of highly paid adults, and that if I were to be at my best in helping negotiate with corporations I must not approach the bargaining table from a cheap room with hamburgers in my belly but from an immediate environment most closely approximating that of the enemy. His most telling argument was unvoiced: that by refusing to live it up I was, implicitly, joining forces with those towards whom he was increasingly growing violent, the "deadheads" — the puritans — of the Left.

Provoked by Alston, I soon learned the ropes of corporate existence within the AVB-CIO, how to book a seven-dollar-a-day hotel room and in which restaurants to eat, how to eat Lobster Newburg instead of hot dogs, how to drink until late at night in the bar of the hotel, how to carry on stoical flirtations, how to comport myself with men two and three times my senior. What I did not then realize was that the feverish, table-pounding, occasionally whoring, exciting life of the AVB organizer on the road was not the way he lived most of the time; that back in Detroit most of them lived quiet family lives. No, that is not completely accurate. Any union organizer or staff member was a member of one faction or another, and factionalism disrupted everyone's normal routine. Feverishness, excitability, the running high temperature of antagonistic, almost apocalyptic politics was the established tone of Detroit. To this day, John Alston does not know that I knocked down one man in his behalf and was myself knocked spread-eagle ass in the restaurant of the General Motors Building, and I did not regard this at all out of the ordinary. I remember wanting to tell John about these incidents at the time, but our code prevented it. It was fortunate that we did not share the same taste in women. He was addicted to the beautiful tough union women who were leftovers from the war days of AVB organizing. Since I could not yet aspire to such magnificent animals I confined myself to the lower echelons of the union world — the women shop stewards, secretaries and shop workers. Throughout most of that year, although the Finnish girl, Sylvie Torvald, was my steady girl, I had a deep and terrible crush on another shop steward, a woman called Mollie.

Mollie lived in the upper half of a brownstone house on Briggs Avenue. The bottom half was owned by Paul Wooster the chief legal counsel of the AVB, and the mandarin of the Left puritans. Mollie shared the upstairs flat with Helen. When it became necessary for me to move out of the Sverdlov's on Seven Mile Road, Helen, Paul's assistant and colleague, invited me to sleep on her front-room couch and I accepted.

In the house on Briggs Avenue, we were all on the same side of the factional fight, except Cora, Paul's wife, who looked upon the fight within the Vehicle Builders' Union as a conspiracy cooked up by her husband to obstruct the smooth running of their daily domestic battle. Far from avoiding the union, she besought her editors to assign her the beat as often as possible. An acrimonious and unforgiving woman. Paul, John Alston, Helen, Hiram Sverdlov and one or two selected others served as K. T. Tolliver's brain, his technicians in the all-out brawl against Victor Hauser. The deepest hatreds in the union were those between Hauser's back-room boys and ours.

My stay at the house lengthened into months. I slept on the

front-room couch and Helen and Mollie slept in the back. Mollie was a committee woman at Ford Local 600 — "Little Moscow"; a slim, wiry high-cheekboned woman of indeterminate age. She and Helen had made friends at Bryn Mawr, rejected their well-to-do families and plunged into union work during the war when so many young women were attracted into it. Mollie's father was an overseas missionary who had made a fortune in banking before receiving the Call, Helen's a rich Florida industrial rancher, descended from freemen. I worshiped Mollie. I did not want her. But more than anything I desired her admiration. To my dismay, she treated me — fondly. The only people John Alston never derided in my presence were Helen and Mollie.

It took me a while to understand why the people in the house on Briggs Avenue, though generous to me, were longer in accepting me than some from The Other Side. Paul Wooster was the acknowledged poobah of the Detroit AVB Left colony, and Wooster objected to Alston's having brought me in without prior consultation. The fact was, Alston and Wooster, who had once been the union's Damon and Pythias, were almost open enemies at this time. Like myself and Bruce Fischer, the boy I had almost visited in Albert Lea, Minnesota, they had never really understood each other. Alston had made almost an art of affability, of learning how to get along with "the guys"; Wooster was a cold, locked door. Both Alston and Wooster knew that it was Alston's maverickness, justified and otherwise, which provoked their ugliest quarrels, and neither went out of his way to adjust this. I think this was because they needed to have their friendship broken, John so that he might, with psychological freedom, leave the union, Paul so that, for the same reason, he could continue in the labor movement. Had Paul and John had it in them to confront each other the Left would have been different and better for it. It says much for the postwar atmosphere of the union movement in America that these two men — the one rigid and unyieldingly Russophile and bookishly anti-capitalist, the other groping in romantic fits and starts to engage his ideology with the American experience — were literally afraid to carry on an intellectual dialogue, and that their arguments were always electric with suffused, repressed emotions. They were to reconcile, years later, only when the Left was a shambles.

For such a cohesive and uni-minded group, the Wooster faction-within-a-faction was itself riddled with similar personal enmities, jealousies, ugly tension. I was caught in the middle. Alston demanded of me unquestioning loyalty to himself and an identification with his animosity towards the others. To relieve the unbearable pressure of Alston's demands upon my loyalty, more and more I began to try to make a life outside the union. He disliked me for this. More and more, I found myself, despite my differences with the "deadheads," siding with Paul Wooster against Alston because of the flippant and corrosive manner in which Alston was phrasing his arguments. All meanings accepted, Alston was looking for a way out. Often, the situation was for me painful and ludicrous. On the road, and at union conferences, Wooster and Alston competed, the one discreetly, the other shamelessly, for my company, almost as though I were an attractive woman; I can remember once in Cleveland having taken a room with Wooster so that we might work on a statistical wage chart in preparation for the next morning's conference, and Alston meeting me in the coffee shop with a thin, white grin on his tight, sharp features, "What's the matter, boy, you like him better than me?" and laughing coldly. This having constantly to choose sides in my own political family was tearing me up, but I never could get Alston to discuss it calmly. He could out-argue me always.

Now, in all this, I may give the impression that John Alston was a flash-in-the-pan, a union playboy, and that's all. A lot of people thought this. (Remembering, in the union movement, a flash-in-the-pan is one who fades within, say, ten years.) To this day I do not know the truth. I do know he did not have staying power. But while he was around I think he was on to something, and it was, and is, his tragedy that he could never bring himself to fight within himself to systematize his thoughts, to render them coherent. I believe he had the intellectual stamina but I think he also knew that to do this would commit him to a sinking ship, that of the Left in America. And when the chips are down, the Johns of the world must choose survival at the expense of the meaning of their whole previous lives. (To Alston's credit, he did not jump from the sinking ship but went down with it and spent several years floundering in the muddied waters of aimless and empty disillusionment and disuse; but all the time he was scanning the horizon, calculatingly; he did not accept any of the offers of help from the vessels that did come by — Paul and Helen went to work for small, beleaguered Left unions, Sverdlov took a post at a Kentucky college, I went on the bum — but waited until a formidable, shiny and expensive ship appeared and only then did he allow himself to be picked up. He married a millionairess. In my heart, I do not believe I have ever forgiven John Alston this, and it surprised me, and humbled me, when I visited Chicago, that Paul and Helen, now married, felt they had nothing to forgive Alston for and were, in fact, eager to hear news of him.)

As a paid member of the union staff I was supposed to remain aloof from family quarrels. My job, I was warned by Hauser himself (who signed my pay checks even as I assisted in trying to unseat him), was to service the million members of the union, period. But this I found impossible. Staff members, I soon discovered, were hired primarily as factional combatants, and I was expected, I think even by Hauser, as a matter of course, to do my bit in an atmosphere that was daily becoming more acrid. "Chop chop." You never knew when the man in the next office, or even your best friend, was out knifing you; it was an unmerry game of union-made musical chairs, a natural milieu for opportunists of all stripes to climb the main-chance ladder. Fortunately, the business of the union was not at this stage complicated by the intrusive presence of professional criminals who ran the lucrative numbers games in the various auto factories. Such men existed, and a few of them even held low union office, and sometimes it was necessary for top officials to make a tenuous accommodation with them in plants which they strongly held, but they were not, as in the Teamsters and Ladies Garment Workers, an important influence.

In this situation the Left, faced with unreconcilable alternatives personified by K. T. Tolliver and Victor Hauser, began to fall apart of the weight of its own untenable arguments and tactics. There was terrific internecine squabbling, expulsions, disciplinings, fear; the more the New York center of the Communist Party found itself in the cul-de-sac of its own formulations, the more frenzied its efforts to inform its membership with militant obedience. It was a situation tailor-made for upper-class radicals who, above all, needed tight crises where they could justify abdicating their intelligences, their inbred predilection for sensing and defending nuances and gray shades, to resolve all doubts and differences by opting for the crudest form of loyalty to "the working class"; i.e., the Party. Paul and Helen and Mollie, the Sverdlovs and their sort — shone. The heat was on, and if they could not analyze dispassionately this new and unexpected phenomenon of a capitalism which refused to fall apart and a working population that was not at all unhappy about the state of affairs, they could do the next best thing, show the Red flag, their mettle and their pride of participation in a movement into which they had not been born. With Alston and myself, who *had* been born into it, it was quite a bit different and considerably less a matter for dialectical melodramatics. Neither of us felt the slightest need to show our loyalty and were, in fact, irked by demands for it. What we were both worried about, each at our own level, was the way in which our vehicle was heading downhill and towards the abyss. We knew this, and said it, and tried to convince others of it. But it proved impossible, right up to the eve of disaster, to prove to our colleagues and comrades that the ball game no longer belonged to us.

Though I think Paul and Helen would deny this now, they hated us for crying havoc. I think I loved John Alston for not being blind. Under moments of attack from our own side, we could achieve closeness and kinship. When the editor of the Ford branch newspaper was expelled from the Communist Party for advocating the "ultra Left" policy of workers' councils, John and I, individually, went out of our way to be seen with him in the corridors of the union headquarters at a time when the Wooster-Sverdlov clique, with whom the editor had been on the friendliest terms, adopted a policy of icy nonfraternization. About the sole ally John and I ever had in this fight-within-a-fight was the reporter for the *Daily Worker*, an amiable and relaxed character named Al Williams, who, though it was his bounden duty to oppose John Alston (which he did), looked with considerable distaste upon the genteel fanaticism of the Wooster group. The only other allies John had (but not I: I had not their talents for serio-mock sybaritism) were chosen from a small, select band of cool union professionals — "he's a pro" was the highest accolade John Alston knew how to bestow upon another human being. These men and women, so different in personalities and even politics, always had one thing in common: they knew, in John's definition, how to "live" and they had been in one way or other, or were about to be, *broken.* This concept, taught me by John, still has a powerful hold on me, and to this day my closest friends are those who have been broken by the world and emerged "strong at the broken" places. It is unfortunate that I should have to phrase it in such a sentimental way, but were I to dress it up it would convey a false sense of what I today still believe. This whole idea may carry with it for some people a stench of self-pity and I think it does. But that does not worry me overmuch. I have never been afraid of self-pity.

Right then, mid-point between the two annual conventions, trampling towards the climax of what would, by more or less common agreement, settle the direction if not the fate of the labor movement in America for the next years, John's closest friends were, in my opinion, a wholly admirable group: Juanita Holliday, a leggy redheaded factory organizer who gave up her Roman Catholic fiancé to stay with the union; Mel Melosky, a fat prematurely grizzled ex-paratrooper with one side of his face shot away who did part-time jobs for the union; Eleanor Farrell, ex-fashion designer and bookwriter who had organized for the AVB in the war; Joe Tubman, a Negro lawyer in Victor Hauser's faction; Chris Rooney, a Negro organizer married to Paul's secretary; a man who owned a saloon on Seven Mile Road; a pretty little secretary who worked for Jess Hauser; and Lloyd, a civil engineer who didn't like unions. About the only thing these people had in common was that they played poker. I was just then beginning to learn how to play "real" poker (i.e., embroidered poker — high-low, baseball, etc.) at the hands of people like One-Eye Joe Gold and K. T. Tolliver himself. One of the saddest things about the English is that they are not a race of poker players.

Poker, all-night and quietly held jazz-and-liquor sit-ups, an occasional tranquil luncheon to relax from the factionalizing — these were the principal recreations of John Alston's little group. But, in the main, our energies were poured into the coming fight. Our job, the job of our small group, was to provide the intellectual and statistical ammunition for the Left-of-Center faction. It is interesting that in doing this we lost our vision . . .

The chief argument in the Hauser armory was that K. T.

("Kremlin Tolerator") Tolliver was merely a front man for the Communist Party. This was not true. But it was true that much of the militance, some of the funds, half of the brains and a large part of the emotional drive of the Tolliver faction derived from Red sources. The remainder of Hauser's grapeshot concentrated along these lines: that K.T. could not creditably join in public debate with corporation presidents; that Tolliver was administratively inept and squandered union funds through fumbling and in pursuit of straight flushes and blondes; that Tolliver should never be forgiven for being sucked into blind adherence to the wartime no-strike pledge and a "Teheranized" future plus advocacy of incentive pay; that Tolliver was too close to John L. Lewis and that he had temporized, from the Left, on signing the Taft-Hartley affidavits.

Anti-Hauser arguments similarly ranged from the demagogic to the true; that Hauser was an egomaniac whose need for personal publicity fouled his role as union leader; that Hauser had absolutely no scruples and would, if need be, make a deal with the Devil or the corporations if it would help him secure himself as president of the union, then president of the CIO and ultimately president or at least cabinet member in the government; that Hauser neglected basic shop issues, such as speed-up and Negro discrimination, in favor of grandiose schemes which looked impressive on paper (especially newspaper); that Hauser was much too chummy with business leaders; that the contracts he negotiated were poor; that Hauser was hatcheting Phil Murray, the revered head of the CIO; that Hauser had agitated among wartime workers against the no-strike pledge while he was selling them out in Washington as a member of the War Production Board; that while eschewing communism his staff was riddled with Socialist Party men, etc., etc.

There was no doubt which side I was on. The more I worked for Hauser the more I became convinced he was a danger to the labor movement in terms not only of ultimate goals but also bread-and-butter issues. But I did no more than sense that "life itself" (to use another of our hack phrases, fortunately usually accompanied by a self-deprecating grin) was furnishing a basis for Hauser's rising star; that despite Hauser's embarrassing intimacy with government and corporation officials, his substitution of smooth collegiate methods and rather leechy diplomacy for rank and file militance, and his incredible plays for a good press — this man reflected a changing union and a changing America. It was not an easy situation for insiders to understand.

The people who most hated Hauser were not us but the militants and old-line shop stewards: theirs was the clearest case. These old ones (in the auto industry you are old at thirty-five), with their memories, looked back to the thirties as the high point in their lives because they had a chance, for the first time, to fight back and give the front office the well-deserved works, and now here was Victor Hauser, flanked by teams of social psychologists and campus economists, proposing replacement of this (granted, frequently anarchic) militance with a morbid philosophy of "sound labor-management relations," "centralization of union authority," "co-operation," "responsibility." Had a major unemployment crisis hit in '46 and '47 Victor Hauser would have gone down the drain. It didn't. Hauser bet right, we bet wrong. We paid.

As Hauser's and Tolliver's representatives fanned out into the local regions to log-roll in anticipation of the long-awaited showdown, union headquarters on Woodrow Wilson Avenue became like two armed camps. The first and second floor was "his"; the third floor was "ours." We didn't speak to them, and they didn't speak to us. We communicated, when we had to, through the medium of secretaries and business managers, except that even they were forced to take sides. Nobody could assume an independent position; there was no middle ground. Neutrality was meaningless (e.g., the office manager was "his," the chairman of the clerical workers' local was "ours," the staff bursar "ours," the cleaning personnel "his," etc.). I no longer had time for anything outside union work. I rarely saw Sylvie. My only refuge was a cellar jazz shop on Second Boulevard much frequented by Negro musicians who were just beginning to adorn themselves with goatees, dark glasses, berets and Muslim names. While they prayed to Mecca in one part of the dark, dank shop, I had earphones on my head discovering Joe Turner and Sidney Bechet and the ineluctable delights of Art Tatum playing behind anyone's vocal. Gillespie and Prez would, for me, come later.

From time to time it was my duty to travel to various local unions and regional conferences to lecture on my "speciality," which I had learned overnight on John Alston's ultimatum that I make myself uniquely useful or get out of the union. With the aid of a Marchand calculator and generous, if irritable, help from Helen and Paul Wooster, I had become a weekend wonder on comparative wage clauses, piecework and incentive pay schemes. These trips I took to Milwaukee, Cleveland, Rochester and other medium-size factory cities in the northern industrial plain were among the nicest experiences I was ever to have inside the AVB. For it was in these cities that I met not only the shopwork delegates but also the old-timers, the men and women for whom the union vision was a live and practical thing. They loved telling their stories to me, and I looked forward to hearing them. They made me understand — in countless bars, back parlors, cheap restaurants, hotel corridors — what the Amalgamated Vehicle Builders had once stood for. They reminded me, when I did not know, what it had been like in the auto cities after 1930: how, in 1932, Ford and Ford only was producing and then because of orders placed by Russia; how they had marched on their factories, stormed them, sat down in them and remained sitting under a rain of blows and injunctions; how the bourgeoisie believed the AVB meant revolution and how some of the AVB members believed it too.

It was on these trips that I began to understand the fundamental clash of interests not only between the corporations and the factory workers but also between two distinct generations of *workers*. The old-timers, the ones who had done the first fighting and created the skeleton framework of the union, in one degree or another had seen themselves as the vanguard of an irresistible tide of social change which would fundamentally alter relationships within America. But the next generation, the ones who came after them and reaped the fruits of that first organizational harvest, simply wanted things a little better. More deeply, what I learned on these trips was the nature of the radicalism held by the older workers, the vanguard. It was here that my friends back in Detroit were wrong; they did not understand how it worked in America. For, when all was said and done, the revolt, even the revolutionism, of these pristine industrial rebels was not something outside the American experience, nor conversely did it come out of a marrow-of-the-bones sky-shouting fundamentalism. Most of these older workers had migrated to the auto cities expecting *conventional* success, had come in order to participate in the big American dream of onward and upward by way of individual effort. It was only when the system broke down, when it failed to provide not only the rewards but even the competitive context in which prizes could be won — personifying this failure in the vengeful genius of Henry Ford — that a gripping sense of revolt stirred the auto workers. But, at heart, theirs was a revolt of the disappointed and not of the fiercely despairing. Sometimes, and in a disastrously incoherent fashion, I would try to explain this to John and Paul and Helen but by this time they were entirely wrapped up in counting, recounting and predicting delegate votes. We were all captured of an obsession on almost exactly the level of the ward-heeling politician. (Harry S. Truman, who was then President, would have understood and sympathized with us more spontaneously probably than any other public figure.)

As the battle lines were drawn, I was thrown more and more into the company of Paul Wooster and his group. I did not particularly like Paul, because I did not like mandarins. But I did like the two girls whose house I was living in, Helen and Mollie. Unlike the others in Wooster's group, they knew how to have a good time in our odd moments of relaxation. Paul, on the other hand, was shy, standoffish and consequently hyper-political. His marriage to Cora was splitting apart at the seams. Cora detested Helen, whom she (wrongly at the time) suspected of having an affair with Paul, and chose the most inopportune moments to blunder into their working schedule at union headquarters. It was her insistence on this idea that gave Paul and Helen the idea, I think. Myself, I was still worshiping Mollie.

Throughout, John Alston continued to play an ambiguous, not to say ambivalent role. He was unhappy with his union job, his life in Detroit and, by an almost impersonal extension, his wife. He felt, I knew, like going into new territory. Detroit cramped his style now. Now that he was no longer a top official but just one of many political drones he was having to pump-prime interest in his work by jazzing up his work with a glamour and an excitement which truly did not belong to it. While his politics were directed at Hauser, his personal rancor was reserved for Paul Wooster and the submandarins. The more desperate he grew, the more emotionally lazy and careless; as never before he tried ordering my life. Either that, or he forgot about me for weeks at a time.

Even though I was working in the midst of Communists, Alston maintained a strict and close-mouthed neutrality on this subject. To be asked to join the party in those days in Detroit was commonplace. Communists were everywhere, down in the shops, up at staff, on the sidelines. It was an open secret that the Tolliver forces conferred with party liaison men. Wherein derived the power of the party? The answers to this question, contrary to the mysterioso music played by the popular press, were fairly simple. The Communists had a philosophy based squarely on what they hoped were the interests of the workers; they were tough (but by no means *that* tough); they were disciplined (and *that* disciplined); they had proved their loyalty to the union many times over (to say they did this for their own special reasons was to beg this particular question); they were articulate, and selfless and *ready;* above all, they were needed. In the early days when the union was gunned, spied upon, spat upon, what was needed were small, compact, mobile bands of fast-moving, sophisticated organizers; i.e., the party people. It is a matter for the history books now that old John L., who despised Communists with a legendary fervor, went straight to the party for organizers as soon as he broke away from the AFL to form the CIO, when he needed help fast from any quarter. The trouble came, not in the early days when the Communists were doing a good and often heroic job but later, when there was time on everyone's hands to pass resolutions. By the time I got to Detroit the fire had gone out of the party. As yet, however, none of us, least of all the party, knew this. We did insist upon treating it as though it were the Vatican. A disservice to it and to us. For too long it had been, at least within the CIO, too many things to too many men.

Now, it is a matter of simple amazement to me that so many otherwise intelligent and perceptive men and women inside the AVB took their "line" from men in the industrial section of the party who clearly did not know their job. At that time, the man the party had assigned to the auto industry in Michigan was a Spanish Civil War thug (yes) who held considerable fascination for me because he was so perfectly a hybrid of Machine-Gun McGurn and Stalin when he was Koba agitating the Baku oil-field workers. The main trouble with this man — a former combat paratrooper, twice winner of the Silver Star, ex-captain of the Lincoln Battalion — was that he knew next to nothing about how automobiles are put together. He had been sent in when his predecessor went haywire on liquor and the kinds of pressure which only Detroit can generate. He is now in prison on the Smith Act; I know because I signed a petition for a rehearing of his case. He was the only Communist of whom I was always, in his presence, afraid.

Detroit uses 17.4 per cent of the nation's steel, 65 per cent of its rubber, 70 per cent of its plate glass, 33 per cent of its radios. Keep these statistics in mind as I talk.

The volcano simmered. And not only inside the AVB. The entire CIO was squaring off against itself for a final showdown between Right and Left. God help us all, the crucial issue became not workers' councils or hourly versus piecework rates but the Marshall Plan. Tolliver and Hauser were so eager to get at each other's throats that open warfare — which would have pleased nobody but the corporations and not the wisest industrial negotiators in them — constantly threatened. Occasionally, Philip Murray, president of the CIO, had to come to town to temporarily soothe and paper over differences.

The poison was spreading far beyond the union movement in Michigan. Factional lines, reflecting the Tolliver-Hauser split, were drawn in everything from Benevolent Aid Societies to the American Veterans Committee. In the long, terrible battle, the A.V.C. was destroyed, Michigan liberalism was forced into an irrevocable and impotent anti-Communist posture and friendships born in the heat of the sit-down days buckled. All I knew at the time was that nobody was going to win. That much, if nothing else, was obvious.

One night, six weeks before the convention, Tolliver and his cronies on the executive board called a special all-night conference at Tolliver's home to which John and Paul Wooster and the AVB research director were invited but not me. Helen and Mollie and I stayed up all night at the house on Briggs Avenue waiting for John and Paul to tell us what it was all about, although we had a pretty good idea. For the past two days Helen and I, under Paul's supervision, had been using the Marchand calculator totting up delegate votes, and we had concluded, no surprise, that Hauser had us badly licked. It was these figures that we gave to Paul to take to the conference. When John and Paul came in, towards morning, they made several wry little jokes but wouldn't tell us what happened.

Then, fast breaking, in a last-minute maneuver, Tolliver gave the go-ahead to the Left on a scheme to capture the convention. Negotiations were begun, by our little group, to incorporate a farm implement workers union into the AVB. It was a left-wing union, and if the merger could be accomplished before the convention Tolliver would (or might) have the votes to defeat Hauser. It was the wrong move. Wrong and fatal. It gave Hauser just the issue he needed to push him over the top. He publicly accused Tolliver of selling the AVB to the Communists for convention votes, and since the farm implement unionists had outsmarted themselves by demanding convention votes simultaneous with virtual autonomy within AVB, the argument was telling. I was involved in the negotiations with the farm implement people in Chicago, and I don't think any of us smiled once during this period. We were all desperate men involved in a duplicitous scheme which in our hearts we knew was going to fail.

The annual convention was in an uproar from the first morning. Our faction lost disastrously. Victor Hauser red-baited without quarter and with some justification. He was re-elected president and this time swept the executive board. He was in control. One of Hauser's propaganda shots had been the "exposure" followed by denunciation, of the Wooster-Alston clique as Communists or fellow travelers; Tolliver, though faced with certain defeat, chose to stick by his brain trust. It was all over.

Thereafter things went to pieces in my part of Detroit. Tolliver accepted a charity job with CIO and retired from the AVB union scene. Overnight the machinery of the Left collapsed. Paul Wooster left Detroit to become legal director of a small, avowedly Red union, taking Helen with him, and divorcing Cora, who came within an inch of testifying against her husband at an Un-American Activities Committee. Mollie remained in the shop. I knew she would.

In defeat, something was released in all of us, a kind of elation, and also all that pent-up bitchiness. Personal relationships suddenly zoomed up into sharp focus: more often than not they could not stand the scrutiny and splintered. Everything happened fast. I was even thinking of taking Mollie away with me, out of the shop, to where I didn't know. Ever since the evening Helen and I had compiled the Marchand tally sheet of delegate votes, John Alston had been telling me to get out of Detroit. We both knew the real reason for this was that our relationship had gone dead. He didn't want me around as a reminder, as someone who would one day turn on him. It was his great obsession, this: that his best friends would betray him.

One night, some of us were in Alston's playing stag poker when Mel Melosky made a crack about Mollie and himself, which I laughed at with the others. And then a sudden chill enveloped me as I understood what it was he was talking about. I played the rest of the game with cold fingers. When Mel went upstairs to the bathroom I went with him. I was so choked, standing by the mirror as Mel peed, that I could barely speak. I said, Mel, you've got a goddam filthy mouth. Mel buttoned up and got very tough. We raised our voices. I felt like crying. John Alston came up and separated us, and I went home, out the back way.

John showed up before I did on the following Monday at the small office-in-exile that Hauser had given the Fringe Benefits Department (us) in Hamtramck, and which we shared with Betty, John's secretary, who was perennially breaking up with her husband, Lonnie, a buffer at Packard Local 180 and a member of the same A.V.C. chapter as John and I. I came into the office late, and John shut the door after me. He was about as gentle as I remember him. He was using the same old words, telling me it was time to grow up and all, but I do believe he was trying to soften the blow. I told him that just because Mel said that Mollie had started going to bed with him was no reason it was true. Mel, I said, might be boasting to cover what the war had done to his face. I had never seen him and Mollie together, he never came to the house. There was absolutely no reason to believe Mel. John smiled and said, No, I guess not. But, good Lord, I was *shocked.* There was no change in Mollie towards me because she thought I had known all the time. Still, every time I saw Mel Melosky I felt like punching him. Mel wasn't a bad guy, but I still do.

The other inhabitants of the Tolliver factional apparatus, if they were staff members, either went back to the shops or abandoned the union movement altogether. John Alston was in this latter category. Relations between us were not happy towards the end. Only when we both went up to help plug holes in a crumbling eleven-month-old strike in West Allis, Wisconsin was there a short burst of idyllic friendship. It was a brute of a walkout, probably the most viciously fought of the postwar strikes. The plant was owned by a family of America Firsters; the local leadership was militant; wages were bad, management was spoiling for a fight. It was like a blazing scene from the thirties, goons dragging pickets inside the plant gates and beating them up for "trespassing," trucks full of scabs ramming the massed union lines, mounted cops charging full tilt at strikers and being met with a barrage of ball bearings rolled under the horses' hoofs. (John had an arm broken during a side-gate scuffle when a scab car knocked him against a wall. The arm knitted poorly, and today he must carry it a little high and crooked.) Up at West Allis, away from Detroit, John and I tried to reconstruct our friendship. But eventually the strike petered out, all but lost, and we returned to Detroit and the tensions that were pulling us apart.

Long ago I had sensed the affinities between John Alston and my first teacher, fat gorilla-like Alan Pick, and it did not make me feel good. I knew I had disappointed Alston by not developing in the direction he wanted. To me, Spain would always mean Franco; to Alston, increasingly, bullfighting and Hemingway. My friends bored him. His friends — they were exotic habitués of the curious little demimonde between the union and Detroit's criminal rackets, rich eccentrics, assorted women, war correspondents, mountain climbers, liberal stockbrokers and "unconventional" Grosse Pointe chatelaines — repelled me even when I stood in awe of them; they all shared a quality of self-conscious, even frenzied "good living." Alston said I was a young puritan. The outright rupture came when I took the floor at a union conference to talk against Alston on a minor point. Our friendship, which had always been rooted deep in Alston's complicated demands for complete loyalty, dissolved that night.

This time, at leave-taking, there were no farewell parties, few tears. Everyone just drifted apart. John Alston and I, as we shook hands in his house the day I left, tried to pretend a feeling but it was hollow. And so the time in Detroit came to an end. The affair with Sylvie ended on a note of no regret. I wondered what to do with myself, where to go to find that special prospect I was sure lay out there somewhere still in front of me. Detroit had been tough and disenchanting, the year, I think, I learned that the man (or boy) who believes fairytales, is a fool and may well wind up a knave. My mother and father had told me many such fairy tales, and now it was time to lay them gently, reverently aside for what, above all, I desired: the truth of life. Germany had been one such truth, Detroit another. And now I felt I knew enough to go out and make my own truth and not have to depend on the Alan Picks and John Alstons.

Some of my friends, especially Mollie, urged me to forget the sour, ward-heeling, instructive atmosphere of union headquarters for the sweeter, purer air of the factory floor. Always, I had thought that's what I would do when it was time to quit the union. But now I couldn't. I had been educated out of the factory. It looked too drab and too confining. I had some of John Alston's blood in me.

I was twenty.

And now, it felt strange to be sitting on their couch in Chicago with Paul and Helen, happily married and Detroit a distant memory. I didn't know what attitude to have towards them. I felt ashamed at how little I had done for myself and for anyone else since Detroit, but they did not appear ashamed for me. The fact is, they seemed rather proud of my outside accomplishments. I was surprised, delighted even, when I saw they took real pleasure out of my having worked in Hollywood. Also, I was a little hurt. It was as though they had not even expected me to stick it. I had wanted to, if only to show them that there was a place for people like me.

Like many of those I had been visiting across the country they were in no hurry to reminisce, which made me feel awful, that I was living in the past. I did not think I was, but I did want to *find out*, all of us trying to think it out, what the meaning of those years had been. All that afternoon the Woosters and I just sat around and made small talk. They said Cora no longer bothered them, although for a time she sent them some nasty letters. They were, they said, thinking of having a baby, adopting one. I really loved those people when they said that: Paul, once so locked up, and Helen together trying to make it. Helen joked about Paul's paunch and it was the first house I had been in for a long time where I couldn't feel any malice between husband and wife. Perhaps you shouldn't take my word for it, however; I'm told I have a tendency to romanticize peace between men and women wherever I find it.

Afterwards, on the road to Cleveland, I remembered that Paul and Helen and I had not mentioned what was happening in Hungary, not once. Mostly we exchanged information on our friends from Detroit. I found, to my disgust, that I wanted them to join with me in some quiet form of denunciation against my one-time teacher and friend, John Alston. But they proved not only loyal but genuinely fond of John, as though they had never really expected him to last the course either. It made me feel slightly cheap. All Helen would say was, You and John quarreled didn't you? I just shrugged. They sensed I did not find talking of John easy, and we did not mention it again.

As we spoke of our friends from Detroit the pattern worked itself out here too. Most of them were now in private business, some even working for corporations. Few had grown the stronger or used the experience to step up from; all were now in obscurity, working in insurance agencies, as camp guides, television repairmen. The few who had managed to escape to the universities had almost all been winkled out by the various Un-American committees on their ceaseless crisscrossings of academic country in search of targets. I wondered aloud, on that couch, if many of our friends had gone over to the FBI and Helen said, "No thank God, not many; fewer," she said with a wry smile, "than I would have predicted." That was the first inkling I had that Helen, too, had been on to some of the "deadheads." "The funny thing is," said Helen, "we all keep away from one another, and have all these years, as though we had committed a murder and didn't want any more to do with each other."

Helen cooked us a fine dinner. She took tremendous pleasure from seeing us eat her food. It was strange. We talked a great deal between us, and touched on nothing important. Yet there was no tenseness. Helen and Paul had been through something pretty bad together, I could see that. They had not found each other wanting, and now they were over it. I never thought I would live to see the day where the center of gravity of the lives of Paul and Helen would be outside the trade unions, or politics, but I had been wrong. As the women's magazines say, they had found each other. I don't know how else to put it.

I asked if I could go to sleep early, and then, in the room they gave me, I did a little phoning. It took me a while but I succeeded in contacting Sy, Fifie, Schlomo and Angie. I told them I was in town for a couple of days and suggested we get together tomorrow evening at Mincie's Hot Dog Parlor. Angie said Mincie's no longer existed but caught on and suggested a barbecue joint on Ogden Boulevard. Angie, Schlomo and Fifie said they would try to contact a few of the others. Sy sounded suspicious and would have wanted to do all his talking by phone.

I went to sleep, wondering what it would be like, the first gathering in over ten years of the Knights Athletic Club of Greater West Side Chicago.

I had a lazy morning, as Paul went off to his job. Helen and I spent a couple of hours over the morning coffee discovering each other again. She had regained her attractive old habit of referring flippantly to that which was important to her, and then in the middle of the conversation, she said, "I don't want to bowl you over but I'm not terribly interested in politics any more." Now, coming from any other person, even her husband Paul, this might come as a surprise and that's all. But Helen was the most political woman I had ever known, barring perhaps one or two who belonged not in the movement but a sanitarium. And then, as I looked across the coffee cups at her black, large smiling face I realized what we all should have realized a long time ago: that, given enough rope Helen knew how to have a good time and had been waiting only for someone to ask her. Paul hadn't exactly asked her — but he had let her. It is banal as hell to use a word like bloom on a woman, but that's how it was happening to the Krupskaya of Briggs Avenue, Detroit, Helen Wooster née Washington.

We finally got around to Mollie. No, Helen said, she hadn't seen Mollie for about a year though Mollie sometimes spent part of her holidays in Chicago with them. She was still working at her factory in Detroit. It was now thirteen years she had been there, I thought but didn't say. When the Korean war broke out, Helen reported, the management had Mollie fired but the women who worked with her in the soldering room fought like tigresses to keep the security guards from bodily throwing her out the plant. For about six months Mollie took up a station in a small tea shop-candy store across the street from the plant and held daily court with her colleagues from the soldering room. Eventually, when political tempers cooled, Mollie got back into the soldering room where she is now, once again, chief steward.

We talked some more that morning, and I was surprised, and guilty, at how many of our old friends had gone back into the shop after the factional defeat. Many of them were still there and Helen urged me to go to Detroit. But I had no place in Detroit now. Just before she went off to the library, where she said she spent a lot of time now helping Paul do research, she said that Mort Wallace, a good friend of ours, had been thrown out of the second-floor window of Packard's after the Korean war started, and he was now in a Wisconsin rest home with a broken back. (So you see, defenestration can also be a home-grown and not uniquely Czech product. *Vide* Cal.) The political situation in Chicago, she said, was that there weren't enough left-wingers to go around and make a single meeting and for the first time in twenty-five years pacifists, Trotskyists, Communists and free-thinkers were coming together. "You should see," she said, "some of those Trotskyists and Unitarians," and laughed. She laughed even louder when she said, "And you should see some of us."

Later that morning, from Helen's kitchen, and feeling very nervous about it all, I phoned Dena Strauss who had been secretary of the youth organization in which I had been a "leading member" such a long time ago. I had not been exactly what you call popular with Dena Strauss, but that had been years ago. The last official time I had gathered with the youth leaders had been at a meeting of the Garrison School staff, when I had been, more or less, in disgrace and, or so I was informed, in danger of having my epaulettes stripped. The meeting had been called in the aftermath of a financially unsuccessful party in the home of a Doctor X on the splashy near North Side. At the meeting Rafe Hawes had gotten up and asked why the money to hold the party had not gone into a better cause, such as "Negro work" or "woman work" or "youth work." To answer him the Negro co-director of the school rose and spent about forty-five minutes explaining how, even if the school had to lose money on the affair, it was indispensable to secure the alliance of progressive middle-class elements such as Doctor X. This was part of the "line" at the time of Teheran. This was also at a time when I thought that policy was hogwash. I said as much, as tactfully as you can at seventeen, at this meeting, and then Alexander, the school co-director, rose again to explain the need for an alliance with the middle class. At the expense, someone asked, of the working class? Sometimes, said Alexander. Doctor X, he explained, was a "key" figure in this alliance. At which point the school receptionist entered with a message that Doctor X had just died. There was absolute, stricken silence. I leaned back in my chair and, involuntarily, chuckled. It was a hell of a thing to do. After that, it was generally understood that (a) a tentative offer of a junior post at the Garrison School was not to be pressed, (b) I was to be regarded as frivolous, untrustworthy and very probably tainted by my one-time membership in the Young Socialists.

Of course, it had been a damfool thing to do, to laugh right then. The truth is, I could not help it. Dena was quite cool on the phone but in her old gracious melodious way; with a tinge of bitterness she said she was an old married woman now with three children and a doctor for a husband. It amazed me that she should continue to bear a grudge. As diplomatically as I could I got around to the subject of Nick. Yes, she said cautiously, Nick was living with them at the moment. My heart pounded. Nick! I had found him. I didn't even try to sound casual, and asked after him. She said Nick had had a hard time for a while. His first marriage smashed up, he went to the university, then into a steel mill, then back to the university to train as a psychiatric social worker, which is his job now. That would be like Nick, I thought. Trying to help kids the age he was at when he needed help. He was, Dena said, going to get married again. I told her that was terrific, and that when Nick got home would he call me? Briskly Dena said that Nick was in her house right then. A moment of silence followed. Nick must be in the same room with her now, must have been listening to Dena talk about him. I asked if Nick would come to the phone. She asked me to hold the line and muffled the speaker. Then she came on and said, quietly, "Nick doesn't want to hear from you."

I didn't even ask why not. Why he wouldn't talk to me. The cork felt pulled out on me. All I wanted to do was hang up. But for some reason Dena kept me on the line, and we went on talking, about one or two people we had known, and how long I would be in Chicago. Very distinctly she said, "I've changed a lot. I'm not the way I used to be." Angrily, "Listen to the radio. There's the reason I changed." But I didn't want to hear it. I wondered if Nick had changed his politics also? It seemed hard to believe. Then I did a cheap thing. I said to Dena, Tell Nick I saw Cal. He's in Coeur d'Alene. I heard her say to Nick, "He said he saw Cal in Coeur d'Alene." I didn't hear Nick say anything. When she came back to the phone she asked me where I was going and I said I wasn't sure. Almost militantly she replied, "You never are, are you?" I shouted, for Christ's sake, Nick used to be my best friend! She didn't say anything. I hung up. (It had been to Dena and Dena only I had explained, before Detroit, that my leaving Chicago forever was an act of faith in the future of American social change. I would release myself, to be ready at all times to fight, plan, build and prepare for this by studying at the fulcrums of power and change in America. Detroit was the place to go. Dena had said, over lunch at Walgreen's, one man can't do it. To which I had replied, Only one man can do it.)

After that, I dialed a lot of numbers very fast. But they had either moved or disappeared. Then I had a stroke of genius. I looked up Zoya's name in the phone book. It was still there. I phoned. Her mother answered the phone, suspicious at a man's voice. No, Zoya wasn't home, who was I? I said, Me, remember, an old friend of Zoya's. Yes, she said vaguely, I'll give her your message. Five minutes later, as I sat slouched in the kitchen chair staring at a wall calendar, I was surprised when the phone rang and it was Zoya. She sounded exactly as I remembered her, girlish and enthusiastic. I said I would be right over. I felt in a rush, dressed, made sure I looked all right in a mirror and ran out to the De Soto which had a parking ticket on it. I tore up the ticket and headed out for Austin where Zoya lived. I had to ask directions at least five times. I didn't know Chicago any more, and that was the truth. It looked like any other city to me now, this place I once knew like the back of my hand. I made my way out to Austin by routes which were as strange to me as if they had existed in Portland, Oregon, a city I have never visited.

The old neighborhood where I remember taking Zoya home after Youth meetings and trying to kiss her in the hallway: the buildings, which I had once looked upon as the embodiments of middle-class affluence now looked shabby and aging; like a shanty-Jewish lower middle class slum. Everything was cramped. The huge automobiles parked at the narrow sidewalks seemed almost to dwarf the three-story porticoed houses. I found Zoya's house by the address, having forgotten what it looked like, walked up three flights of dark narrow carpet-smelling stairs and rang the bell. Her mother answered the door, looking exactly as I had remembered her, small, Jewish and suspicious. Then Zoya bounced in, and we both waited for her mother to go away to a party on the South Side. Mum obviously didn't want to leave me alone with Zoya, so I put on my formal, English air and Mum went away, reassured. As soon as the door was shut Zoya took my hands and made me stand away from her and said, "I can't get over how handsome you turned out." You too, I said, half meaning it, remembering how many years it had been since I used to take Zoya home and as I raced down her hallway stairs listen to her cries as Daddy, a dentist, beat her for coming in late. She kept saying, "I can't get over it." I suddenly felt grown up, sophisticated and successful. We went into the kitchen for coffee, and then she started pouring drinks. Zoya could really belt it. I gazed at her. She caught me doing it and said, "I'm not fourteen any more." I had to admit, no, she wasn't. She still had that magnificent, lush figure behind that skirt and cashmere sweater, but those lines under her eyes were darker and deeper than they should have been.

Zoya had been my girl when I was sixteen. I had thought, from her figure that she had been sixteen too, but it turned out she had been only fourteen. She wrote plays in blank verse then and was ruled over by a stern and iron-tempered father and a shuffling mother. It seemed incredible to me that she should still be living in the same place. But I was happy she was happy to see me. She was marveling at me and I felt perhaps the years were not for nothing. I asked Zoya if she would like to go for a drive, and she said, "A car of your own."

Zoya and I drove all over the West Side. The neighborhood had changed out of recognizability. It was all Negro now, this one-time place of brownstone flats and synagogues and basement clubhouses. It had never been quite a slum, and now it was. The house, on Christiana Avenue where I had lived for two years was now a decaying Negro-inhabited tenement, its front door hanging from the hinges as though in a photograph of a tenant farmer's cabin. Everybody on the streets was Negro. It was exactly as the South Side — Richard Wright's south side — had been when I left Chicago. What disturbed me was that it was such a *sad* place. It's always the same, when you can tell that the previous inhabitants have left in a hurry and the new ones are feeling prickly and defensive. They stared with open hostility at me, Zoya and the car. Negroes, said Zoya, are pouring into Chicago at a fantastic rate, and now one third of the inner population was colored. Later on, I walked around the old neighborhood and tried to talk to some of them. Many were recent arrivals from the South; none were friendly. Negro policemen in side-car motorcycles raced boldly about the streets. Zoya said, "The Negroes are turning Chicago into a slum." I turned and looked at her. She said, "I'm not against Negroes. But truth is truth. And they're so huffy. I work with some Negro dental technicians at my hospital." Then she told me some long, complicated story about how a Negro did her out of a job at another hospital. She sounded bitter; like any middle class Jewish girl whose neighborhood had been "invaded." I asked her if she was still politically active, and she said, with a giggle, "No, I haven't been to a political meeting in years. Gee," she said, "that sure does take me back." I reminded her of the times I would take her home and kiss her in the hallway, and she said, "I never did like you kissing me." I said that hurt me, and she said I had been too sexually advanced for my age, that we all had been.

We drove all over Chicago the center of which, like most of the cities I had visited, was a huge slum. Freeways spraddled this slum so that professional people could zip in and out to their offices from their suburbs without having to come into contact with the decaying core of the city. Whole neighborhoods — Cicero, the near West Side, Congress Street — I had remembered as being respectable were now substandard. Chicago looked like a wild city. Zoya seemed mild and casual about it. In the Loop she suggested I take her home because she was expecting a phone call from her mother. We drove back to Austin.

In the flat Zoya fixed us up with some drinks and put a flashing Chopin piece on the record player. She belted away three scotches. I sat on the couch and watched her. The apartment was quiet, the shades drawn. I toyed with my drink. When the Chopin piece was finished, I said, That was grand, Zoya. She sat back. "Yes," she said, "I collect Chopin grandly. That was Daddy's doing. I miss him very much since he died." She came over and sat on the couch and I said, When is your mama coming home? She said, "Why don't you kiss me?" I put my drink away on the table and kissed her. She lay supine on the couch and put my hand on her breast. I kissed her some more and then we went into the bedroom. She said, "When I was going to dental school I was marvelous at taking off my clothes; but not recently." I said, I don't like to hear you talking like that, Zoya. She smiled, a friendly blank smile. She took off everything except her brassiére. When I tried to take it off she said, "It's more fun for me with it on." But, later, she took it off. She closed the blinds and all the time I was inside her she smiled up at me. "I used to do it a lot with the boys at the school, but not any more," she said. The more I was in her the younger she looked, and this pleased me enormously. While we were resting she got up and went to the telephone and said, "I'm going to call up Rebecca." And she did. "Rebecca," she said, "guess who's here?" They spoke at considerable length on the phone, mainly about me, and then I got up to talk to Rebecca. She sounded puzzled, and we talked inconsequentially. Rebecca had fallen in love with all of us in turn and finally married a truck driver. She was a fine, sardonic girl, and I could just see her asking, What are you doing over at Zoya's? Which, in fact, she did. Rebecca had always been the one to see straight through to me. My father had wanted me to marry Rebecca. But, for me, she had been too old-country Jewish, too homely, her blunt squat features expressing a hurt because she was not pretty, and a hurtful vulnerability rendered into a crude-ranging toughness in approaching life that I would grow to understand only years later. Rebecca and I did not exchange much information; I think she sensed how much this would have hurt me. We promised that I would call later. Then I took Zoya back to bed, only to have her pop up and call Rebecca's *sister.* It was a long conversation. A couple of hours later, dressed, we had coffee in the kitchen. Zoya looked nice and those pouches under her clear young eyes were less prominent. She went into the shaded living room and played another piece, then came and sat on my lap in the kitchen. She was engaged, she said, to a nice Jewish boy, a lawyer. I congratulated her. She said, "Why don't you save me?" With that same empty friendly smile. I laughed, as good-naturedly as I knew how. I kissed her on the forehead and said I had to be going now, it was almost evening. She saw me to the door and I said I would call tomorrow. She said, "No, you won't." I said, Of course I will.

But, of course, I didn't. It was late afternoon, and growing cool. I drove in past Cicero's principal shrine, the hotel lobby that used to be Al Capone's headquarters, over to Roosevelt Road and cruised down the Road towards my old neighborhood. I felt wonderful, ironhearted and satisfied of lust. I was not coming home again sick with nostalgia. I was young Engels, just from Barmen, the foreign visitor viewing with a cool and detached eye the tortured sprawl of Manchester. Except that here, in this city, I needed no guide, no Mary Burns. Soon, however, I was to change my mind and wish that I had one. Because I no longer knew this city which I called home.

It was coming on towards night and the streets, which I had remembered as so riddled and stuffed with raucous odoriferous immigrant life, seemed strangely abandoned, as though the Negroes who now lived here were yet afraid. I could not, after cruising a while, blame them. A brooding sullenness, a sense of malevolence. You could see it in the way the Negroes had not yet appropriated the neighborhood as their own, had not turned the bars into local centers. They went too much about their business; either that, or stood on stoops and glared. I don't mean watched or gazed or stared. Glared. They were expecting something. And I knew what. A challenge. I have never, in all my traveling through America, seen a city so tense and waiting for a race riot.

I parked the De Soto on Roosevelt Road and walked over to Louie's Cigar Store where I had one of my first jobs as a bookie runner and which I had left when my mother found out and whacked the daylights out of me. I had liked the job. It had been exciting. Every week the lieutenant of uniformed police from the Pulaski Road station walked in, said Good evening, Louie, everything peaceful? and walked out to his car with an envelope in his breast pocket. A couple of months after my mother forced me to leave the job, which had entailed running and collecting, Louie's brother, who had helped run the bookie, was shot dead in a billiard parlor. I had been coming home from school when a kid told me Hymie, Hymie the Goneff, has got his. I ran over to the billiard parlor which occupied a second-floor loft over a bakery. The ambulance men were just carrying Hymie's body down, and a bunch of us kids crowded onto the stairs, which were spattered with bright red blood beginning to darken into the dirty wood. I never did find out the exact circumstances of Hymie's murder. The bystanders all had conflicting accounts, which is the trade mark of a fast, efficient and professional murder job in Chicago. And it wasn't because the cops were around, because they weren't. In fact, I was there ten minutes on those bloodstained stairs before the lieutenant of uniformed police, the same one who collected from the cigar store, finally showed up. All we could find out that day, was that two men had called Hymie out into the hall, one of them had hit him and the other had shot him with a small machine gun. Those stairs became something of a shrine too. Not so much because Hymie was murdered there — gang killings were not that all uncommon — but because a machine gun had been used. This was long past the days when machine guns figured prominently in gang killings, and it was terrifically glamorous for us. Six months later I had so exaggerated the story that I was going around telling the kids, few of whom believed me, that I had actually seen who did the killing. Louie must have heard about it, because my mother told me he had a long talk with her when I was at school one day and politely asked her to ask me not to say that I had seen the men do it. My mother gave me another licking then, because she thought I had retaken the job with Louie at his cigar store as a runner.

The cigar store was now a liquor store. I went in and spoke with the proprietor, a Negro. He was unfriendly and did not unstiffen when I told him I had once been a bookie runner there. He looked at me as though I might be a cop, and said it was no business of his. I tried to resume my role of private pollster, and asked the man how Negroes in the area were going to vote. It was a stupid thing. It might have been all right to ask how he was voting, but not otherwise. Gruffly, the Negro, a muscular gray headed fellow, asked me if I didn't have better things to do with my time. I went out and went next door, two shops away, into a bar on the corner, which in my time had been a rug store behind which one snowy day Izzy Walzer and I had a terrific fist fight because I had told Izzy I was afraid to fight him as he had a bad heart; after I won the fight Izzy pushed me into the snow and looked so excited I was afraid to get up; I kept asking passers-by to please go and fetch Izzy's mother or father. I must have knelt in the snow in the alleyway all of two hours, kept by Izzy and the fear he might keel over of a heart attack, until he got bored and went away. I never forgave Izzy. Never. It is a terrible thing to hold over a guy, your own heart disease.

As soon as I walked into this bar I knew Chicago, or at least this part of it, had really changed. It was like a bar in the Negro section of Greensboro, North Carolina. Ramshackle, a long wooden counter, a few tables and chairs, bullfighting and jazz posters on the walls, cases of beer and 7-Up stacked up against one wall and a small juke box. It wasn't even like a bar in Harlem. I walked into a wall of cold blunt hostility. White Man Unwelcome. Fair enough. I asked the fat bartender in a neat business suit behind the counter for a whiskey and water which he served up, as far as I could tell, without looking at me and then he went down to the other end of the counter. The few men and two women in the place looked at me, though. I wondered and they wondered. I thought, Wyatt Earp would have known how to handle this situation. But I didn't. That was always the problem. You just couldn't turn around, rest your elbows on the bar and say, *Look, I am not to blame.*

I walked down to the end of the counter where the bartender was picking his teeth. (I used to think bartenders picked their teeth and stared at the ceiling only in movies; I don't know, maybe it is life copying art again.) I asked him who he was voting for, and he rumbled, Democrat. I said was he going to vote Democrat despite their record on civil rights? He said, "What kind of a damn pollster are you, anyway?" I smiled and said, I am a pollster in depth. In depth, man. He looked at me as though I were on the stuff and said most everybody, if they were voting, which he doubted, would go Democrat. He gave me his card, and he turned out to be a ward captain in the local Democratic Party. I told him I had used to live in his neighborhood, and he straightened a little as though I were about to follow it up with a value judgment. What he said was, "That is of no interest whatsoever to me." The thing is, I understood exactly what was happening. We were all on each other's wave length. It had all the feel of an aftermath of a racial incident below the level of a riot. I knew that if I said something like, I'm a member of NAACP too, they would have thrown me out. Then I thought, ah fuck them. I was getting very tired, in Chicago, of presenting myself to people and not getting presented back. I finished my drink, went over to the juke box and stuck in all the change I had in my pocket, pressing down a number of times on the button beside someone called The Kitti-Kats singing "Isle of Capri" and then walked out. That would fix *them.* I got back into the De Soto and drove over to my old school, Hanson Elementary. I parked on a side street and watched the dusk capture it. It was impossible to feel nostalgic, or much of anything else either. This entire trip had long ago lost its perspective. I was in the middle of trench warfare. I was standing waist-high in muddy water, helpless, appalled and I could not pretend to see any of this in perspective. *And* in my old neighborhood too. It was almost better to feel crazy, because then you were a Jonah in the belly of a whale which was your own mind. It had its own comforts.

I suppose at this point I should write about how I tripped fancifully around the old, well-remembered places, strolling up and down stone stairs my head whirling with remembrances, testing a loose balustrade here, smiling fondly at an old sweet shop there, but I didn't. I walked about a bit, tried to speak to several Negroes on the street, got a more or less indifferent response, climbed back into the De Soto and got out of there. I wasn't even *feeling*. The old neighborhood just didn't mean anything.

I drove a few blocks over to Ogden Boulevard and parked in the rear of the barbecue joint where the Knights and I used to hang out. It was a big barnlike affair, with red neon signs everywhere and laminated tables and, of course, a juke box, not much different than it had been. I took a large center table and told the waitress I was waiting for friends. At this point I was feeling, to tell you the truth, damn silly. Here I was waiting around for kids — *men* — none of whom I had seen for more than ten years, because we had once belonged to a basement club. Still, I said to myself, why the hell not? I was not exactly wrapped in an aura of nostalgic anticipation, or even fidgety. Actually, I think I was being a little bored with Chicago at that moment.

The first one who came in was Sy, redheaded Sy, who recognized me right away. He came up to me cracking wise all the way and we shook hands. He said, "First thing, are you successful?"

Now isn't that a hell of a thing to be asked in your own home town? I said to Sy, I am so successful I am breaking of it. He said, "Yeah, how so?" I said, Well, in Hollywood, I had two private offices and two secretaries and Humphrey Bogart called me by my first name. Now what kills me is that Sy sat there taking it all in without a smile, and possibly even respecting me for it. I should say right here that Sy was probably one of the brighter of our gang in the old Knights. His ambition had been to be a radio writer. I asked him what he was doing and he said he was a probation officer. He was married and had a baby daughter. He had aged terrifically. When I had last seen him he looked an old seventeen, and now he looked a young forty. His red hair had turned brownish gray and he looked not haggard but wizened; blunted. He had been a peppery, cynical and defensive boy. He said that Schlomo, Fifie and Angie were coming.

Meanwhile, we sat and talked. All we talked about was the Knights. What had happened to them. Sy and I used to have key-chain fights, the point of which was to cut the opponent's face. Although I have never been what you would call athletic, I was good at this corner sport. The boys did not respect me for reading or even for being president of the Knights, but they did respect me for knowing how to cut an opponent's nostril with my flashing key chain. ("Yay, lady! lady! Turn around — I wanna tell you something! You dropped something! . . . Aw right, have it your way — bleed to death!")

We had all been close at one time. The club had been our home. Most of the other boys had been away at war, and we all felt a little ashamed about not being in uniform. Eventually I relinquished presidency of the Knights to a fat loquacious slob named Richard who led us one night into a riot with the wops from east of Sacramento Boulevard. The fight was on the lawn of Manley High School, and one of us, a new boy named Arkie, who was an escapee (we later learned) from a reformatory near Little Rock, was almost killed with a rock. Some of us, including myself, were pulled in for a guest appearance at juvenile court. The judge was really something. He solved that particular ethnic problem by ordering the Jewish boys, supposedly us although we numbered a lot of non-Jews in the Knights, to stay west of Sacramento Boulevard and the Italians east. It did not, needless to say, work out that way. Partly because the Italians numbered among them the Romano gang. They terrified me, those Romanos. They seemed not to care whether they lived or died. I got into a fight with one, Ernie Romano, once, and he terrorized me through two years of high school. Every time I saw him I broke out into a sweat. Even now, when I visualize his bland swarthiness, I miss a beat on my heart.

Well, for us, the club, the Knights, was life. Hanging around with them was life. By the time Richard came along to take the presidency away from me I didn't care, because by then I had met Cal and was studying to be Engels to his Marx.

I kept asking Sy about the old Knights, and damn if he didn't know where nearly all of them were. Horatio, my special friend, who we had all expected would build the tallest bridges in the world, was a druggist on 14th Street. Avrum was in prison, this time on a forgery charge, after three appearances for child molestation. Ralph, the card player, the bluffer, Sy said, was dead, of polio; Ralph the puncher, the swimmer; one night, when we had been "trailing" girls, our favorite sport, one of the girls whom we followed into the bushes with a wop kid turned out to be Ralph's sister and Ralph had run screaming right into the bushes after her; now he was dead. Ed, stolid-brained, heavily handsome, was playing semi-pro baseball for a team somewhere in California. Stan, the tall and righteous rabbinical student, was a furniture salesman in Santa Fe, New Mexico. Taciturn, utterly fearless Al was in Joliet penitentiary, charge auto stealing. Izzy, with the heart condition, had become a dentist. Oscar, Mexican, whose old man had been in prison, had dropped out of sight. Fritz, the red-faced Trotskyist, was a high school teacher. Tom, at seventeen, alcoholic, lost, way out in right field most of the time but a nice guy, was a chauffeur; somehow we all had thought he would turn out to be a writer, or a genius of some sort.

About Angie, Fifie and Schlomo, I would soon find out, said Sy, grinning. "So tell me," he said "are you happy?" You go to hell, Sy, I said. "Same old jerk," said Sy.

The truth is, Sy and I had never been in exactly what you call love with each other. All in all, he was now acting very defensive and *superior.* He said, "Well, the Hollywood big shot. Are you still a *ganzeh* Communist?" (Sy would never forgive my having recruited him into the Youth Movement.) I said, My aching back, Sy, let's not talk politics. He sat back and pretended to give a big belly laugh, "That's rich," he said, "coming from you." I guess it was, too.

The second person to come in was Fifie. The little bulb-nosed *goneff* who used to play clarinet and had three fingers and his teeth shot out at Omaha Beach, miraculously not permanently scarring him but causing his face to wear a slight perpetual pucker, as though he was always just on the point of getting ready to tune up on the clarinet. About five years ago, during a meeting I was holding in my house, in L.A., Fifie had shown up, from Chicago, loudly demanding that I fix him up with a Hollywood starlet; he had left the same night sadly disappointed in me. Fifie was a shrewd, unintelligent Jewish boy, undersize and whining, and as soon as he opened his mouth I saw that he had not changed. I wondered, with a kind of stupefied love, how he had ever been one of my best friends for so many years. He openly moaned about the loss of his hand the way you or I would grieve about $100 we had been conned out of.

Later on, Angie came in with a fat, pretty woman whom he introduced as his wife. She then went away. Angie had been the new fish, agile, crafty eyes and lies, a scared one too; now he was slow and portly, looking like a young Lou Costello. He was, he said, a teacher of carpentry in his high school. Almost immediately he began to talk about his students, with genuine fear and dislike. Of all of us, Angie, small but not weak, had hated physical battering. We had all known this and used to have a trick of picking him up and throwing him from one to the other of us while he shrieked and cursed us. He was, I could see, still wearing a large steel cross around his neck. Unlike Oscar, who had been an altar boy, and who had more or less led me almost into the Catholic Church, Angie had always been a hypocritical Catholic. We used to needle him mercilessly about this.

Looking at Angie, I was reminded of Father Lenihan. I asked Angie about him. Angie replied oh yes, he knew where the Father was, had a parish in Berwyn now. But I could tell from the way he spoke that Angie wasn't sure who I was referring to. It was a bad habit of Angie's never to admit he didn't know the person under discussion. Idly, I wondered what would happen if I went out and tried to find Father Lenihan. I was half tempted but decided that would have been too cornball. The truth was, I hadn't seriously thought about him since I left the Church which, properly speaking, I had never really entered. He had been the one to whom I had gone for instruction; a Jesuit, naturally, who I think must have seen me as a prime catch indeed, a Jew who wanted to be a priest. If he hadn't overreached himself he might have nabbed me too. Just before my first communion, which I swear I really was approaching in a state of grace, he handed me a little brown booklet called *One Hundred Sins a Catholic Boy Might Commit* or some such title, and told me to go home and study it, and if I had committed any of them to be sure and confess it to him just before I accepted the wine and wafer. Needless to say, when I got home I found I had committed about 40 per cent of these sins, and if Father Lenihan thought I was going to tell him all about my Sin of Onan, which to my mind was by far the worst of all, he had another think coming. I just didn't show up for the communion ceremony, and in the months afterward whenever we passed in the street Father Lenihan used to give me a gaze of intensely compassionate disappointment. I imagine that is how professional fishermen look upon The One That Got Away. But I had to hand it to him, the good Father never said a word against me in the neighborhood. The sad thing was that thereafter I was too ashamed to use the gym facilities of St. Agatha's Church, of which Father Lenihan was one of the priests. St. Agatha's had the best indoor baseball lot in that part of Chicago.

Finally Schlomo came in, still the teller of dialect jokes, still with brilliantined hair, tall and jerky. He ordered servings of our old dish, bar-be-cue, french fries and cole slaw, and we laughed because we all remembered what we used to order.

Then we sat around. I mean just that. We ate furiously, and talked the smallest talk imaginable. Here we were, hadn't seen each other for well over a decade and, within thirty minutes we were plain bored with each other. I with them too. Boredom of course, is never that. It's always disappointment. At any moment I expected a holiday spirit, some sudden sense of boys on an outing, or at least aging husbands just for an hour away from their domesticity. But, instead, we just sat at that table, thoughtfully shoving barbecued ribs into our faces. I have never known the past to be so far distant. Sy kept up a running patter, I think mainly to needle me, on the socio-economic changes in Chicago since I had left. Fifie kept saying, "You didn't find me no broad in Hollywood, big mouth!" as though I had *said* I would. Angie kept talking about the installments he had to pay on his house. I wished I had brought a bottle of White Horse in with me.

I said, Say, how about me going out and getting a bottle, but Sy got in fast and said, "No, what do you wanta do that for?" I guess, except for Fifie, they all had to go back to their wives. The thing is, not one of them really knew what had happened to me since I had left Chicago, but they didn't ask any questions. When they had first come in I was dying to ask them, to find out how they were living now and how they got that way, but suddenly all I could do was yawn: it was like a sudden attack of hiccuping, or asthma, except that I was expressing it in yawns.

I said, Schlomo, what are you doing with yourself these days? He had fallen unusually quiet for Schlomo with whom dialect jokes used to be a minor, chronic disease. He said, "Nothing much." I could tell from the way the others were acting too normally I'd better not pursue the subject. For one thing the odds were even that Schlomo was due to go in, or had just emerged from, some prison somewhere. The nearest to Schlomo I have encountered in reading is the character of Sparrow in *The Man With the Golden Arm.* He was always and forever cooking up deals, figuring the angles, plotting a caper, with a mournful, long-faced and unhappy expression as though he knew someone would catch him. They almost always did too. Before I left Chicago he had been "behind" twice, once for car stealing and once, of all things, for bond forgery or something complicated like that. On his visit to Hollywood, Fifie told me that Schlomo had made one big killing: he had robbed a big fur store in the company of some other thief who had promptly collapsed of a heart attack a day afterwards. Schlomo had gone down to Mexico City and lived for four years on the proceeds of that one job. The idea of tall, rabbinical, dour, weepy-eyed Schlomo in the land of guitarists and señoritas was very funny. I couldn't resist asking him across the table, Schlomo, tell me now, how did you find Mexico?

Immediately he brightened. He liked talking about Mexico. He became positively enthusiastic. It was the only thing I had ever heard him talk about knowledgeably. When he correctly pronounced Popocatepetl I almost fell over. The others were only mildly interested. "One lousy thing, though," said the Schlomo. What was that? I asked. "The Jewish broads," he said. The what? I cried, not believing my ears. "Yeah," he said glumly, "they are down there too. In fact, worse." "Worse than Chicago?" asked Sy skeptically. "I'm telling you," said Schlomo. "They're all the daughters of refugees and people like that, families, papas and mamas grab hold of you like you was their life raft or something as soon as they find out you're Jewish, they wanna have their daughter marry you and not one of the south-of-the-border *schwartzas.*" We all laughed quietly, thinking of Schlomo eluding marriage-hungry Viennese mamas in Mexico City.

But the laughter did not lead to anything. It just died away. And there we were, supping. It was as though we were inside some social vacuum tube where our every action, lifting a fork, saying a word, had had the meaning sucked out of it by the very shape of our existence. While we were waiting for coffee, I reached into my trousers and unslung my money belt, extracted the books of traveler's checks and slapped them on the table. Schlomo picked up the checks and thumbed through them, finally announcing, "One thousand. You're traveling heavy," said the Schlomo.

"What are you showing off for," said Fifie. Angie said, "Gimme half, I got problems." Sy said nothing, just smiled evilly. Ah hell, I thought. What I had meant to do was create some kind of joke we all could share, and that was it. But they didn't think it was much of a joke. I slunk the money back into the belt and stuffed the belt into my trousers pocket. All I wanted to do was get out of there. Fifie had stopped talking about his hand stump hurting him, and was nattering about how he had been part of a Bureau of Internal Revenue "commando" which had gone through the accounts of a famous Chicago gangster in order to catch him out on evasion charges, which they did. Fifie was very proud of that, and for some reason it saddened me more than anything. Because, you see, before Fifie lost his fingers at Anzio beach, despite his pinched mind and blunt soul he could play an almost professional Mozart on his clarinet. I suppose eventually he would have given up the clarinet anyway. The last memory I had of Fifie and me as kids was the night the police called at his house because it had been rumored he was the salesman of eight-page "dirty" books. Since he is very short, and in a bad light looks innocent, he had managed to convince the cops it was two other boys. But about two that morning I heard pebbles practically cracking my bedroom window. It was Fifie, standing out under the moonlight in the snow-drifted alleyway. I dressed and went downstairs, and we spent the next couple of hours digging in the middle of Douglas Park burying the obscene books, and that ground was as hard as a judge's heart. As I say, we dug until almost morning, in a cold sweat of fear, not because the johns were after us, which had happened before and would happen again, but because of the offense with which we would be charged. It would be very difficult at Hanson Elementary living down probation for selling "eight-pagers." But the cops never did come back, and for all I know those tiny books are still buried behind some bushes, near the corner of Albany Street and 13th. If you are interested.

And then and we all knew it simultaneously, it was time to break it up. I could tell from the way they were talking that they had not had anything to do with one another, other than passing in the street, since our club days. Well, that was natural enough; what was I complaining of? I suppose, the same thing I was complaining of, demanding of, other people across the country: that they, in some way, in any way salute the importance of what we had done together so that something of our history would become meaningful. I kept telling myself, in that jukeboxedup barbecue joint, that the healthy way of looking at all this was to say, Well, all that is in the past, it is only the present that matters. But, in my heart, I really did not feel the present mattered one good goddam. I suppose that at this point I should take a bow, humbly and say that this was a purely subjective reaction. But I didn't think it was. I think why I felt so bad was that the more everyone I knew became furiously occupied with the present the more it seemed to not matter. There *is* a way to buy a house, and wash your car, and talk about the price of lettuce, and grumble about your work, and even to worry about paying installment bills, but the way everyone *I* knew was going about this made me think it simply didn't matter; they were all busy, busy sleepwalkers, buying their way into a life from which everything in America was insulting them. Like that boy I picked up outside Omaha, eating, sleeping and going to the toilet in the shadow of hydrogen bombs lashed in the belly of primed bombers, or near it, and not even being *afraid.* I don't know. Maybe one of these days I will run into a psychoanalyst, or somebody, who will explain it all to me; I mean, about how because I feel a certain way I "project" the same feelings onto everyone else. ("Project" was a favorite word of Hilda's; I will tell you about Hilda later.) And maybe he even will convince me. But I'll still walk around with a tiny wisp of suspicion that the way I was feeling might be the way everyone else — like Schlomo, Fifie, Angie, Sy — was also. Maybe not. Since this is the chronicle of how I started to go mad I guess I am suspect in matters of grave social import.

So I broke it up by telling them I had to wake up early in the morning and get out of town. This was something of a lie inasmuch as I expected to spend another day in Chicago. Sy, before anyone could say anything, declared as how they would stick around a while. The bastard. Making me look the party-pooper. We all shook hands, solemnly, as though I would be coming back next week, and then I walked out. I suddenly hated Sy. I could have hit him.

I got into the De Soto and reached over for a bottle of White Horse when I remembered there wasn't any there. I started up the car and cruised along Ogden Boulevard until I found an open bar, a cheesy, small place called John's On. I went in and had a couple of scotches and started to talk to this man next to me. I swear, he even *looked* like Ernest Borgnine. This place had a mangy juke box too. Fortunately the owner had a sense of humor because it kept playing thirteen-year-old tunes like "There's a Star Spangled Banner Waving Somewhere" and "Rose of San Antone." I told this burly man with the five-o'clock shadow next to me that I had been to a reunion of some of my old clubhouse friends. He said, "Yeah, that's interesting." No, I said, it wasn't interesting. He said, "I get together every month with my old clubhouse gang. We have a lot of fun. You should too." I said, You sonofabitch. He said, "That's why you don't have fun." But I could see him measuring me, and I suddenly became afraid he would knock me on my ass. We had both grown up in the same neighborhood and I think the reflexes are basically the same. Anyway, I figured I had too much to drink. Two scotches. I went back outside and cruised around all over the West Side. I recognized the streets and alleyways. Nothing had changed structurally; it was just built over and decayed under and with different people, mainly, as I said, Negroes. It occurred to me that the bar I had just come from hadn't any Negroes in it. And it was right in the middle of the Negro section. As I said, you could smell riot in the air. It was a brisk October night, the kind I used to love in Chicago. Dark, cool, lonely. I cut over to Independence Boulevard, past 12th Street and cornered left on Grenshaw almost to Pulaski Road where I pulled up. Yes, there it was, the old clubhouse. The building was exactly as I remembered it. I got out of the car and went to the iron fence and stared down into the well of the basement. The landlord had made our old clubhouse into a flat. I could see someone's lights burning behind the curtain. I leaned on the fence and stared, no longer feeling ironhearted and satisfied of anything, my brain dead and clogged with nostalgia which swept over me like sweet nausea in waves, each wave bigger and heavier than the one before it, until I realized they were coming with a regular rhythm, and now I was in the fist of that old brain music again. I was tempted to jump back in the De Soto but I made myself stand there, on the sidewalk, until the clubhouse became a flat, merely, again.

I drove straight back to Rogers Park and where I was staying with Paul and Helen. I parked and waited until I could see all the lights go out, and then I went upstairs, to the room they had given me, undressed and went to bed. I had one more day left in Chicago.

In the morning, while Helen was out at the library, Paul and I had a long talk. He said that the situation of the Left unions generally was, after several years of government harassment and raiding by right-wing unions, better than might be expected. A great many mergers had taken place between small Left unions and the larger, more conservative internationals.

How were these Left unions faring within internationals which, until recently, had been their bitterest enemies and main source of raiding?

Paul thought and said, "The old hard division of Left and anti-Left is breaking down. Fast no; gradually yes." In the Chicago region of the UAW, for instance, Milt Burns, a well-known left-of-center who had taken his International Harvester unionists into UAW from the Left union, United Electrical, was now being openly spoken of as organizational director for the entire UAW region. "This," said Paul, "would have been unthinkable when McCarthy was alive." I told Paul that in traveling across the country I had heard or seen nothing to support the view that leaders and staffers from formerly independent (Left) unions suffered purges or serious discrimination in their new unions. Paul said, "Most of the purgeable people have been already. The others, such as myself, do their jobs and lie low."

In his own union, a small outfit called the Association of Tool & Die and Allied Crafts, the situation was, as usual, complicated. Last year, Paul said, it had merged with the International Union of Maintenance Technicians, a conservative AFL union, on the assurance of keeping itself intact and autonomous. But now the Maintenance Technicians had decided to become part of Victor Hauser's Amalgamated Vehicle Builders, our old union. The problem, Paul said, was that the Association of Tool & Die men were to be part of a "package" deal only on pain of disavowing some of its top officials, most of whom were Communists. From the couch where he was sitting Paul threw me a copy of the newspaper of the International Union of Maintenance Technicians with a front-page editorial denouncing communism written by a young firebrand whom I remembered in New York leading May Day parades in his paratrooper's uniform. This was the price exacted by the Technicians' union for interceding with George Meany, AFL president, on behalf of the Communist leaders of the Tool & Die men. Hauser's terms for an eventual merger of the three unions were clear. Tool & Die must get rid of its Communist president, in return for which it could retain its own staff personnel, such as Paul, regardless of politics. A deal was setting. The legal counsel of the regional AVB headquarters a conventional lawyer who knew nothing of Paul's former role in the union, had approached him to help out in the merger negotiations with an eye to coming onto the AVB legal staff.

Paul grinned. "The way things are going," he said, "I'll be working for Hauser in another year." His superiors in the small craft union were now impeccably conservative trade unionists. "They do their job," Paul said. "There is no political problem because there is no politics." When he said it, I swear Paul sounded more relieved than sad.

Paul was suspicious of the long-term contract but said it would become a permanent feature of the industrial picture, and nothing could stop it. He said the entire union membership had become "almost overnight" depoliticalized, if by overnight we mean a historical process lasting ten years. I laughed and said, Overnight. He laughed and reddened and said, "Old habits, comrade, die slowly. The guys in the plants," he said (even after fifteen years in trade union work, Paul sounded uncomfortable saying guys. He once confessed to me that he never had found a convenient and natural way of referring to them, men, members or guys), "the guys in the plants are doing pretty well. Financially. But they are also very sensitive — more sensitive than I have ever seen them — to slight quivers in the lines on the economic chart." They want, Paul continued, to see trouble long before it happens so that they can do something about it. Taft-Hartley, he said, was not much of an issue, although Negro discrimination was. Everyone, he said, was looking for an excuse to vote Democratic; all the trade unionists, that is. I told him that was how I had found it.

I had been doodling on a piece of paper while listening to Paul explain the situation in the Midwest, and thinking to myself how undogmatic he sounded. He had gone back to his empirical roots. But then, when he stopped talking, I sensed something and looked up. Paul was staring at me. He looked old and relaxed and haggard, his face suddenly drawn and empty. He said, "You know, brother, the Left is finished. Us. We've had it. Three strikes. We're out." It was as if both of us had let out a silent sigh. Perhaps mine was not so silent. After a time, I said, Where did we go wrong, Paul? In Detroit, I mean. That's where it was pretty much decided, I think.

"Yes, I think so," said Paul. "That was where it *was* decided. And when we were there. I don't know. We took such a beating I try not to think about it. It was, in truth, a mighty train wreck. Who the hell put all that fucking grease on the rails has been a topic of stimulating domestic debate, but neither Helen nor I can lay claim to a single position."

Paul went into the kitchen and came out with a bottle from which he poured for both of us. He sat down like a tired man. "I don't know," he said. "I wasn't telling you the truth when I said I don't think about it. It haunts me. But the truth is, when it comes to talking about it, I have no stomach for rehashing. The Hauser-Tolliver issues, most of them of course weren't really issues but tactical points in two contesting public relations campaigns." In the next few minutes, Paul reeled off *every* single tactical point we had ever made against Hauser: that Hauser was an intellectual fancy pants who was using the labor movement merely as a springboard, that he was chummy with the bosses, that his cosmological blueprints made good newspaper copy but added up to a kick in the balls for the workers, that the contracts in his home local were lousy, that his name had been attached to a statement of the National Planning Association calling for lion-lamb cohabitation and for speed-up, that his wife had promiscuously investigated all candidates before selecting Victor as Most Likely to Succeed, that Hauser did not wholly venerate Phil Murray, that he had instigated wartime strikes while kissing the toes of big brass in Washington, that he wanted to stifle democracy in the union.

In no time at all Paul was virtually talking to himself; he sounded as though he had gone over the ground a hundred times before, looking for an answer. "What did his side say about our side?" Paul murmured. "Okay. That Tolliver and his boys were louts and numskulls propped up only by the local Communists, that Tolliver could not respectably join battle in public debate with a C. E. Wilson or Henry Kaiser . . . Ah what the hell is the use! They just don't synchronize. It all adds up to, why did we hate Hauser? You see," he said, still talking to himself, "it's really two questions. Why did we, as intellectuals, hate his guts? God help us, he represented what the majority of workers wanted at that time and place."

Then Paul broke off. "Oh my oh *my*," he murmured. "I can't figure out whether we did the right or wrong thing. For a long time I thought we did the right thing wrongly. Now I'm not so sure. Finish your drink and we'll watch television."

Then Paul got up and went over and switched on the television set and sat on his haunches, staring at it. It was as though he had gone berserk. I had never seen him like this. Just then Helen came in the front door, and Paul hurriedly snapped off the set and took her smilingly in his arms, the way a good husband should. We had a late lunch, and then I went out into the rain to drive around a little. Just before I went, Helen said, lightly, neutrally, "The fighting is very heavy, the radio says, in Budapest." Paul went right on eating. I figured it was a good idea to get out of there tonight or tomorrow morning.

I drove around the West Side of Chicago most of the day in the rain. Visiting various places. And as I drove I listened to the radio. They were now reporting the Hungarian uprising at hourly intervals, the same as sporting events. It gave you a curious feeling, going around to all the spots you remembered in your home town, including the street corners where you at one period in your life broke up Communist meetings and in another period yourself stood handing out leaflets, listening to American, nasal voices tell of the butchery in Budapest. I knew I should have been feeling profoundly, I mean feeling this linkage between what I had once passed out leaflets for and what was now happening in Budapest, but I didn't. I just kept thinking, this will be it. This is the start of World War III. But as soon as I remembered that the news reporters were now coming on hourly instead of every fifteen minutes I knew the United States wasn't going to mobilize anyone for anything; not a few days before the election.

Late in the afternoon I parked on 22nd Street and rang a bell in a brown brick tenement. I was terrifically surprised when the person I expected came to the landing on the second floor. It was Rima Shiffs. She asked who it was, and I yelled up my name. She asked again who it was, and I said, We went to school together. She muttered something which floated down to me, like, "I'll bet we did," and said to come up. I walked up the ratty and evil-smelling stairs. Rima had been the good-time girl of Hanson Elementary. One night we had a party at her house, and my best pre-League, pre-Knights friend, Jackie Berg, took Rima into her parents' bedroom. Trouble was, Rima had an idiot brother who picked just that moment to not only come to our party but go into the bedroom. Rima told us later that she was lying under Jackie when she saw her brother wrench the half-length mirror off the full-length bureau and bring it down on Jackie's back. Poor Jackie, he was taped up for a month.

As soon as I walked into Rima's place I knew she was on the tricks. It didn't surprise me; we had all expected it. But, my God, she had aged fast. She sat on the couch in a wraparound, and smiled automatically. It was like some bad scene from Hollywood. The living room was a combination of furniture probably left her by her Swiss folks, heavy and stolid with fringes on everything, and cheap modern, and Rima in her wraparound quite ugly. I sat down and said to Rima that I had gone to school with her. Then, before she had a chance to say anything, I got up and walked out, down to the De Soto and drove straight back to Rogers Park. Paul and Helen and I sat around all night, talking. I noticed that even when we were talking seriously Paul had the TV set on. Twice he got up, once to put on "Studio One" ("Sometimes they have fairly good stuff") and once for "I Love Lucy" (no excuse). I couldn't believe my eyes. Paul praying to God was a more believable sight than Paul watching "I Love Lucy."

We chatted in a friendly manner, and then I went to bed. Just like that. One minute we were talking, and then we were all washing up and passing each other in the bathroom.

I woke up about four in the morning, quickly dressed, packed, wrote out a note apologizing for not staying for breakfast, said to give my regards to Mollie, and went out to the De Soto which I had had oiled, gassed up and lubed yesterday afternoon. There was another parking ticket on the wet windshield, which I tore up, got in, consulted the radio for the latest, took a swig of White Horse which I'd brought down with me, took a dexedrine spansule, and got rolling.

Chicago was peaceful and comely at five in the morning, even with the radio crackling out the first news of Csepel Island. Dark, wet, the lamppost shiny streets covered with a fine snow of dead leaves from the overhanging oaks, the cars parked nose to bumper on each side of the sleeping streets. I took my time getting out of Chicago but had to stop in Whiting, Indiana, just over the state line, when the damndest dee-pression came over me. It lasted about an hour; so I just laid my head back on the seat and went to sleep, slumping quickly and waking up instantly. And then I started out again. It was as though the whirring tires of the car had become my two feet, and I was walking smoothly and not riding.

Gary, Indiana, at seven on a dark October morning is probably the most beautiful thing in America. You drive through gray sleeping working-class towns, which have an unblemished record of riots whenever a Negro has occasion to move into a new house, Whiting, Calumet City, East Chicago, an unbroken succession of steelworkers' homes, cheap bars, gas stations, aluminum signs of incorporation, signs of dug-in conservative solidity, the immigrant come to America and realizing its promise by burrowing in, curiously bleak, curiously *functioning* little townships, and then on into Gary itself, dead as a doornail this time in the morning except for the lines of automobiles carrying steelworkers to the mills. Just outside Gary I turned off the main highway leading to the various works entrances onto a secondary road skirting the shore of the lake and rimming the steel mills. It was a dark and wet morning, and for several miles the lakefront was illuminated by bursts of fires and towering gas flames and a necklace of industrial glows out of the steel furnaces. It is strange how the slow, moving sight of those furnaces immediately catapults you into the realm of art. I have myself never worked inside a steel mill but I have a fair idea of who the men are and how they live, and every time I see those glowing furnaces outside Gary I *contemplate* broadly, even artistically. They are a beautiful sight. As soon as I passed the last mill, I spurted forward on Highway 20, going east.

I forgot all about talking to people, about polling them, about finding out what was happening inside America. I was now having a race with myself. Fright sat at my right hand, emptiness lay behind my eyes as though scotch-taped there. I thought a great deal about writers, and writing, as I streaked through those small industrial and market towns of upstate Indiana.

And what writers must do with their writing.

I see no salvation in personal relationships, in political action, or in any job I might undertake in society. Everything in me cries out that we are meaningless pieces of paste; everything in me hopes that this is not the end of the story. For there is something in the atmosphere of America which multiplies and enhances the basic nausea of experience while preventing, or hindering, that which might counteract the inescapable, papered-over vertiginousness: a direct apprehension of discrete phenomena, America straight. Has all that I have been enabled me to break through to the essential reality, this irreducible, absurd, self-evident fact? That man is alone and can only relieve but not redeem his loneliness. That, to the extent we try to deny this — and most things in America aim at denying this — to that extent we participate in a living lie which must corrupt if not destroy us.

I looked at upstate Indiana and thought of how far we had come away from even the wannest of Thoreau's strictures and dreams. The end is peace, a swift laughing togetherness of men in a kind of accomplished innocence. Michigan City, Indiana. In a pig's eye.

Csepel still holding out.

As soon as I was on the open highway I lit up some marijuana cigarettes which I had been carrying since Los Angeles. I smoked three in a gas station lavatory but they did nothing. I was not at all far out, or unattached. I had all of me inside me, but I did not like it one bit. I was so drunk on futility I was willing to try anything. Maybe that was how the Indian Bird was when he got into a mood to rob a bank.

On and on, on Highway 20. America from Chicago to New York is one vast medium-sized medium-industry medium-ugly town, called by different names, having different tax rates. What was it Housman said? "Deceived alike in origins and expectations." More to the point was Ezra Pound's epitaph on something which could have been America, "The age demanded an image — of its accelerated grimace." Man, that is Chicago, Elkhart and all the way through to the New England coast. An accelerated grimace.

I took a slight detour, and when I arrived in Fort Wayne I went into a drugstore phone booth to call the last of the Corpuscle Quartet, Stu. I hadn't seen him for ten years, but just before I left Los Angeles he had sent me a letter saying that he was working in his father's supermarket, was eating and living well, writing poetry, and had started up a local cinema society and would like to see me. The letter was quite bitter. Stu was the poet of the quartet, the folk singer, pimple-faced and mimicking, nervous as a cat, moon-faced and a comedian in all the whining spheres. He stared out at you behind thick spectacles and quavered revolutionary songs to a boogie-woogie beat. It used to kill Cal, who did not like to joke about politics.

Stu himself answered the phone. I yelled, Hey, Stu, it's me, Stuvengo old boy. He said, quietly and calmly, "You can't come over. I've got scarlet fever. We'll have to talk on the phone."

You had to give one thing to Stu, he never lied meanly. *Scarlet fever*. I should have hung up on him. I said, For Chrissakes, Stu. He said, "I mean it, I'm contagious as hell." I told him I wanted to hang up but he insisted we talk over the phone. I had absolutely nothing to say to him, not after scarlet fever. And, another thing, he was using me. For some obscure reason of his own. He started out coolly, then peevishly, then irritably and now really angry. He insisted that I was making fun of him. He said I was being superior. I don't know who he was talking to but it sure wasn't me. I said,

Either let me come out or I'm hanging up. There was a pause; then he said, reluctantly, "Okay, come out, but you'll have to talk to me through a door."

And he was as good as his word. I drove out to the address he gave me and found it an oldish, turreted house, endowed with large eaves and large windows, altogether a relic, the kind of house a judge or local newspaper publisher might have purchased in 1890. I rang the bell, and a pale-faced maid answered. She ushered me to the back of the house where arrangements had been made. The maid looked tense and surprised; I had expected that.

There it was, by God. No wonder the maid had looked surprised and unhappy. In front of a large single oak-brown door was a straight-backed wooden chair, facing sideways, under a stairwell. I went up to the door (wondering if the maid was peeking) and knocked heavily and aggressively. Stu piped up, in that gravelly, squeaking voice, "Don't come in! I'm contagious!" The hell of it was that if I had called his bluff I still wouldn't be able to say if he had a serious illness or not. He habitually looked awful, and his face, as I remembered it, was always death-colored and marred by pits and pocks and pimples and spots. Stu, I had to admit, was a pretty awful-looking boy. But I used to like him, not without a kind of unwilling derision (it was the same for the others, I knew) but like nevertheless. He was the only one of us who had talent.

Stu's voice, now as I was speaking to him, was carefully trained to sound like someone on his deathbed, frightened, self-pitying, weak. He had sounded like a foghorn on the phone. I sat down in the chair, feeling, I can tell you, foolish. We spoke through the door, which, without trying it, I knew would be locked. Stu said he worked days for his father, in the shop, and did writing at nights. He was sending a story off to *The New Yorker* that evening. Some of his poetry had been published in a local anthology and he was thinking of borrowing enough money from his father to turn the largest local movie into an art cinema house. In Fort Wayne, Indiana.

I said all that sounded very interesting, and he shrieked, "Don't you patronize me, you bastard." I seriously wondered whether perhaps Stu might not have gone insane in the years I had not seen him, and might not now be lying in a dark and shrouded room, a tragic reminder to his parents of a scar in their blood line. But no, as I had come up the front walk there had been a yellow Dodge convertible parked in front of the house that could have belonged only to Stu.

Conversation lagged. He had not asked me a single question about myself, nor had I expected him to. Self-centeredness was to Stu what wood was to a tree: one did not resent the natural. Still, it made normal converse, even considering the door between us, difficult. I said it must have been quite a change of life for him to come and live in a smallish town. Well, that did it. He railed at me for something like fifteen minutes, accusing me of accusing him of becoming a small-town refugee, a Babbitt, a philistine. "This is America, boy!" he shouted, "and it's about time you learned what it's all about.

"You and your fucking big towns," he shouted. "Disgusting and miserable, the life, the people in them. You want to know," he said, "what it's like in the big city? It's like this. It's lonely, son, lonely as hell. It's coming home with the rock in your stomach which becomes a hunger for food but you don't eat because perhaps someone will answer their telephone and you can invent an excuse for going over to eat at their house." (Here Stu drew a big breath.) "And what else is it? It's like going *lunatic*, deeply, pervadingly, by slow, steady stages. It's reading a bad book and refusing to let go of it because then you either have to face your own sweating aloneness or the typewriter which is aloneness plus. It's being unable to make contact. Why? At work, the people are shells. Outside, who is there to touch? Nobody. Not a goddamned friggin soul."

I tried to say something but Stu just stopped a moment, then plunged on. "It's jumping with delight," he said, "when the telephone jangles and being unable to stop the torrent of arrogant, drunken words, all the time you want to be a swell fellow but because you're so goddam lonely and isolated and self-walled you resent it, and possible charity, oh God extend a little charity, and you snarl and bicker and make meaningless jokes, and if it's a very good girl, or if you're so far gone you don't give a screwing jump in hell anyway, you mumble contritely, Come on over, baby, and save me just this one night. And so you, the boy who breaks his back seven times a day not to be beholden to anybody, are suddenly monumentally obligated, obligated in such a way that cruelty is the only way to discharge this special obligation. Christ, what in hell is the meaning of life, of anyone's life in that big city of yours? It's not living, it's preventing a breakdown, that's all big city life is. I think I may be close to one, but I have no way of knowing. Fight it, boy, fight it until you haven't an inch of breath in your lungs, because there are going to be a hell of a lot of more important, no, not important, more *useful* battles to fight in the future and you might as well not get any practice in buckling at the knees."

At which point he shut up. Neither of us said anything for a long time. Then I whispered, Stu . . . I received no reply. I called out several times. When there was no response I got up, placed the chair under the dark stairwell, walked out of the house to the De Soto and drove out of Fort Wayne. I had seen the last of the Corpuscle Quartet.

One good thing, though. I had stopped noticing the girls. For the past two hundred miles, and before that, I had felt like leaping from the car and bearing all the girls I had seen to the ground. I mean, all the girls. Whether to kill or love them, God alone knew. I was no longer trying to solve mysteries, simply fleeing fears.

About women. I never know whether I will like them until that moment when, their backs slightly arched, their arms are akimbo reaching to unsnap the brassière. Never before then.

For the first time in my life I not only understood Shakespeare's Lear but identified with him.

I passed up another hitchhiker.

I thought about how unnatural it was to spend so much time on the road when there isn't a depression going. But there are all kinds of depressions. If it's an economic one, then people don't say anything if you go on the road. If it's moral or cultural, people say you are filled with neurotic self-pity. Around here, near Sandusky, my thoughts were full of a book I had read while in bed in Los Angeles. It was called *Scum of the Earth* by Arthur Koestler. It was about anti-Fascist refugees in France in 1940. The whole tone of the book said, You don't know how lucky you are if you are a non-refugee. I kept trying to remind myself of the situation of those refugees, telling myself that I didn't have it so bad, nor did my friends, what were we complaining about? But it just didn't wash. If you haven't experienced something like that you have to make do with what you have experienced. And it seemed pretty bad. Oh, not in any way you could really *list*. That was the worst part of it. Because you never knew whether it was in your mind or outside in the world. I suppose each generation makes its own trouble. But I think there should be a way of reminding ourselves of our blessings, relatively I mean. Suppose, for example, all tiny babies were subliminally motivated by means of ultrasonic sound waves to absorb, in the cradle, maybe even in the womb if science progresses that far ahead, a kind of *collage* of memory of the suffering of refugees on the road in France in 1940. I have heard of experiments along this line, teaching kids in infancy to be oriented towards Latin by playing them Latin recordings in the nursery. So when these children, the children in my experiment, grow up, way far back in their minds they will be aware of what it was like at one time to suffer to the point of not wanting to survive. And looking around them they would be happier. By comparison, if you get my meaning.

I was now traveling on the geography of my temper.

The speed of the car, the way I handled the wheel, each stop I made, was dictated not by the road but by the ferocity of the music which, no matter how many tricks I tried, rang and reverberated and inhabited my head. I was totally at its mercy. I vomited like clockwork. I passed out with almost the same regularity, never, thank God, before I had time to pull over to the side and carefully lay my head on the seat.

Why didn't I pack it in altogether? Hard to say. I suppose I thought it would go away and, perhaps, this time not come back. Probably I would have turned off the road had I known of a place. But I didn't. I knew no one in the northern part of Indiana and Ohio. I kept thinking about that Veterans Administration Hospital in Wyoming. I remember hooking my thinking on it, irrationally, almost obsessionally. I was tempted, again and again, to turn back, but was always kept from it by the thought of having to go back a thousand miles. Don't ask me why I fastened on *that* hospital. But it was that one or none.

Also, I kept drinking White Horse. Today, it is the only Scotch label which I don't feel *anything* about when I look at it.

Towards evening, I stopped off in Cleveland, called a friend of mine, someone with whom I had worked in North Carolina, a woman Communist. I phoned from a drugstore on the west side of town. Almost the first thing she said was, "Have you been listening to the radio? We worked, we turned mimeo machines, we argued and passed resolutions and made enemies out of friends, and look what we got for our pains; tell me what good it did." We spoke for a few minutes, and I hung up, and got back into the car.

Outside Cleveland, on Highway 20, in the rain, I did turn on the radio. Austrian radio, the announcer said, had established contact with Csepel Island which declared its intention never to surrender. The election returns were coming in, but it was too early to tell the winner.

About twenty miles west of Ashtabula, at about 70 in the rain, I started looking around for some more White Horse. I had thrown the last bottle out but thought I remembered the remnants of an old bottle in the glove compartment. Angrily, I shoved my hand in. It felt like a tiger slashing at it. When I put my hand back on the wheel it slipped and sloshed all over. I slowed down near the glow of a motel court and saw that my fingers and palm were bleeding. I had shoved them right into the shards of glass from the broken bottle I had thrown out of the car back in Nebraska, which I had gone back to pick up, in the rain, under the gaze of the boy with only one arm. I had forgotten that the glass was there.

I sucked at my hand but it continued to bleed. So I drove on to Ashtabula, arriving about ten in the evening, and called in at a drugstore to ask for the nearest doctor. I was told there was one just around the corner. The drugstore clerk and a customer stared at me, and when I passed a mirror I saw that I had streaks of blood on my mouth. I walked around in the rain until I came to a large, comfortable-looking clapboard house. I walked up the steps and rang the bell. The doctor himself came to the door and I showed him my hand. He was just finishing a late dinner and told me to go into a side room, which was equipped as a surgery.

The doctor was a Lionel Barrymore type out of the Doctor Kildare movie series. He was pretty old, somewhere in his sixties, and untidy. There were soup stains and cigarette ash over his vest and he looked half blind, but he sat me on his examining table without a word and went after my hand efficiently. I kept looking down at him, silently begging him to ask how I had done it. I really did feel like talking.

But the old bastard did nothing of the sort. There I was, a complete stranger sodden with rain, probably stinking to his ceiling of White Horse, my face smeared with blood and that hand possibly cut when I punched it through a mirror in a rage, and he did not ask me a single definite question. He just wanted my name and address for his files. He bandaged my hand and told me to have someone look at it when I got somewhere. He said there was no glass left in my hand, but he didn't congratulate me on it. Just said it. I paid him five dollars and he stood up, waiting for me to leave. I don't know, maybe he was just a tired old man.

As soon as I was outside, on his porch, with the rain beating down on his lawn and the door shut behind me, about ten-thirty on the night my country was electing a president, I suddenly thought: my hand doesn't hurt. It gives no pain. All the time he had been bandaging it I hadn't felt a thing. Suddenly it hit me like a truck: I was having a mental breakdown. I felt like going back and interrupting that old doctor at his late dinner and pounding at him: WHY DIDN'T YOU ASK ME ANY QUESTIONS! DIDN'T YOU SEE WHAT WAS WRONG WITH ME?

But I didn't.

In my diary, for the night of November 6, there is the following entry: "Curious. I am having a nervous breakdown." I felt a little awed, considerable detached fear and an obsession with a single solitary notion: to push on. This too, I felt sure, would pass just as soon as I made the *right* kind of contact.

Beware the man with a broken dream. He will turn on you.

I walked to the car, got in and drove. I was without resources, and in some senses without a mind. I knew I had to check in somewhere. I drove all night, slowly, sweating, nervous, losing myself off the road several times at the approach of head-lights which blinded me. Oncoming cars frightened me. By the time I stopped the car I was exhausted, almost cheerfully, from crying.

It was morning, sunny and bright, and I was in a place you never heard of, called New Erie, New York. It is a small industrial town in the furthest northwest corner of the state. I had relatives there, I remembered. Or at least I hoped they were still there. It was the first time I had ever gone to blood relations for help. The first time in my life.

There was an old man sitting by the window, already, that early in the morning. Staring, his hands resting on two canes. The house was painted yellow and was old and nice-looking, off a side street near railroad tracks which led through a grove of trees right down to the shore of Lake Erie. As soon as the door opened to my knock, and I saw that it was my cousin-in-law, Eva, I knew I would be all right for the next day or two. The first thing Eva said was, "An auspicious occasion, Pa. Eisenhower is President and look who is visiting us."

*

Eva said, "Hello, long time no see. Lee is fixing his car at the garage, he'll be back soon." Eva's kids, a girl about thirteen and two boys about twelve and ten, came into the living room and stared at me and then dashed out to school. They were blonds, all-American types. Eva herself was a buxom, fair-haired woman with Scandinavian features. I never could get used to her calling my cousin Lee. In the family we always called him Simon, his name. But when he had been an organizer he had to change his name to Lee Brown or something like that, and it was then he met and married Eva. They were both tough, durable, unimaginative, family-loving communists, even though they had broken with first the Socialist Party, and later the Communist Party, and still later with a group called the International Workers' Party, with which they were now, as they were to tell me, reconciled. During the Spanish Civil War, Simon, or Lee, was my idol. He and his brother Archie had flipped a coin to see who would go to Madrid, and who would stay home with the folks. Archie won the toss. He went to Spain and came back with his eyes crossed, something to do with the noise of guns. As soon as he came back he went to work in a shipyard as an organizer for the union and rose to a fairly high position before the Red scare got him. Today Archie is a plump, jovial automobile salesman in Monterey, California, who attends yearly meetings of the Lincoln Battalion veterans and once a week goes to his Democratic ward get-togethers and acts as Assistant Scoutmaster for his boys' troop. But people like Simon and Archie — in fact, practically my whole family, they are just lying low. The minute political channels are opened again, if ever, in America, they will all be swimming like crazy. Archie likes to act like a pillar of the community but I know he is just waiting to get moving again. A few years ago, when the counter-revolution broke out in Guatemala, some California friends and myself were on the point of going down to join the Arbenz forces. I went to Archie and asked him for some money, and he put his hand on my shoulder and said, Kid, you stay here. The fight is tougher. I said, I know, Archie, that's why I want to go down there.

After Eva took me into the side-porch room and introduced me to the old man sunning himself — he was her father, silently senile, from the old country, Denmark — we had breakfast in the kitchen. Eva and I didn't know each other too well. To her I was a bohemian. She and Lee-Simon had organized together for years, like my mother and father. It had made them both tremendously conservative, having to fit in with the dull, cautious towns in which they moved from year to year. And I knew they hadn't become conservative and unimaginative in their own way, for I had known them as a child, but had grown so because of proximity to, and a desire to please, manual workers.

Then Lee-Simon came in. He stopped short, staring, and said, "Well well well." In that instant you could see him go through a complicated ratiocination, pleasure at seeing me, a small apprehension about whether I would upset the routine of his house or give him a name among the townsfolk. Then he decided it was all right. He came over and shook my left hand and asked tactfully if I would like to clean up. I looked at myself in their kitchen mirror: I looked bad. Stubbly chin, dirty face and T-shirt, blood all over me. Eva, she hadn't said a word, not a word. That was Eva's way, and I seldom could tell whether it was from indifference or antagonism. I think perhaps somewhere along the line Eva was not deeply in love with any of Lee-Simon's family. The fault lay with them, because they had never approved Lee-Simon's marrying a *shikseh* — and a fair-haired one at that, who couldn't be passed off by any stretch of the imagination as a *hamisheh.* I could understand Eva's nettlement — what the hell, Lee-Simon's folks were *old* Bolsheviks — but it was strange to be bracketed with the family, most of whom I hadn't seen in many years and who in any case had more or less disowned me because they could not understand anyone who changed political allegiances. *They* never had. My Uncle Boris, for example, who was the only one of the lot I loved, as he lay on his deathbed had asked his wife Bessie which side of The Picture was facing outward. Bessie had replied, The nice side. Boris had roared in anger, Before I die I want to see the *true* side facing out. From what I understand they had a terrible row, in their rickety little house on Pritchett Street in Eagle Rock, Los Angeles. And when Boris began to sink, Bessie relented and turned the picture around, and the sons, Lee-Simon and Archie, brought the old man down to the parlor couch to gaze at it, all the time Bessie muttering fearfully, McCarthy he isn't dead yet, McCarthy he isn't dead yet. You see, The Picture had been in the family for many years. One side was a bucolic scene of hills and cows. On the other side, which I remember being turned out all during the thirties, was a magnificent didactic panorama of "The Storming of the Winter Palace by the Bolsheviks." Old Boris was the best trouser maker in America. The last time I went to see him, I had driven up in a friend's new Cadillac in order to impress him. He had been sitting on the porch. After a few minutes he said to his wife, Bessie, Send the boy away. He shouldn't have to see my dying of cancer. It was the way he said it. Gentle and *sympathizing* with me. When he died I received the call at the studio. But I didn't go to the funeral, the one to which Lee-Simon had flown out from New Erie to attend. I came in for a lot of criticism for that. What they didn't know, the family, was that on one of my last visits to Boris he had confided, *Boychik*, listen, don't go when I'm buried. I know you don't like such things. It would be hypocrisy. He used the Jewish word for hypocrisy, *tsveeyes*. That was what my Uncle Boris was like. He is a good reason to believe in a heaven.

Lee-Simon put his arm around me, avuncularly, and said, "Hello stranger, you're getting fat." I said, You should talk. Simon, whom I always remembered as muscular and happy-humored, was now a stolid, paunching A-1 credit-rating solid citizen. Also he had grown a crazy Lew Ayres (late period) mustache.

As soon as we were around the kitchen table, though, I knew that I would be all right as long as I remained in this house, with this family, but that I would have to go soon, within a few hours. If anything happened to me, I didn't want it to happen near them, I didn't want any of my family to know about it. I like to think it was to spare their feelings, though I doubt it. More than likely, it was childish pride. They disapproved of me and had always predicted a bad end for me. I hated to have them proved right. Which I didn't think they were. But it would look like it.

Lee-Simon asked me what I had been up to recently, and I told him about a few of the jobs, emphasizing the non-middle-class jobs and completely soft-pedaling the last two years in Hollywood. When I told him about the stint as a taxidriver and the contaminated union, Lee-Simon said, casually, "It sounds like a good opportunity for an organizer." That really hurt. Lee-Simon would have gone right in and tried to organize those drivers into an alternative union. There was no use telling him how phlegmatic the drivers were, how many of them were "lumpen elements" just passing through, ex-cons and the like. Lee-Simon was not an aggressively courageous man but he knew his duty. Looking at him now across the table I realized that I had never really known him. I had seen him on three separate occasions, once before he married Eva, twice afterwards, when he came to our house to recuperate from beatings, once from Indiana state troopers, once from sheriff's deputies hired by a corporation in Arkansas and once by organizers of a rival CIO union — in that progression lies some of the recent history of the trade union movement. He, Lee-Simon, had always been anxious for me to settle down in some community. He had always said, You can't do good Party work or union work bumming around the way you do. You've sown your wild oats. Now get yourself a wife and family and make something of yourself. By which, of course, he meant organizational work. It was advice the tone of which might be used on any erring cousin by any uncle anywhere. I could never quite get it across to Lee-Simon that it looked a trifle unkempt and unbecoming from a convinced revolutionary. He was a revolutionary, too, as was Eva, even though their present dug-in lives belied it. Had, I believe, a revolution, by some miracle, occurred in America, they would have abandoned their children to participate in it. And yet here they were, Eva on the Town Council and one of the vice-presidents of the PTA, as she was telling me.

Lee-Simon interrupted, after I said my piece, and tactfully suggested a wash-up. I took an hour in a long, hot bath, and I suddenly felt it was wrong to have come here. I was inflicting myself upon them on the basis of virtually no relationship whatsoever and my oft-proclaimed coolness to the family. And, also, seeing how they lived was sealing the fact of separation from America for me. The alternatives were clear: stagnation, stability, normality — or what Lee-Simon and Eva called "crazy bohemianism." It may sound glib to put it like this, but there was, as in the trade unions, no decent alternative between Hoffa and no union, between corruption and defenselessness. At least that was the jaundiced way I was seeing it then.

As I rubbed myself down with a towel, in the bathroom cluttered with family toiletries and childrens' bath toys, I made an oath to myself to act respectably and responsibly as long as I was here. And, if possible, not to become embroiled in a discussion. If I knew Simon and Eva, they would now be bending with the wind and sincerely regretting a great many actions of the various political parties with which, at one time or another, they had been affiliated, without relinquishing in the least that plodding, unattractive faith which sustained them and enabled them to do so much good work. I wanted to make no enemies today.

As soon as I went downstairs Lee-Simon took me on a conducted tour of New Erie. He was the chief organizer for the union which controlled several ore-processing factories in the vicinity. I knew, without his having to tell me, that he had come to this quiet little town because the party — *some* party — had sent him. Lee-Simon was accustomed to burying himself. I think that was why he must have married Eva. She was a fanatic burier.

Lee-Simon led me down to the ore-loading docks and said that

New Erie was the third-largest ore port in the Great Lakes. I said I had not known that, and he said few people did. He was quietly proud of this town. Only gradually did he get around to asking me, really, about myself, and when he saw I didn't much care to discuss it he let it alone. Lee-Simon is the most tactful communist I know. He asked what I thought of the elections, and I said, Fuck. He said, "I voted for Eisenhower."

We spent that whole morning and part of the afternoon talking union shop. He was involved in a political situation unthinkable a short time ago. In his union, he said, Communists were fighting each other over whether or not to merge with AFL-CIO. Dispute over this issue was cracking comradeships which not even the "revelations" of the 20th Congress had. Lee-Simon said that his best friend was regional director for his union just over the state line in Pennsylvania. Now they weren't speaking. "Not only that," said Lee-Simon, "but Pete" (his friend) "says he might lead a raid on my locals here because I want to take them into the AFL." I said, Whatever happened to party discipline? Lee-Simon replied, "Whatever happened to the five-cent cigar?"

Let me explain some of Lee-Simon's situation, and perhaps you will learn something.

Ever since the Cold War began in earnest, and the American union movement split politically, the Left unions have had their backs to the wall. More powerful unions, in with the current mood in the country, began raiding mercilessly. As it became clear that these raiding tactics were making serious inroads on Left union membership, many of the most thoughtful people inside unions such as Lee-Simon's began trying to devise ways of salvaging something. The AFL-CIO merger seemed a propitious time to explore the possibility of salvaging what remained of the union by taking it into the "mainstream," as the AFL-CIO was now being called. I couldn't tell from what Lee-Simon was telling me exactly what the situation was, but some facts did emerge clearly, and it fitted in with what I had been hearing all across the country.

Suffering almost daily losses of membership from raiding, a number of locals and districts of Lee-Simon's union had been offered what they thought were good surrender terms by AFL-CIO (right-wing) unions and, upon reflection, decided to abandon the parent organization for these other unions, especially the International Association of Machinists and my old union, AVB. Lee-Simon said the terms on which most of his locals were being offered into IAM were fair: basically, that the "stranger" locals should come in as semi-autonomous unions, full preservation of internal democracy and no purges of staff people. Apparently, though Lee-Simon was not explicit on this point, Communists were in the lead of this breakaway movement from the union they had helped found. Although Lee-Simon was fiercely anti the Communist Party, he sided with the party on this union issue.

Lee-Simon, to take the example of another union, said that inside the Left-led United Electrical Workers (UE) where he (and I) had many friends, a similar crisis existed. It was a matter of record that Jim Carey, president of the anti-Communist International Union of Electrical Workers (IUE), under pressure from his membership and secondary leadership, had offered the top UE men, all left-wingers despised by Carey, high posts in IUE if they brought UE around. But the UE leadership — Fitzgerald, Emspak, Matles — had shrewdly procrastinated until pressure (from George Meany, the Association of Catholic Trade Unionists *et al.*) could be organized to torpedo negotiations. The recent UE convention, about a week before I got to New Erie, had spent considerable time blasting the breakaway leaders, such as Lee-Simon, as "rats," "traitors," etc.

Lee-Simon said the only UE districts which were not in the process of "merging" were the so-called "Matles districts." Matles, a Communist-minded vice-president of UE, declared he would continue to hold out, that the guarantees offered by AFL-CIO were questionable, that UE should withstand all blandishments so that it might negotiate from strength. I asked Lee-Simon if Matles also took the position — as did other independent unionists, such as Harry Bridges' longshoremen — that the merger of AFL with CIO had been precipitate and contrary to the best interests of labor, and that an independent Left union movement should continue to exist outside AFL-CIO as the "conscience of the union movement."

Simon immediately got into an argument with me. He assailed "this type of thinking" as unrealistic, destructive and utopian. UE breakaways, he said, had no choice and were doing the best thing under the circumstances. In his own union, he said there was strong sentiment in his factories for rejoining the "mainstream." I said, you mean grass roots sentiment. But Lee-Simon's sense of humor was not one of his strong features, and he said, "Yes, grass roots." After some questioning, however, he admitted that two of his locals were balking. "Those people," Lee-Simon said, "have stuck with us through years of red-baiting, company pressure and all kinds of trouble." So now he said, they're not about to walk themselves into the AFL from which they came and which they remember with no cordiality.

It was interesting that when he spoke rapidly Lee-Simon said AFL for AFL-CIO. It was a Freudian slip which, when I pointed it out, he stubbornly resisted. I said, You wait and see, the CIO will become watered down by AFL. "No," said Lee-Simon, "the AFL will be bucked up." You want to bet? I said. Lee-Simon smiled. "I never bet on anything but the Revolution." It was an old joke between us.

From the docks, Lee-Simon conducted me in his old car around town but kept me away from his factories. It struck me he was not so much ashamed of me as afraid I would say something untoward that might upset his relations with the workers. It also turned out that Lee-Simon was a civic alderman, a volunteer fireman, a member of the local board of education and president this year of the Community Chest. He said, winking, "Not bad for a Bolshevik."

Somehow I didn't feel like winking. I wouldn't have minded Lee-Simon's being all those things, or his being a Bolshevik, but the two together? Not that I felt it was subversive, or that Lee-Simon was being especially dishonest with his neighbors. I just had a feeling that in living in a place like this Lee-Simon had done what all good immigrant boys do — assimilated. What I feared was that Lee-Simon might be kidding himself that he was doing it all as part of a political mission rather than, in a sense, coming home to what he basically was: a good citizen.

Lee-Simon was very excited — or as excited as his slow-going nature allowed him to be — over education. New Erie was a screwball town on education. Next month, a $5,000,000 bond issue for education was on the ballot. Everyone in town, said Lee-Simon, agreed that new schools were needed to replace the dilapidated ones. The middle-class and upper-class people in town were organizing to support the bond issue in order to secure better schools. The wage workers and poor were preparing to vote it down. They had done so every year for the past five years. They thought the answer should be federal aid, government help, and that the bond issue would cost many of them, who were small homeowners, too much in taxes. The Company, which more or less controlled the town, and to whom federal aid was anathema, vigorously supported the bond issue. Lee-Simon's union — usually forward-looking on social issues — had taken one look at the temper of its membership and decided on a posture of strict neutrality.

I said, Just when you think you know it all something like New Erie, New York, happens. "You can say that again," said Lee-Simon.

In the late afternoon his three kids came home. Eva told me that the older girl was going to a singing teacher and was competing on local television. The older boy wore a football uniform. The girl came up to me and asked if I had ever met Jimmy Dean. I said, Yes, once, in a director's office at Warner Brothers. She retreated, ogling me, and went out of the house, with her brother. Half an hour later she was back with, I swear, fifteen teen-agers, all of whom wanted to ask me questions about Jimmy Dean. Eva invited them into the house, and Lee-Simon went out to a meeting, not asking me to come along.

I loved talking to those kids. Most were between eleven and sixteen. Rachel, Eva's kid, competed with one of her school friends to ask the most questions about Jimmy Dean. They all sat in front of me in a wide semicircle, with the old grandfather doddering blindly away on the darkened sun porch and nobody paying him much attention. I always have admired the idea of a bunch of young kids sitting at my feet, though I could have liked a more congenial topic than Jimmy Dean. They all said they would have *died* for him. They wanted to know what he had really looked like, what he had eaten, how he had dressed, if he had had girl friends. I admit

I did a little dressing up of the truth; I mean, I had only met this boy once but I put my imagination to it and what I told those kids in New Erie, New York, was probably not more wide of the mark than the myth dished up by the Warner Brothers publicity agents. The trouble was, after a while I was *lecturing* them. You could see them grow restless and giggly. Also, Eva became distinctly uneasy. I was telling these kids how a myth for the public is created, how their minds are manipulated, and then I got on this subject which I thought I was through with, how the manipulators become, finally, manipulated by the very lies they tell, how these lies distort their spirits more than those of the consuming audience. I went on and on, and Eva's smile faded, and pretty soon I don't think anyone was listening. Well, hell, *I* didn't bring up the subject of Jimmy Dean.

One of the little girls, with a pony tail and a charming smile, said, "I think you're cynical." Eva stood up and said, "Mary Jane, I think you're right" — and then broke up the meeting by shooing everyone home. Which was just as well. I had been recommending books to those kids. I was past *The Way of All Flesh*, which I recommend to everyone under twenty-five, and probably would have gotten to *What Is To Be Done?* if I hadn't been stopped.

After the kids had gone, Eva turned to me and said, "Why do you tell young children such things?" I said, Because everyone lies to them so much. "But you know," she protested, "they couldn't understand a word you were saying." She said it as though I had been raping them or something. All right, I said angrily, but it's no crime not to understand or be understood, it happens all the goddam time. "Don't curse in front of my children," she said. That was when I knew I had to get out of there, mood, hand, notwithstanding. If only she had said *the* children. But, no, it had to be *my* children. That finished it.

I went upstairs to take a nap which lasted until about ten in the evening. When I awoke, I went out to the stair landing. I could hear voices below, in the living room. I sat down on the top step, like a kid at his mother's party, and watched. It must have been a meeting of the Town Council's sewage subcommittee, because all they talked about was the stubbornness of a neighboring township over some disputed drainage. There were about seven or eight people in the room, not counting Lee-Simon, who was comfortably sipping beer while ensconced in an easy chair, and Eva calmly knitting. Lee-Simon was obviously the chairman. Everyone downstairs was a solid citizen of America. Lee-Simon and Eva looked right at home among them; they were where they belonged. Even today, I wonder what Lee-Simon and Eva had to do to themselves, to their characters, to their (if you will) souls in order to make themselves acceptable to these small-town Americans. Or was it that this was what they had wanted all along? The thing was, until you knew their history you would have thought Lee-Simon and his wife *were* small-town Americans. But I had to hand it to them. In a way, they were marvelous. It couldn't have been easy for them to win the confidence of their fellow citizens, not with Lee-Simon being area director of a union which was regularly red-baited by the local newspapers, the town's biggest corporation and rival unions. I could just hear the local alderman or drapery shop owner saying, They say Lee-Simon is a kind of a communist but we never see it around here.

The sad thing, of course, is the way I remember Lee-Simon coming through Chicago on one of his organizing trips, sometimes with an assumed name, and telling me all about the war in Spain and what Cousin Archie was doing there. Lee-Simon had been my earliest real-life hero. And now he was chairman of some sewage subcommittee. Oh, sure, I know the arguments. People grow up, revolutionaries calm down, you have to make do, all the rest. But still.

When I looked up at a little noise, I saw something that near scared the life from me, at first. About three feet away from me, outside a room with a closed door, sitting erectly on a wooden chair on the same landing where I was, was Eva's father, staring down at the meeting. He was almost completely shrouded in darkness. I didn't move a muscle. Did he see me? I whispered, Hello old man. He turned slowly and gazed at me. Then he reached out a long, bony hand and pressed my shoulder. He went back to watching the meeting.

I swear to God I almost broke down.

I went back to my room and thought about sneaking out of

the house and getting a move on. Still thinking about it, I fell asleep. It must have been about two or three in the morning when I heard a noise in the room. Who is it? I asked. Lee-Simon said, "Go back to sleep, I was looking for something." The hell he was, I thought. One of the nice things about Lee-Simon was that you could always tell when he was lying. He ground his teeth. Audibly. I mean personal lies. If you don't think it's reassuring to have a friend or relation who grinds his teeth when he tells a lie just think about it a minute. It was positively *charming*.

He came and sat on the bed in the darkened room. We talked a while. He said, "How's your papa?" I said, Well you know, Lee-Simon, I don't see him very often. He said, "Why do you stay away from your own family?" I said, Lee-Simon, I don't know the answer to that one. I must be scared of them. "They're nobody to be afraid of," Lee-Simon said. For you, I said, not me.

Then, for some reason, he told me something I had not known. He said that he was not really Archie's brother or Boris's son. He had been adopted in 1922 when his own parents had been deported to Russia in the aftermath of the Palmer Raids. He said he hadn't known about it himself until Boris told him the night, down in the family basement off Coney Island, when they had flipped a coin to decide who would be going to Spain. Bessie, Boris's wife, he said, had never liked him. "But," he said, "I made it my family. I worked at it. It became my family. You could do that." Oh no I couldn't, I said. It's too late. "Ah, what's going to happen to you?" replied Lee-Simon. I said that was what people had been saying to me, one way or the other, all the way across the country, and I appreciated the interest.

"Okay, goodnight," said Lee-Simon, and shut the door.

In the morning Eva woke me, in a friendly manner, and we all had breakfast, including the three kids. The old man was back at his station on the sun porch, staring, not making a sound. The kids were unusually silent. They kept looking at my bandaged hand. I think that when their mother shooed them out last night they had gathered somewhere and made up a mildly sinister theory about me. They looked as though if I had said boo they would have jumped. After breakfast, I said goodbye. I asked if I should say goodbye to the old man, but Eva said her father's hearing was bad. I wonder.

They all came out into the street to see me off. I promised to send the kids autographed pictures of various movie stars, and then I drove off.

I was feeling all right and knew it would last about eighteen hours. By that time I hoped to be in Boston where I confidently expected a whole new chapter of my life to open up.

One good thing, as I drove out of New Erie, I wasn't driving too fast. A nice, steady 50. That was all I had needed. A good night's rest. I felt all right. The day was crisp, sunny, early.

I by-passed Buffalo and in the afternoon came to Auburn, New York. It felt good dropping in on someone not because I needed to but just for the hell of it. His name was Alfred Munster, and it tickled me to see him in his new milieu. He was the owner-in-law of the largest department store in Auburn. I parked the De Soto in the big lot at the side of the store and went in and asked for Alfred. I found him standing in the middle of the radio-and-television department, hands behind his back, slim, impeccably dressed as usual, primly gazing at an old movie on one of the several television sets going. I came up behind him, after a salesgirl pointed him out, and whispered between my teeth, Hello, Monster, I thought the whole point of leaving Hollywood was to *leave* it.

I swear to God he jumped eleven feet. His face flushed and he looked more unhappy to see me than anyone had anywhere in the country. I said, Relax, Monster, I only dropped in to say hello, I'm on my way somewhere else. He gave me a thin, dapper smile and we shook hands. He couldn't help swiveling his neck to see if anyone was looking, as though I were an old pal from prison. I said as much. He said, "Well, in a manner of speaking you are." He was actually wearing a red carnation in his buttonhole.

Alfred had been assistant story editor at the film studio where I was blacklisted. And now he was married to the daughter of the man who owned this fancy emporium. Alfred had the bright eyes and erect carriage of a young man who thoroughly expects to inherit Papa's business.

As soon as he could decently do so he took me into his private office, which was lavishly furnished and interiorly decorated in Alfred's own inimitably fruity way. If I am sounding nasty it is only on account of Alfred's being a *type;* but he himself is not such a bad person. Although I will listen to argument.

As soon as we were in his office I started cracking wise about his new status. He grew very uncomfortable. I could never resist needling Alfred, even though, if the truth were known, I felt deeply sorry for him. He was a slim young man of thirty-four or thirty-five; difficult to tell his age and he never would. A not unhandsome ferret face, long thin nose, eyes slitlike and set apart. A face utterly incapable of extremes of emotion. He was, as always, dressed in the height of fashion, with the merest hint of sportiness. Whenever we used to walk along Sunset Boulevard together I always had to count on an extra ten minutes to wherever we were going because of the time Alfred spent inspecting haberdashery windows. He was a one-time bit actor, Canadian-born, and during the late thirties had existed on the fringes of Group Theater, an experience which had stamped him neither with private nor social passion (of which he was almost totally deprived), but perversely, with an edgy, asexual defensiveness towards the loud, the declamatory, the bold. In Hollywood, he had lived alone in a fantastically furnished house in the most fashionable area just below Sunset Strip.

Nobody at the studio ever seemed to know much about Alfred. He was one of the very few who did not talk about themselves and did not gossip about other people. Nobody appeared much interested in Alfred, which seemed to suit him. He used to spend long hours alone in his office looking gloomily, asexually into space. He always dressed neatly and was freshly scrubbed.

I said, Alfred, this looks like a very nice setup. A very nice setup indeed. He looked at me queerly for a moment and then reared back in his brown-plush leather chair and yelped with laughter. He remembered that that had been the opening line of a script we had once been ordered to write at the studio. The executive producer in charge of production had just seen a film called *The Killers* and then had read a short story by that name written by Ernest Hemingway. The following morning he told his story editor, a woman named Kay Kellerman, that he wanted a story like it within forty-eight hours, except that he wanted a part in it for Rita Hayworth who was then on contract to the studio. Kay told Alfred to put an outline down on paper, and Alfred came into my office and said, Look, character, I can't write but I hired you to. (Alfred had been the one to hire me; I'd just come back to Los Angeles from New York, and was on my way to the Chrysler auto plant in Bell, California, to look for a job when on a hunch I stopped off at this studio and asked for an "inside" job on the basis of free-lance work I had done for them in New York. Alfred, wincing at my getup — I had just come in off the road, literally — hired me.)

So Alfred and I spent a whole day putting a story together, which, strictly speaking, was a violation of the rules of Screen Writers Guild of which we were definitely not members. But the head of the studio, now deceased and gone to hell, was always pulling cheap stunts like that. He used to go through the studio at night turning off the lights. In the middle of our story the studio boss sent down word that the heroine was now to be not Rita Hayworth but Judy Holliday, also on contract. At the end of forty-eight hours we had concocted a story, the first line of which, spoken by a gangster wearing calfskin gloves and a golf cap as he stepped into a roadside café, was "This looks like a very nice setup, a very nice setup indeed." But the story was never made. Rita Hayworth decided to marry Aly Khan, and Judy Holliday became pregnant.

After Alfred served me a cognac from his sideboard, there was an uncomfortable pause. I knew what it was about too. Not that I had showed up. But that it would have been most natural for us to start talking about the old days at the studio, in the story department. Alfred had a guilty conscience about that, as did practically everybody in the story department who had held on to their jobs — and they all had — as a result of my run-in with the studio. It is true they funked it. But I wasn't holding any grudges. But people don't really ever feel comfortable about martyrs, and I was one. That is my fate. When I was young and liked the idea of martyrdom — who was it — Shaw? — who said that martyrdom was the only profession where you could become famous without having ability — on more than one occasion I found myself a junior-grade martyr. Usually politically, mind you. Which meant that I was appreciated only by *the cognoscenti.* But martyrdom nonetheless. Trouble was, even after I lost the taste for this sort of thing — along with Lobster-Newburg and Hemingway — I *still* found myself martyrized. It really wasn't my fault. The political situation in America was a holy mess.

Take at this studio, for example. Liberty Pictures. I had made good. I was the fair-haired boy of the story department. I loved the job. It was the easiest I ever had in my life. For four hours a day I lay on a white fabric couch and read books and screenplays and wrote synopses of them along with my comments on whether they would make films or not. The other four hours I spent sleeping or reading periodicals. During the two years I spent with Liberty I was probably the best-informed man in Hollywood. The reason I only worked half the time was that I was fast. I mean I read and wrote fast. When my co-workers asked me to slow down I did. After a while the job became boring. But it was easy. And I was being paid about $150 a week. Practically all the bosses knew I slept half the day but they were afraid to say anything. I was The Fastest Typewriter in Town.

Well, anyway, the day finally dawned when it all had to end. I was summoned before the vice-president of Liberty Pictures who told me how much he liked me, how much he admired my work. He was gray-haired, with a nice Palm Springs tan, and a comfortable belly. Actually he looked a little distinguished. After telling me how nice and talented I was he began to talk about the sacrifices our boys were making in Korea for the Free World. I didn't know what he was getting at. I asked. He pounced. He asked me whether I didn't feel like helping our boys in Korea. I said, I'm too old to volunteer and anyway I did my time in World War II. His demeanor suddenly changed. He said, with iron in his voice, I am not making jokes. I could see that. I sniffed in the air that my career at Liberty Pictures was drawing to a more interesting conclusion than it warranted. I perked up and became interested in the conversation. Vice-president X (he is dead now and I have no rancor in my heart to abuse his memory) with great solemnity pulled out of his teakwood desk drawer a dossier. He said, weightily, "We have information on you." I said, Who gave you the information? He said, "That's of no matter." To me it is, I said.

"I will brook no impertinence, young man," he said, "we hire former FBI agents to look into certain things. This is what we found out about you." He then proceeded to list my crimes, which were that I had written for the university newspaper editorials of a "controversial" nature, and that I had been elected shop steward in the story department only a few months after I was hired. He put the dossier down and hinted darkly of other subversive accomplishments on my part. His attitude was that of a stern father. He said, "Well?" I said, Well? He said, "What do you have to say for yourself, young man?" I said, I'm as patriotic as the next man, meaning it as a joke. It was a damfool thing to do, because it gave him a chance to pop off for another ten minutes about our boys in Korea. Then he swiveled around to face me: "You," he said, "have a contribution to make." I nodded my head, as though to say, Glad to.

He spoke at considerable, and if I may say so, tedious length about the contribution of the motion picture studios to the war effort and how important it was for the studios to show a united and patriotic front. I said I believed in a United Front too but he didn't get the joke. He then pulled out a sheaf of papers and announced that they were affidavits submitted by the top stars of his studio. He mentioned the name of a friend of mine, a writer, who had recently done likewise. He said he wanted a similar affidavit from me, stating I was not and never had been a Communist. I asked him if I could glance at one of them and he handed a thick one to me which had been done by a big-name female star of the studio. I had time only to read one or two paragraphs. It was revolting stuff. How the sight of starving men in the depression had so affected her that she had been vulnerable to manipulation as a dupe of, etc., etc. I said, It appears that more than a simple statement may be wanted. "A few details," said the vice-president, who thought I was coming around and, considering everything, was being not unfriendly. In fact, he was positively *buddy*. I said I didn't much cotton to the idea of writing affidavits, and he said, "You know we've had our eye on you for quite a while, and we like your work. There is talk of making you into a full-fledged writer here." My God, what a lie, I thought. My story editor went out of her way to keep me away from story conferences because I never could help laughing at all the wrong times. I do not say this in too superior a way, mind you. We all have to make a living. But, good *heavens:* "This looks like a very nice setup. Very nice setup indeed." Come *on.*

I listened while he talked. He waved his hands expansively towards a huge wall safe. "In there," he said, "are hundreds of affidavits of decent men and women, citizens of America, who were not too proud to display their loyalty to the studio and their country." And the FBI, I said. He became serious, melodramatically serious and sympathetic. "I want you," he said, "to think of your future in Hollywood before you give me any rash answers. I've batted 1.000 in this league so far. You wouldn't want to spoil my record — son." I almost puked in his face. Before I could say anything, he said, "Go home, think about it." How long do I have? I said. "Until tomorrow." He chomped down on his cigar and called for his secretary, who showed me out with an impassive expression. I have always hated the secretaries of big executives.

I went downstairs to the story department and called a flash meeting of all the story analysts. Because, you see, that's what I was. You might have thought with all this fuss I was a $3000-a-week writer. I collected them all in my room and I told them what had happened. When I stopped talking — nobody said a word. I looked around at the faces. They were pale and guilty. Someone said, "Gee, that's tough." I sat back. I knew that tone of voice. If this were the Army someone would have said, "Go and have your t.s. ticket punched by the chaplain." I turned to Rona Fillimore, the most militant of the bunch, a middle-aged termagant whom I liked very much, an ex-druggist's wife from Cairo, Illinois, who had run off from a bridge party fifteen years before and made her way in Hollywood. I said, Rona, you know this is a matter of principle. She said, with her usual admirable candor, "Shit. Look at us. Scared silly. There's your principle." She started to cry and stomped out of the office. I dismissed the meeting and phoned the president of the Guild, who said it was a private matter between the studio and myself. When I walked out of the studio that day at quitting time all the doors in the long yellow corridor of the story department were closed. You have to remember that this was in August, in Los Angeles, in a building without air-conditioning.

That night I had dinner with my friends Harold and Essie Hardy. Harold edits *The Pacific Liberal,* a west coast magazine.

He is a nice, pompous sort of guy, very cool in a clutch, descended from a long line of parsons. Essie is an ex-newspaperwoman. At that time she was on leave to an academic foundation in order to write a history of the Hollywood blacklist. When I got finished, Essie, sensing a good story, said Boy oh boy. I said I figured that if I played the studio along we might discover enough to give us a clue to the inner workings of the blacklist machinery. Harold and Essie agreed. For the next few nights I went over to their house in Benedict Canyon to tell them everything that had happened at the studio. (It later all came out in a book published by the Fund for the Republic. I am the "C" mentioned at the beginning of the book.)

The next day at the story department Alfred Munster, the assistant story editor, took me out to morning coffee and said, Don't be a schmoe. Go along. You'll only hurt yourself. All that jive. Around noon, the benevolent vice-president summoned me again. This time his manner was crisper. He stated that what he wanted —I mean, after another ten-minute harangue on my responsibilities to the boys in Korea—was a piece of paper disavowing not only past or present membership in the Communist Party but also a pledge that the campus Communists had not written the editorials for me. If, he said, I had ever been a Communist he would want dates and specifications. By this, of course, we all knew in Hollywood it was meant *names* also. Finally, he said, he would like a general disavowal of any "immature" ideas expressed in the college editorials. I got up and thanked the man and asked for a few days to think it over. He didn't like it but agreed.

The funny thing was that I *did* think it over. I consulted with my lawyer whose advice, simply, was, Lie. I said no. He threw up his hands and said I didn't have a chance. I could sue the studio for all sorts of things, and possibly even win at the end, but it would take about ten years. "Lie or leave," he said. "There's no more principle involved. You small fish don't even have the consolation of a good fight." That talk with my lawyer sobered me, and I spent the next two or three days at the beach near Venice, thinking about my life. I felt as if it was not a joke and that I had to be careful of my motives in this thing. Thus far, I had acted like the political animal I was; attacked, I was occupied with plans for counterattack. But, and

I think this was for the first time in my life, I reflected upon the repercussions in my own and other people's personal lives if I chose to fight the studio. I suppose I would not have begun to think in this fashion had not politics, in America, by that year, been reduced to private gestures.

For two or three days I lay on the Venice beach and thought. Then I went back to the studio and asked for an appointment with Vice-president X. His secretary ushered me in with that same blank expression, and I wondered how many men and women she had seen walk into that huge and ornate office and walk out with meaner souls than they had gone in with. Mr. X was sitting there, colder and sterner than before. It was the first of several interviews in which I purposely spun out the negotiations in order to find out how the blacklist actually worked. (Blacklist was illegal, by both federal and California statute, and the studios furiously pretended to noncollusion.) At night I went to Essie and fed her the information I had learned during the day. Finally, came the day when Mr. X demanded a full and unequivocal statement from me without further delay. He insisted he wanted the statement for his safe and that nobody would ever see it except in the event I got into trouble. By this time I had learned the processing route: my statement would be forwarded to New York, where a kangaroo court consisting of a well-known newspaper columnist, a lawyer and officials of the American Legion would read the statement, check it against their files, and then teletype acceptance or refusal to the one man in Hollywood who acted as liaison. I wanted very much to know who this man was. I knew it had to be someone in the studios where there was a private teletype wire. I also found out that the big Hollywood union, IATSE, and its president, Roy Brewer, were involved, but to what extent was unclear.

I would have liked to draw the situation out further in order to help Essie expose it all, but the thing had become a farce. I am a lousy spy. So I told Mr. X to go take a flying leap. He said, "Young man, I will extend you a last opportunity to save your career in Hollywood." I called him a sanctimonious old sonofabitch, and he stood up and said, "If we were on private grounds I would thrash you." I had to laugh at that one. I mean, he was acting like someone from the upper ranks of the British Indian Army or the Foreign Office who had just been rudely insulted. I must say he did it well, considering that for many years he had been the chief business agent and gunman for the film projectionist's union in Chicago, had served time for common assault and had never graduated high school.

I got up and said something articulate, such as Aw come on will you! (It has always been a failing of mine to become very angry at moments such as this. I remember one night at a crowded Student Council meeting on the University campus where I was the star performer: there were about three hundred people crowded into the Council chambers, all waiting to see whether I would be fired as editor of the paper. I had spent half that day preparing careful, subtle answers to all kinds of questions. It had been impressed upon me that I must not be irresponsible, for I was the official voice of the newspaper. So I sat at the end of the big conference table, legs crossed, calm and compliant. The first questioner, the Dean of Students, or perhaps it was the vice-president of the Council, asked me something stupid, like what did I think about Russia. Then I became angry. As I recall I said something clever, such as, Even if I liked you, Dean, I wouldn't know how to answer a silly question like that. After that, I became angrier and angrier until the vote of the Council was a mere formality. It is, as I say, a character failing.)

At the door I turned and said, Does this mean I'm blacklisted? Mr. X looked at me and said carefully, "There is no blacklist in Hollywood, as you full well know." Does that mean I can apply for a job at another studio? "There is nothing," he said, "to prevent me from having lunch with, say, the story editor at Metro." I see, I said. If you don't make trouble over this, he said, we won't. You mean, I said, if I take it to court. "Then," he said, "it will be you making the publicity, not us." He had me there. I shut the door and went downstairs to the story department, packed my things and left without saying goodbye, except to Rona Fillimore, this woman from Cairo, Illinois. Rona was the grittiest person I ever knew in Hollywood. She is dead now, so my saying this cannot embarrass her. Whenever I asked Rona what made her leave Cairo, Illinois, she used to say, Those damn bridge parties. She was a small, round woman, a kind of peppery little thing whose favorite stance was hands on hips, legs apart, head cocked to one side, saying, Well, he (or she) *is* a sonofabitch.

I went into Rona's office and she pulled out a bottle of champagne. She said, I bought this for the occasion. We sat in her office and drank the champagne, mainly in silence. There wasn't much, you see, to say. She said, "I'm sorry I didn't do more." I said, Aw what the hell, Rona, you know as well as I that I was thinking of quitting anyway. She said, "Thank you for trying to salve my pride. But I want to apologize. Not only for me. For the whole story department. Don't judge them too harshly." I told Rona there was nothing to judge. She said, "Don't give me that. The thing is, you have to remember most of these people were involved in the big Hollywood strike that failed. And they've never recovered. Oh, hell what's the use? When you lose your guts you can always find an excuse. I think I'll go off and get psychoanalyzed. Now seems as good a time as any." I went over and kissed Rona on the cheek and left the studio. Everyone knew I was leaving, and all those story department doors were still shut. In fact, Alfred found it convenient to be ill that day. After that, whenever I met any of my former colleagues they all looked slightly defensive and shrunken, as though I had done them an injustice. You never know.

Anyway, that is how I came to be blacklisted. Not exactly what you call an electrifying story.

And now here he was, Alfred, fashion plate of Liberty Pictures, low man on the status pole, surrounded by the sideboards, offices and accoutrements of his new position. I must say for him, Alfred did not lord it over me. Or offer me advice. Or even attempt a more intimate relationship than we ever had when he was poor (I felt sure that was how he must think about it). All these things have been done to me, one way and another, by friends risen in the world. Instead, slim and impeccable, Alfred sat back in his leather chair, sipping cognac, as though he had simply assumed his rightful place in the world. That it should be as the manager of the largest emporium in Auburn, New York, was something he had to suffer gracefully.

We chatted a while. Then Alfred moved with elegant discomfort in his chair and said, "I'd love to have you come out to the house except that just tonight we're due at the country club for an affair." I looked carefully to see if Alfred had acquired the knack of telling mild jokes, but no, he was serious, or perhaps more subtle than I remembered him. For a moment I was tempted to tell him that that was all right, I was staying over. But I am not by nature a sadist. I said that was too bad as I was leaving town in a few minutes.

Alfred walked me out to the car lot. As I was getting into the De Soto (you could see Alfred examining the car and trying to figure out if I had come up or down in the world) I pointed to the building and said, Eee, Alfie, you don't do yourself 'arf proper, in imitation Cockney (a joke between us, dating from our having worked on a sequel to *Mrs. Miniver*, never filmed). Alfred drew himself up rather nastily but what came out was, "It will do, it will do." I think perhaps he did not mean to say that exactly. We shook hands and I drove out of Auburn, New York, leaving behind me Alfred Munster and his empire.

By nightfall I was on my way towards Albany on a beautiful, smooth-banked, fast freeway. I had promised myself not to take any more freeways: they were too conducive to busting me up. But, somehow, I had driven onto this one. It was obviously new, almost shining, two double strips of gleaming black asphalt through swelling, autumnal country, an orange-black sky descending, beauty outside and something less than beauty inside. I had promised myself that at the first onset of a "symptom" I would turn off the road and go to a hospital. And now it had happened again. For I had obviously stopped at a toll gate to pay the collector for admittance to the turnpike. The IBM card was on the seat beside me. But I could not remember it.

I kept driving. Whamming past town after town until I was in the middle of the night. I couldn't go slow. I did a straight, steady ninety past Cherry Valley, Schenectady, Albany, Troy. I could have been in a humming motorboat in the sky. Two good things, however. The oncoming lights did not, as yet, scare me off the road. And I was off the White Horse. There was a half-full bottle in the back seat, next to my duffel bag, which looked like a dead man curled up, but I left it alone. I was driving, conservatively, on dexedrine, benzedrine and Miltown. But not White Horse. No lush me.

Fortunately, my hand started hurting. This, somehow, prevented the music from entering my head. I resolutely kept the radio off. I didn't know, or care, whether Csepel Island was holding out. That was *their* problem.

I wanted a woman, on that turnpike, in that night. I vowed that on entering the first large city off the road I would find a woman. Even if I had to go to a whorehouse. I thought of all the women I had known and how little meaning there was in the blur of their names and fleeting memories. I cursed the atmosphere of America, its puritanism and oversexualism welded so tightly together we were all pressed to death. I cursed America for sexualizing *everything*. I cursed myself for being caught in the web. Flaubert once said, our soul is a sealed book to the clergy. Well, in America, the soul is a sealed book to everyone with hysterical sex on the brain, befuddling it, making the reading and acceptance of souls, and therefore fraternity, impossible. Berenson calls it *acide*, life without taste, life smothered not in sex but pornography. Women. Cheated by men. But men are crucified by women's retaliation: their abject, passionate immolation in trivia. I don't know. Was I right? Or was it simply that I had never known inspiring, delicate, nourishing strong love? That is, love.

But I suppose it is true: you do not fall in love at the start of a long voyage you have planned for a long time. I am a born metaphor, deathly afraid of the outward signs of megalomania. And yet for years, possibly since adolescence, I have dryly and studiously examined the indications of my own life as a clue to the country at large, as though reading a psychic thermometer. I cannot describe to you how excited I became when a teacher in high school told me what "microcosm" meant.

Two things occur in a country which has lost its political soul. The children blame it on the parents, their sightlessness, and the children listen to music. America, once a land of immigrant Prometheans, has become the country where the record collector is king.

Why are people always trying to make a "character" out of me? The road is my work as the office is theirs. I am not the more eccentric for it. I will not have them push me out of society, their lives, in this way. It is their way of keeping me on the move, as though frightened I would light on their doorstep. Perhaps I should accept this role. Otherwise, I am always stretching out my hand in the least effective way: by tying my malaise in with theirs. I have always found the conversation strangled when, in the middle of a discourse, I say, in an attempt to draw a bond between us all, "You know how it is."

I think of Swede and wish he were alive so that I might talk to him and hear him laugh and say, as he used to when we worked in the biscuit factory, Boy, you *do* think something of yourself, don't you!

I wonder if I will live through to the time when my morality will not even be able to prevent my son from turning thief. Did I read those words somewhere or did I just think them?

How can you marry the world? I want to marry it — it just doesn't want to marry *me.*

I repeat myself. Hopefully.

On the Turnpike, and by dawn I was off it, high as a kite in my mind but keeping a good strong grip on the wheel, and rolling somewhat slowly across Massachusetts. Strange. It was the first time in my entire life I had been in Massachusetts. It gave me a peaceful feeling. The moment I sped across the Massachusetts state line from New York I felt, *now, now my life is changing.* Nobody knows me here. I can be anything I want. In Massachusetts — I will be a writer.

And then, really for the first time on this trip, I felt lifted up by a vast, imaginative, free-floating surge of good will towards everybody and especially myself, the kind of feeling you are likely to get about the second or third minute after you have put on a record such as "Aunt Hagar's Blues" by Louis or "The World is Looking for the Sunshine," Jimmie McPartland — a clear happy trumpet sound, clear and thin and absolutely pulsing with all the good hopes. I felt *young,* rolling up over the yellow leaf-matted hills, the countryside in the morning one riotous, blending explosion after another of Constable colors, the trees thick and low and full of *wood,* the slim untraveled road an inch thick with fallen yellow and light brown leaves, the crest of the hills a crow's-nest from which to scan in satisfaction a sea of tidy oak forests, the small college towns quiet without being sleepy, very reassuring after that night on the Turnpike.

*

Boston.

I parked the De Soto near Boston Common, and walked into a comfort station where I changed from blue jeans and T-shirt into my very special Oxford brown wheeling and dealing suit, the one that Harold and Essie had helped me pick out in Beverly Hills, the one I always wore in Hollywood when I borrowed one of the other agent's Cadillacs to go out to the studio, after a lunch at Romanoff's or La Rue's, to consummate a deal. Down in the comfort station I put on the old-school tie I had specially bought for that suit, and went back to the De Soto and put back my bag and set out for 7 Common Street. On the way I passed a street mirror, which was lucky. I was dressed to kill — I looked like a financier's gangster son on his way to hear the trustees read the will — except that I had a two-day growth of beard.

So I ducked into a barbershop and ordered the works, shave, shine, shampoo. It took about an hour, but it didn't relax me. I was very excited. I spent that entire hour talking to the barber, telling him what a great fellow I was and what I had seen in crossing the country. To tell the truth, I do not believe he was very interested. Once he asked if I had stopped off in Cincinnati, where he had a sister-in-law. When I came out the rain had stopped and it was a fabulous day, bright, clear, brisk. Boston was terrific. Old and stable and busy, with the automobile tires making whooshing sounds all around the Common, and traffic tangles but no one was yelling at anybody else. It had a wide, brown, subsided, strong color, Boston. I found a bar, with a German name, and went in and started to drink. This bar, like everything I had seen in Boston, was terrific. Very genteel, and masculine. Deep brown woods, a huge silver mirror behind a long, Italian marble bar and a brass rail extending the length. The bartenders all looked like your Irish father, and the few afternoon customers looked like the heads of publishing firms who had just ducked in to have an informal snifter while they mulled over John Steinbeck's or William Faulkner's new book, whether to accept it or not. Everything looked magnificently conservative.

I tried to strike up a conversation with my bartender, and it pleased me that he would not. Obviously, you had to win your spurs by coming in regularly for three years before they would say good morning. Boston. I drank about four or five scotches, very quickly, and then began to sweat. I paid for my drinks, gave the bartender a small tip because I did not want him to think I was a parvenu, and weaved downstairs to the lavatory. It was a terrific lavatory, not at all consonant with upstairs; I mean, it didn't have deep aged browns all over the place and shiny brass. It could have been the toilet of any bar. Terrific, I thought. Don't truckle to the new-rich bourgeoisie. That's the stuff. Boston!

I straightened myself in a small wall mirror. I looked flushed and excited. Then I realized I was stinking drunk. There was nobody in the lavatory. Fuck it, I shouted at myself in the mirror. Bluff the bastards. You're as good as they are. You're better. Drunk you can do what they do sober. When you cross the threshold of 7 Common Street you straighten up, boy, stiffen that spine like a West Point cadet and play it *so* cool. At this point, a little Negro man came out of absolutely nowhere and said, "Are you addressing me, sir?" Now wouldn't you know that is the way they talk in Boston?

I threw the man half a dollar, jauntily, and yet not without a certain dignified conservatism, and said, Mister, you are looking at *the* literary sensation of next year. I am going to knock this country straight on its everloving ass. I am going to write up such a storm my fellow citizens will have to take cover. I am *great.*

Coming upstairs, I made it a special point to walk steadily across the barroom floor, my bartender was watching. But outside, on the sidewalk, I told myself that would not do. Nothing to excess. Straight-backed, silent in my interior, wise and judicious. Wisely and judiciously I walked up the slightly hilly street, on the east side of Boston Common, to 7 Common Street. Ah, marvelous. An old, virtually moth-eaten building, of straight oak pillars and quietude in the musty corridor. Exactly as I had hoped.

I asked the elevator man to direct me to the offices of the publishing company, which he did, and I stepped out on the third floor and announced myself, in a mild stentorian manner, to the receptionist, a blond and conservatively leggy girl who looked as though she had been at least two years at Barnard or Radcliffe. She smiled when I gave my name, and I wondered if she had read any of the manuscript I had mailed her company. I was then ushered into a small room overlooking the Common which was entirely taken up by a small, timid secretary, a roll-top desk, and a woman named Abigail Quinn. She urged her chic, superbly attired and businesslike bulk out of her chair, shook my hand and asked if I had had a nice trip. She said she was sorry that Miss Edmond, the lady with whom I had been in correspondence, was not in the office, but that she, Mrs. Quinn, was competent to deal with me inasmuch as she had read my manuscript, enjoyed it and wished to discuss it with me. I took a seat beside the roll-top desk and decided that within the next five minutes I would have to find a middle ground between the two roles of wild genius writer and cool Hollywood businessman. I was so fuzzed on White Horse, dexedrine, Miltown and the rages of brain music which beat with alternating triumph and despondency inside my head that my legs and arms felt encased in frozen concrete. I laughed, dribbled, was charming, crossed and recrossed my legs and altogether presented a picture of confident, arrogant authorship.

Mrs. Quinn, the chief working editor of the firm (I learned later), was polite, sympathetic and had a way of rearing herself back in her chair and roaring with laughter. I asked her if she liked the idea of what she had seen of my novel, and she asked me to explain what I had in mind, because, yes, she did like it, and perhaps an advance could be arranged.

Well, now, you have to understand practically all my life I have dreamed of a publisher, in just this sort of office, and behind that kind of roll-top desk, with a timid secretary half listening in as though hanging on my words of acceptance or refusal (though, as far as I know, she was thinking of a dozen other things), offering me an advance for a novel-in-work. Lovely phrase. Novel-in-work. My instinct was to grab it and run. I mean, it really was what I had been dreaming of, particularly these past few years in Hollywood. But the rug-merchant reflexes I had acquired stood me in stead. I lazed in my chair and allowed as how I would go on down to New York and see if I could get a better offer, no offense meant. I had submitted my novel for the Fellowship, and if I did not get that I would shop around a while. This huge, shrewd woman looked at me, as though trying to figure out whether I really was as good as all that. At the moment I sure did feel I was. I was a *genius*, man. And not only that, but I could take care of my own business affairs too.

During this entire conversation I had to hold on to the edge of my chair to keep from falling off. I mean, I suddenly felt the whole weight of the trip pressing down on me and forcing me off the chair. I was operating on sheer gall. Nothing was coming from inside but a kind of wily reflex. I put my hands behind me to hold on better. All of this must have made an impression, because Mrs. Quinn kept saying how much she liked the book, but that of course I had every right to seek other offers. Oh hell, I thought, I didn't force her hand.

We had a long talk about books. And then I realized I had been talking too much, and that if I went on talking I would give the whole thing away, so I shook Mrs. Quinn's hand and heard her say her offer would always hold. I walked out of the building tremendously let down. What had I expected? You see, I should explain that I had more or less forgotten what the novel was about, since becoming ill in Los Angeles. I thought that perhaps by hearing someone talk about it I would remember. But, no.

Well, I would go on down to New York and open up my suitcase and study the manuscript and try to figure out why I couldn't remember. Five minutes after I got into the De Soto and started to drive out of Boston's traffic tangle I couldn't remember what had happened in the publisher's office. The liquor had drained out of me and so I knew it must be something else. I had an awful feeling of anticlimax. I had felt, in crossing the state line into Massachusetts, so certain the acceptance of that novel would lift me clean up and over this mood which had been dogging me, and now I realized, with something like dread, that it had not. Leaving Boston, I kept wanting to shout at myself, You've made it boy. Relax.

But it didn't work. I suddenly thought, with an icy calmness, Omigod, it's a fluke. Something in that stuff I wrote must have touched that lady somewhere in her memory box and that's why she's giving me the advance. So I turned the car around, on a junior Turnpike, and zoomed right back into the Common. To hell with bargaining, I was going to take the offer. Then it started to rain, just as I was looking for a parking spot. It was about five in the afternoon and if you have ever tried to find parking space at going-home hour in the middle of Boston you will know why I just gave it up, especially as I thought how foolish I would look coming in and saying please thank you, so I just headed for New York again.

It was dark and pouring rain, twilight dark, on the highway south of Boston. The road was slippery and I was deciding on how to begin my career as a writer. I promised myself I would notice all the little details of existence, as I never had before, because to tell you the truth I do not have an eye for detail, and I am as yet too ignorant to solicit revealed essences, which is why I never did think this business of being a writer was for me in the first place.

As darkness closed in I pressed harder and harder on the accelerator. South of Boston the road is fairly straight and rises and falls like gentle concrete waves. I rolled down that shadowed, rain-slick road, with the beautiful autumn oak trees planted like God's telephone poles all along the way, and making for a lovely and scenic drive, and I put down the windows even if it did soak the baggage in the back seat. Somewhere in the back of my head I sensed it would never be better, with hope, than now, or worse, with the sick confusion in my brain, than now, and I had that old De Soto up to 100, very steady on the wet road, whipping past the oak trees and slamming down the asphalt troughs and clawing swiftly up the upsteep hills when — and didn't you know it? — I saw flashing red lights behind me. If it had been a sedan I would, the way I felt, have tried to outrace it, but I could see that it was a motorcycle. No chance.

So I stopped. I can tell you from 100 on a wet road it took me about half a mile to bring it down, without skidding, to a full halt. Then I waited. This is the part I loathe. The way the john parks his vehicle in front of you, and methodically takes off his gloves, and reaches into his pouch for his notebook, and practically stretches and yawns and enjoys the scenery before he condescends to come over for the full song and dance. Honestly, I do not mind traffic police. More or less, I have found them not so bad, a trifle less corrupt than vice-squadders. But why can't they jump off their bikes, and give you the lecture and ticket, without all this knocking the mud off their boots and hitching up their belts? It is one of the four thousand reasons why I do not enjoy cops.

This particular song and dance went as follows: Cop: (very calmly) May I see your license? Me: Of course, officer. Cop: Out of state? Me: As you see, officer. Cop: Do you drive this way in your own state? Me: What way, officer?

See what I mean? He said, "I clocked you at 90 miles per hour, mister." I was positively crestfallen. My speedometer had read 105. American technical ingenuity, my ass. The police officer read me the full lecture. He asked me if I was a G.I. I said no. He said, "I would have given you a break. As it is, you will have your license taken away by the State of Massachusetts." Suddenly I felt that was unfair. I like the state, I hardly knew it, what did it have against me except forty or fifty extra miles per hour by an untrustworthy speedometer? The cop took down my name, make of car and license number and let me go. Which was a piece of luck. He told me, of course, that I had to appear in court next week. That will be the day, I thought, driving away and showing the cop my exhaust.

That cop never should have stopped me. The drive in the night and rain down to New York was a nightmare. For some reason the cop stopping me had done it, had frightened me; no, shaken me. I didn't know why, but it had. Curse him. I did 40 all the way into New York because I had become scared of the oncoming lights. I could hardly hold on to the wheel. But I had to make New York City. That was the end of the line. I could get off there.

So tense that it felt like coiled-up springs ready to pop behind my eyes, I made it, arriving in the middle of New York City, after a miserable hour of 30 m.p.h. because I was afraid I would go off into a ditch. Like a homing pigeon I had landed on Sheridan Square, Greenwich Village, and now that I was here I didn't know where to go. So I just sat in the parked De Soto and stared out at the streets, which were glistening. It was a fairly warm night and the rain had stopped. I got out of the car and began to walk up and down the streets of the Village, a kind of parody of the lonely hunting, aching young man's walk up these same streets which I had committed as part of my biography five or six years before, when I had been young.

It felt slightly reassuring to be lonely. At least I was feeling something, and not that awful panic as though my parachute had failed to open that had stayed with me ever since Boston and the start of the drive through the rain. I went into several comfort stations and vomited in all of them, and then I felt better and began to notice things around me. The Village looked prosperous. Not like the old days at all. The boys and girls all looked like B-plus average students from Harvard, or NYU students trying to act like Harvard. I stepped into a phone booth and called Jessica and Benn. Jessica said I could come over tonight if I wanted and that I could use their flat for the next month because she was flying out to Denver to see her parents. I thanked her and said I would be over, maybe. It was the same as ever when we spoke together, brisk and slightly shamefaced and a little breathless. Jessica was a strange one, and she thought I was too. My calling her this way was a peace offering inasmuch as we had not been on speaking terms for a couple of years. A late convert to Marxism, she could not forgive apostasy in her teacher. Like me and John Alston.

After I hung up, I immediately began again stalking the wet, dark, crowded streets of the Village. It was simply amazing how many people there were. I resented their zest. Passing the Washington Square fountain, I couldn't help sitting down and laughing. Here I am again! Why? Who knows. Sitting on the rim of that old fountain, where years before, jobless and full of prospects, I had sat anticipating myself and the women I was to love, I felt very excited and horribly depressed by the interest the publishing company had shown in my book. I didn't think I could do it. But maybe, maybe if someone was waiting for the book, such as this woman in Boston, I would write it.

I went into a drugstore on 8th Street and phoned the Savoy hotel, got the Lathenases, and told Maurice that I had arrived in New York safely with his car and would see him the next day probably. The first thing Maurice told me was that my old girl in L.A. was now having a love affair with my doctor. I pretended to be happy for her, and when I hung up became depressed as hell again. I went back to the fountain and sat down and began thinking about the book a great deal, as the night closed in, close to midnight, people leaving the park, which was becoming cold. I was still dressed nattily. In about an hour the queers would start filtering through the cold, abandoned park towards me. I knew this part of the Village pretty well, poor bastards. I figured, for the novel, that I would do the first section in the first person, on a bold and intimate level, Gorki, and a little like a wonderful book I had once read called *Temptation* by John Pen, about a Hungarian boy growing up in the interwar period and going to Budapest to work as a bellboy in a rich and fabulous hotel: then, in the latter stages, I would switch to third person, cool, spare for perspective.

Sitting on the fountain, waiting for the queers to descend, I wanted to lay every girl I saw in New York. But *really* lay. I was restless, tired and conscious that I was irrelevant to the lives of most of my old friends. I looked up at the cliff-dwelling lights of Lower Fifth Avenue and knew that if I did not then get a woman I would go clean out of my mind. Or what was worse, do something with Jessica.

I went over to Ninth Avenue, to a lovely bar I remembered, named the Tame Mare. But as soon as I went in I knew I was in the wrong place, or the wrong time, or the wrong damn something. The San Remo crowd was there, virtually hanging from the rafters; the queers and phonies and hoity-toities. No need for me to have worried about the punks in Washington Square park: they were all here. I pushed my way to the bar and asked for George Hyland, the co-proprietor. He didn't remember me too well. I just said, George, what *happened?* He shrugged and gave a small grin. "Dylan Thomas," he said. "They found out he used to come here." I said goodnight to George and left that place.

Well, that was that. Why do they have to put their clammy hands on *everything?*

I wandered around the Village, still in that Sunset Strip suit of mine, for another hour, then went over to Morton Street and rang one of the bells. A sleepy girl in toreador pants-pajamas (the first pair I'd ever seen) and a Japanese robe came to the front door of the huge tenement house. I gave my name and said, Remember? She hardly looked at me and said pleasantly for me to come in. I followed her down the corridor and we went into her flat, which was a low-ceilinged, extremely dark room-and-a-half. Everything in it, as I remembered, was Japanese. No furniture, just cushions. The radio was playing Brahms and I took her in my arms, willingly. She felt wonderful. Her name was Olive and she was the most available girl in the Village, friends, enemies, indifferent. I had known Olive off and on, no pun intended, for several years. I suppose she was what you call a nymphomaniac, but aside from the fact that she would permit a great many different types of men, on the spur of quick decision made somewhere behind that rather lovely, ovaloid and Japanese face, she was not outstandingly eccentric; in fact, a rather quiet, mildly intelligent girl who was, when I last saw her, a secretary to a theatrical agency. I have known nymphomaniacs but never one who made love in the uneccentric, unhurried and pleasurable way Olive did. I used to try to theorize to friends that perhaps Olive just liked it, but they said no, poor child, it was ghastly, ruinous compulsion of which she had to be cured.

Okay, if they said so.

I took (or if you will, bore) Olive to where I remembered her matted couch was, and I am fairly certain that she did not completely recall who I was. One good glance in the light of a street lamp, and she had decided to take her chances. She spoke to me for the first few moments in a friendly, affectionate way: Don't Hurt, Easy, Let Me Lock the Door, There, Do You Mind the Radio, Let Me Undo It, Oh It's Cold, Put the Blankets Over Us, in the dark low-ceilinged apartment on Morton Street. It was the pure act: a kind of companionate, urgent strength. You say hopeless and anonymous? I have never known it to be hopeless with Olive. There is anonymity and anonymity. I *gave* it to her, and my senses returned.

I walked out into the street, feeling not badly at all. Olive was sleeping soundly. You never left money for her. Not that she protested. I remember her once saying to us, Sometimes a man feels sordid giving me money, and if it makes him feel any better, why argue?

I drove the De Soto over to 15th Street and lugged some of my baggage up to Jessica's apartment. She was up, waiting for me. "Hiya, kid," she said in that tense, high-pitched voice of hers. She didn't look good, thinner than usual, drawn and tired. It was Jessica's way. She was a low-price fashion designer, and drove herself four or five months steadily, then collapsed and had to be flown out to her parents' house in Denver to recuperate. This usually happened twice annually, in rhythm with the garment seasons.

Jessica operated on raw, nervous energy, always had, always would. I dragged my stuff into her three-room apartment, and she got drinks. As usual, the moment we were together, a wall went up between us, which we had always tried, and this was no exception, to get over with giggling and chattering and a kind of desperate sincerity . . .

I had gotten to know Jessica at the university, in California, during my last sad, sweet term there. The fight had been lost, I had been fired as editor and I was just a student now. I spent most of my time boning up for my final examination, the "comps." In the library I discovered a segment of the campus population I had almost forgotten about, the unknown, industrious young men and women who lived off-campus, commuted by bus and streetcar, and studied hard. At first it was a jolt, and then a pleasure, to meet the library "cave dwellers" who didn't know me from Adam and didn't recognize the name, except to ask where had they heard it before, had I been on the football team or something? They didn't give a damn about me except in how I met the strict, civilized, rarefied standards of cave dwelling. There were three of us: Manny, a rabbi who had lost faith; Ken, an African; and Jessica. We palled around together. Afterwards, Manny went to Israel, Ken went back to Sierra Leone, and Jessica I tutored.

Jessica was half Cherokee, half Scottish, a rangily built former night-club singer and general high-stepping daredevil. Once, because it seemed logical, Jessica and I had tried to make it, but the chemistry just wasn't there. The truth was, I could never quite see Jessica as a girl. She was more one of the boys, and by the time I saw that this was something of a pose to prevent her becoming hurt, it was too late, and she had begun disinclining towards me. Anyway, she was devoted to Benn Hacker, quarterback son of one of the "Hollywood Ten," who when in training was convinced that sexual intercourse drained a man of his vigor and coordination. So Jessica began going around with me during football season. She had come to the university because Benn was there, and a few years later they were married. I had brought Jessica up politically. For the past two or three years we hadn't been talking, mainly on her initiative. Jessica was not very political in-the-head but she had inexhaustible reserves of violent gut-loyalty. Also, she had her own way of doing things. Last year, she had been arrested after refusing to take shelter in a mock air-raid alert. She was an impulsive girl. Back in college we had had a ball; Jessica owned a souped-up Mercury which she used to drive (with me in it) tantalizingly close to parked police cars, yell an insult at them and then whoom out of there fast. In cold print it looks childish. The thing about all this, is that Jessica and I always felt we were special to each other but had never succeeded in finding a way of showing it. I think it was my fault.

We stayed up talking until five in the morning. Jessica spoke more frankly with me than she ever had. She and Benn were separated and negotiating a divorce. She was waiting for his phone call now. His new girl friend was jealous and he had to get out of the house to call her. Jessica's mouth was set in a rueful smile as she talked about Benn and herself. Several times she said, "He just won't grow up. Maybe it's a vitamin deficiency." You have to remember we hadn't spoken a peaceful word to each other in thirty-six months. I was afraid of Jessica's speaking of Benn because she would have no alternative to despising me if I didn't respond correctly, and I had an unbroken record of never having done so with her. But then I could see that she was so fatigued with overwork and strain that it didn't much matter, that her attempts to confide in me just now were a kind of photographic "shadow" of past attempts and that she really expected very little. Far from reassuring me, this gave me apprehensions.

As we waited for the phone call from Benn, we found we didn't have much to talk about. Her entire life was wrapped up in her work; the other two people we had had in common — Ken and Manny — neither of us had seen.

There was a knock on the door, and Jessica gave a little jump. (For the past two years the FBI had been knocking on her door at all hours, trying to get at her passport, which eventually they did.)

When the door opened Hilda came through it like a damn cyclone and almost swamped me, with Tad on her heels laughing with delight. Hilda and I kept embracing, and then Tad and I, with Jessica somewhere in the background, grinning. Before I go any further, perhaps I had better tell you about Tad and Hilda. They were, although we could not remain in the same room without quarreling, my two best friends in America . . .

In Los Angeles, when I knew I was recovering, and therefore would no longer have an excuse to remain in town, I shut off the television set and got out of bed and dressed and went down to the car and drove up to Coldwater Canyon to see Tad and Hilda, who lived in a lean-to split-level pinewood house which looked as though it had been designed by the idiot father of Frank Lloyd Wright. It was a hot, hazy afternoon, and they were both home, fretting over whether Tad ought to go and take a job in Atlanta, Georgia, with an oil company. (Tad was a theoretical geologist.) Hilda was nursing the baby and looked fine. She was a dark, swarthy, dolphin-hipped girl who looked like an Uzbekistani princess, had been married three times, psychoanalyzed twice and had been my first secretary at the Benedict Agency, and is also the best friend I have of my adult days. I have known Hilda for years. She is my quarreling sister. It is not possible for us to be in the same room five minutes without her trying to boss my life. Or it was. Now she has Tad and doesn't interfere so much with me. I miss it. A lot of people don't understand about Hilda and me; they think I have a secret hot for her. All this is over, and wasn't much in the first place anyway. I met her when she ran an advertisement in the Los Angeles *Times* for her apartment. When she came to the door we practically fell into bed. Since then, Hilda has always claimed that I found her in a promiscuous period neurotically based on a fixation on her father or mother, I forget which. My story is that I was irresistible. To make the story even shorter, after we were through, Hilda sat me down on the couch in her front room and shook her large, Jewish head with a kind of brisk sadness and said, You're a baby boy, you shouldn't go around seducing grown women. Needless to say, I took umbrage and finally we yelled at each other, which more or less set the tone for a relationship.

It was Hilda who persuaded me not to take that spot-riveting job at Packard-Bell and to come to work for the Benedict Agency. It was also Hilda who, on my first day out as a go-getting agent at the Valley studios, watched me come back and locked herself in her office and cried, and when I asked what was wrong, said, I'm sorry I got you into this job. I had been against her marrying Tad because one day when she should have been taking my dictation she went down to the Santa Monica beach in her awful leopard-skin bathing suit and picked up this brown, tall, handsome young geologist and took him home with her. I railed at Hilda for several days. I said it was time for her to stop sleeping with every man she met. Eventually, however, despite my warnings, they began to live together in this crazy-looking house in Coldwater Canyon. Tad swore he would never marry Hilda, which he could well do because he was already married. Hilda swore to both of us that she would get Tad to marry her because she knew — "subconsciously" — he wanted to. I used to spend hours in the Agency lecturing Hilda on the ethics of not blackmailing a man into marriage, particularly after she succeeded in getting Tad to make her pregnant, which really infuriated me. Through it all, she quietly maintained that it was the only way to get Tad to propose, which he did, with me prophesying doom all the while. On the night before the marriage Tad woke me up at two in the morning and came over and said he couldn't marry Hilda because she disgusted him; she was, he said, so *ugly* he could hardly bear her sight. But the following afternoon they were married in my apartment, with Hilda's brother, a San Francisco policeman, as disapproving witness. This was, of course, after Tad's divorce.

That wedding scene should have been photographed. The sun pouring in through the venetian blinds, making patterns on the daisies which I had strewn, half in joke, half seriously, all over the place. Tad straight and self-conscious in his best suit, Hilda about eight months twenty-nine days pregnant and looking fantastic, the rabbi, this small, pug-faced friend of ours named Manny (who went to Israel and became an archeologist) and the second witness his wife, Joy. The whole situation was funny, if you have that kind of sense of humor. Manny had once been Hilda's boyfriend, and Joy was the girl Tad had gone to when he was in his Hilda-ugly mood. In the middle of the ceremony Manny forgot the words and I began hysterically to giggle. Somehow we got through it all successfully, Manny predated the marriage license, and we all went out to Scandia's for dinner, on me.

Tad was a good husband for Hilda.

After I drove up to their house in Coldwater Canyon, I sat down on the couch and said hello to them. They regarded me with some coolness because the last time we had been together we had had an argument over what to name the baby. I had wanted Drury. They had said no, it was a terrible name, especially for a girl. Finally, they had begun to squabble between themselves, and Tad had told me to get out, everything would have been all right if I hadn't shown up. That had been weeks ago.

We kept off what the child should be named, and just chatted, about this and that. Then Hilda started to cry. Tad said, Oh for Christ's sake Hilda. She said, I know he's going to start traveling again. I just *feel* it. Tad said, So what if he does? Hilda became angry and said, Oh for Christ's sake yourself. Hilda stood up and yelled at me, *Jerk.* She gave the baby to Tad, practically threw it to him and went inside the bedroom and shut the door behind her. Tad looked at me, and said, Why do you always start arguments here? I thought, oh what the hell and went out to the porch, and down the stairs to my auto. Tad came to the porch and held the baby aloft and shouted, The name is Drew Ann. I looked up at him. He was smiling broadly. I waved, got into the car and drove off, back down to the street where I lived, and climbed back into bed for another week, but not before switching on the television . . .

Anyway, that is who Tad and Hilda are. They said they had flown into New York for Tad to accept this oil company job. I threw Tad a quick glance, and he said, with a brown, nervous smile, "I'm going to be a rich businessman, how do you like that!" I told Jessica it had been an awfully nice thing for her to do, to have called Tad and Hilda to surprise me, and she said she thought I would have liked it. Yet, in some vague, dull way I felt disturbed, almost disheartened. In the old days Jessica would have been eager to talk to me after we hadn't seen each other, and now she was placing other people between us. No, I thought; that is too far-fetched. It was a nice gesture. I have to stop looking into motives *all* the time.

We all went down to 14th Street, to a cafeteria, for a dawn breakfast, and talked a lot. I was too excited to eat. Tad and Hilda were delighted at my delight. They were leaving for Los Angeles by plane that evening, to prepare for Atlanta, where Tad had agreed to sign on as office manager. While we were still at breakfast, Jessica said that her plane was leaving in a couple of hours and hardly with a farewell left the cafeteria.

She slipped out, just like that, pausing only long enough at the cashier to pay her separate check. I went up to her at the cashier's desk. Jessica said, "Stay in the flat as long as you want. If a girl named Margaret calls tell her that Susan got married and I'm out at the house in Denver. Be good." I stood stock-still, not knowing what to say. Hey, Jessica, I said. "Be good," she said, and raced out of the cafeteria, as though I were a plague carrier. When I went back to the table, Hilda said, "You two had a quarrel?" Yeah, I said, about three years ago. "*Jerk*," said Hilda with that patronizing affection which always drove me wild, "always chewing at the same old bone. Why don't you save up money for a good psychoanalysis?" Tad moaned, good old Tad. I drew myself up stiffly and said that Jessica and I were not sleeping partners. Hilda shrugged and laughed, "So that's the reason." She had me there. I wonder if it was. That, I mean.

Jessica going away like that disturbed me, but I vowed not to let Hilda or Tad sense this too much. After breakfast, I took them back to their hotel and promised to call in the evening. Then I went back to Jessica's flat, let myself in with the key she had given me, and roamed around it, in the dark and dawn light, for a couple of hours, enjoying its relative largeness.

I spread-eagled myself on the bed in the bedroom and read stretches of *You Can't Go Home Again* by Thomas Wolfe until the late morning. I became excited. Suddenly, now, in New York, anything became possible. I began to work feverishly planning my book, lying on the large bed in Jessica's apartment, reading about "George Webber" lying in a Munich hospital and totting up the things he has learned. And I thought: that this too has happened to me. And the truth was a series of homilies told me by simpler people, homilies I rejected.

I rolled over on my back and chuckled for about an hour, remembering my interview at the publishing company. I got up and walked to the window, and looking down on 15th Street I brooded pettishly. Was the Boston firm a good enough house? How could it be? The building was old and musty, Mrs. Quinn seemed not at all eager to jump in and edit me, it was all so lackadaisical; and I loathed the fiction books on their list. Large, boring, pseudo epics of America, the "American experience." Yet who was I to yap?

Looking down from Jessica's window I kept repeating to myself: I am a writer.

The phone rang in the living room. I answered it. A girl's voice at the other end. Again, anything was possible. It was the girl, Margaret. I talked, booming, cocksure, into the phone. We talked for about half an hour. I said something about meeting her in Harlem, and she made a crack about Negroes and I said, What's the matter, don't you like Negroes? She laughed and said, with a kind of sadness, "Maybe not, I am one." I felt a fool. I brazened through a date for that evening at Chumley's, in the Village. When I put down the phone I felt terrific. I went back to the bedroom but I couldn't sleep and Thomas Wolfe no longer had anything to say to me, I had to get out onto the streets and *see*.

The first thing I had to do was get rid of the De Soto. I went downstairs into the cold, dry, gray morning air, and looked at the car. It was dirty and solid, its entire front end a paste of dried mud and dead leaves, the windshield almost opaque with spots and dead insects splattered. I sat down on the steps of Jessica's apartment house and looked at the car. I felt nothing for it. I had for my old 1940 Pontiac, the one I had left back in Los Angeles. But not for this. For some reason it made me angry. I knew I should feel something for it; the rear right spring had, after all, held up. But now all I wanted to do was be shut of it.

I drove through the early morning traffic to the Essex Hotel, on the south side of Central Park, lied to the doorman telling him I was a resident and had him put the De Soto away. In the lobby I phoned Maurice and Julia, got them out of bed and demanded their presence downstairs for breakfast. Maurice sleepily said for me to leave the car, they would be in touch, then hung up. I gave the doorman the keys and walked out and into the park, wondering what it was like to be so rich, like Maurice Lathenas, that I did not even inquire as to the condition of my car driven across the country.

I climbed a rock on the south side of the park and watched the streams of traffic grow heavier and thicker as the sun rose and the day warmed, and then merge in the middle of the park and pour down Seventh Avenue, and I thought of all of the cracked lives and wounded families which the collapse of the left had left in its wake, and when I pictured the actual individuals involved, visualized what they were all doing now, with very few exceptions I saw it wasn't all a bad thing. There was a compensation. Because, although it was easy to make fun of and name as absurd, to pity, even to have contempt (at your own risk, reader), they were beginning to take their lives apart, they had been forced to, and the odds were that as persons they would emerge better than I had ever known them. There were exceptions, of course. Like Kevin-John, the alcoholic Little League salesman. And Cal and Josh, blacklisted screenwriter and core-maker, who would go down with the ship without once seriously questioning what it was all about. But the others, the others, there was a chance they might become stronger at the broken places. For what? Toward what purpose? I didn't know. I was tempted to stay in America and see it, help it, join in it, benefit by it. But, in my heart, I knew I wouldn't. The process would be too slow, too tedious, too unrewarding except in some kind of final summing up. I would not be able to stand the gaff of the terrible disillusionment which was sweeping over them. I had been all through that, for myself, and I did not want to watch it in others. I was now ready to make jokes about it, and I could not stand to be with people who were not yet ready for humor — and the next step. No, I would have to leave many of them behind. Suddenly, sitting on that rock, I felt *fast* and *up*. I looked down. My hands were balled up into fists. My God, I hadn't felt this way since Chicago, years before. I felt totally alone, at the center of the universe and *ready*.

After that it was mostly anticlimax. I mean it was at that point that I had left my own country.

I stayed in the park, on the rock, watching the traffic all that morning and on into the afternoon, thinking of what New York had meant to me. It probably wasn't the town I grew up in, but it was where I had felt most conscious of growing. You see, just as soon as my final exams were over at the university, my protégé, Gus, and I rammed across the country to see what our future was. In Cleveland we saw the headlines about the North Koreans attacking the South Koreans, and Gus had leaped out of the car and brandished a paper in my face, almost crying as he shouted, All right, explain *that.* (Gus was my *political* protégé.) We went on to New York together and then split up. I went down to Barrow Street to offer my services to a small socialist journal called *Review of the Month,* but they didn't have any money to pay me and the two men who edited the review made it known, more or less politely, that I would only be in the way. Which was too bad, because that was why I had come all the way across the country that June, to offer my services to what was left of the movement. They didn't laugh at me, or patronize me; it was just that they were grizzled and a little politically weather-beaten and I don't think they wanted anyone young around the place. So I went out into New York and fell in love with all the girls.

I fell in love and roamed the railroad ties of sunlight under the elevated tracks on Third Avenue and hungered for recognition and wondered what I would do with my life. It was in New York that I moved into the Village, and went on and went off the weed all within a week, and it was there for the first time in my life I committed adultery with a friend's wife, and starved for status, and lost my oldest friend when I shrank back without knowing how not to. It was in New York that I shared the top-floor flat with Zack and Henry, who had been at college with me, and where we learned to depend upon and loathe each other, and where I first started to write and went back to playing handball and made my decision, when I was feeling frightened and lonely, to go back to school and take my Ph.D. in American Studies, and where, all in all, I played the young man as hard as I could to keep back the awful sensation that *something was going wrong.*

I did a lot that day because, for some reason, I felt that time was not on my side. First, I walked north and cut through the park to East 66th and called on my friend Bruce and his wife. They were, luckily, in, Bruce having a day off from his job, and we went walking in the park. We were formal with one another and not very communicative. It was always the same way between Bruce and myself, and I had never liked his wife, even though she had been raised in an anarchist colony in New Jersey (her full maiden name was an anagram on John Peter Altgeld). At the university Bruce and I had been close, or at least that was what most people thought. They thought we were each other's best friend. This was mainly because we had roughly the same politics at the time I edited the paper when he was chairman of the intra-university co-op organization, my only backers on the Student Council, during its darkest hours before the Administration closed the paper down. The fight for the paper was our fight. We had led two student strikes together, won and lost together, but we were far apart, as far apart as two men can be who work closely together. Bruce never let me inside. I don't think he ever let anyone inside, including his wife. He was a hulking, pale boy, a farm boy from Minnesota, and very locked up inside himself, dry and afraid, I suppose, to come out. He was a secret novel-writer. Also I don't think (even though he married one) he liked Jews. I know that sounds funny to say about anyone as radical as Bruce, who organized on the docks and became a steeplejack and almost went to jail when he told a House Committee to fuck off. But I think it's true. If you pressed Bruce hard enough, emotionally, he would bare his teeth, usually at me. I don't know, maybe it was because he once saw me kissing his girl at a college party, although I think it predated this. (She was the only girl who really engaged his passions, and now she's dead. We never talk about her. Never.)

To outsiders it always looked like Bruce and me against the world, together, Athos and d'Artagnan. The truth was, Bruce and I had things on each other. I knew that, behind closed doors, when the heat was really on, politically, he had a tendency to crack, to evade and compromise. Outwardly, and in many ways genuinely, he was the most moral person I've ever known. But there was just so much pressure he could take. Several times in the heat of campus battles I had to almost forcibly prevent him from backtracking. Not all the way, of course, but enough to vitiate the principle. This too, we never spoke of. What Bruce had on me mainly was a certain irresponsibility and laziness. I loved to write front-page editorials but I was not much interested in the relationship between campus dormitories and suburban tax rates. Bruce was. He was a devil on facts, on technology, on economics. When it was my turn to write a dullish editorial I just lazed around until Bruce would offer to do it, although he was not a member of the staff. So we had a kind of justified, mutual contempt for each other, we were a little afraid of each other (I because locked-up people always frighten me, such as nuns; Bruce because he knew I could not resist trying to get to know him, and not leave him be, as he was) and I am not even sure we liked each other. But we kept together, I think, for appearances, like an old respectable married couple, because it would have dismayed our supporters and friends to know that a split had developed between us. You see, Bruce and I stood for something. At least in those days we did. They were our best days. That is the third thing we don't talk about.

So Bruce and his wife and I walked in the park for about an hour, and then we parted. As simple as that. Our histories had diverged, and now as friends we did. I honored his history, even if I wasn't sure he did. After the university, he had gone back into construction and demolition, as an organizer, but had been fired, not by the company but by the union. As we walked in the park, Gelda said that Bruce had received three jail sentences in the last eighteen months, once for picketing an Atomic Energy establishment, once for traveling with a Negro in the front end of a segregated Greyhound, and once for sailing a dinghy into Brooklyn Navy Yard to protest war preparations. Now he was trying to make a living as an obscure clerk in a small New York civil-disobedience organization. He was not complaining, but he resented my advice to go out west and resume scholarly work. His genius was for data research and every time I tried to tell him this he balked. Maybe he thought I was trying to patronize him because he looked on me as a potential novelist; I don't know. I don't know anything about Bruce.

In the late, cool afternoon I went on up to Amsterdam and 99th and called on my old teacher and Svengali, Alan Pick, the Marxist who looked like an ape. Alan lived in a railroad flat, in one large room of it, with paintings on all the walls. It was a shock when he came to the door. I always remembered him as hulking, aggressive, snide, hairy, a kind of Bakunin of the music world, a Scriabin of the dialectic. Now, at the door he was actually slim, crew-cut, in velveteen pants, the old Mussolini jaw now in retreat. He invited me into his room, and we lay on couches (there were no chairs) to talk. He didn't bellow once. Old Alan had certainly changed. Now it was almost difficult to remember what a powerful hold he had once had on our platoon of teen-agers in Chicago, when his word, on anything, had been law. He told me that he was teaching music now, in a school in Long Island, and had gathered around him a small corps of young composers who subscribed to a new theory of his about musical "color." He had, he said, advanced chordal "color mixing" from the palette of the score to the canvas of the orchestra, from pointilism to a kind of proharmonic slab-ism, and waved towards the hi-fi record player out of which were issuing low sounds of a definite musical nature. I had to admit they were interesting. Not unlike Alan when lecturing.

It wasn't easy for Alan to talk to me, and I supposed I would have the same problem with John Alston, if I decided to see him. Just once, Alan tried the old stuff, to grill me aggressively on what I had been doing the past years, but I stopped him cold by telling him that I was here on Rafe's behalf. That stopped him cold. "Oh yes," he said, "what about Rafe?"

I said, You ought to stop sending those letters to him. He doesn't want to see you. Alan stared at me a long time, and then he gave a small, malicious giggle. Right away I knew what he was thinking, and I could have socked him for it. I told Alan, Rafe isn't queer any more. He's not anything any more. "Sure, sure," said Alan, still giggling. But I could see that he was hurt. Rafe had been his one true love, the boy he had almost destroyed, and my oldest friend. You sonofabitch, I said. "I think," Alan said, "perhaps you'd best go now." I could see I was hurting him. Not only that about Rafe; but that one of his students should no longer be under his thumb was a real, physical pain to him. I wasn't enjoying it and so I went to the door and walked out. About half a block away, just as I was descending the IRT subway stairs, I looked back and there was Alan, in his velvet pants, a beret on his head, shouting, "Come back, I want to talk to you." I hurried down the stairs. I wasn't afraid of him, I just didn't want to be involved.

It was the same feeling I had had passing up hitchhikers on the road. "Come back, come back, I want to talk to you," Alan shouted.

I took the IRT up to the Bronx and climbed Jerome Park hill to the apartment house where my Aunt Sue-Sarah lives. I couldn't tell you in a million years why I was going up there. Although the family felt close to me, I did not to them. I never visited them and did not go to their funerals and weddings and altogether was a bad son. I think I was going up to the Bronx to see if I could get any news of my father. When I speak of my family it is all on my father's side.

My aunt was in. We had a long talk. She was still a pretty woman, in her late fifties. She said I was a pain in the heart to the entire family because I would not give them *nachus*—grandchildren. I told her that if her pretty daughter, Sheila, a Hunter College girl, would consent, I would gladly give her a special *nachus*. My aunt became very angry, and I had to tell her I was joking. She said she did not like jokes of this sort and that the longer I remained without a home the more such jokes would cast a shadow over my life. That was her phrase, cast a shadow. She said her own children were giving her trouble, especially Sheila, who was known to be dating a boy who was not Jewish. I laughed. Aunt Sarah said, "Go ahead, laugh, it will be out of the other side of your mouth when you have your own children. I contribute to the Communists, I read Howard Fast, I make speeches against McCarthy—but Sheila will not marry a *goy*." I said, For Chrissake, Sarah. "Sue if you please," she said sternly. I told my aunt that she knew as well as I that Sheila would never marry a non-Jew, she was too much her mother's daughter for that, I only wish she would, it was only her way of asserting independence, that there was no cause for worry, Sheila was basically not an independent person. "I will not have you influencing my daughter," said my aunt. I said. My aching back, Sarah, I haven't *seen* her in eight years. Mollified, my aunt got up and made me some chicken soup with *knadlach*. I couldn't eat.

She reminisced, suddenly. "You know," my aunt said, "I was always jealous of your mother. Not my brother, your father, but his wife. Your mother knew this never, I always hid it. She was the intellectual of the family. In the lower East Side they called her the 'Angel of the Soapbox.' " For the next couple of hours my aunt gave me memories of my mother, how she had organized her first sweat shop at thirteen, her first meeting with my father. "Oh yes," my aunt concluded, "she was the smart one all right. But what did it get her? A father like yours." And me like me, I said. "That's right," she said. "All right," she said, "so I wasn't so smart. But I raised a family, soon both my children will be married, I will have plenty of *nachus*. And calmness. I will have had calmness. Your mother never had this." It isn't everything, I said sullenly. She smiled at me bitterly. "Look at you," she said. "You would give your whole life for a little of that right now, wouldn't you?"

After leaving the Bronx and my Aunt Sue-Sarah, I went back to Greenwich Village. I had not learned where my father was or if he was alive. I didn't even know if I minded. The thing I wanted to avoid was suddenly and without warning meeting my old man on the subway. The chances of this happening were not good when you consider I didn't know where he lived, what he looked like now and if he was alive. But it kept worrying me nonetheless. I had several fantasies on the subway; one, that I would recognize him and him not me, two, the other way around. The fantasy that appealed most to me was that we would recognize each other, sitting opposite, at exactly the same moment, spend several moments gazing at each other in a transport of indecision, smile at each other in a despairing, sagacious way and one of us would arise at the next station and get off. I hadn't seen my old man in seventeen or eighteen years.

I met no one on the subway and made my way down to Chumley's, an English-type theatrical bar in the Village. I waited about half an hour, and then this girl Margaret, with whom I had made a date earlier, came in. She was a very pretty girl, with big teeth and a small waist. I shook her hand and spoke in my deep, grave voice and was careful not to laugh too loudly, and it soon became obvious that this girl was not very interested in me. I found this irksome, as I was beginning again to feel lonely and like laying half Manhattan island (the half that was female). I do not know why, but I have never interested Negro women. This depressed me. Also, the fact that as I spoke to Margaret I realized that I had neither status nor point of view. I was a bit shocked by this. Usually, when I come off the road, I settle down quickly, back to myself. But it was as though I were still at the wheel of the De Soto talking to Margaret. I didn't know where I belonged, to which party or country or family. Margaret didn't know either. "I'm one of those don't-belong Negroes," she said.

I became very enthusiastic when she said this. I tried to get across that that was approximately my feeling too, but she wasn't having any. She looked at me skeptically, and I said, Well, we can't *all* be Negroes. This did not go down at all well, and the evening steadily deteriorated until, about an hour later, a girl-friend of hers walked in, a white blond girl, which disheartened me when I realized it was a put-up job and that Margaret had not trusted me. The three of us sat around talking, and I tried to explain this theory of mine that there has not been, as Tennessee Williams and God alone knows how many other writers would have us believe, a breakdown in communication, but that in fact we are communicating superbly well to each other a message the very clarity of which was unmanning us. We understood only too well. And we are shaken, quite appropriately. I told them that the only way to sustain ourselves in the situation was to stop trying to communicate so hard with each other. The core of the problem, I said, was Individualism. When we have to live for other people in phony Togetherness ways it becomes impossible for us to realize ourselves as individuals and therefore to really live for other people. By now, both girls were becoming very bored. I realized that they must have spent a lot of time listening to people talk this way in the Village. But I was serious. That was when I made my mistake. I said, Take us for an example. A single man and two unmarried women. Why is it that the situation in America now permits of only two alternatives, either getting married or biting the nails of spinsterhood? The blonde, faded and with a good figure, blew up. Why *shouldn't* women have careers, she said. I gave up. I paid for the drinks, said I had a sick headache and got out of Chumley's. I was disappointed that I had not made connection with Margaret. Before I left America I had a terrific desire to leave behind a connection with one of the early Americans, like an Indian or a Negro.

Back in Jessica's flat, I received a phone call from Arturo Mishkin, who said he had found out I was in town. We arranged to meet at the Russian Wolfhound, a restaurant-bar, on 57th Street just off Seventh Avenue (if memory serves). Arturo came in, chipper and wisecracking, and we had dinner together, on him, as he was sound-supervising a Hollywood film on New York location, using an assumed name. I ordered chablis with crab, shashlik and Pommard '40, and couldn't eat any of it. Arturo talked compulsively and proudly exhibited some obscene witticisms told him by his twelve-year old daughter, whom I disliked. He said he now had a mistress, realized his wife was really his mother, had marked up his twelfth year in psychoanalysis and understood, finally, he was a crum. That was his phrase. "I understand finally, I am a crum." Then he reached under the table and showed me a package which he said contained two work prints of a film he had just sound-mixed for a European government. That was also his phrase. "A European government." I asked him which one and he said, "One that is on the side of the angels." I laughed, possibly too bitterly, and he said, "Oh you're one of those."

Yes, I said, deserting the sinking ship. Arturo drew himself up proudly and said, "You were never on it, you crum." I said, I thought you were the crum, mildly. And, of course, Arturo got sore and shouted, "You *know* I envy your masculinity, why do you use it as a weapon against me?"

Well, I mean, twelve *years* of psychoanalysis.

He calmed down and coyly suggested that he might do me the honor of letting me take his package of work prints to a friend in Paris who would then, he even more coyly suggested, transfer it somewhere eastward. I said, Arturo, you really are famous, don't you know they put people in the electric chair for things like that? I thought he would faint. He did grow mighty pale and begin to stammer. I told him I meant it as a joke, and he leaned across the table and breathed fiercely, "If you ask me, you have a depraved sense of humor." Okay, I said, why don't we all have a drink and you take those work prints home or take them to Paris yourself, the way you look you could use a little vacation, that little old mistress of yours is wearing you out, Arturo, ol' kid. Well, that did it, of course. *You* try making jokes with a man twelve years in psychoanalysis. He grabbed his package and ran right out of the restaurant without another word, of course leaving me feeling rotten, not least because he brushed away my hand from the check which he paid by flinging some bills at a waiter near the door. It was all pretty embarrassing. The assistant manager, who looked like the Tsar's aide-de-camp (the one who is sleeping with the Tsarina) came up to see if I was drunk, or stabbed to death, and I got up and wandered towards the bar.

I drank a certain amount at the bar and then a troupe of West Indian steel-banders came in, had a single drink apiece and left behind one of their number, a slim, well-turned out young man about my age. He introduced himself to me as the manager of the steel band. I asked him how business was, and he said, "Lousy, rotten, terrible, man." The worst of it was, he said, that by profession he was a painter and not at all from the West Indies but from Janesville, Ohio. In fact, he hated steel-band music. "Not only," he said, "do I not dig it but I regard it as the most monotonous music in the world. I try not to listen but the boys get upset because they know I don't like their music. They keep threatening to look for another manager, which is okay by me because it would give me a good excuse to go back to Ibiza."

I asked him what Ibiza was and he said an island in the Balearics. He loved Ibiza, had just come back and wanted to return. All he wanted to talk about was this island. He said it was the only place to live and paint. He finally gave me the name of the man who ran the newspaper kiosk on the quay and said this man would help me find a house — $28 a month. "Kiddo," he said, "as soon as I get myself a Guggenheim or marry rich I'm streaking back for good ol' Ibiza." And then he fell off the stool. I leaned over and started to pound him on the back. The bartender came over and said, "That's no way to put him on his feet," and then the assistant maître-de, the Tsarina's lover, came up and hissed, "We do not want any trouble in this establishment." So I pounded Don harder on the back and shouted, Hey Don, get up, they don't want any trouble in this establishment. He looked up at me and it was clear he did not know who I was. That kind of drunk, you can never tell them when you start out drinking with them. He was the first black-skinned man I have ever seen fall off a stool. Several people helped him back up to his seat, and he went on drinking as if I were not next to him. I thanked him for his tip about Ibiza and said I would probably go there and then I left the restaurant and walked restlessly, wandering, first over to a jazz joint in Sheridan Square. I didn't feel like picking up girls any more, at least not tonight. The band was awful, but I did see someone I knew. I went over and we chatted. Wilfred was drunk. He was always drunk. Are you on a job now? I asked. Wilfred said no, he was through being a private detective, he was on the overnight desk of American Wire Service in New York. Wilfred and I had been on the overnight in the L.A. bureau, where he had augmented his income by private detecting in divorce cases. The only thing decent about Wilfred, when you came right down to it, was his wife, a Saigon girl whom he had met when he had gone there with the Army. We talked a little about old times, over the noise of this band, which advertised itself as old-time New Orleans and had a saxophone in the front line. Wilfred was almost out on his feet, and I had to prop him up. He said he and the Saigon girl were separated, that he hated his job and was thinking of turning homosexual like everyone else and would I like to join him. He said this loudly, and the crowd around us turned to look and laugh a little. Wilfred then grew sleepy and said, "There ain't no fucking leopard." I had to laugh at this. When I first went to work for American Wire, I was on with Wilfred, who was overnight editor. A report came in that a leopard had escaped from a local carnival and was terrorizing the city. I went out to report it. Wilfred, drunk as usual, kept saying, No fucking leopard, take my word for it. I interviewed a score of policemen and citizens who had seen the leopard. This was my first by-line story. I went out to Highland Park and spoke to a man who showed me the scratches he had received when the leopard leaped on him. After cruising around in a police car half the night I went back to the office and began my story, "Tense, raw-nerved police officers tonight patrolled the fear-shadowed streets of residential Los Angeles . . ." All the time I was writing the story, Wilfred, so drunk he could hardly sit up, kept muttering, "Ain't no fucking leopard, ain't no fucking leopard." I became very angry, and I stood up and yelled, The cops have *seen* it. Wilfred had slumped even lower in his chair and said morosely, "You'll see." Of course he was right. It turned out the escaped leopard was a hoax, perpetrated by a cooky salesman from Altadena.

I left Wilfred in the jazz club and went over to the square in Washington park. It was about one in the morning, and I sat down on the stone fountain, only I was not waiting for the woman I was to love. The park was cold. I had no place to go. A girl came by, in a cloth coat, and sat in the shadow on the other side of the fountain. I thought, What the hell and got up and walked away. I went over to 13th Street and stood in front of the house I used to live in. The street was dark and the house was dark. I wondered if anyone I knew still lived there.

It was in 1950. I had left the record company because a first success had paralyzed them and given them aesthetic lock-jaw, and I left the house where I lived in Gowanus because my friends were frightened about the outbreak of the Korean war and had asked me to leave. So I got out of New York by bumming my way south to visit with friends in North Carolina. I had just then begun to write and was quite happy about it. My friends at the Taussig mill in Durham asked, as friends do, what I was doing with myself these days, was I working for a union or on a shop floor, and this made me feel awkward. What indeed? I wandered further south, until the heat and Jim Crow forced me back to New York.

I felt hurt. My friends in Brooklyn did not ask me to come back. They were busy throwing out most of their books, carting them over a block or two to other people's trash bins. There were short, sharp days of panic among us in New York, a little self-dramatizing but also with some foundation for worry. A bill had already been introduced into the Congress authorizing, if memory serves, the construction of three concentra — I beg your pardon, relocation camps, in the event of a national emergency. If memory continues to serve, it was that raging New Deal liberal, Hubert Humphrey, who presided over the House-Senate conference to adjust the bill, I have no doubt, friend, in order to soften its more intemperate procedures. I felt sulky about Del and Kate and Big Tom and Gina in Gowanus; they were jazz musicians, of the Prez school, and so one expected better of them. The thing was, pregnant Gina was fiendishly afraid she might have a miscarriage if the FBI came around, which it did fairly regularly in those days, in its polite and affable way. And so, they explained to me in their living room one morning while their dog, President, solemnly barked, I had to go because my reputation from California might do them an injury. This was very silly, because Tom and Del were notorious in their section of Brooklyn, and I was unknown. But in those first days of June and July, 1950, there was no point in arguing, even with friends.

So I went to Greenwich Village where the other homeless people were. What shrunk me was what got any of us who had just come out of the university on the G. I. Bill, that the Army would come and get us again. I had nightmares about this. Factory owners wouldn't hire you because you were of draft age. I had one or two friends who persuaded psychiatrists to certify them as homosexuals to evade the draft; this was fairly common in Greenwich Village in 1950, and may still be. I got into a mood and decided the only thing was to self-consciously "do" the life of the young man from the provinces, a manuscript under one arm and a typewriter in the other.

But it wasn't easy any more. I didn't know anyone down there in the Village, and I soon saw it had gone seedy and sappy and *trés bourgeois*. Of all the surprising things, I began to feel nostalgic about the campus where people had known me, where I couldn't walk across the quad without being said hello to by admirers, friends and even enemies. Answering an ad in the *Villager* I moved into a flat in a large semi-tenement on 13th Street.

It was what they call a railroad flat, with seven or eight box rooms strung along a single dingy corridor leading to a communal kitchen, where most of the trouble occurred. The people living in the railroad flat were young Village people, tight, wild, never judging for fear of being judged, and broken. But not strong. Just broken and on the down side. It was like a book-lined Skid Row. I was *home*.

Gracie was my girlfriend in the flat. She became my girlfriend a couple of hours after I moved in. I thought this was hospitable. Gracie, with a gamin's face and darting eyes, who spent most of her afternoons in an orgone box. (It is too complicated to explain what an orgone box was, or maybe even still is, go and ask.) Woodward was a one-legged, ex-Air Force transport pilot who was writing a novel but hadn't gone past the first chapter in three years of living in the flat, and you could hear him pumping on his good leg down the hallway every midnight sharp to make love to Bettina, an interior decorator from Moline, Illinois, who had changed her name from Betty when she moved into the Village. Quentin, in the next room to Woodward, was a young folk singer who loved my girlfriend, Gracie, and used to sneak into our room around dawn and play the mandolin for us, or rather for her. It was eerie, I can tell you. Fuzzie, in the next room down, wanted to be a radio announcer, masturbated constantly in the unlocked bathroom where he used everyone else's towels but his own, and liked to show newcomers to the flat a clipping from the St. Louis *Post-Dispatch* about his half-brother murdering their mother with an axe. You *neve*r knew when Fuzzie was telling the truth. He is in Dannemora (NY) prison now, on a self-defeating charge, that of attempted suicide in the BMT subway. Eleane, whose boyfriend was a bona fide Persian prince studying at Columbia and who was on the needle, lived with Dot, who *always*, every Saturday morning, tried to do away with herself by stuffing up all the cracks and apertures in the common kitchen and turning on the gas, succeeding only in making herself and Fuzzie (whose room was next to the kitchen) sick. One day Woodward, the peg-leg, became mighty sore over Dot's carryings on and called her a name and said he would be glad to help her next time. She threw a knife at him, which hit but did not injure me, giving Gracie, usually deeply equable, an excuse to go for Dot, who had once been her love and girl. It was also that kind of house.

It was a house without rules, loud, raucous, stop-and-start. Except that whenever they heard me at my typewriter they quieted down and went about on tippytoe, all very self-conscious and elaborate. If *they* were unable to work and create, they wouldn't stand in *my* way. They were determined on encouraging me, even if they didn't know what I was writing and only fobbed me off from one day to the next when I tried to tell them. I loved them so much that I announced, in the kitchen, that I would one day write a story about all of them which I would call "The Railroad Flat on 13th Street." This news they accepted with gravity.

And then one day I came home to find most of the inhabitants of the flat on 13th Street sitting around the kitchen, their rooms and the bathroom reading my manuscripts. Nobody said anything much. But afterwards, after coming by my room to leave the manuscripts, they weren't so careful to keep quiet. In fact, they made plenty of noise.

About a week later, riding the subway, I looked at a bum across the aisle and saw with a shock that it was a man who looked like Swede, now down and out. I took him to 13th Street, gave him my bed and fed him for a week. Woodie and Bettina passed it around that my secret vice was picking up old bums; everyone in the house started treating me differently until one night the man went away and never came back. I moved out and went to California. I think I was twenty-three in those days.

I went back to Washington Square. The girl was gone. Fifteen minutes later a plainclothesman came by the stone-dry fountain and asked me for my identification. I gave him one of my two press cards, which I always do with cops, and he said I perhaps ought to go home to sleep, and police couldn't be everywhere at once with all these muggings. I said I wasn't drunk, and he said, "I didn't say you were drunk, I get paid with your money and I'm just telling you for your own benefit." I asked him why it was that New York cops, more often than anyone else, felt it necessary to invoke the tax structure. "Look jack," he said, "go home and go to sleep, guys like you make me weary." He saw the expression on my face and said, "I'll give you half a minute and then I'll book you for a queer."

That really got my goat. I stood up. Why a queer? I shouted. He said, "All right." I said, Why not a pickpocket or a burglar or a murderer? Why always a goddam queer? *What have we got on our conscience?* So he took my arm and marched me through the trees over to a squad car that was parked on the street. Still holding my arm he ducked down and said to his partner, "Call in this man's name, age and draft number." His partner, also in plain clothes, took my wallet and radioed my vital statistics somewhere. While he waited I was taken a few yards away where the detective lighted a cigarette. I didn't say anything, and neither did he. "Bob," called his partner. The detective said to me, "You know better than to walk away," and went to the police car. When he came back he had his partner with him. I tried to force myself to completely relax my body, and told myself that if they piled into me not to run away and not to hit back. But they didn't. The partner stood staring at me a while, quite dramatically in fact, which I suppose was to impress on me that he would remember me from now on. The first detective said, "All right, get your ass out of this part." I didn't argue.

I walked back to Sheridan Square, to the jazz club, to find Wilfred but he was gone and the club was shut. It was about two in the morning. I didn't remember the clubs shutting so early. Probably a consequence of everyone, including the junkies and Bird-lovers, emigrating to the suburbs. The streets of the Village were deserted and quiet. Everything had changed since my day. When I lived in the Village it had been commercial and going expensive, but now the thing seemed one entire false front. I could not imagine a Village where, at two in the morning, of an early November, you couldn't see scores of characters stomping around. You might not have approved these characters but they would have been there.

Walking up Sixth Avenue past the jailhouse on 8th Street, I got an idea for a film script. It had to do with nymphomaniacs and junkies and jazz musicians who *commuted* to bohemia. I was laughing so hard I forgot about the cops in the park. I wanted to tell the idea to someone, so I stepped into an all-night Wimpy's and phoned Zack. He had been asleep and for a few moments he didn't know who it was. I said, Zack it's me, I've got a tremendous idea for a film. He said, wearily, "It couldn't be anyone else. But before you come over you might as well know I've got Dave Margolis living with me, we're sharing an apartment."

I said, That's impossible, that's like putting black and white together. Zack said wryly, "You make funny jokes, boy." I felt my face glow red in the phone booth. I said, Well you know what I mean, you and he used to be four million miles apart. He said, "We still are. But he just got a divorce and needed a place to stay." In the background I could hear Dave's sleepy voice cry, "You don't have to tell him the story of my life, who is it?" Zack said it was me. Dave yelled enthusiastically and said for me to come right over. Still more wearily, Zack said, "You heard the man." I said, You still mad at me, Zack? He said, "Man I ain't mad at nobody no more. That's the trouble."

I hung up and hailed a taxi which took me up to my old flat on 76th Street and West End. (When Henry and I moved out we had turned it over to Zack.) It was on the top floor of an old brownstone. I heard a tinkle on the pavement the moment I stepped out of the cab: the key. I used it on the door and walked upstairs. The door was open and I walked in. Zack, in a tacky old bathrobe, came up with a grin and shook my hand. He had decided to be friendly. I could tell he was grinning only by the light of the hallway. The flat itself was pitch-dark and had a crazy, acrid smell. Zack said, "You might as well sit on the floor, there's so much junk around." So we sat on the floor in the dark. I asked Zack how he was, and he said, "Keeping."

Dave came in and said, "Aw put the lights on, they're dead to the world." Zack got up and put on one small dim bulb. The flat looked pretty much as I remembered it, a bachelor's place, cluttered and matty and yet looking bare. There were masks and candles and gilt-edged books on the couches and chairs, and a *menorah* on the mantel with a large open cardboard box near me in the center of the room. I looked into the box and it had scraps of white paper in it. Zack grinned. Dave said eagerly, "Voodoo, man." I looked at Dave as though to say, Don't give me this "man" stuff, but I didn't say it. Zack looked a little embarrassed. "Yeah," he said, "we been doing a little voodoo. You know, black magic." Dave said, "Keep it cool, man, the chicks are asleep." I wished to Christ Dave wouldn't use language like that. Zack said, "Ballet dancers." Dave said stentorianly, "Bellies and hearts of steel." I said, You sound in training to write a lousy book. He said, "Look, bygones are bygones, let's not be unpleasant." In olden days he would have strode across the room to manfully shake my hand. The fact that he did not now do so augured ominously of his immersion into his new world.

"What is it, kid?" asked Zack. "You need a place for the night?" (Dave glanced at him sadly, as though he wanted Zack to say "pad.") I said no, I was okay for that, I just felt like coming by to say hello. "I think that's terrific," said Dave. I sighed, not sure that I didn't prefer Dave the old way. It was unthinkable, these two living together. It had to do with values.

I was never able to really pin down Zack. He was suspicious of me in college and thereafter. Political, his entire life was political, for Zack was a Communist, and a good one.

Thin, unhandsome, lazy-looking, a brilliant student, a Sunday-school Baptist and an orphan: he had the athletic spirit but the bones had proved too brittle. (I had been one of the two men responsible for breaking his ankle in a football game on the street outside Co-op Barracks.) In so many ways the party had made a man of Zack. At the university he made his friends entirely among white people but was a Negro among them, not like my friend Stirling. That is, he made his friends among whites until his party decided that it was the time to "strengthen our ties with the Negro people" and that Zack was the logical person to "lead the struggle." So Zack admitted his error, and truly felt ashamed at "deserting" his own people, and theorized and generalized and painfully made friends among the campus and city Negroes and realized, not dimly but acutely, that here was where he belonged. Zack understood at all times that the Negro's "pride of race" was a secondary, defensive reaction, and he disliked joining in celebrations of racial achievements. His sense of proportion, if I may use a much — and justly — maligned phrase, was (in those circumstances) a rare and splendid thing. He resented braggadocio, and even when the detours lay most heavily upon him, he rarely permitted his political work to degenerate into flamboyance. Zack icily drawling to me, after I had delivered a magnificent and arrogant speech in my defense before a crowded Student Council chamber, "That was fine speech, man," deflated me more profoundly than any other reproof at the university.

Zack's cool tactical sense, his mild manner, and embarrassment at personal friction, prevented him from becoming a Leader of His People. He was fantastically devoted to bebop, and publicly prided himself upon a technical grasp of modern jazz, which was in contrast to his intellectual self-effacement in the fields where he might easily have dominated. I liked Zack because he never let failure go to his head. He understood, what few of us did, that the frat boys and square characters who controlled the classrooms and student life of the university made so much of the campus radicals not because of what we did or were (damn little) but because they needed to have a local bogeyman to match the larger, more abstract national prey. It was the frat boys' way of Doing Their Bit.

Not many of us knew how difficult it was for Zack to go back into the Negro community, which did not have as high a respect for him as the whites.

Zack's other problem was girls. His was not a talent for happy love affairs; his luck was almost primordially bad. Although he did not discriminate against Negro girls, he almost always went for white, Jewish things, who usually believed he was too dry and humorless and ego-involved. I think myself that he was a very ethical boy. He used to laugh at himself by calling it bourgeois-liberalism. This laugh was short, dry and rasping. After college, he went to work in a San Fernando high school from which he was fired after a visit to the valley from the House Un-American Activities Committee. I hadn't seen him in two years, and knew only that he had married a little Negro girl who had divorced him. The last time I had seen Zack all he had wanted to talk about was woman trouble.

Dave was a different kettle of fish. How he tied in with Zack God alone knew. Since he had a nose for these things, I suspect he was in the neighborhood doing unconscious research for a book about the new, demoralized and disengaged generation, of which I suppose people like Zack and myself were the original disengagers, three cheers for us. Dave never did me serious wrong but it was easy not to like him.

He was a "Jew boy." He looked like a Fascist stereotype of a Jew. Thin, flat-lean, swarthy, greasy complexion, face scarred and pocked, big watery eyes in a much-boned, vivacious face, and a long nose. He walked hunched over and you always expected him to rub his hands together. He was a throwback.

Dave lived in a different world on the campus, the world of fashion, fraternities, smoothness and that special, ritual pomp of campus social life reserved exclusively for the sons and daughters of the well fed. He was comfortable, taken care of, on the income his father had left his mother, a nice modern Jewish woman who went to the theater, did not speak with an accent and played bridge. Dave had joined the big-time Jewish fraternity at college, learned to play Shearing at the piano and cut a place for himself in the niche of local jazz musicians and novelists-in-being. He wrote a college musical and went around in a fraternity sweater and white saddle shoes: one of the boys but also extremely conscious of his difference, his Jewishness, his inability to completely assimilate (because of his appearance) into the predominantly and sometimes hysterically Anglo-Saxon college community. He took the other way out. He became the cosmopolitan Jew, the urbane anti-ideological Jew who showed nothing but contempt for the Jewish boys who sneaked into gentile fraternities because they happened to be wholesome-looking. He became master of the Yiddish dirty joke — replete with accent. He learned to speak Yiddish. He learned sensitivity to the subtle norms of campus anti-Semitism. And, like Zack, who did not go out with Negro girls, Dave was rarely seen with a Jewish girl.

I had last seen Dave several years ago in Los Angeles where he had apparently settled down to life as social columnist for one of the evening newspapers. He had married our graduation year's Senior Prom Queen, a vacuous beauty of unimpeachable white, middle-class Protestant origin. (To marry — or even be seen dating — the Senior Prom Queen has been one half of the Great American Dream since even before Scott Fitzgerald sanctified it.) As far as I knew they were still married.

Dave's morality operated in a narrow area, and when speaking to old college acquaintances, especially the radical ones among whom, perversely, he chose to make a few friends, he had fallen into the habit of aggressively apologizing for his occupation as a gossip columnist. On last seeing me, he had said, Look, kid, ya gotta make the cabbage before you can carry the torch. You expected his hands to come together in a Shylockian rub. The one thing of which he seemed most proud (even, I was told, when not in my presence) was that he had defended my right to edit the university paper to the Student Publications board. He was graduating then and had nothing to lose, but I grant he did make an impassioned (always in low voice, eyes peering out melodramatically from lowered brows) plea, defending the record of this man (me), but not even by implication attacking the stupidity of my detractors, for that would have been "ineffective" and anyway who knew when one of the detractors would be an employer. Am I being unfair? Of course. Am I being fair? Fairer still . . .

Zack broke out a bottle of brandy. We sat around the false ceramic fireplace and did a little drinking. All the voodoo stuff in the flat put me off. It just wasn't Zack's style. I wished Dave weren't there, but he looked positively joyful I had found him in such company.

Zack said that he was now working on electronic computers, his original trade and love, in New York, and that he had made it up with his brother, with whom he had quarreled over politics a few years ago. But more than that he wouldn't say. "I'm bitter, man." I said, There's nobody to blame. He said, "What was the use of it all? You tell me." I said, We bet on the wrong horse, that's all. He said, "Don't give me metaphors, man. Tell me, what was the use of it all? We worked and worked. For what? To kill Jews in Brest-Litovsk?"

Zack was strange this way. Sometimes it seemed he had been hit harder by anti-Semitic revelations inside Russia than many of the Jewish comrades. I remember seeing him about a week after a Canadian Communist had reported a conversation where Khrushchev had said that the Jews were tailors, individualists, rabidly educational, incapable of socialist solidarity. It was at a party given by his girlfriend, a cashmere-sweatered, laughing, joshing Jewish girl, the daughter of a Hollywood agent. He had been leaning against the wall, and when I came in he coiled his long, brown arm around my neck and whispered, It all makes me want to puke — *all.*

Zack was sitting on the floor, his back against the couch, the bottle of brandy in his hands. He began to cry, sniffling and sobbing. He shrugged at me once or twice but couldn't stop. Dave looked quite calm, as though he had seen it before, and almost commanded Zack, "Go get one of the girls." Zack got up and disappeared into the bedroom. Dave, still standing, said, "He's been like that ever since the news came in about Budapest. Nothing can stop him." Dave sounded a little in awe. Finally, Zack came out of the bedroom and plumped down on the couch. He looked worn out, crumpled, his thin bony body wrenched and dried up. He said, "You're lucky, you always had Bruce and Henry."

Bruce and Henry had been my two best friends in college, more or less. I said, Don't talk like a fool, Zack. Henry is an alcoholic in Fresno and Bruce is a eunuch who's afraid to touch a typewriter. He shook his head stubbornly, "At least you had them." On paper this may sound as if Zack was self-pitying. But he was, from his point of view, stating some sort of fact, a little of which escaped me. He was feeling, I think, that he had come out of it all with nothing to show.

Then Zack lay back on the couch and said, "Man I need a psychiatrist." Dave said, "Tuesday, Zack, the appointment is Tuesday." I told Zack to move over on the couch and I sat down beside him. He said, "Don't talk to me no more. Don't give out with any jokes or metaphors. I just want a psychiatrist." I said, Zack, if we look at this the right way it can be a sort of beginning. Zack jerked up his head to look at me in amazement, then lay back again. Dave said, "Dale Carnegie yet." I said, Dave, when did you start paying dues? He said, grandiloquently, "It's a great big human problem now." I said, Look, old boy, I mean, the barn has burned down, it gives no more shelter. The thought of Dave nursing Zack was touching and infuriating.

"Fuck you, too," said Dave. I saw that I had hurt him, and I was sorry. Okay, I said, fair enough. He went over to a bureau drawer and came back with a bottle. He got out two capsules and put them against Zack's lips. "Drink up, buddy," he said gently. Zack gulped them down with the aid of brandy. Any minute I expected Dave to say, medically, I think it's best you go now, the way they do in movies. I said to Zack, I want to talk to you. He said, "Come back tomorrow, man. Tomorrow." Dave got up and walked into the bedroom where the girls were. I sat on the couch where Zack was lying. Soon he went to sleep, his head resting against the arm. I got up and walked out.

It was about four in the morning, and I was glad I had my coat on. I walked down Broadway, cool and windy and dark, and I'll be go-to-goddam if a police car didn't draw up next to me near 66th Street. We went through the whole routine again, except that this time no one got out of the car, always a reassuring sign. I put on my educated, semi-Eton, slightly commanding voice ("*Good* evening, officeh. Yes, Iah knoweh it's quite lateh. But youeh seeah, Iam'm havin' a bit of difficulteh with the lahst chapteh of myah bookeh, and Iam'h trying to straighten it out, y'know, with a stroll . . ."). One of these days, don't tell me, I'm going to overdo it. (But this time they went away.)

At 59th Street I cut over to Fifth Avenue and went into the

Essex Hotel to use their house telephone. I got Maurice on the phone and asked if I could come up and get the keys to the De Soto. He began swearing, and then I realized what time it was and that I had awakened him for two nights running. He hung up on me, angrily, but not before asking me if I was in any trouble. I crossed the street to the south side of the park and found my rock and climbed up on it again.

From where I was sitting I could see up into the darkened rooms of the hotel where Julia and Maurice were staying. Back in Los Angeles I had offered to conduct them on a tour of New York City, but I guessed I would not get around to it. If a town has ever been a goal, a mecca for you, you only feel useless trying to explain it to people, especially to people like Julia and Maurice who were too quick to understand. I wondered if all Frenchmen were like Maurice. It started to rain, a warm, spilled rain, and I pulled my coat tighter around me. I was feeling all right on that rock, thinking about all the other times I'd watched rain come down in New York City.

How do you tell anyone about New York? First, Joe Turner singing, "It's been raining all day, baby, and I been home waiting for you . . ." the rich blues sifting through the heavily constant rain splashing down on a summer-soaked New York. To me, New York is a summer city, the day after a scorcher, the day when the grave, sticky rain isn't as welcome as you thought it would be. The town, and its people, so deft at quick adjustment, quickly pull on the raincoats, pull down the hats and draw out the umbrellas from nowhere. The subway is hot and steamy but a wall of cool air stands just outside the station. The rain digs in, not washes away, the grit of the city. The automobiles roll along the glistening streets with a whish-whish, a fine little spray accompanying the whirring tires which leave their treadmarks in the wet street for a few seconds. But the rain does not wash away the hot loneliness.

Manhattan is a hot midday in July. The Third Avenue El screams above pillared, narrow cobbled streets filled with slow-moving old bent men and stunted women and messenger boys and office girls in summer dresses. To anyone from the outside, New York is a town, a race, a people, a way of life apart. When I first came from the West I was almost afraid to gesticulate while talking.

The accommodation to tiny, dirty places is made by New Yorkers, and so I and Henry and Zack made it too. New Yorkers are proud. They have learned to live in a world of rooming houses, hot plates, shared bathrooms, afternoon violences on crowded streets and suffocating subways.

I remember when I first came to New York pondering, as though my life depended on it, why the police were so misshapen, so out of shape, so different from the clean, sunburned, tall Los Angeles storm troopers, why there existed an intimacy between cop and civilian here. I wondered at the Europeanness of New York. Those who call it the most American of cities know nothing of this country. Accents, dialects, foreign tongues everywhere, is like muddy water to the dry gravel and sand of the cemented city. And, this mark well, this is a class city. The classes are more differentiated in speech, dress and way of life than anywhere else in America. My first year in New York was spent discovering it all. The New York of Park Avenue and taxi trips to the Wall Street office and bars of Lower Fifth Avenue. The indifference of the rich, the guilt of the poor, the rats attacking from the Hudson river. And of Kings Highway in Brooklyn, with fat little children racing around the middle-class back yards and the initialed blue awnings and neighborhood romances in Prospect Park. And of Second Avenue (if you are lucky enough not to live on First) with the thick fruity smell of the markets, the perpetually pregnant women, the plethora of stray animals and the knots of busy and lonely adolescents and the peering heads and fat, folded arms on the cooling window sills. And the Harlem Negro. And the pure thin talk-talk world of the Julliard violinist and Columbia U. researcher. And the agonized cheers as the aging but still graceful Di Maggio poles a long one and the somber faces up-turned to the moving flashes of war news on the *Times* building.

More than anything else, New York is a hot day. It isn't too bad when you go to bed. But waking in the morning the body is irritated and wet, wet with the muggy heat, the still cloudy heat that presages the misery of slumped shoulders, narrowed eyes, dragging steps and cloying, moist, swirling heat. Waking, the body has sweated all night and is heavy and warmly logy, but the face is what we feel the most. It is wet and greasy and we stumble to the washbasin and put our heads under the cold water. Better, aah, much better. We straighten up and then know: this is going to be A Scorcher. The reluctant trudge to the subway, on a hot morning, is New York . . .

And leaving the city, that too is New York. The rain stopped, the wind died down and I got off the rock and walked down Sixth Avenue to Jessica's flat. I climbed into bed and read Dreiser. Maybe he could help. I put the book aside and read some of my short stories. I saw no talent whatsoever. I put out the light and went to sleep.

The entire next day I spent in the New York Public Library, writing a chapter of my book. I was very solemn about it, never before in my life having thought of myself as a full-time, professional writer. I kept a dreamy, grim expression on my face and I resolutely refused to look up from my writing tablet. Studying in libraries does something to me. (I found out about this in college.) I feared that if I remained longer I should launch myself at a girl sitting a few seats away.

Some say that hungry men do not have sex on the mind. This is not true. I had not, for some reason, eaten for several days, but it did not prevent me from wanting to lay even the gray-haired desk librarian on one of those long burnished tables with green lampshades. I was feeling, in the library, tremendously lightheaded. It was an old feeling but the first time when I also possessed enough money to buy food. So I sat in the New York Public Library and had visions. They say hunger is good for the soul. I wonder. After the first strong desire for food, all your tactile reactions harden and become leaden weights in the bottom of your stomach.

Your bowels feel hot along the edges and seem to be fused thermally to the largest intestine. Augmented pressures above the eyes cause you to furrow your brows; the headache, unlike any you have ever known, works dead center in the middle of the skull. It is not unlike being drunk but far more sinister as the landscape becomes a sound and swoops in and away, in and away. Delirious thoughts scamper across your hands supposedly busy at a yellow writing tablet and you write with the ease and flow of an Egyptian scribe. A sweat, which at other times would be refreshing, refuses to dry on your skin. It is not altogether oppressive. You feel the heat at exposed parts of your mind, not with the whole of your warm body, as is usual. The eyes are hard to focus. The tendency is to think you want to fall asleep but some hidden, allusive irritation keeps you awake. You peer at the clock and it is quite a long time before you can conceptualize about the hour of the day. Only thirty minutes since you came in — it seems like half a day. Then you feel, suddenly, too heavy and lassitudinous to be irritated. Periodically, a burning sensation inhabits the throat and you yawn though you are not sleepy. You write a note to the girl down the table and notice, without involvement, her eyes go wide in puzzlement going into fright. Hurriedly, staring, she packs up her books and flees. You retrieve the note. It is incoherent, a covey of inky squiggles. Idly you wonder if she will call an attendant.

Hunger . . .

I have always considered that I never took up a scholar's vocation because of the peculiar muskiness of the sexual fantasies which assail me in libraries. In the late afternoon I went down into Brooklyn Heights, Cranberry Street, to visit with a man, B., who had for many years been economic affairs editor of *The Daily Worker*. We sat around until the evening talking about things, mainly the party, from which he had quietly resigned a few years ago. He was working on a book expounding a new thesis of "colloidal boom" to explain why the American economy had not suffered the periodic depressions we used to forecast. He was a civil, bespectacled man with a son and daughter in school, a 21-inch television set and a talkative wife. Looking at him you wouldn't think that he had just missed out being prosecuted on a charge of Soviet espionage. In its indictment the government had tried to prove that when B. was in Indochina he had been carrying messages from the French Communist party to the Chinese Communist party. (The indictment was thrown out of court.)

B. had been a party member all his life and had gone to school with my friend John Alston, whom I was still undecided about whether to see. B. was a solid rather than a brilliant scholar and had what people like to call a first-rate mind. For years he had had in the party a reputation as a friend of the malcontents and heretics although this rarely showed itself in his daily column on economic affairs. Nobody in the party now spoke to him, and few people outside, because when he quit he did not repudiate. His wife was very unforgiving. Unlike B., she had been expelled from the party last year for "white chauvinism," arising out of an incident at a dinner party where she had refused to give up her seat to a drunken Negro. She told me the story in their front room in considerable and voluble detail, while B. squirmed. When she went into the kitchen to make dinner, B. said, "Poor woman, she can never understand that they got at me through her." I said, But it's all over now. He said, "Even when it's over sometimes it's the only thing you have . . ." He did, however, receive a few compensations by way of humor, he said. Last week, on the very day that Earl Browder (former deposed head of the CPUSA) made a pilgrimage to the office of his one-time arch enemy and chairman of the SPUSA, Norman Thomas, my friend B. was invited out to an expensive lunch by the *New York Times* anti-Soviet expert and asked if he wanted to take a job on the *Times*. "I may yet, I may yet," B. mused.

B. spoke at length about the past and future of the Communist Party. His analysis of past "mistakes" was, I thought, to the point but he could not bring himself to believe the party was a completely dead duck. He agreed with me that the existence of a militantly Marxistic organization, however small, or strategically unimportant, was one guarantee of that tautness in a nation's political life without which a certain political (i.e., moral) erosion was almost inevitable. That was why, he said, he had fought in the past few years for a reversal of party policy on basic doctrine. B. went up to the attic of his flat and brought down carbon copies of letters which he had written to the party leadership. I read them quickly and found them sober and prophetic. B. had been a prophet, but none had known this. I took him to task for not having publicly stated his position much earlier. He replied that to have done so would have canceled his effectiveness vis-à-vis the party leadership, and then he smiled heavily, and said, "I see your point." I asked him what reception his views had had, and he said a very bad one. The official operating leadership — William Foster, Betty Gannet and Pettis Perry — had rejected outright his thesis that the party systematically and hysterically overestimated the "war danger." The younger, "underground" leadership was more sympathetic but communicated its view that "the present danger" was no time to rock the boat. I said, I've heard that somewhere before. B. shrugged. I pressed him for reasons why, with all his influence and prestige, he had failed to strike a spark of response among the Communist hierarchy towards a more realistic and American policy. Was it, I suggested, Soviet influence? No, he said wearily, he doubted it. Then? He pushed his long, aristocratic fingers through his thick gray hair and said, "Oh, you know, the thing that has been dogging us all our lives, a failure of guts."

We sat in silence for some moments. Then he brightened and leaned over to switch on the television set. B.'s wife came in and said, "God how I hate television; B. practically sleeps with it." B. sat back happily and he and I, while his wife grumped back into the kitchen, watched a police drama. Several times during the program B. remarked quietly, "Interesting, isn't it?" Over dinner, which I half ate, B.'s wife said, "It's his way of coming back into the world." B. reached across and patted his wife's hand. "She thinks I'm overdoing it," he said. "Perhaps I am."

Early evening when I left B.'s house. It was a nice night, not too cold, and I walked down to the Battery with the idea of taking a ride on the ferry. But I didn't, and got into a subway going uptown. The subway train wasn't crowded, there were only a few people in my car as we swayed and roared up towards 14th Street. After the doors shut at 14th Street, I heard music. A thin, high screeching. "Blue Skies," after a fashion. A man came through the door at the far end of the coach. He was a tramp, a beggar, in an old tentlike patched coat, wearing dark, green glasses and holding his head at an angle while he steadily played "Blue Skies" on a shining tenor saxophone. He began to move towards the center of the car. The few occupants stared at each other in embarrassment. An old Puerto Rican lady leaned forward and dropped a coin in the beggar's cup. I hated that old beggar and decided not to give him anything. I almost got up and walked into another car when, at 19th Street, I almost banged my head against the window with my fist. The saxophone had multiplied itself. Another man, a second beggar, had appeared at the opposite end of the car. He closed the door. Now both turned to face each other and almost simultaneously gave forth a blast. The first beggar went on, the second stopped, not so much in bewilderment as in wrath. Then he too took up a tune.

Both musical beggars did not advance but stood their ground and began blasting at each other, trying to get the other to retreat and disappear in defeat. "Blue Skies" versus "Roses of Picardy." Blue Skies was not too old, with no edges to him, any type of body under that great coat and a head cocked in angry, querulous protest at the ceiling of the subway train swaying and rocking and rushing up towards Harlem. Roses of Picardy was much smaller, neatly dressed, and with a large wooden sign hung around his neck: Blind Please.

They stood there. And then they began to screech. Not blow awkwardly but swell out their unshaven faces as though trying to blow one or the other out the door. My fellow passengers were drawn up, metaphorically speaking, in fetal positions of fright and withdrawal. One woman got up and brushed past Roses of Picardy to the next car. The sound of the two saxophones had penetrated, and passengers from the coaches at both ends were beginning to stand up and see what was wrong in our car. Then Blue Skies began to move forward, back in the melody again. Roses of Picardy screamed and stood his ground, but as soon as he heard (or possibly saw) the other man's music coming nearer he, too, though evidently with less eagerness, began shuffling and stepping forward. They were equidistant from the metal pole in the center of the aisle. Nobody got up to leave. They were not playing, the two beggars, in any kind of counterpoint. Roses of Picardy began making waving motions with one hand, as though to warn Blue Skies or the other passengers. They advanced upon each other, grumbling, hawking, hooting. The train was an express from 72nd Street. I knew what I should have done. I should have gone up to one of them and dropped a large coin into his cup and said, Now look, be a good fella, stop playing or go back the way you came, I'll lead you. I just sat there, with maggots crawling around inside my guts. I know it sounds crazy, but as soon as those two beggars came into the car I knew they were my shadows, my doppelgangers. I didn't want to find out what would happen when they met in the middle of the car. But they did meet, and before the train stopped at 125th Street. They came together exactly in the middle of the car where the metal pole separated them. They were blowing into each other's ear. They had arranged their faces so that at any last moment they could smile and side-step each other. Instead of lashing out at each other at the moment of contact they both put a hand out to the metal pole. Then they stopped playing. The car was noisy, full of hot, rushing gritty air. My eardrums pounded. The saxophonists leaned against the metal pole as the train roared into the 125th Street station. They leaned in attitudes of languorous exhaustion, mute. The doors slid open and I bolted. I hit the wrong turnstile and almost split my stomach open.

Up on the street, at 125th Street and Lenox Avenue, I walked around in the night. I couldn't clear my head. What were the two beggars doing? Fighting? Had they turned on the passengers? Committed suicide? Or, were they twined around the metal pole playing a duet in perfect two-part harmony? I started to walk south, towards Chelsea.

On 84th Street and Lexington Avenue I sit down on a bus bench. Almost as soon as I do a Negro woman in a shabby red coat with a dirty gray fur collar lurches furiously along the street in front of my eyes. The children pay no heed, the delivery boys speed by on their bicycles. The woman crashes to the sidewalk and lies completely unconscious, her body lying in an attitude of unmistakable pain. Later, you are to discover she is drunk, but now she is bleeding and her glasses are broken and one arm flops over the curbstone. The people around her, and me, stop in their activities: the doorman of an apartment building gazes across to where she lies, the children stand up in their tricycle saddles, a passer-by half turns, inspects her curiously and passes by. A woman carrying groceries sits down on the bench. I say, No one will stoop down to see if she is still living, to bind her once more to the human race. The woman on the bench says, "Ah, she's a drunkard, I'm sure someone's phoning right now." I say, Jesus Christ, and the woman moves over to the far edge of the bench and begins to look up Lexington for the bus. It is, I say, a phenomenon of a society becoming increasingly dehumanized, desensitized, a society which is losing the thread of nerve, which is deadening its own ganglia, that synapses the eye and the heart, which is paralyzing its own apparatus of stimuli, transmission and human response. The woman with the groceries gets up and walks away.

She lies there, and no one will help. No one. Not me. There is something terrifyingly normal and sane in all this: the normalization of insanity, of inhumanity. After a few moments, she rouses, sits up on the curb. She cleans off her blood, looks unintelligently at her split glass frames. She rises and stumbles off. I wait on the bench. The buses stop. But the woman with the groceries was a prophet. Twenty minutes later a police car pulls up and finds nothing. The two police look irritated.

Near Jessica's I stopped off at a bar on Sixth Avenue and 15th Street. I had a beer and while chatting with the man next to me about whether or not Don Newcombe really was a choke-up guy in the late innings of a game, I fainted to the floor. When I came to, the bartender, a woman and her husband and a policeman were bending over me. I thanked them and walked slowly around the corner and upstairs to Jessica's flat. It had started again . . .

I lay in bed in Jessica's place for the next two days and nights, too weak and frightened to go out. Tad and Hilda phoned, but I let them go off to Atlanta without seeing them. I put in a call to the VA mental hospital in Wyoming, but canceled it. I gathered together all the readable books in the flat in a heap next to my bed and read through them until, exhausted and eye-sore, I could drop off to sleep. The shades were drawn all day, and day was not much different from night. Before, I had never really liked Thomas Wolfe but now I devoured his books, all of which Jessica owned. As I did not like Whitman I found much of Wolfe repulsive, but I knew I could write in no other tradition. And one other. Not that of Debs, Donnelly and Haywood, but Reed, London and Darrow. Once during this dark period I phoned someone I knew for a "fix" but did not go out of bed to answer the door when he came and knocked and stood outside, quietly swearing. The phone rang, several times, I did not answer it. On the evening of the first day

I put a bottle of White Horse to my lips as I lay on the bed and drank half of it almost without stopping to breathe. It knocked me unconscious. On the evening of the second day I picked up the telephone when it rang at 11 P.M.

It was the managing director of the publishing firm in Boston, to whom I had been briefly introduced. He apologized for breaking into my sleep and said he had tried several times to get me earlier. He said that it had been decided to award me the Writing Fellowship for that year. I thanked him, said I would fly up to Boston for the signing of contracts, hung up, and lay in bed in the dark room and tried to let the words register. After a while, I turned on the lamp next to the bed and using the heap of books to write on I sat up and made out a will. When morning broke I pulled back the shades to let in the new light. I went downstairs, bought some stamps from a machine next to the bar in which I had fainted, and mailed the will to my bank in Beverly Hills, California. It was a bright clear autumn day, with a cold stiff breeze sweeping over the streets just beginning to fill with workers, not yet hurrying to their offices and shops. Then I went back to the flat, packed a bag and took the train, not a plane, to Boston.

In Boston, I signed a contract for the Fellowship and was taken out by the head of the publishing house. The lunch was at his club. As often happens when I am in august surroundings (the waiters are seventy, the wine unlabeled) I felt like a gangly West Side boy and drank a great deal to counteract this. I liked my host and enormously enjoyed being flattered and told that I was a brilliant and promising writer. I did not, of course, believe this. Nor did I tell him that, for all practical purposes, the outline of the novel had been wiped as clean from my head as though it were nothing but chalk dust and the past few days a wet rag. I also, inexplicably, went a little berserk. I *had* to explain to this gentleman what it was all about (he was a proper, cultured Bostonian): I tried to make him see what had happened to our generation, a subgeneration really, and why so many of us had ended up, or were about to do so, in suicide, breakdown or its equivalent in the suburbs. I think he was trying to understand, but he kept saying "Well, I don't know, not too many of my friends have had mental difficulties." So what could I do except try to *prove* that his closest friends were in terrible shape? The afternoon, mainly owing to his tact (*Boston* tact), passed off better than might be expected, and we walked in the Common and discussed pigeons, which he fancied, and Ezra Pound, whom he published. He also told me about Ross Lockridge. This scared me badly.

I went back to the office and met the advertising staff and everyone told me what a fine fellow I was, and the managing director and Mrs. Quinn sat with me in her office and discussed the book. The trouble was, they did not tell me what they wanted, and I did not tell them that I had forgotten it. Finally, one of the publishing house girls took me home with her in the company of a traveling representative and another girl, and we stayed up late drinking wine. But I boasted so much the young traveling rep stalked away, and I had a picture of myself as a blow-hard. I do not remember much of that night. The rich food of the club after a couple of days of not eating, and the wine, went to my head. I traveled out to a bar I knew in Scollay Square where I met an Irish girl who took me home to tell me her troubles. We had a terrific drunken fight over religion, and some time around dawn I went over to Cambridge and called on my friends Gus and Olga. I took them out to breakfast to celebrate my good luck, and then had lunch with P., a Harvard economist, then under indictment by the State of New Hampshire for subversive doctrine. I grabbed his lapel over lunch and shouted, Who's going to take over? Answer me that! He was a handsome, courtly fellow, and he disengaged himself from me coolly: "Nobody. Nobody's going to take over. There's nothing left to take over." I went back down to New York that night.

When I arrived in New York it was as though Boston had been a dream. I did not know what it meant. I immediately made for the Public Library and spent the hour before closing writing furiously on my large yellow tablet. Then I walked back to the flat. Suddenly, walking down the street, I became full of the absolute beauty of myself in the world, and I longed to have a future. Unfair, I felt like crying out. It was unfair. There was so much I *liked doing*, and I resented, bitterly resented, as unjust, this heavy dry cloud that hung over my head. For the first time in my life I knew what the blind and crippled must feel. I could not console myself that it made me feel better. It did not. I did not wish to make common cause with them. I just wanted to live.

I was in such a state of excitement and exaltation that, with the tablet under my arm, I ran slowly down to the Battery and back, to tire myself out.

I awoke to a fantastic autumn morning. Cold and sharp. Somewhere behind me Tad and Hilda had gone to Atlanta, and Julia and Maurice had left for Paris, and I was in New York. I walked down 42nd Street in the late morning. The cinemas were starting to open, and the creeps and midday shoppers were crowding the sidewalk. Violence was thick under the surface. Men and women walked the streets muttering to themselves. One old man dogged my steps, saying, "I learned . . . oh yes, I learned." With the cripples and disjointed ones all over the place I was almost happy for the loonies. My hunger for women sometimes made me feel as I were taking leave of my senses. I went back to the Public Library and sat down in the West Reading Room. Hiram Sverdlov, in whose flat I had rented a room in Detroit and who had played his parlor organ at three in the morning while completing his biography of the poet Hood, was now Chief Assistant to the Media Director of one of the largest television agencies, offices half a block south of the Library. But I didn't look him up. I realized now I didn't like Hiram. The fact was, I disliked the hell out of him. The more I thought about it, the more I saw how much the Left had become a haven for nay-sayers.

Sitting in the Library I was immensely exalted by the women there. There was a girl at the next table. If only, I thought, there were a tiny radio in all our hearts to send out signals and wait for answering signals from the also-hungry. I was so excited by everything, I left the Library and walked all around the garment district, and wanted to shout, Writer! . . . I am a . . . writer!

And just then I watched a child die. On 28th Street. The day was still cold and sharp, the air milky, and the child wore knickers and an old wool cap and he was dark and ran swiftly and low on the ground in his black and white gym sneakers. He slid off the back of the big garment truck as it stopped for the light on Seventh Avenue, and he ran behind a Cadillac sitting in front of an expensive restaurant. One or two people walking past the restaurant noticed him, and slowed momentarily, wishing him ill or good luck I did not know. The traffic light flashed green and the boy darted out into the street and grabbed the guard grates on the truck's rear. As the truck slowly lumbered away, the boy found difficulty heaving onto the tailgate, and succeeded only in sliding one leg aboard. Suddenly the truck swung around the corner where I was standing, thinking my God I am a writer now, not fast, but heavily, and the boy's leg slipped off the grate and he hung on as the truck rounded the corner and then the boy was swept away from the truck, striking the cobblestoned surface about twenty feet from where I stood near the awning of another expensive restaurant guarded by a liveried doorman, and he was crushed by the bus whose driver had no idea of the existence of the child. The screams from the watching women were slow in coming.

I watched. A crowd gathered. The boy was swallowed in figures. When it became apparent that I was interested and not horrified I began to shake. As soon as I could, I walked away. I walked for a long time, and in the afternoon I was on 54th Street near Park Avenue. I sat on the stoop and looked at a white, four-story house across the street. The stone ledges on the house were all done in a bright maroon, which was probably Hector Loomer's idea. I sat there for I don't know how long. That was the house where I had learned. It was where John Alston lived with his new wife. For some reason the first thing that came to my mind was the trip south that John Alston and I had made, at the end of which John had told his wife, my friend, Rhea, that he wanted another woman. I had done the driving most of the way. It had been the last time John and I were to be together. He had said that he wanted me as a buffer between himself and Rhea in front of the children, and I had gone with him as an act of friendship. John had not usually been so frank with me.

I remember we left New York on June 6, the anniversary of D-Day, which was also the day when the Air Corps had rejected me as a Pilot Officer cadet because one eye was ten points off. That day I had not been able to restrain a certain tragic gaiety, until I went downstairs to the street and saw the headlines about the invasion of France. The people in the streets had been elated, and I had felt utterly miserable because I thought I was now out of it.

I told John about this as we were leaving New York for the South, and he had said, That was your lucky day. If you'd passed your exam you'd never have met me. He meant it partly as a joke, but I knew the part he wanted me to take seriously. It was a kind of a plea (John never could make up his mind which was which), to back him up to the hilt on whatever he was about to do. I knew I wouldn't, not this trip, and that it meant the end of us. I knew that somewhere down South, because I would not take his side, I would lose a brother and a father.

Getting out of New York was sad. I did most of the driving because of John's bad arm. We were in his new woman's Chrysler station wagon. Leaving New York, even temporarily, gave us both a sense of despondency, of friends slighted, and tasks left undone. At night, about eleven, the city is solemn and calm, not unyielding as in the hot rushed afternoons . . .

The white stoops of Baltimore dim in the night . . . The trucks darting in and out of traffic lanes, handled like heavy, agile birds . . . The two people in the car, the man and the youth, pass the time and tell old stories and reminisce, and exchange old enthusiasms . . .

Conversation overheard in a Richmond, Virginia, washroom: "How you know it's so good?" "I tried it. Had the scabies. Got it off some damn nigger on a streetcar. It's a sort of parasite. But you have to be careful how you apply it — don't get it next to your balls or they burn right up. Oo, burns bad . . ."

Through Washington with its noisy memories of V-J Day, of the Judge's room. Chickie married an MP and has a child; Dennis has two children and is an assistant scoutmaster. In the early morning haze the capitol buildings appear deserted and ponderously dreamlike.

In the South now — the Negroes are different — furtive and self-contained. Sign: "Jack's Colored Tourist." Frank and subtle, just a friendly warning to the visiting northern man of color.

Jumbled red remains of dead dogs and chickens on the hot asphalt.

After the tidy gentility of Maryland and Virginia — the side which the South presents to the North — into the real South, the Deep South; alfalfa fields in the hazed sun, wrecked shacks and hardened, fearful farmers. It is so strange. After all the talk and donations and editorials — to come down here again and find the outwardly placid atmosphere, the blanket of custom, it stifles, the Natural Fascism.

And the slowly rolling thunder of multi-engined warplanes, two years after Korea.

Bennetsville, South Carolina — AA booklet says, "has charm." No. Just a more quaint aspect of the ancient, hideous ornamented stupefaction. Colonnades and Coke. Youths lounge about sidewalk in front of drugstore with restless, flushed and incredibly vacant faces. Most amazing — the Negroes adjust to it. No hint of violence in relationships between Negro and white man. Each has his role. The Negro must work. The white must supervise and see to it, including applications of kindnesses, that the Negro works and within this framework the Negro is "left alone." John Alston and I have the first quarrel. It is over a cow. I hit the cow during the night.

Old matriarch with elephantiasis of the lower limbs sitting on her porch, her slender babyfaced daughter reading the comics to her. Sixteen-year-old girl in the white dress, moving about the café with the assurance of a woman, Jesup, Georgia.

Mill village in Georgia; the whites, gray and primeval, living in stilted shacks; fifty yards away, separated by a stand of gum trees, the Negroes live, in duplicate circumstances. Separate but Equal.

New York City, life as I know it, is a world away from the Deep South. No relation to their lives. How connect the acoustics engineer living and working in that crowded corner, New York, and the poor-white cracker draining turpentine from an old tree in a Georgia marsh. I ask this. John Alston replies, harshly, "You'll learn in time not to try."

The horror is the Georgia "cracker." Depravity rigid.

The South is a man's world. Southern women therefore more brutal to Negroes in administering code. Women all look drained of sex, men fearful of manhood.

Turkey buzzards alighting on the road, wings flapping with hideous slowness, long soft neck straining forward.

And then the visit to John's wife, maintained in exile. In a cottage off the quartz-blue Gulf beach, John and I play with the small son while the wife sits on the chintz-covered couch, smoking steadily and wondering when John will bring up a divorce. But, at the last moment, he has lost his courage and uses you as a buffer. Your own position is intolerable. Back in New York, in the lengthy discussions on life and marital strategy, at which occasionally the other woman was present, John's wife, Rhea, whom you had not seen since Detroit, was a cipher, an obstacle to be circumvented, somebody who stood in the way of John's happiness. But down here, on the beach, meeting Rhea again, Rhea the Detroit wife, you remember she is a good woman, one of the best, and you feel sad and contemptible because friendship betrayed you into helping shield John from the consequences of his broken marriage, and all the truths are in the air. The fear of the coming break, the prospect of an old age in loneliness is in Rhea's eyes. You leave one morning.

John is on the beach waiting as you walk dripping out of the Gulf, in the morning. I'm going back to New York, John. Suddenly he is absolutely frightened. His face goes white. Oh yeah? he sneers. Hearing himself, he puts on an adult grin and says, Some pal. Later, on the highway, outside the cottage, before Rhea or the kids are up, you lift your thumb. John runs out, his unknit arm swinging awkwardly, and says, Here's some money, take a plane. No. John puts his hand on your shoulder and says, Hey old boy, you're still on my side in this thing, aren't you? And the thing you have feared all these years does happen. Your friendship with John Alston has gone. It is a dead thing now, suddenly inert and showing its white belly. You say, Sure, John, sure sure sure.

You go into town to get the bus for New York. Inside the terminal you head for the washroom. It says White Men, and you hesitate, startled, and a fearful thought strikes you — are you a white man? Yes, you are relieved, you are, and walk in.

Negro porter in the bus terminal treating you with the smooth assurance of the defeated.

A woman gets on the bus and sits down in the seat next to yours. You go up to Raleigh together. Night closes in, you turn to her. She smiles, her gold teeth hardly visible in the dimmed interior light of the bus. She puts her hand between your legs and leaves it there until the morning. Above you, standing in the aisle, an Air Corps sergeant with no pupil in his left eye and a haggard wife.

They do not speak to each other during the trip. Near midnight, you suddenly look to the back of the bus. Negro infantry sergeant, silent and sullen, refusing to answer your eyes.

The bus relaxes and becomes neighborly as destination nears. We didn't know we would like the bus driver who took over at Baltimore. But he is all right.

I got up from the stoop and brushed myself off, crossing 54th Street . . . I rang the basement bell because I knew if anyone was home they would be in the glass-enclosed garden out back. I was about to turn away when the door opened. It was Doorie, the hulking Negro nanny. She looked at me strangely a moment. I said, Hello, Doorie, and when she didn't register I clapped my hand over my mouth and bellowed like an Indian. That broke up Doorie, she remembered. In the old days, when I worked for the recording company upstairs, she and I used to steal away to her attic to listen to her collection of old 78's. For some reason whenever Woodie Herman's "Cherokee" came on, we used to sit around the gramophone and quietly go Woo-wa, woo-wa. It doesn't sound like it in print but we thought that was very funny and jivy.

Doorie shook my hand vigorously, which it was her custom to do with everyone from delivery boys to her own husband, whom she had been in the business of divorcing when I knew her. She led me through the spotless, stainless-steel kitchen, chuckling ruefully and shaking her head and saying over and over again, Woo-wa, woo-wa. "They're all in there," Doorie said, at the steps leading down from the kitchen to the enormous sunken living room. I said, Let me go in alone, I want to surprise them. Doorie smiled affectionately and went back to cutting up some chicken in the kitchen. Doorie was built like a football halfback, wasn't too intelligent and sometimes acted as though Emancipation had never been proclaimed. I remember once encountering her on a Lenox Avenue subway train and trying to get her to join NAACP. She wouldn't talk to me for days after that.

As I walked through the living room I noticed it had three television sets, one ordinary, one color and one with all sorts of gadgets around and on top of it, making it look like a radar set. That would be John's set, I thought. I could see past the glass wall into the enclosed garden that there were people out there. I felt queer and suddenly remembered a remark John had made to me shortly before I left Washington for Germany. And above all, he had told me, never even think of dying for a cause; it is the mark of the slob.

I paused on the threshold, glad that I had remembered to wear a suit. Antonia, slumped petitely in a canvas chair, smiled at me, and said, "What a surprise, how nice to see you." One thing about Antonia, you never could surprise or throw her. Hello, Antonia, I said, it's nice to see you too. A man in terrycloth T-shirt and shorts with an arm held slightly high and crooked was standing on a board balanced on a small metal barrel in the corner of the glass-encased garden. He started to jiggle violently from one side to the other and fell off. "Well, old pal," he said. It was John Alston. He came over to shake my hand. I swear he looked pleased to see me. But I didn't kid myself. I knew as soon as his mind started calculating he wouldn't be so pleased.

There were two other people in the room, and like John they were wearing shorts. The garden was centrally heated. They were a man and a wife, a gossip columnist team whom I had once seen on their television program. They both looked much older and faded than I remembered from TV.

Antonia looked confused about my being there, but John climbed off his toy barrel and said enthusiastically, with the kind of shy, phony enthusiasm I knew so well, "Hey, lookie here, waw buddy, a new way to reduce, you could use it." And he climbed back up on this board and started swaying and balancing all over it. Antonia was embarrassed. The TV couple laughed. John counted breathlessly, forty-eight, forty-nine . . . fifty and jumped off, smiling and sweating. I wished to hell I hadn't come. Doorie came in and said to Antonia, "The gun men are here." Antonia got up quickly and said, "Oh let me take care of them, John," and left the garden. I knew she wanted a little time to figure out how to deal with me. As she left she gave me a little, frightened smile. I felt like saying, The time when you had to worry about any such thing is long past and that is our mutual sadness, kiddo. It must have been like that, I thought, with my father and mother, my mother tensing up when, every year or two, union organizers from New York would drop into the house, not to suggest anything at first but just to say hello, and my mother knowing that after they went my dad would soon follow. But if I didn't know it before, I knew it by what John now said, he wouldn't be budged, not even if I offered him on a silver plate a chance to save the world.

"Going huntin', old son," he called, although he could have spoken normally if he wanted. "B'ar huntin', Jackson Hole, in the Tetons." He was using an exaggerated mountain-man twang, and the TV couple looked at him curiously. So did I. John said, deliberately, "I got a hunting lodge up there. Want to come along?" He stared at me with an aggressive grin. I said, I'm going away, John. "Where to?" he said. Europe, probably, I said. "It's about time," he said and poured everyone a drink. I don't want a drink, I said, I just came by to say hello. "Sure," he said, "sit down, relax, take a load off. I'll help Tony with the guns," and he left the room.

The man of the TV couple said, "Come on out and let us show you the tomatoes." I went with them into a glassed-in corridor where boxes of things were growing. "Chemical fertilizer," said the man. "It's the only thing. Here, look at this." He showed me onions and flowers and various vegetables. The wife sat in the sunken living room drinking. "Are you interested in chemical fertilizers?" asked the TV man. No, I said. We went back into the room.

The TV man explained at considerable length that John and Antonia had turned their entire indoor garden to experimenting with chemical fertilizer. I figured that was John's newest kick. When I had last seen him it was skiing, and before that trying to get sponsors for a filmed version of the *Upanishad*. Chemical fertilizer on 54th Street. Jesus Christ.

I said, Where's Hector Loomer? and they said, "Who's Hector Loomer?" Well, that took care of Hector. I wondered if he had been fired or just had wandered off one day and not returned. Hector and I had not been exactly great friends but he did teach me to cook. I remembered the day Antonia's husband broke down the door. We, the recording company, were all upstairs, on the third floor, with the sound equipment and RCA mikes and turntables that Norbert, Antonia's husband, had hated so much. John said, Go on down there and clean him up, kid. I said, For Chrissake,

John, he's in as good a shape as I am. He may have a gun, Charlotte said. Why do you people have to have such corrupt lives, Arturo had screamed, in a perfect fright. John had insisted, You can take care of him, kid, remember West Allis? West Allis had been the place where John and I had been sent during an eleven-month strike and where John had broken his arm. A cop had fallen off his horse when the pickets threw ball bearings under him, and he had grabbed me. I had socked him and run and after that John was always telling people what a tough guy I was. That was one of the things I didn't like about John, he was always trying to make me out tougher and smarter than I was, and when I didn't live up to advance billing he would go off into a kind of sulk, like an old man whose son had failed to make the varsity.

I suddenly vividly remembered that afternoon. It was strange to see the record company in physical panic after the months of slow, cumulative hysteria. We all knew Norbert was coming, and none of us knew what to do about it. Antonia was somewhere downstairs in a sedated sleep. John knew what was expected of him, and so he stayed calm, like a hero before the battle when all the cameras are on him. Myself, I didn't feel heroic. Adrenalin pumped into my blood channels, I felt high, the nerve at my Adam's apple pulsed sharply. A ponderous, undulating urgency built up in the house as preparations were made to meet the crisis. Charlotte went around the room stowing away delicate sound heads and recording equipment. John draped the old phonograph cylinders in white canvas, not because he gave a damn but to have something to do. He was waiting for something to happen and then he would be all right. Arturo was off in a corner sketching furiously one of his gigantic crayon butterflies, and Hector Loomer, fat and mustached Hector, was running upstairs and downstairs, calling out from below, He's not here yet. Nobody knew what to do. At almost the peak of excitement, when decisions seemed hopelessly compromised in a paralytic tangle of indecision, the violence occurred. Hector was upstairs with us and suddenly we heard the glass in the front door crash and tinkle. The door had been locked against Norbert. Tension upstairs flooded up and over a queer plateau. My blood was pounding. John was sitting on a table, smoking calmly. I winked over at him and he smiled. I was now ready to take Norbert if that was required. Everyone's actions seemed to slow down after the sound of tinkling glass downstairs had died away, no decision was reached, conversation was dreamlike. Charlotte, trembling, said to John: What's Rhea going to do? John: It'll work out. How's your mother? This from Arturo. Okay, she's not been good: John. Charlotte: What do you mean, good? John: She's a selfish woman. Hector, sharply: You never knew that before? You've been in the family as long as I have. Everyone turns to look at Hector, trying to fathom his statement. He looks back defiantly. Charlotte: The whole world's selfish. John: Sure. Nothing happened for five minutes. Then Hector went downstairs and soon the house was filled with sounds of small bits of glass being swept up. Hector ran upstairs and said, They're still down there, talking, something's gotta happen soon. We waited. Hector went downstairs after we heard the front door slam. He came back up to us. He said, You mean she didn't call the cops? What a shitface. Hector's bitterness was most acute; he had hated the husband for a long time. He shrugged his shoulders and went downstairs, muttering, I feel old again . . .

I remember thinking that there was something admirable about Norbert that day. One does not ordinarily think of fortune hunters as breaking down doors. I think even John, who was expecting the worst, had been surprised . . .

John came bounding back into the garden, proudly saying, "Antonia's choosing the guns." The TV man jerked his head to his wife, signaling her to join him at the far end of the artificial garden. John and I were left alone. Carrying his bad arm more aggressively than I remembered, John lit a cigarette out of a small silver case and offered me one. When I shook my head he said, "Don't you smoke?" I don't know why he felt he had to rub it in. I said, No, John, I don't smoke. I haven't smoked for years. "Oh yeah," he said, "that's right." He brightened. "Did you get a look at my experiments. I worked it out myself. A combination of glucose and sulfates, hey, isn't that genius." He led me to the TV couple and we all stared down at John's and Antonia's artificially cultivated onions and flowers.

John turned to me, in front of the other two, and said, "What have you been doing with yourself, old boy?" I said, One thing and another, mostly I've been out in Hollywood. (We hadn't written for some time.) "Make a million, ol' waw buddy?" he asked. No, I said. And then I told John I had been an agent. (I wanted to see his expression.) John said, "Well, man, you've really made out in the world." The awful thing was, he was not trying to be tactful. He was marveling. Just then Antonia came in, and I said, I've just been telling John I was a Hollywood agent. She looked at me in that brief, frightened way she had which always made me want to say, You've got five million dollars in Chase National, what have you got to be worried about? But, of course, I never said any such thing to Antonia. The truth was, I liked her. Our relationship was formal, touchy and distant. She thought I was a nice, confused man with probably not much of a future. It was unnatural that we had ever been thrown together, in work and in our personal lives. But there it was. I never could get over the hope that some day Antonia would leave me, say, $15,000. She had everyone else in her will, John, and John's sister, and Charlotte and Hector Loomer and probably even Arturo. But no, on reflection, I didn't think I was in Antonia's will. Still, you can't help having fantasies, even cruel and crass ones, when you know only one heiress in your life . . .

In my last term at college I received a telegram from John Alston saying that he and some friends were coming out to California. I had not seen John since Detroit. They came out, and that was when I first met Antonia, Arturo and Charlotte. John was still married to Rhea, although he was acting charming and possessive around Antonia, who was small and blond and wore a perpetually flinched look. I met them all at the Glendale station and took them to a hotel in Beverly Hills where I made a big deal out of dinner, hosting and ordering the wine. John beamed. He had taught me how to do things like that, even though we both knew I was showing off.

It was obvious from the start that John and I had not only grown apart but were inhabiting different worlds. I was not much interested in his, nor he in mine. I kept them all away from the campus but in the end John found out about the trouble I was in. I walked into their hotel one morning to find them all in the coffee shop reading the morning L.A. *Express*. I was on page one. The *mishigas* is far too complicated, and a little boring, to go into here. In its way the story was flattering. It made me responsible for virtually all the left-wing student activity on the west coast, hinted that I had been a union goon in Arizona and was something of a revolutionary soldier of fortune. If the story had appeared in an English newspaper I could have collected about four billion pounds libel damages. The headline ran: MURDER HINT IN RED PLOT AT UNIVERSITY.

What it was all about was that a student socialist had gassed himself in the basement of the Co-op Barracks, and his hysterical father had gone not to the police but a state un-American activities committee. Together with our Dean of Students, Larrimer, one of the very few people I have met who could safely and accurately be accused of compulsive machiavellianism, he concocted a public committee appearance before television cameras, before which Larrimer, without actually saying it in so many words (there *is*, after all, some kind of libel law), implied that for all practical purposes Communists ran student activities at my university and had "captured" the newspaper and various student boards. He, Larrimer, had even gone to the trouble of comparing column inches of space in the campus newspaper, before I became editor, and later. Apparently, under my editorship, leftish and liberal sentiments had 538 column inches more than conservative statements. This was surprising good news. The "angle" on the news story was the hysterical father's accusation that somehow or other the campus Reds had murdered his son or driven him to suicide. I never knew the boy. The eerie thing about this was that it was about the fifth suicide in as many months on campus, two of them socialists.

Well, anyway, this morning my picture and Dean Larrimer's testimony were on the *Express*'s front page. Charlotte was indifferent, but Arturo and Antonia looked up from their papers and coffee at me with surprise and a little respect. I was pleased at this. John folded his paper away, grimaced and said, Slob. He turned to the others and waved at me, Gratitude for you, he said. I send this kid to be polished at college and this is the kind of thing he spends his time doing. He swiveled around to me: I told you to keep your nose clean. I told John I had tried. (I had, too.) You could see he was both pleased and displeased.

Arturo and Antonia wanted to know what it was all about. Charlotte said, Leave the chap alone, he doesn't want to talk about it. (Actually, I did.) Anyway, said Arturo to Charlotte, you're a Trotskyite. Trotsky*ist*, Arturo, Charlotte reminded him. (It wasn't until shortly before I left Argus Records that Charlotte told me she and Arturo had lived together during the war.) They were a strange crew, all right, four deep-dyed New Yorkers in the sunny, placid forests of Los Angeles. They didn't belong here, in Beverly Hills, and I didn't belong with them. By now, I had learned why they were out here — to be presented with an Oscar for the sound track for a small, inexpensive film a charitable foundation had made called *Stuyvesant Street Blues*. The sound track was an Argus specialty, a sharply edited, beautifully modulated documentary of excerpts from dusty historical cylinders, street sounds patiently collected, live dialogue and secret conversation, art song and folk song, abstract sounds and a narration by an old farmer-poet backed by a specially commissioned chamber trio. The film had taken the Foundation six months to shoot; Argus took two years for the sound track. The company had been operating for several years on a modest scale, periodically issuing small volumes of spoken theater, modern poetry, far-out jazz, historical collections with modern music, and the kind of city folk music (Chicago hillbilly, East Los Angeles *canción*, Army songs, Detroit "dirty dozens") commercial companies and the Library of Congress had no time or interest for. Argus, by its existence, argued quietly against kitschcrap. *Stuyvesant Street Blues* had been their first ambitious and sustained project, which they had intended, as with all their "audio formations" as they called their recordings, to stand alone and only for small audiences, and it had made them all suddenly famous. I went with them to the Academy Award presentations, and took my girl, Cri Cri Viertel. Although Cri Cri and I had broken up by this time, I took her because I knew John would be impressed. Cri Cri was a star, more accurately, a starlet at this time, on the downgrade but only a few close personal friends knew that. John was, as I had expected, quietly impressed.

John and I weren't together much when he was in California. One night, it is true, we both went out to the suburb of Tarzana for a booze-up with old Dan Henry Humble, my friend and John's friend, from the —th Infantry. It wasn't such a nice time as you might think. We three sat around a small, dark bar in Tarzana and tried to put a good face on what we had been doing with ourselves since the Army. Dan Henry was president of the Ford local union but was about to go on staff as Assistant Regional Director and was sensitive about taking a pie-card job. John Alston was embarrassed about not being in the union any more and kept making awful jokes throughout the night about Dan Henry's new staff job. And I was not exactly proud of my record at the university. The night turned out uncomfortable for all of us, the jokes kept getting worse, and finally we broke it up, although I think we had intended keeping it going until dawn. On the way back into town in the new powder-blue station wagon he had rented, on Argus' money, John savaged Dan Henry, not for taking a staff job, but because Humble had refused to place himself in the succession for the International Executive Board of the union. I said, Dan Henry likes a peaceful life, he doesn't want to turn into a pork-chopping bastard. Crap, said John, he's getting yellow. I didn't argue the point. I think John wanted me to.

So John and his group took their award and went back to New York. I dropped into their hotel an hour before their train was due to leave, and John and I had a drink in his room. He said, mildly, Look me up when you come to New York. And that was that.

What I hadn't told John was that by this time I had been, more or less, kicked off the college paper and was studying film. I think now I didn't tell him because he might think I was interested in it because it was a cousin to his field. John being John, he probably would have seen it as some type of crazy, subtle triumph. As it turned out, I was glad I didn't tell him, because when I left college I thought I knew something about sound — and a day with Arturo and I knew nothing. Arturo could make you feel more ignorant by telling you how much you knew than anyone else in the business.

Probably, by the time I left college, I knew that sooner or later I would wind up working for Argus Records. For one thing, it was the best small record outfit in the field. But, also, I suppose, I knew John expected it of me. To tell the truth, I expected it of myself. It was inevitable that John and I would have a last go at friendship.

Well, after John and his crowd had gone I felt a sense of something having slipped through my fingers. It turned out to be fairly ignoble when I analyzed it later. John had obviously found himself a berth. I wanted one too.

As I've explained, the last semester at college was a quiet and good one. I was off the paper with nothing better to do than study, and I spent most of the time in the library with Jessica McMasters and the African, Kenneth Nkumba, and the rabbi, Manny. I had time to ask myself certain questions. Why, for example, when I discovered that this particular university was, for me, a fraud, and that there was no point, again for me, in the academic life, had I hung on? What had I found on the campus to keep me there three years? I had come to the university with no clear purpose, except a vague idea about "polishing" myself and then jumping back into the fray. But what fray? And where? The world of the factory, of the League and the union and of 2 A.M. meetings suddenly seemed very distant and small, too small to hold the formless dreams I now dreamt.

The week before my final exams I walked into the Dean's office, by no invitation. He was, as always, friendly and unctuous. I asked him straight out across his desk what my chances were if I applied to a graduate school. He smiled, clasped his hands behind his round, well-shaven head, leaned back and said, Don't. I smiled too. He really was a bastard. I asked him if there was an academic blacklist. He said, If requested by the deans of graduate schools, to supply an impartial opinion about the attitude of any individual student to his responsibilities, seen of course, in the wide social context, I would hardly have an alternative, put yourself in my place. (Those were his exact words.) As soon as my exams were over, I made my way to New York. I would be a writer . . .

For a month I did not contact Alston. I accepted an invitation from Rafe Hawes to come and live with him and the O'Haras and Lorenzos. Then I hung around the "slave markets," the employment agencies, one of which sent me to a junior executive's position with the William Morris agency. I got the job because I knew shorthand. It may impress you to know that, in my prime, I could type eighty words a minute, touch method, and take shorthand (Pitman) at one hundred w.p.m. How I got that way is less impressive . . .

The gang I was in before the Knights, the Christiana Street

Streeters, was caught *en masse* car stripping at the same time that the city of Chicago was conducting an experiment in social work "rehabilitation." Ordinarily those of us who were first offenders would have been let off on probation. But this time the Judge shuffled us off directly to a battery of social workers who, after having us submit to occupational tests, sent their reports in to the Judge who gave us our choice of going to the schools he recommended or three months in Montefiore Reformatory. (This experiment was short-circuited upon legal protest by the Chicago chapter of the Civil Liberties Union.) Only one of us, Teddie Shiffler, chose the reformatory because he already had a job waiting for him with his father's rug-cleaning firm. The rest of us were siphoned off to various technical, college prep and specialist high schools. Me, I was told I had an aptitude for business and was consequently dispatched to the McCormick Commercial High School, situated in the heart of the brothel and burlesque district of Chicago. I spent two years there and learned typing, shorthand and to detest business in all its forms. The principal of the school was a former LaSalle Street banker who regularly met one of his more voluptuous students in a bar on Harrison Street after school. (I know, because I began meeting the same girl, a little after this time, when we had the same clerical jobs in a local office.) If the object of the social workers was to keep me on the straight and narrow, they showed the customary lack of insight into how working-class communities operate. McCormick Commercial had about four hundred girls and twelve boys, three of us chosen from widely separated car-stripping gangs (none of the three knew this at the time, as we were busy trying to be respectable). Every afternoon, when I got back to Christiana Street, I had to endure cries of "Pansy" because I was going to a "girl's school." It goes without saying that I sought redress by plunging into what, I believe, is called, an "anti-social phase" and outdressing everyone on the block in the uniform of the period, pork-pie hat, satin shirt, peg pants, reat jacket. Zoot, man. But I digress. Again . . .

Finally, when I did call Alston, he was furious that I had not gotten in touch my first day in New York. Then he hired me on the spot to work for Argus Records. I knew, as he hired me, that he should have consulted with the other members of the company, but I also knew that it was his way of ensuring they would resent me and that he would have in me a ready-made ally with no causeways to anyone else.

After the series of defeats on the campus in California, which only in New York could I admit had stung, I felt taken care of in Argus, though it was I who did the taking care. Three years had passed since Detroit, and the Korean war was on.

It was a strange, mad, genius-stricken group, hipped on the unexpected success of their first film and planning a second audio story, this one on prison life. Arturo Mishkin, bald, timid, talented in too many directions, practically living with his psychoanalyst (also doing Arturo's two daughters and wife), was Argus's engineer and audio director. Whatever he touched, even when not looking, had a way of turning to art, high art. Charlotte Hughes, the archivist and editor, scared of not being young any longer, scared of a lot of things; a supreme craftsman and fiercely convinced of her own ineptitude. Tall, gaunt, ugly Charlotte who kept a bull fiddle in the studio as a way of draining down tension, and whose prime hobby was to haunt Spanish Harlem with a concealed tape recorder in her worn black suitcase, the suitcase with a hole in the side.

John Alston took care of the business side of Argus Records, which was paid for by Antonia, the millionairess, who also designed the record sleeves for the company. Although I had no evidence to go on, I was pretty sure that John had set his cap for Antonia. My reasoning in the matter was pretty shabby: I would have done the same in his shoes. She was pretty, she was vulnerable and bright, and she was very, very rich. Sooner or later, I knew, John would ask me to act as "cover" for him and Antonia, who was married to a muscular moron named Norbert, to whom she had given a plastics factory so he could have something to do during the day other than walking their jointly owned team of greyhounds on Park Avenue. I didn't much care for Norbert. Having married for money he was forever sensitive about it, and took it out by playing on a semi-pro football team in Queens.

Almost from the first, I was also used by Charlotte and her boyfriend, Lincoln Hudbetter. Linc was Negro, and younger than Charlotte who was obsessed with approaching middle age. She and Linc never went out without a white person as "cover." Charlotte was afraid, and Linc was a respectable middle-class Negro, and America is America. They should, perhaps, have married long before; they were afraid of that too. Linc was an industrial-relations psychiatrist in a suburban auto factory. He and I played stickball Sundays in Central Park. We used to go running around the Reservoir. He had a problem. He wanted children. But he didn't want them half white. The day he told me this, while we were lying on the grass after an early morning jog, I sat bolt up and said, Linc, you're a goddam reactionary. He said, with a sad, white-toothed grin, That I am, that I am.

For me this was a new milieu. Through Arturo and Charlotte, I came to know the world of the New York sound engineers, musicians and archivists, and on into the world of film documentary; where people really cared what they did with their work. I lived day and night for sound, watching Arturo at the mixing console by the hour and going home to Brooklyn to read Grierson on reality and Eisenstein on montage. It was an inbred, intense world whose inhabitants spent most of their lives in artificially ventilated control cubicles bent over a panel of knobs and switches and who rarely discussed technique among themselves and yet who lived by technique. Under Arturo's haphazard tutelage, I learned to mix and edit not with my brain or ears but with my fingertips. You can't mix with your brain, Arturo used to hum while running channels of tape from the console to the echo chamber and back again, you can't mix with your brain. Your guts, he said, your intestines, the dark corners of the small intestine, that's where you mix from.

In Detroit John had drawn the lines. I was to see everything just so long as he supervised the tour. In New York, this was no longer possible. I roamed freely. But there was another world, viewable from the equipment-cluttered rooms on the third floor of the mansion on 54th Street, and that was Antonia's world of eastern wealth, whose inner limits were strictly set between Beekman Place, Wall Street, Westchester and Hyannis (but with fast highways to Europe, art and public office). Because they were accepting her money, even as they gave her a niche of her own, a work to call her own, but accepting her money nonetheless, Arturo and Charlotte pretended that this world of Antonia's did not exist. Every morning they would come to the mansion and let themselves in by the back basement door and run upstairs past the first two family floors as though pursued by demons. Not once in all the time I worked with either did I hear them mention or refer to Antonia's "other" life.

Twice a month Antonia, a legal orphan, closeted herself with her financial adviser and for those two days Charlotte and Arturo were unaccountably beside themselves. Once, and only once, did I myself refer to Antonia's money, and that for the last time. One day a young novelist, who had just risen to best-seller status, came to the house and told a movie story about jazz, to Arturo, Charlotte, John and myself. He said that a studio was bidding for it but that he would like to produce the screenplay in collaboration with Argus Records. He said he would do this and named a price which by Hollywood standards was exceedingly modest. Charlotte immediately said that no, but thanks, the group couldn't afford it. I laughed. Arturo, Charlotte and John released cold glares on me and I never mentioned the subject again. Because, you see, despite Antonia's millions, the group liked to pretend that they were operating on a shoestring. After a while, they actually came to believe it. The sound track of *Stuyvesant Street Blues*, for example, was advertised as costing $18,000 and all over the world sound recordists and movie makers marveled. But when I saw the books it became obvious that the track had cost twice that — still no mean achievement but not $18,000. So, as I say, the one unshakeable convention was with reference to Antonia's money. The fact that they were all in the will probably had something to do with it too. The end-result was that Arturo and Charlotte avoided Antonia's "other" life ("the bottom," we got into the habit of saying, gesturing shortly with our thumbs down) like the plague. John didn't. He played his cards well. Slowly, carefully, so as not to rouse resentment or suspicion, he naturally revolved around the bottom of the house until he was at the center of it. Also it had something to do with the fact that somewhere along the line I think he fell in love with Antonia, well and hard.

Myself, I was fascinated by the way Antonia lived on the first few floors of the house. (We, Argus, had the third and fourth floors, back to front, with a ten-by-ten-foot glass-covered hole cut between the floors and a metal ladder in between for easy access. The third floor was, in effect, the control room where Arturo and Charlotte kept a bank of tape and recording machines, the pre-amplifiers, a "gram bank" of turntables and the control panel at which Arturo sat and worked. The fourth floor was a studio where we kept the mike booms, Charlotte's bull fiddle and echo chamber. Norbert had the attic, where he played on rainy days with a $5000 toy train set. Football and toy trains. Norbert.) Every now and then I saw Antonia going out to the theater or having East River Drive friends in for drinks. But John, who was in, wouldn't let me in. He said no. One day, without my having to ask, although he probably thought I would some day, John said, turning his thumb down, Verboten, kiddo, understand?

Possibly by way of compensation, John and Antonia picked out a mistress for me, a well-turned-out TV actress named Nadine, the young wife of a genial homosexual scene designer who enjoyed having dinner with us. It never failed to give me the creeps but I figured that as long as I was in New York I had to be a New Yorker.

I knew that Argus Records was sick. "Stuyvesant Street Blues" had won a special Academy Award, cabled compliments from Pudovkin, Chaplin and Cocteau, prizes at most of the film festivals. Nobody spoke of the visuals, which barely did their job; attention was riveted on Argus' sound track. It was the first American documentary of its type to bring in mass audiences. M-G-M offered the group a berth at its studio which the group did not even consider. (John did but was outvoted by Arturo and Charlotte with Antonia, as usual, passively acquiescent to the majority, for after all had they not saved her from a life of empty boredom?) And now they were frightened. Could they repeat? Charlotte and Arturo, John and Antonia, indisputably they had created a magnificent and touching production in sound; I swear this. Then, slowly, I watched them crumple. They hesitated, sulked, talked endlessly, cleaned equipment, interviewed writers, singers, musicians, old cowboys, did everything but choose a subject to record. They simply could not make up their minds. Months went by. Arturo, for want of something better to do, ordered whole libraries of prewar political broadcasts and recut them on his mixing panel, instructing me in his mock-humble Jewish-tailor voice as he went along. He decided to make the Duke of Windsor's abdication speech into a Dylan Thomas soliloquy, with a cool jazz background, and almost succeeded. Neuroses got quite out of hand. Petty spats developed, enveloped. Then, at last, recording began on a second documentary. It was the wrong one to make. The dialogue and "wild" sound were done in a prison and a mental institution. It was too close to the bone. It wasn't a good "formation." Not bad. But not good either. The group was watching itself too closely. If you are interested in real art, and how it is organized, and the vexing, possibly insoluble question of a collective art, this part of the story should be a cliffhanger. If not, too bad. But it is my belief, after all this elapsed time, that what bugged Argus was essentially an artistic and not a personal tension.

This second major production was too self-conscious, with a full orchestral score, a turgid use of echo chamber and an overly austere use of prisoners' dialogue. Issued as an album, its critical and public reception was polite, only. BBC, a few of the VHF education stations and some universities asked for copies. Sales were of course negligible. The group, all of us, turned in on each other, devouringly, accusingly, savagely, yet held together. The atmosphere in Antonia's place, on the upper two floors, the studio and control room, smelled thickly of the acrid fumes of disappointment, fatigue, the sourness of frustrated effort. A search for a third story was begun.

I wasn't living in the mansion. I was in Brooklyn and it was an antidote. Rafe Hawes, the cat-eyed young Mexican, had finally broken away from Alan Pick, and he and I were sharing his room in Brooklyn. Somewhere above, I have explained about the Lorenzos and O'Haras.

How long could it go on, the days of tension at Argus Records, the nights of laughter and argument with Rafe and the O'Haras and Lorenzos? Finally, Rafe went away with one of the Gowanus high-steel Indian youths to a job on the Al-Can highway. Without our saying so in so many words we agreed I had failed Rafe as a friend. It would be egocentric to say that Rafe went on the Al-Can because I shrank away from him that sunny afternoon in Central Park, but I cannot help being haunted and ridden by the belief that he would be a better man today if I had been then. It is not water under the bridge. It is a sense of low-key, permanent shock that lives with me. It is not something one asks forgiveness for, or rhapsodizes over, or even tries to turn into art. It is something you either live with or don't.

And then Rafe was gone. I was alone with the O'Haras and Lorenzos and it was different. Korea, McCarthy, the Smith Act trials; the house in Brooklyn was uneasy; after two FBI men came around, politely inquiring, the panic was on.

It was becoming impossible at Argus Records too. Having been gripped by fear and impotence of an entirely different order, they ceased making records and then even pretending to. Our days were filled with reading esoteric novels in the control room, going to the 42nd Street flea-pit movies, running off pornography to ease our boredom, and playing poker. Four times a week John and I played poker in his house out in Jackson Heights, while Rhea made sandwiches and I played with John's small son. The players were John, myself, Arturo, Charlotte, rarely Antonia, the man from across the hall and the man from upstairs (John lived in a housing project), and Linc Hudbetter. The poker games began to be expensive, and that was when I knew that things had started in earnest between John and Antonia. Raising the betting limit was John's way of showing nervousness.

One night, after the poker game, John and I drove along Bay Parkway in a long stretch of muteness. Then John said, All right, old boy, you're grown up now, Daddy has something to say. I said, I know what it is. He said, Are you sure? I said, Like you said, I'm grown up. We drove on, past the winking shore lights, in silence, until, suddenly, John slapped me on the back and burst out, She's terrific, isn't she? She's got *millions,* son!

As events developed, when John asked me to side with him I had to tell him then, as later, that I liked Rhea and had to stay out of it. The few times I did act as cover I felt lousy. I knew that sooner or later John would never forgive me for witnessing what was going on. I couldn't win in a situation like that, and we both knew it. To have gone along — the way I was feeling — would have been contemptible. Fighting him was betraying him. I tried to stay neutral. But not for long. For days something brewed between John and me. Argus was at the end of its blind alley, something neither

John nor I could help. We killed time. I reran some of the old pornos, remixed a section of the 1934 Nazi party rally in Nuremberg the way I thought Arturo might have, cutting in Bessie Smith, a wild track of Fred Astaire tap dancing and some stray female dialogue we had stored away in cans, and tried to write. John sat hunched up on a chair in a corner of the upstairs kitchen for hours at a time reading comic books and the *Wall Street Journal;* then, in a blundering, compelling rage he tried to provoke me by telling me how to court my new girl, a Bronx nurse named Barbie. That made it up and over, boys. Almost helplessly, I burst out at John and asked him how could he think to live on stocks and bonds, on the workers' blood. I'm afraid I used that phrase, the workers' blood. He didn't get angry, just gazed over at me mildly and said, When you've done something in the world, then criticize. That one really hurt. We had it out. I told John to clear out of Argus Records, it was watering his jizzem. John said, out of the blue, You'll never learn to love. It was that kind of argument . . .

So there we were today, on my way to Europe, John and Antonia and myself, and this TV personality couple, in the artificially fertilized artificially heated garden of the house. "A goddam agent," said John proudly. I knew what he was thinking: that I had learned to make my way during the Big Pause, the nonrevolutionary period, as had he. John had been like me, bred up for seditious leadership, fundamentally we didn't know anything else. And now this. A Hollywood agent and a kept man on his way to a Utah bear-hunting lodge.

Conversation in the garden lagged, then stopped. I must give it to this TV couple that they were embarrassed. John turned to them, the way he does, and said, pointing at me, "An old AVB-CIO buddy, we met in the Army." The TV couple nodded politely. John's voice rose a notch. "Tough old cob," he said. (I knew what was coming, all right.) "Once, up in Minnesota," he said, "we saw him knock a cop off his horse." I said, quietly, John, it was Wisconsin. "Yeah, that's right, Wisconsin," he said. He fell to loudly musing, "1947, the second round, we almost changed the world, didn't we, kid? Well, how's the old novel coming?"

I knew that had been coming too. It was approximately what he always said when he was at a loss. Speaking carefully and choosing my words, I said, Actually I think I just got a prize for it. "Hey," shouted John to Antonia, "did you hear that? Our boy's finally made it." He turned to me and said with absolute sincerity, "I think that's marvelous, boy." "So do I," said Antonia. "How about coming bear-hunting with us?" said John. A deadly chill came over all of us, and I thought, Oh what the hell, it's crazy to carry a grudge against your own folks. They did the best they could.

I said, No, thanks, but I had to go to Europe to write this book. "Hell, no," said John, "you come up to Wyoming and stay in the cabin all winter." "Yes," said Antonia weakly, "there's lots of room." I shook my head, feeling more discouraged than I can remember.

John got back on his slenderizing balancing board and began to gyrate wildly. He kept repeating, almost gibbering, "You stop this nonsense about Europe, everybody does it, and you come up to Wyoming with us." I said, John, get off that foolish thing and talk to me like a man.

The TV wife said quickly, "Pardon me, the ladies' wee-wee for me." Her husband sank back into the shrubbery with his drink. Antonia looked cold and stolid. John stepped off the balancing board, looking mildly surprised. He slowly drew his mouth back over his teeth in the kind of exaggerated grimace I had often seen him make at long union meetings when he was bored. He shrugged, then slumped his shoulders, as though to say, I've tried to get you to talk to me in the only way I can talk to anyone and now you're being your old priggish self.

I walked into the sunken living room and flopped into a huge, wine-red soft chair. John and Antonia came in after me. John poured her a drink and then one for himself, "You want anything?" he asked hoarsely. I shook my head. We were exhausted. The TV man seemed to have disappeared into thin air, though I assumed he was still somewhere among the shrubbery, as his wife was still among the plumbing. I looked around the room, at its deep black carpet, at the brown Olde English walls, at the two television sets and the one with John's radar gizmo on it, and I remembered that I had once liked this house very much . . .

There used to be days, when none of us could figure out where to go next, and nothing was about to happen, and everyone's neuroses were temporarily and accidentally in suspension, up on the third floor, in the heart of the house, the control room, it was there that a wonderful peace settled. The madam, Antonia, led on and baffled by the furious, indecisive squabbles, is gone; downstairs, the baby, not missing Antonia right now, plays quietly in a corner of the enormous living room. His nursemaid, the hulking wise gentle pliant Negro woman, rests, thinking of the cross-husband she must bear. Upstairs, in her attic room, I rummage about and play the latest jazz records lowly, causing incredibly deft and rhythmic piano sounds to sift downstairs. The little sounds of the house—a toilet flushing, windows contracting in the sharp wind, the huge dogs padding around, are immeasureably comforting. Outside your window the people pass slowly and obliviously, New York people, without personality. They, far down below, make no sign of hurry or of anger as if in deference to the quiet that reigns in the house on 54th Street. And you slouch sensually on the maid's bed reading with ninety per cent of your mind a novel while one flight below Charlotte broods over her trays of antique cylinders of Edison, rent-party piano, Lenin, Debs and Caruso, recleaning them for the thousandth time, and Arturo continues sketching insane butterflies. You read your book . . .

I looked across at John and wondered how he would react if I suddenly said, John, the real reason I am writing this novel is in order to find a point of stillness in the rush to my own extinction, which at the moment seems close. But, what the hell was the use? John would simply ask me to come up to Utah and Antonia would grow paler. I was dearly tempted to ask Antonia, How can anyone with so much money be so frightened? I know it sounds like a simple-minded question but put it to yourself, ask yourself whether you would be like that (barring glandular irregularities) if you had *that* much money. I don't want to sound unsympathetic to Antonia. Actually, I think I had been measurably in love with her for a long time, in the abstract.

Then John took command. He said, "Antonia and I have to be going out soon, you'll have to excuse us." My face burned. I felt lousy. What an awful way to wash up a friendship, or get heaved out of your substitute father's life, or whatever you want to call it. I was being dismissed. The TV lady came back from the ladies' wee-wee, and I stood up and we all stood around. Antonia looked about ready to cry. Me too, for that matter. John said, "Look you up if we get to Paris." I said, Me too, if I get to Utah. Shook hands all around. Antonia began to bite her fingernails. Like a figure in a drawing-room melodrama, Doorie showed up, right on schedule, and took me to the door. Goodbye, Doorie, I said. She looked at me a little sadly, and I shut the door behind me and walked up 54th Street towards where the Third Avenue El used to be and no longer is.

And I thought: and yet, in all this, I honor the man who was my teacher.

When I got back to Jessica's flat there was a telegram under the door waiting for me. It said, "Reconsider" and was signed by Laura Collins, back in Hollywood . . .

I sat down on the bed and remembered Hollywood . . .

I left Argus Records, the house in Brooklyn and the railroad flat on 13th Street, and my girl Barbie; I went to work on the docks but was personally thrown off by Albert Anastasia, the Enforcer himself, in a way that is not necessarily relevant to these pages. (In England, I read that the Enforcer got his finally, with a .32 Smith & Wesson and a .38 Colt, in the barbershop of the Park Sheraton Hotel in New York City while his bodyguard was across the street having a cup of coffee. Meaning no sacrilege on the dead, I like that bit about the cup of coffee.) I tried hanging around New York but getting kicked off the docks that way had knocked the stuff out of me, and I went back to L.A. I was going downhill, not too fast, steadily and with no malice aforethought. I went through more than one job, and in each but the last I was a conscientious and loyal employee. Dug ditches for Con Edison in West Los Angeles and knocked walnuts off trees in Pacoima, served time on the overnight desk of American Wire Service (where I pursued that man-eating leopard) and drove the morning shift for Yellow Cab. I worked a power saw for a Santa Monica Boulevard ventilator-making company, took part in two stock-car races (placing in neither) and finally went off to look for Indian Bird out near Cache, Oklahoma. E.J. was nowhere around so I went back to L.A., started to write a novel, gave it up, got mixed up in an Easter dawn teen-age riot down at Newport Beach and had to have stitches in my nose and wondered how long I could avoid going to work in a shop, the shop floor of a factory.

I went back to hacking for Yellow Cab, which was my first real experience as a Negro, what Ralph Ellison calls invisible, being looked at, spoken to and seen through. I quit when a buddy, the man who had taught me the ropes, stole my cap and map book out of my locker, and I decided once and for all to find out about the factory. I took a job at a television plant, as a spot welder, only to run out during lunch hour. The walls were closing in on me; the restriction, the mobs of workers, the regimentation, like to drove me mad. I kept on running until I hit Skid Row, but now, as it never had before, it terrified me. Frightened and unsure of myself, I took another job sitting alongside seven other misfits cleaning 16-mm film.

It was the last job I was to have before swinging aboard Hollywood. The building in which we worked (in the basement) was a dazzling white concrete three-tier split-level ultra-modernistic copy of a short, jagged dream of a man. It was situated, slanted downhill, on a sunnily blistering corner at the very top of Sunset Strip, just before the green belt leading to Bel Air and my old university begins.

A single business occupied these premises. The men who conducted the business ate lunch at La Rue's, two blocks down the boulevard, every day and arrived for work at 10:30 A.M. in new Oldsmobiles and Chryslers and wore spun-shantung suits and called each other "honey" and "doll," although they chewed cigars. Sometimes they brought their wives to the office. Office space took up all but the basement portion of the building, which is where we worked, the helots.

We had a single workroom allotted to us which was about half the size of the company president's office, although it was we who kept up the mechanical end of the business. We, the eight of us, sat on high metal stools, four facing four, six of us not yet thirty years old, in a neon-lit vault kept at a deliberately cool, exceptionally dry temperature which gave to our sun-thickened voices a lunging, crackling quality. We all had the same job. To sit between two spools, technically known as re-winds, holding the left hand at the top of one spool to act as a brake while rotating, for more or less eight hours a day (plus overtime) the right hand in a clockwise direction, which kept in motion a continuous and moving band of film we were supposed to let pass through our left hand (when it was not acting as a brake) holding a cotton rag soaked in methylethylene or similar cleaning fluid. The film we worked on was 16-mm prints of old, not to say ancient pictures which the Hollywood picture studios had sold to provincial television stations. The building on top of us was engaged in syndicating and distributing these prints. None of us really knew how the business worked, except that our labors were responsible for something in the vicinity of thirty million citizens west of the Rocky Mountains devoting a major portion of their evening hours to the film we were allegedly cleaning.

The work was comfortable, intolerably dull and very badly paid. Our employer, a portly and Viennese gentleman, gave it to us to understand that the low wages were commensurate with our inabilities to rise above such jobs as he offered us. He had an inactive, unaggressive contempt for us as native-born Americans who had failed to improve ourselves while he, a victim of Hitler, was most definitely on the way up. For some reason six of the eight of us in the basement seemed to approve, and even respect this man. The exception, besides myself, was a shambles of a boy named Hans Landau.

Hans was a distant cousin of Antonia Landau's, of Argus Records in New York, although he had never met her. (The Landaus were divided into *haute bourgeoisie* and literary-theatrical talent, the bulk of the latter having removed themselves to the west coast of America almost at the moment of debarking upon the American shores from warring Europe.) Hans's father was a novelist and physician; Hans's mother, a dress designer for Hollywood stars, was even better known than the father. Hans was the black sheep of an only-son family.

Hans and I had often seen each other here and there in Los Angeles but we did not get to know one another until it was our fate to sit opposite on the 16-mm re-winds. The two of us were somewhat set apart from the others: I had had "education" and Hans gave the impression. But the democracy of the miserable is a rigid, spiteful establishment, and we were committed to it, Hans and I.

Although he was blood-related to the company president, it did not — until the moment of strike — occur to either of us that he should use the relationship for, say, exemption from the silly, humiliating bullying of our foreman, an eighteen-year-old boy named Elkin. We detested Elkin — so clean shaven, well built, rosy-cheeked — and bullying. He was bright but not intelligent, and to all our quarrelsome complaints — about the wages, the twenty-minute lunch break, his persistent efforts to make our work less slipshod (which it was) — he would say sneeringly, Why don't you leave? Quit. You don't have to stay.

He was right, of course, much righter than he knew, in taunting us this way. To Elkin, dodging the draft and marrying the daughter of one of the president's assistants upstairs, marrying in other words into the business. it seemed a simple enough matter. Why *didn't* we leave? But none of us could. We had all wanted this job because it called upon so little of each of us. And for that reason, a terrible reason, we could not quit it. Who else would hire us? We hated ourselves, and each other, for it. But there it was. We were cowards in a coward's job. Elkin did not know this, because his foremanship was only the first step on the ladder for him. He was ambitious and worked hard and I don't think I have ever met anyone who humiliated me, by the very act of personal contact, the way Elkin did. He was always looking at me in a kind of amazed, amused way. Also I was afraid, slightly, physically afraid of Elkin. He played football for L.A. High School and was tremendously strong despite a lithe, fairly slender build. He was cunning enough to sense that I was afraid, and that if a challenge came it would come from me, and that therefore he could bully us with impunity. It's not easy to describe what I mean by bullying. There was the usual ragging, and nagging about schedules, and picking and carping, but none of us minded that too much. Foremen are foremen, even if they are only eighteen. No, it was what I tried to touch on before. His brutishness about reminding us, each in a way vulnerable to us as individuals, that we were hopeless failures while all around us lay, literally glittering in the sun, the evidences of success and affluence which he, Elkin, would one day, climbing above us, attain. In the mornings, for example, he would always be in the rewind room ahead of us, ready to cry out, Good morning, you bums. What Elkin did not know, I believe, is that we were, in some large sense, bums. At least we all felt it. It was like the Skid Row again. As we sat all day monotonously rotating our arms, the long rolls of film slithering and wavering through the rags in our fingers and sending out wave upon wave of cleaning fluid odors, a pall of numb, almost hypnotic hopelessness used to fall on us, until by the end of the day we hated each other. We never saw each other after work. It was unthinkable.

So there were Hans and myself; and next to me sat Theodore, the stoolpigeon. Theodore was stunted, crippled down one side of his body by a childhood paralytic stroke which had whittled him down to under size and caused him to drag both one foot and certain parts of speech; with bright almond-shaped eyes and a misshapen, pear-shaped head, with tremendous b.o. and endowed, through his stupidity, with a certain curious thrusting intelligence which would swarm upon you at the most unexpected times. A crypto moron, a physical moron three quarters of the time, he possessed a certain insight into the lives of those he worked among. With our hearts and souls we despised Theodore. He was the *lumpen*, the Van Der Lubbe of our little work force, someone who we felt in our hearts should have died at birth. He jeered constantly at Hans, who also was lame.

Across from Theodore sat Widdick, a handsome, almost dandyish young man who was just, he assured us, "passing through." (That's what they always tell you on the Row, and your heart sings when you see them stop and stay. That's when you know if you don't leave the Row, right then, at that moment, you never will.) Widdick kept his own counsel, did his work quietly (and was the most careless of the lot) and didn't seem outwardly defeated. It wasn't until the strike that he announced to all of us that he had been a plant security guard and had pistol-whipped a thief, or would-be thief, aged thirteen, and had been fired in disgrace. He ended by telling us, in a neutral tone, I sometimes hit small kids.

Next to Theodore sat Sidney, a smiling, wincing, movie-magazine devouring piece of plump, overripe fruit. Sidney was all right; he had been, literally, born that way. A few less jogs of his old man's torso and Sidney would have come out as a girl very likely. He would have made a fat, homely girl but a better one than the boy he was. Sidney was very intelligent. But he had, as they say, confused values. He was a walking, talking, waddling compendium of mass culture. Age fifty, not a year less, with the clear flesh of a young Etonian. He studied Jimmie Fidler's column as though it were an apostolic epistle which he constantly carried with him and often stopped work to read silently. He knew, always knew, which pictures were in production and who was starring in them. You would be surprised at how irritating a habit this is, especially when the man in question does not know it is irritating. The thing about Sidney was, he took the plots of movies *seriously*. Sometimes when I was exasperated beyond politeness, I would shout, Sidney, I used to make up those plots. Then I would describe to Sidney why a film is made, precisely who wrote the story and how. But even though I would often do this with all the quiet persuasiveness at my command, and even though he lived directly across the street from RKO Studios, Sidney sustained a deep, sure identification with the hideous *sincérité* of movie plots. To everything I said, Sidney simply smiled cordially and replied, Now that *is* fascinating. No, Sidney, I would say, it's terrible, don't you see how terrible it is. And he would smile that serene, Bible-reading smile of his, and say, with a kind of amiable ruefulness, It's so ingenious. Sidney.

Opposite him worked the Actor. One-eyed Tammany Jones. It was not his real name of course. With his agent's approval he had chosen Tammany. But not even his agent knew he had only one good eye: no eye patch, and full movement. When I told him the derivation of his *nom-de-travail* he, like Sidney, said, Now that's pretty interesting, isn't it? He spoke with a faint lisp and had broad shoulders and was letting his sideburns grow in the hope he could land one of the roles going in the TV westerns which were being shot all over town. He too was only passing through, and would alternate periods of fraternizing and snobbishness. The best thing about Tammany was the way he stood up to Elkin.

Elkin, when he did re-wind work, sat at the end of the work table across from Werner Zampi. Now Zampi had a curious story. After comparing notes, Hans Landau and I decided that he was, or had been, a Fascist. Zampi was a small, sallow and obsequious man, a north Tyrolese who had, he told us, been a film editor with the

Italian Army. He had been a p.o.w. at Fort Sheridan, in Illinois, repatriated to the Tyrol and had then come back through marrying a half-Jewish girl of American citizenship. Sometimes the boys, in a joking manner, would try to get out of Zampi his attitudes to Mussolini and Hitler, but he would always spread out his hands and say, Aheye, leave that to the politicians, I am no politician. Zampi was a bitter little man, a fully qualified editor to whom the Hollywood union would not permit entry. He had, however, discovered that by kicking back part of his present and future salary to a certain union official he might be permitted a job, and he was, while working with us, in the process of negotiating such a transaction. It goes without saying that this, his first and second occupational experiences in America, confirmed a certain image in his mind, and Hans and I were always expecting him to burst out one day with, Hitler was not *all* bad.

From Hans, Zampi stayed strictly away. The first day on the job, Hans told me, as soon as he had learned Zampi was gentile, Tyrolean and ex-Blackshirt, he had gone up to him in the basement toilet and bluntly explained that he, Hans, was a Jew and had given Zampi orders not to refer to it. Although it was a little difficult seeing Hans giving anyone orders, I believed this. Hans was, considering the rest of us down in that basement bent over our re-winds, a moral titan.

Whether Hans had been born this way, or had suffered a childhood brain injury, was something his father and mother had never adequately explained to him. The official story was the usual one of falling on his head from the crib, but Hans said that his parents told this version too perfunctorily for his comfort. According to outward physical appearances Hans was all right, just so long as he stood still. He was large, bulky and completely, plangently bald, with a sad, elephantine drooping face and eyes that are usually described as liquid. But when he got moving he was all a shambles. His speech was trudging and slightly slurred, and the only way he knew to point a finger was to start out by moving both hands in canceling-out motions, pyramidally, until he got the effect he wanted. If you happened to find yourself standing anywhere except directly in front of Hans, and suddenly you said, Hans! he would throw himself together in a kind of uncoordinated, convulsive fit in order to locate, alternately cringing and craning his body, where you were. He wrote poetry and short stories and was, he knew, like myself, a failure in life.

Most of the day we sat, all of us, hunched over our re-winds without a word to each other except for the impolite grunts and short gestures needed when we required the film cement or razor blade. This silence was broken only when one of us, usually unprompted, would suddenly blurt out a story of an insignificant incident which had occurred during the previous days. Invariably, nobody else picked up the thread, except for a single round of comments around the table, whence a dull, whirring silence would once again descend. This silence, which we shared had a texture-all of its own. It was malign, inbred, spiteful. Occasionally, someone would suddenly brake his re-wind in mid-film and slide off the stool, cursing as though with a mouth full of ashes. Such occasions caused no stir of surprise among us: our turn to do the same would come, or had just come. We loathed the easiness of our work, our stations and each other. All that is, except Hans and me.

I loved Hans. I was the George to his Lenny. No, that is unfair and not correct. Hans looked mentally deficient and was not. In point of fact, he was sensitive, decent and the legitimate heir to a far-ranging culture, that of the Hollywood Viennese. I think now, he was mixed up. Literally, mixed up. Not all the parts of him had ever come together into a blend. He was different from the rest of us in having never suffered a disintegration; he had never been enough integrated for that. His parts, his senses, were all jumbled, and none of them was excellent. Poor eyesight, bad coordination, a trifle deaf, old Hans definitely was under par all right. But he read poetry. He read poetry. Nobody in the re-wind room bullied him, that was the trouble. Even Elkin, our eighteen-year-old foreman, treated Hans with a form of tenderness. I felt like mashing Elkin for his attitude. I knew it humiliated Hans, who more than anything else wanted to be treated normally. The hell of it was, there was this mechanism in Hans which prevented him most times from seeing when people were treating him specially, there was a streak of horrifying, slow thinking in him. But I knew he had found out Elkin (whose motives, in this instance, were high).

Hans and I played special games, over the re-winds, which nobody but us knew about. At first we used to talk together. Formal seminars. To make the time pass faster. One week we held a seminar in "Morality, Retrograde and Progressive, in the Faerie Queen." (Both Hans and I had done work on Spenser.) For a few days we discussed "The Dissemination and Transfiguration of Uni-Theism from the Early Greek Sects to the Middle Ages," or "Influences of Rural Ideology on Early Trade Union Organizations." One day we almost got sick laughing over "Evidences of Anal-Retentive Symbols and Artifacts in Tennyson, Middle Period." The reaction of the other boys was more or less what you would expect. For a while they paid us no attention. Then they got sore. Theodore, the fink, brought a portable radio when the World Series began and stuck it on the wall shelf which was just above where Hans and I sat. When the World Series was over, somehow Hans and I didn't have the stomach to go back to our seminars. We relapsed into the sullen, mutual silence. And then, beautifully, we stumbled on this idea, this plan, this grand design to rescue civilization from itself. In all modesty, I must put it down that the idea originally came to me — but also, had it not been for Hans's initial reaction, his burst of spontaneous encouragement, the world today would be a poorer place indeed.

About ten or eleven days after the World Series, as we were monotonously working away, I was suddenly stricken with a blinding, magnificent sense of reality. Perhaps, in later history books, this moment will be likened to the maid Joan's first vision or St. Paul's trauma. Be that as it may, it struck me that this material which was running through my ethyl-soaked hands, at the rate of three feet per second (timed, naturally, by Elkin), was motion picture film. On the film were prospects, vistas and perpectives which, when projected by a machine into a cathode ray tube and electronically distributed to American homes, created a series of mounting images which formed one leg of that monster table, "the mass media." What better way to devote one's spare (and more than spare, *working*) hours than to lead the way in sabotage?

So this one afternoon, I suddenly stopped my re-wind and picked up the piece of film. I sabotaged it. The method was simplicity itself. Part of our job was to check the film for breaks or chips in the sprocket holes. If we came across a break we stopped the re-winds, snipped half a frame from either side of the defect, cemented the film together and rolled on. A missing frame, or even two, possibly three (depending upon the action) is rarely detected by the audience. It so happened that many of the prints going through our hands were in old and dilapidated condition. They should have been replaced by newer prints. The management, of course and however, wished to squeeze the very last ounce of profit they could from these old prints, even if their scratches and breaks did irritate a mass audience. My own feeling was that if management wished to take the risks, I would be happy to oblige by supplying them.

So I held the strip of film in my hand for some time, savoring a historical moment. Hans but nobody else stopped their work to watch. He smiled faintly at me, in the way he had. I gazed almost affectionately at the slightly torn sprocket hole in the piece of film I was holding. I then cut through the film with my razor blade, took up two feet of film, cut through again, cemented the ends, dropped the two feet of amputated film into a trash bin at my side, and rolled on. Hans stared at me. I smiled at him. A moment later I repeated this procedure, removing from the film another twenty-four inches of action and sound. The picture was called *Farewell, Dear Murderer*. All told, I took out seven or eight stretches of film story. I knew that many television stations never took the trouble to screen the films they bought, and the ecstasy of my vision of the reaction of the Late-Late-Viewers as they bumped and jolted through a more than normally incomprehensible story almost brought tears of joy to my eyes. To you, out there, this may sound vicious, or hostile, childish even. Such is the fate that awaits all great seminal actions of a revolutionary character.

I ripped whole sections of film out of the spools all that day. Working with friends of Arturo Mishkin at Argus Records in New York I had acquired the knack of "reading" film by just holding it up to the light and using the individual frames like letters of the alphabet. I did this now. Gradually, from day to day, I refined the method from indiscriminate sabotage to calculated torture. I would "read" the film until I came to the climactic scene of a sequence —

the cowboy dashing to the rescue of the lady, the revelation by the master detective of the criminal, the seduction which the plot had been leading up to — and then, simply, remove it. The fact that I was doing this veritably under Elkin's nose pleased me. You may say, as you read this, lugubriously, such is the state to which he was humbled. Yes, probably. But all I can remember is a singing heart. From that first day onward my job took on meaning.

And for Hans too. His initial reaction had been incomprehension. He just stared. It took him, actually, about half a day to see what I was up to. I spaced my actions and I did the job smoothly, but when Hans finally caught on he began to snigger wildly. Some of the boys looked up in irritation, but Hans kept his head and I was saved, to fight on further days.

It goes without saying that Hans followed suit. At coke break that afternoon he sidled up to me in the corridor outside the re-wind room. Terrific! he said, clapping his hands together like some great big happy half moronic, half-intelligent bear and giving that cough-chortle of his. I winked and held my finger to the side of my nose and we went happily back to work, busy all afternoon, snip snip s-ni-p. Once, late that first afternoon, we started up our old seminar. We called it "An Investigation into the Possible Merits of Cultural Luddism in the Twentieth Century." But that was gilding our beautiful, gorgeous lily, and we shortly stopped talking and went back to our jobs. Snip, snip, s-ni-p.

After the first day or two, Hans and I settled down to a more leisurely pace, mutilating the film less from compulsion than whenever the fancy struck us, or more accurately, whenever we ran across a piece of film which we felt too lazy to patch efficiently. We would dearly love to have seen one of our efforts on the idiot screen, but unfortunately our product went to Denver, Portland, Salt Lake, even San Francisco — everywhere on the west coast except where we lived. Hans and I, because we admired San Francisco, decided that we would not damage film destined for that city. It was a definite contradiction to our action theory of Cultural Luddism but the basement re-wind room was nothing if not a residence of unthought-out contradictions.

The important thing is that it gave us a purpose, a sense of mastery over our fate. It followed, logically, to form a union and go to the management with our demands. Hans began attending meetings of a small CIO union competing for film technicians against the giant, corrupt union operating in the Hollywood field. He finally persuaded a field organizer to come out and see the place. This field organizer was a very competent, very unhappy man. Big and ugly, with a broken nose, a real union pro, he and I quarreled almost upon first meeting, and the second time we met, at union headquarters, his secretary came between us before blows could be struck. At any other time I think we might have liked each other. But his job in the film technicians' union was either exile or compensatory for a factional situation in the Meat-Packers Union from which he had come and which had formed him, and he was in a perpetually unslung humor. For my part all I desired was that our union be organized methodically, from the ground up and according to traditional and democratic principles. But Sam, the union organizer, did not see it this way. He had already seen what we were and concluded, no doubt correctly, that the sooner a union was, or was not organized, the sooner he could have done with us. His attitude towards us was not much different from that of the company president. When we met at the union office I told Sam, the organizer, I wanted to see the terms he was going in to negotiate and he said that it was not the usual union practice. I laughed and made a mistake, I called him a porkchopper. That was when he tried to throw a punch. Hans started to cry. Violence always affected him, and Sam and I soothed him on the office couch.

But Sam insisted he would not divulge the terms of the contract he would ask the company to sign. He said, There might be a stool-pigeon among you. I said there was, Theodore, but what the hell difference did it make. He said, There might be more than Theodore. In deference to Hans, I did not cock my arm. The next day, Hans and Sam and I talked to all the boys, except Elkin, at a local lunch counter, and a week later we held an unofficial election. Five of the eight voted for the union, and then we unanimously elected Hans our shop steward. That same afternoon the company president invited me up to his office. He said I was the brightest of the group of film-cleaners and that I had no business in a dead-end job and wouldn't I be happier elsewhere? With a straight face I said I was happy where I was and wanted to make my future film-cleaning for the company. (Snip, snip, s-ni-p.) He became very angry and called me a cocky sonofabitch. But the most surprising thing happened. Instead of sitting back and calmly laughing, I clenched my teeth and began to hate the company president. I felt stung and humiliated by what he was saying. My reaction to his words took my breath away. I have been in several company negotiations and I knew, as do all trade union negotiators, that the worst thing you can do is to make a personal enemy out of the company representative. Anger, like statistics, is a tactic. But the one thing I didn't feel was tactical. I felt myself choke up. You're scum, shouted the president, you're a troublemaker, you're using that poor ninny down there, Hans, wait until I tell his family. Then he dismissed me. All that afternoon I deliberately refrained from damaging any of the company president's film. That victory I would not give him.

It was strange to watch what was happening to the boys as a result of the coming of the union. Immediately upon Sam the organizer's coming down to give us his pitch, silence flew away from the re-wind room. Intrigue and quarrels flew in. But the silence was gone. Elkin jeered at us for wanting a union. He said it was ridiculous. He said the workroom was too small. He said many true things. But the idea had taken hold. We plotted, conspired, argued amongst ourselves. In my heart, when I compared this to what I had once planned for myself, and been close to in Detroit, I felt it was silly and demeaning. But I was determined to play the situation with such dignity as was commensurate with a vast organizing drive against a monopolistic, implacable employer. I think that perhaps in the back of my mind I had some idea about our group's redemption once it had passed through the union experience. It did not exactly happen in this way.

For one thing, Theodore immediately began his stoolpigeon activities. Now Theodore, although he did not know this, was in the long line, the ancient tradition. He was the cliché stoolpigeon. Golem-like, nasty, transparently double-dealing, managing always to leave behind him a certain ratlike spoor. The nice thing about Theodore was that he made no attempt to act the double agent; he ranted against the union incessantly. His staple argument was that it would do nothing for us while exacting our dues, and that the union officials were simply in the game to line their pockets or to hold on to their jobs. This attitude was more or less shared by the others around the worktable except, paradoxically, Elkin. Elkin was rather intelligent about this whole thing. He frankly declared that if he were not marrying into the business he would take a lead in organizing the union because, to his way of thinking, workers ought to have an organization to balance the power of the boss. When the boys around the table were in a good, pro-union mood they agreed complacently with Elkin. When they were busily hating the union for upsetting their previous way of monotony, they regarded Elkin's sympathy towards the union as sufficient justification to be against it. At times, the cleaning table was a babble of all the primitive anti-union prejudices which American workers can dream up, and it was at these moments that I felt most proud of my workmates. By God, the boys had *something* in them after all.

Arguing back and forth among ourselves — with Hans usually in the middle and desperately demanding of me that I relieve him as shop steward — at last produced agreement on a provisional contract which Sam was to go to the company president with. The three weeks it required for us to pinpoint what we wanted were marvelous, poignant weeks. It entailed a horrible task: to look objectively and carefully at the work we were doing and to commit ourselves to it by trying to improve it. It was then that I saw why, for a solid week or two, the worktable had featured such vehement, bitter outbursts against the union. Until Sam the organizer came we could always, each individually, make excuses in our head that we were just "passing through" or else pretend the job simply didn't exist, which I suspect is how most of us dealt with it. But the coming of the union — and by the peaceful, acquiescent instrument of Hans — forced us to consider our relationship to the job, and I don't think it made us too happy. At one time or another every one of the boys except Hans swore he would leave the job rather than join the union. But when the NLRB examiners came around all of us were present and accounted for.

The day before the NLRB election, the company president had a private talk with each of the boys. He threatened, bribed, even blackmailed. He promised Tammany Jones a small part at one of the nearby studios. He told Widdick he would report his behavior to his probation officer. He promised Theodore Elkin's job when Elkin got married. He promised Zampi to get him into the film editor's union.

By this time I was obsessed with the idea of getting the re-wind room organized. It was the most important thing in my life. Hans was temporarily scared off by the company president's threats to cause a family rumpus, and I had to do most of the talking. I am not a persuasive talker, and in fact most of what I said was fairly wild. I almost completely ignored arguments of self-betterment to talk about what a fine and noble thing it was to vote for the union. Strange, in a normal plant most workers would have laughed or booed out of sheer embarrassment. But I must give it to the boys in the re-wind room, they listened. I spoke to them *ensemble* and privately, on the way to and on the way from work, I even visited the rooms where Widdick and one-eyed Tammany Jones lived. I was inhabiting something like a fantasy world, where the seven other boys were a mass of unorganized workers, Elkin the main enemy. My tactics were those that I had seen many times, in Detroit and elsewhere, tactics of organizing a plant in Ohio of 10,000 workers in heavy industry. Elkin began to insult me. I refused provocation. I was proud of myself. I began to think of settling down in the re-wind room while starting a novel. I probably was a little mad. When the boys were called, individually, into the company president's office just before the election, despite Elkin's protests I left my re-wind to walk upstairs with each man, cajoling or pleading or just to keep him company, waiting outside until he was through and then walking back with him. Hans, by this time, was in a state of terror, about one thing and another, but I had no time for Hans now.

The election was held. Two men and a police officer appeared one morning and deposited a large yellow-painted wooden box on our worktable. We filed out of the room, and then filed in with our votes. Then we went back to work. The two NLRB men and the police officer went away with the wooden box to count the eight votes. (I had protested Elkin's right to vote, as he was supervisory, but this was disallowed.) A curious, light silence came upon us, and we worked briskly and quietly for the remainder of the day.

Two days later a notice was posted on one wall of the re-wind room. By six to two, we had won a union. Immediately, open speculation broke out among us as to who had been the two traitors. Elkin kept saying, Don't look at me, and in the toilet he assured me vehemently that he had voted for the union. Possibly he did. For the next few days we existed in a state of suspended animation. We kept staring obliquely at each other across the worktable. We were expecting something. Now that we had our union, what was going to happen to us? The boys grew restive, quarrelsome again. Hans and I, who had stopped sabotaging the film, did not resume. We waited.

Then Sam the organizer came down and presented us with the contract he was going to ask the company to sign. We made a few alterations and improvements and then Sam went away. The boys looked at each other, and at Hans and myself. We declared we knew as little as they, that we had to wait and put our confidence in the organizer. Previously, I had demanded that Sam appoint a two-man negotiating committee but he had refused. He said it would slow things up.

All that week Sam paid visits to the company president's office, and we were immensely overjoyed to see the company legal adviser spending so much of his time in the same office. Down in the re-wind room we were almost happy. For the first time I, and I think the others, did not feel the crushing weight of the intolerably fierce contrast between the air-conditioned squalidness of the basement and the glittering, sun-basted affluent gloss of Sunset Strip literally over our heads, where a thousand times a day the tires of Cadillacs and Lincolns noiselessly and invisibly rode. We had built ourselves our own city.

The news was announced by Sam, now beaming and affable, at a special meeting in the union office on Melrose Avenue one night. We had won our contract. The company president had agreed to sign. The terms were not those we had asked for, but we had not expected them anyway. That was on a Thursday. On Friday morning, in the middle of the day, we all looked up to see the company president standing in the doorway. We felt proud. He was looking angry, almost apoplectic.

Hans! barked the company president (who had never before shown his shantung-silk suit in the re-wind room). Hans jerked himself together convulsively, the way he had, and shuffled off his stool. Several minutes later I went out into the dimly lit corridor. The company president and one of his aides had Hans against the wall; Hans was pale and looked about to faint. It is very difficult to describe the expression of the company president and his aide. They were like men in shock.

Hans looked at me and made a helpless gesture. I said to the two men, Leave him alone. I grabbed the hand of the aide, who drew back and said through his teeth, Don't you *touch* me, you bum. I pondered this statement, the way he had said it, the way he was drawing away from me in revulsion. The company president did not look at me. He shook his finger at Hans. When I get through with you, he said, you'll be lucky if the family invites you to Christmas turkey. Hans was mumbling rapidly to himself. I said again, Leave him alone. The company president in his shantung-silk suit consulted a clipboard production schedule and said evenly to me, Do you handle Denver? I said sometimes. He pointed to the floor where a stack of cans leaned. Open any one of those, he commanded. I opened up the first can and took out the film. The company president grabbed it out of my hand and began, with extravagant, swooping motions to unravel the film. He felt along the edges until he came to a splice. Here, he said without looking at the film, go ahead, look.

I held the film up to the light. Then I remembered. The sequence I was holding started out with two cars chasing each other on a rainy, dark night along Broadway. I felt down to the splice. The first frame after the splice featured a man and a woman in front of a palm tree with the sultry Pacific behind them. Oh Christamighty. I had forgotten all about that. This is your work, said the company aide, it is signed out by you.

Well yes, I said, anything wrong? They both stared at me.

Hans stood up straighter and murmured, I told them when we get the film it is often in disrepair. Good old Hans. I said, That's right, we do the best we can. You bum, screamed the company president holding up the film for me to see, *the best you can.* We'll see, we'll see, and he stalked off up the corridor with his aide. Hans said quietly, I'd forgotten all about that. I said, So did I.

When we went back into the re-wind room we didn't tell the

others. The week finished, and we trailed out of the syndication building and away from the job. I went away for the weekend, down to Newport Beach with some friends of mine, including Hilda Slater. Hilda was in a very neurotic period, just getting her divorce and extravagantly promiscuous. She even wanted to sleep with me, on the sand at night. I told Hilda that would be like incest, and she said, Yes, I suppose so. Hilda said there was an opening at the Benedict Agency but I said I would rather work for Hearst than become a Hollywood agent. Idealist, she said, let's go down to the beach tonight and make love. Hilda was in her lost period. (This was before she met Tad and married him and became a crazy, contented West L.A. matron presiding over business luncheons.) All that weekend Hilda kept saying, Don't be a schmuck, come to Benedict, what's the point of fighting any longer, there's no enemy. I said, Maybe some day, but right now I have something important to do. I didn't tell her what it was until the telegram arrived.

There were about ten of us, five men, five women, sharing the house at Newport for the weekend. It had not been a particularly wild weekend, partly because some of the men and women were married to each other. Several of the husbands made approaches to Hilda, and only one of the wives to me. I was bored. When the telephone rang one of the wives went to answer it and brought back a penciled message for me from Western Union: YOUR SERVICES THIS COMPANY TERMINATED AS NOW. I immediately got on the phone to Hans in Hollywood, and he said that not only he, but all the other boys, except Elkin, had received identical telegrams. I drove back to L.A. late that night, leaving behind four men and five women.

The next morning, Monday, was sunny and hot. When I showed up at the building I found Hans with Zampi, Widdick, Tammany and Theodore waiting. Later, the others joined us. Theodore said, They've moved. Zampi said, Yesss, if you ask me I believe they have moved. I looked. The basement was locked and boarded up. The entire basement was boarded up. Theodore said excitedly, Moving vans came Sunday and took all the film away. They took them somewhere else. I asked Theodore how he knew this, and he said, I stood guard across the street Saturday and Sunday. Old Theodore, the stoolpigeon.

We had a meeting out there on the sidewalk, and I was delegated to go round the front entrance and get an interview with the company president. The doorman and the receptionist wouldn't let me in, they had had orders. I went back to the group and reported. Then we crowded around a phone box and ordered Sam the organizer to come down. He did, after lunch. He went into the building. The receptionist and doorman let him in. While he was inside, Theodore succeeded in another coup, he flushed Elkin out. Elkin came outside on the sunny slanted pavement and spoke to us. He said the company had decided to move its film-cleaning business to another firm, to subcontract it. I said, That's illegal. Elkin shrugged and went back inside the building. Sam the organizer came out and said, We'll charge them with unfair labor practice. Zampi said, What about our jobs? Sam, too, shrugged and said we might as well forget about our jobs until the NLRB report came through, which would be in a few months. He said the union would try to find us jobs elsewhere, in similar work, but could promise nothing. He got into his Chevrolet and drove away.

We stood there on the pavement, the seven of us, under the hot, naked sun and didn't know what to do. Every time we started to think we had to look at the boarded-up basement. Nobody was angry, in fact nobody talked much at all. After a long silence, Theodore said, I know what you two did. He meant Hans and myself. He said, You destroyed film, you made it so people couldn't watch it. Hans, who had been sitting on the curb, got up, as though preparing to defend himself, possibly against blows. The others listened to Theodore. Tammany Jones asked, Is that true? I felt pretty bad and said yes, it was. Tammany whistled admiringly. How long, he asked, for? A month or so, I said. Zampi came up to me and asked with interest, How exactly did you do it? So I described the method, in detail.

Hans came up to join me, and we stood side by side, explaining. Sidney, the fruit, said, Then you weren't being just careless? Hans laughed in a constrained way. I said, No, we weren't being just careless. Zampi said, pointing to the boarded-up basement, That is why we are not working maybe? I said, Partly. Then the whole group went back to asking us to describe, again, in detail how we sabotaged the film. After we got through Theodore and Zampi and Sidney sat on the small grass verge outside the basement and got out a pencil and paper, finally coming up with a computation. Zampi said, Theodore adds up you and Hans ruined twenty thousand dollars worth of cinema film. Hans and I looked at each other. We were impressed. We all sat down on the curb, seven abreast, and watched the traffic on Clark Drive settle back on its haunches up the hill to Sunset Boulevard.

Widdick said, Twenty thousand bucks, boy! Theodore laughed raucously and said, We're millionaires! Tammany chuckled appreciatively and said, We almost drove them out of business. Sidney said, It sounds childish to me. Nobody disagreed with him. But Sidney wasn't being spiteful, just stating a fact. Zampi and Widdick kept asking technical questions about how we had done it without being caught. Tammany said, Those fucking sonofabitches let the film through without inspecting it. He was referring not to us but the television stations. We all nodded vehemently, as though to say, Wouldn't you just know it? Tammany kept repeating, Twenty thousand bucks, like an incantation over us. We sat still under the canopy of what we had done to them before they had done it to us. Hans and I felt calm.

As we were sitting on the curb Elkin came out and said, Why don't you guys go home, the ball game's over. He sounded tough, even menacing. Tammany laughed and pointed at Elkin. Maybe, Tammany said, now the company'll be too poor to give Elkin a wedding present. Yeah, shouted Theodore, maybe they'll even have to can him. Elkin said, What are you guys talking about? He was bewildered. He stood still on the pavement and stared at us. That finished it. One by one we got off the curb, dusted our clothes and said goodbye to each other. Elkin watched, glaring. We even shook hands. Zampi, the Blackshirt, clutched the arms of Hans and myself when we shook hands. It was like a solemn graduating party breaking up. We exchanged addresses and phone numbers. Elkin piped up, Say doesn't anyone want mine? The boys were feeling very good so some of them took down Elkin's telephone number and wished him a happy marriage. Then, one by one, we separated, some going up the hill to Sunset Boulevard, spread out and started to disappear. At the crest of the intersection of Clark Drive and Sunset Boulevard, Tammany turned around and yelled back down to everybody, Boy oh boy, twenty thousand dollars, I haven't felt so good since they shot Hitler.

Goodbye, shouted back Sidney. So long, shouted Theodore. Bye bye, said Widdick. Good luck, shouted Zampi.

Hans and I watched them go. Elkin said to Hans, Do you want to walk with me a ways? Hans looked at me. I said, Go on, there's something I have to do. I walked up the hill, while Elkin and Hans went down.

As soon as I got to Sunset Boulevard I started to run. Running, I passed Tammany and Sidney waiting for a bus to take them down to the center of Hollywood. So long, I shouted. Goodbye, they shouted back.

That day I went into the Benedict Agency and asked Hilda to find out if they still had a job open . . .

I picked up the phone in the shade-drawn, darkened flat and had Western Union send the agency a telegram, NO BUT THANKS.

In the morning I woke up, in Jessica's flat, suddenly intellectually more convinced by the idea of suicide than I had ever been before. I had not sought out the concept; it was always there at first hand. I lay in the large, wide bed and thought of the odds against my writing the kind of book I wanted, and what a cheap way out it was for me instead of looking for my true work, if such there was. Now, as of this moment, I knew that if I were going to try to write this book I would wake up every morning with feelings similar to this, and I might as well start engaging them. I jerked out of bed, dressed and went down to an office near Lower Broadway. The next twenty-four hours was a fast, peaceful dream which I hope you will not be offended by if I lightly mention how I passed them successfully.

The office was called Student Tours, Inc., and its function was to provide cheap off-season steamship tickets to Europe. I went upstairs and was passed along a chain of office assistants until I was ushered in to Hilary. She was a pretty, rather sad English girl with whom I fell into conversation on matters other than my ticket. She asked me when I wanted to go to Ibiza, and I said on the next boat. She made out a ticket, I paid her for it, and we went out to lunch together. I talked a great deal over lunch, partly because I was excited by Hilary. She was my idea of what a modern, traditional English lady should look like, a good complexion, a small high bust, a wide forehead, clear eyes and a light, indecisive voice. At dessert she reached across and touched my face and said, "You don't even know where you're going, do you?" Now, at this point, I know I should have been touched, or moved, or perhaps more excited, but all I felt was a deep unwelcome harassment that anyone else should know. I went to the restaurant bathroom and threw up and when I came back I told Hilary I would like to go out to her place. She said she was married and that her husband did not come home until late and that it troubled her to think of taking me to her place, which was in New Jersey. But we went anyway, taking the lower Hudson ferry, the Hoboken ferry. She lived right on the waterfront, in a green-painted apartment overlooking one of the docks. In her front room she said, neatly and with a faintly troubled look, "Let's not go into the bedroom, I don't want to muss it." I took off my clothes, and she put on the radio and took off hers and was extremely hungry. Taking her back across the Hudson, I said I hoped she wouldn't get into any trouble at her office for coming in late on her lunch period, and she replied no, she thought not, she would say she had been out shopping. She said, on the ferry, that her husband was an engineer trying to be a painter. "He knows he has no talent and so he takes it out on me." She wasn't complaining. Her expression throughout was that fixed, tolerant, slightly ethereal smile she had directed at me when we had first negotiated a ticket for Ibiza. I liked Hilary very much. I held her hand. The boat came into its berth on the Manhattan side and I said, Hilary, I love you. She said, "No. Yes. Yes, you love me." She put her slim, light hand in my hair and said, "Stranger, do we love each other?"

When I left Hilary, on the sidewalk outside her office, she kissed my cheek. Then she ran away into the building where she worked. I walked around Wall Street and did not find it interesting. I rarely do. I just walked around telling myself, You must stop feeling sorry for yourself. But I couldn't stop. It was three in the afternoon. I wasn't due to leave America yet for forty-eight hours. I took a bus to 42nd Street, and went up to the third floor of Liberty

Pictures and asked the secretary who had a desk in the corridor for Jerry Chaplin, the East Coast story editor. The secretary laughed furiously and waved me on past her. Workmen were painting the corridor. I walked into the office, which was a very large room partitioned off by waist-high plyboard walls. The readers and the secretaries were lying around drinking and singing. I walked through to Jerry's cubicle. He had his head deep in a manuscript and was frowning, as usual. Jerry was a worrier. But then too he had a lot to worry about. He wasn't young any more, he wrote historical romances set in the Deep South in the manner of Frank Yerby which did everything Frank Yerby did except sell, he was afraid of all of his bosses, his wife was going deaf, one of his kids had survived a polio attack, and he couldn't even take to drink because it went to his head. Jerry was so involved with his script that I sat down and waited. He was almost completely bald now, a handsome bald man with worry crawling all over him, a nail-biting, odoriferous worry. Life had not been kind to Jerry. A slum boy from Baton Rouge, mother an arthritic cripple, father an alcoholic and then a suicide, Jerry had gotten in a good lot of apprentice worrying. Rescue came. He started playing basketball, was picked up by a semi-pro team and had a try-out with the Lakers. Then the war. By then, married but had to care for Ma, so he went back home and took a job with a steel plant in Baton Rouge, intending to keep it for only a few months. The government froze the job. Marriage broke but Mother wouldn't die. Decided war would be better than steel plant, let himself be drafted and spent three years in Japanese prisoner-of-war camp. After liberation, went out to Hollywood, started writing, hired and humiliated by a half-insane studio manager, tried a steel mill in Duluth, even tried semi-pro basketball again, no go. Drifted with new wife and kid, to New York, started out as a "reader," worked his way up to story editor. He gave me my first job in New York when I needed it, reading and synopsizing books for five dollars apiece, apologizing all the time for the price. Jerry was what you call a nice guy. He just worried too much.

The first thing he said when he looked up from the manuscript and saw me was, "Oi, have I *tsooris*." This, with a still-thick Louisiana accent. I smiled. Jerry hadn't seen me in several years, barring a visit he had done to Hollywood on studio expense. I did the expected and asked after his family. Emily's hearing, he said, was better now, and there was a chance of saving it. Of the three kids, one had measles, one was wearing specs at three, the third peed in bed. He had just been turned down for a raise, his ex-wife was dunning him for back alimony and the teletype at his back was humming busily, a message from the studio chief in Hollywood. I said, What the hell have you got that thing in your office for, why don't you put it out in the corridor? He said, gloomily, "I had it out in the corridor and then the boss came out for his New York trip and told me to put it in my personal office." He gestured around his cubicle. "My personal office," he said. He rambled on about his troubles at home and at work and blamed it mainly, as he always did, on those three years in a Japanese prisoner-of-war camp and he blamed that for a bad, lingering first marriage. Nothing but that, always that, never anything else. "Oh hell," he said finally, "let's have some fun, one of the girls is getting married."

The girl who was getting married was a tall, robust reader with a swarthy complexion. She was Greek Orthodox. There were four female readers, two female secretaries, and Jerry's assistant, a young married man in the room. Most of the women were girls and the girls were not terribly sober. Jerry locked the door and we drank together, and sang songs, and congratulated the Greek Orthodox girl. Then we all went out to Lindy's for cheesecake, sat in two booths raucously, and held our arms around each other. Several of the girls started to cry, and one of the girls who wasn't crying held my hand under the table (I held hers too) and we all became quite hilarious. Jerry's young assistant looked furious when I took away the girl whose hand I was holding. The cab took us to Jessica's flat, and we made love, rough and anonymous, all that afternoon, with the shades undrawn and a pale November light filtering in from the shaft outside. About five-thirty she slapped her head and said, "Omigosh, I've got to finish a report for the West Coast office," so we dressed and I gave her money for a cab. Then I was alone again.

Outside the night closed in. I sat on the bed and stared at the telephone. It rang back, Lucky Mayfield. "Heard you were in town and over at Jessica's," he said, "can I come over and bring a friend?" I said, Sure, thanking God. I played Jessica's musical comedy records on her hi-fi until Lucky showed up. He had a girl with him, a small dark pretty girl with one arm in a white plaster cast. I invited them in for drinks. Lucky was dressed to the teeth. He looked like something off Madison Avenue, Oxford brown tight-fitting natural-shoulder suit, pointed Italianate shoes, old-school tie, stiff white collar over a blue striped shirt (quietly striped), snap-brim short fedora and even a waistcoat. I didn't say anything about how he was dressed. He refused a drink but just sat on the edge of the couch staring at me with a benign, indifferent smile. The first thing he did was ask me if I could help him get a job with some publisher. He was in "rublic pelations" now, and didn't like it. I said I only knew one publisher, and that was in Boston, but that I would write them a letter. The girl looked at Lucky. He said, "Oh yeah, I forgot." But he didn't say what.

I suggested we go out to dinner and Lucky said, "No, wait, I want to tell you what I've been doing with myself since I last saw you." The girl kept a straight face. I felt like asking her how she had hurt her arm but didn't. She said she worked for a New York publishing house. I asked Lucky why he didn't try to get a job in her company, and he said, grinning, "Oh I don't think Anne would like that, would you Anne?" She looked unhappy if serene. I felt uncomfortable. Lucky turned to me, asked for a drink of water and then said, "I sometimes fall off the reality principle unfortunately . . ."

Lucky, too, I had known in California. He came from one of the elite property-owning, newspaper-publishing families, both Mama and Dada. He drove a motorcycle and was built like a fast fullback and was just about the most beautiful boy I ever knew in California, which considering where I was living, down in the south, is saying something. He went everywhere on that motorcycle of his, roaring up and down the beach day and night. His friends were the life-guards and the old Viennese cook in his folks' big Neutra house overlooking Malibu Palisades. Lucky was childish, he never shared candy bars but would girls, he was indrawn and self-sufficient for weeks at a time and, of course, he could be cruel. We studied for our final exams together, that last semester, and I stayed in his house while his folks were away in Italy, probably buying more property. It had been planned for me to stay two weeks, but after two days he said relatives were coming and that he was sorry I had to go. I still don't know what I did to offend him. I think it was that I took his hospitality a little too aggressively; he was rich and I was not. Lucky had this peculiar quality of making me feel lower, very lower middle-class and in awe of his money, beauty and the ease with which he flowed in and out of his surroundings. We boxed together one whole semester in college, picking each other out as partners and agreeing to go lightly. During our last bout we had to mix it up a little for the instructor. Somehow Lucky broke three ribs. I told him that the ribs must have been weakened or already broken from the previous semester's wrestling class, when he had got them taped up, and that I hadn't hit him heavily at all. But all the time I knew him after that he insisted, with a kind of tolerant, knowing yellow-eyed smile, that I had broken his ribs in the ring. It really wasn't true. For one thing, I don't think I'm strong enough. After he kicked me out of his house at Malibu Palisades, we stopped studying together. Until then there had been a sort of coalition: myself, Manny the rabbi, Benn Hacker, Jessica, Kenneth Nkumba, and Lucky. We hadn't actually gone around that much with each other but the rest of the campus chose to think we did. Lucky was the only boy in a family of three sisters, his father was a "nice guy," which in his case meant a moral coward who never got in anyone's way, and his mother was a bully and had been a very good journalist during the war. When I had seen Jessica she told me that Lucky had stayed on at the house in Malibu after graduation and then had used his father's influence to get a messenger's job at one of the large film studios. He had been a reporter for one of his father's newspapers and was now assistant to the assistant "creative vice-president" of a television packaging agency . . .

Lucky grinned and said, "You're lucky, because Anne and I picked you to have a farewell dinner with." You two breaking up? I asked. He said, still grinning steadily, his blond light eyes staring, "Yes, in a manner of speaking, wouldn't you say so, Anne honey?" She sat and picked at the plaster on her cast. Lucky said, "Tomorrow morning I'm going to be taken away." Anne started to cry. Lucky rode it. I couldn't look at Lucky. I knew, without knowing, where he was going. Lucky said, "It's a place called Sweetwater

Sanitarium. I'm touched. Tetched," he corrected himself, cocking his head and making a circular motion with his finger around his ear. "So we decided to spend the last night with you," Lucky said.

Thanks, I said. "You're mighty welcome," he replied. Just then I felt oddly triumphant, vindicated almost. I felt like going to the telephone and calling up the publishing house in Boston and saying, Come on down and see the latest of the tribe.

But I didn't phone Boston. Instead, we all went downstairs to Ninth Avenue and had shishkebab in a white-tiled restaurant. It was not a pleasant meal. Lucky made me promise I would write a letter singing his praises to Boston because, he said, he wanted a publishing job when he got out. He didn't say "get out," but "come down." After a while, particularly after the wine, Lucky calmed down and forgot to be aggressive about where he was going. He stopped discussing homely details about toothbrushes and mail. He relapsed into a shy, grinning, easy silence. I tried talking to Anne but she just poked at her food without looking up. I asked Lucky about his motorcycle and he said, "I'm riding it up to this place." Anne suddenly said, "He hasn't been on it, on one, for two years." I asked Lucky if he thought it was a good idea and he said, "No, probably not, but maybe they'll let me take it to bed with me." I was getting more and more nervous. Lucky noticed and said, "Don't be scared, I don't cry, or shout or break china." I thought Anne was going to faint, so I led the way out of there. We walked back along the street to Jessica's apartment house, the three of us. All the while, I held an imaginary conversation with the Boston publisher, explaining to him why people like Lucky happened. I couldn't remember my argument in his club, but I wanted to; I felt that if I could remember I could put a safe distance between Lucky and me which is what, at this moment, I most wanted. His motorcycle was a two-seater.

From the dark courtyard of the apartment house Lucky stepped out into the street. I looked at Anne. She said, low, "He's going to leave me here, you know that, don't you? He's been planning to leave me here all night." I asked her what she wanted me to do, and she said nothing. I called out to Lucky. He didn't answer either. It was a quiet night, cars went by in the street and none of them a taxicab. Then one came. I was on the sidewalk, halfway between

Anne and Lucky. I tried to shout his name but my throat stuck. Lucky shut the door, and the cab rolled away, stopped for the traffic light on Sixth Avenue, turned the corner and disappeared.

I went back to Anne. She didn't lift her head. She sat on the stone steps and said, "This is to punish me." I said, Look, I'll take you home. She didn't reply. I went out to Sixth Avenue, got a cab, put her in it, and we rode up to 34th Street where she lived in an apartment building like Jessica's. Upstairs, her roommate let us in, scowling. We went into Anne's room. It was like all the rooms in the world decorated by girls who work in publishing houses who take their jobs too seriously. A Rouault, a daybed, straw chairs, *Kenyon Reviews,* a very modern, expensive lamp with a wide, mauve shade. We sat on the daybed and I began giving her a lecture on Mahalia Jackson, of whom she had never heard. She was coming out of it. I told Anne that one of the things that had always troubled me was the fact that I knew Mahalia sang the best jazz blues going, and yet the one time she consented, in Washington, D.C., under the urging and direction of Nshui Erteguin (real name), to sing against a New Orleans ensemble, it just wasn't right, the two parallel lines didn't meet, it was a kinky record. Anne began to perk up and ask who Mahalia Jackson was. I asked her if she liked her work and she said, "I'm passionate about it." I asked her how she had hurt her arm and she said, "Riding in Central Park. It comes off soon. In fact, I could take it off right now if you wanted." I told her it was all right if she kept it on. She brought out a bottle, and to my delight it turned out not to be White Horse. We drank. She said, "I'm sorry I can't put on any records, but it's late and my roommate doesn't like it." Move out, I said. She said she was trying to. For the next ten minutes Anne talked about her roommate. She was obsessed by the scowling, furious girl in the room next to hers. In fact, she was afraid of her. I told her to move out. She said, "My father was a barber on Flushing Avenue, my mother could hardly read, and I spent all day yesterday working on a manuscript by James Gould Cozzens. He came in in the afternoon and said hello." I said it was suicide for publishing girls to take their jobs too seriously, they made movie idols, gods even, out of authors, they became the spinster brides of unworthy men. Anne bridled and stopped drinking. I gave her a long, garrulous, stupid lecture on the necessity of doing one's own work. She kept saying, "And what if you're not creative?" I said, If you want to be a midwife love the baby but not the father, otherwise you'll never find a proper marriage. She said, "You talk like my dad." I asked how old she was, and she wouldn't tell me. I said, It's a hell of a thing to be sensitive about. I couldn't help it but she was starting to excite me. Her dress was black and simple, her skin was white, her hair was long and blond, she was small, and one arm was in a cast. She said, "I was in love with a boy three years younger than me, once. I come from Flushing Avenue and I'm a New School of Social Research girl and we always make troubled marriages. Deeply troubled." She then explained herself.

I asked her why she kept using words like empathize, communicate, mature relationship and so forth, and she said, "When soldiers are in the army they become so angry they only use fucking." It sounded like a plausible theory. She started to take her cast off, and I said she should wait to consult her doctor. She asked me what I was doing in New York and I said I had just been awarded a literary fellowship. Blow me down if she wasn't impressed. She kept asking me questions about what I was going to write, and I kept saying, as a joke, An epic of America, Anne. Little did she know. She took another couple of slugs out of the White Horse and suggested we go back down to my neighborhood for some more shishkebab, which is what we did. But the restaurant was closed, and then she said, "I have to use your bathroom." When we got upstairs, I put on some records and lay down on the couch. Anne came into the room and started to cry for this boy, three years younger than herself, she had once known and loved. I was surprised the plaster cast did not get in the way.

Some time during the night I picked Anne up and carried her into the bedroom, her long blond unloosened hair trailing over my arms. I thought then she was very beautiful. I knew she would not give herself to me, and she didn't. But I could not help but give myself to her. I collapsed the second time, inexplicably, as though struck down by six pallbearers. We lay, apart, on the same bed, in the dark. I was embarrassed.

Anne murmured, for the first time tonight relaxed, "Don't think about it, it always happens that way, it's not your fault." I started to say something when I remembered where I had been, all that day. I laughed. Anne thought I was putting a good face on it and let me. I lay there, in the dark, on Jessica's bed, and laughed . . .

Goodbye, Lucky.

In the morning I awoke and said loudly to myself: Can I write this novel? I must work alone. God give me the strength. Oh please dear God . . . Anne awoke and said, "This is what comes out of not praying as a child." We got dressed, she cooked some eggs, and we parted for the day. I sat down at Jessica's desk and worked an hour or two, then I put my boat tickets into an envelope and addressed the envelope to Student Tours, Inc. But when I realized I had no place to go in America, no place to rest, I put the tickets back in my wallet and tore up the envelope. I sat by the window and waited for the dark. When it came I went downtown to call on my friend Dennis. Next to Rafe Hawes, the cat-eyed Mexican, Dennis was my oldest friend. We met in the Army, when we both worked as clerks for Military Intelligence at the War College in Washington. I respected Dennis. When I was younger I respected his good sense, only later sensing he was making a passion out of equilibrium. He had been badly hurt in the war, when his jeep was blown up by a land mine outside Aachen, and for about two years the shell fragments had a way of working out of his flesh and tinkling to the tile floor while he was showering. In fact, that was how we met, showering together in the War College barracks. I heard this tinkle and thought I saw the cap of a fountain pen on the steamy, wet floor. I always had dinner with Dennis and Muriel when I came into New York. We weren't really close any more, and I suppose had stopped shortly after the war, but it was pleasant to keep up the ritual.

Dennis was a doctor, specializing in what I think are called female disorders. Sensible, ruddy-faced, even-tempered, awkward about emotions, humorously intelligent and academically dull (he flunked his medical exams twice). He had an office near Canal Street and did not seem at all surprised to see me. "Hello, wanderer," he said. Hello, sheik, I replied. It was an old joke between us. While he had been hospitalized in Washington, he had given me small packages every week or so to take to Muriel in New York. Every weekend, on Saturday afternoon, I would meet Muriel in Battery Park and present her with the package, but she would never show me what it was. At first I thought they were rings, but whenever I inquired Muriel always colored and changed the subject. Finally, my curiosity got the better of me when I returned from overseas and visited them in their small Greenwich Village apartment. I asked Dennis what had been in the packages. Dennis laughed, and Muriel, now pregnant, also did. Dennis said, I'll tell you some time when Muriel isn't around. Oh go ahead, Dennis, Muriel said. It was Dennis's turn to blush. Well, he said, Muriel has a tendency to break out in a rash. He paused. Muriel supplied, Where babies do. And so, said Dennis, I stole penicillin ointment from the War College hospital. It was in short supply at the time. Oh, I said. Muriel said, You'll never make a good romantic, kid, you're not tough enough.

Dennis closed up shop early, and we drove along the Parkway to his place, in the middle of one of those gigantic housing projects near the sea. Dennis had grown older, a little more disappointed, and he spent a lot of time telling stories of how wise he was, how full of insight. I didn't understand some of the stories, and Dennis said it was because I was not yet married and settled down.

Muriel was surprised to see me but put the child away early to cook a marvelous Chinese pork supper. One of the nice things about visiting Dennis and Muriel is that they are still in love, this after eleven years together. Dennis was never a success with women, I always had to find him one in Washington, but Muriel liked to kiss him, you could see that. Instead of responding like an overheated spaniel, Dennis took Muriel's love with dignity and calmness. They would stay married forever. I envied them. So I got a little aggresive and made a few cracks about life in a housing project. Muriel, a great believer in psychoanalysis although she has never been analyzed, kept saying, "What's your problem, bud?" But Dennis became aggressive. He said he was local schoutmaster and treasurer of the neighborhood Neighbors for Stevenson campaign. *Mazultov*, I said. Without any of us being aware of it, after dinner we suddenly found ourselves, Dennis and Muriel and myself, defending our lives, our ways of life. Dennis did some hot, unkind probing and refused to be shushed by Muriel. I was now sorry I had made cracks about suburbanites. I said, The trouble with you, Dennis, is that you don't generalize any longer. Dennis really got sore then. "Your life," he said, meaning mine, "is empty at the core — that's why you're going to Europe." He had speared me.

I took one look at Muriel's face and knew right away that something was wrong. I said, What's wrong, Muriel? "Dennis," she turned softly to her husband, "leave him alone, you're being hard." That was when I knew and it frightened me again, terrifically. *I* had caused that expression on her face. The look of a woman who has just seen an auto accident. The evening was drawing to a bad-tempered close. Dennis did nothing to conceal it. I wanted to placate him but I really did believe he was sinking into a kind of thick, gentle morass. I said, on the spur of the moment, You know, I just won a big literary prize. Dennis looked unmoved. Muriel said, "Hey, we know two more people, friends, who just have, too. Where does yours come from?" There was no point. I couldn't rouse them. I said it was time to go. I kissed Muriel and this time, for the first time, she made no mention of my ever coming back when I passed through. Dennis drove me to the subway train, which this far out is on stilts in the air. We made a few Army jokes and said goodbye to each other. He didn't look back as he drove away to the housing project. I climbed up the old wooden stairs and got on a stationary subway train and waited for it to go. Opposite me, sleeping, was an old, disheveled, sad drunk, in a lurched, motionless position on the wicker seat. He reminded me so much of Swede. I went over to the old man and stuck some five-dollar bills in his pocket. He slept like dead. A small, tubby married couple came in at the opposite end of the car and plumped themselves down virtuously. I cried out, Don't worry, I'm not rolling him. They turned and stared at me contemptuously. I shoved my hand in the old drunk's suntan pocket and held the money aloft. See, I shouted. The old drunk awoke and weaved himself up and towards the door. I tried to put the money in his way but he just shoved me aside and wandered out onto the platform. The doors shut with a bang, and I hung on to a strap, all the way to the river stops. The tubby little couple, wrapped up in overcoats and furs, got out at the De Kalb Street station and immediately spoke to an inspector. The inspector looked at me between the shoulders of the tubby couple, and then he got into the coach. I stood at my end hanging on to a strap, and he stood at his end balancing on his feet and staring, with no particular rancor, or even interest in me. As soon as the train stopped across the river, at Canal Street, I got out, ran up the stairs, vaulted a small fence in a small park, and walked fast uptown to Jessica's flat. Nobody followed me.

I awoke to my last morning in America.

Just after dawn I got out of bed and packed my things. I was taking with me what I always do in a serious move, my old army duffel bag, the bottom half of the infantry pack I was given at Fort Meade, Maryland, and an old brown suitcase I had bought in Detroit. I slipped some money into an envelope and left it on the desk in the front room to help pay Jessica's rent, and then I went into her closet and stole a small, inexpensive checked-tartan carry-all bag. I needed the bag to put my small things into. Jessica had not given me permission to take it, and the money I was leaving behind would more than cover the cost of a new one. Also, in her closets, she had a score of various types of luggage. I didn't know why I was stealing it. I needed one but there was time to go downstairs and walk over to 14th Street and buy one. I sat down on Jessica's bed and I gazed into the closet, keeping one hand on the tartan bag, and wondered about it all. I knew I was going to take it away, I knew it was not important and that I shouldn't. Then I made the bed, gathered up my baggage and in two trips by the small elevator brought it downstairs to the courtyard. A taxicab took me to No. 88 North River dock, near 48th Street.

I was one of the first people at the terminal station. It felt peculiar letting someone take care of my bags when I had worked only a few piers away. I rode the freight elevator up to the loading shed where my things were ticketed and taken away. The long, tall echoing shed was beginning to fill up with passengers for the ship, which was moored to the side of the loading shed. It did not look like a large ship. I stood near the purser's desk at the bottom of the gangplank and searched for a kindred spirit, specifically someone who looked as though he had a political face. I needed that kind of face.

The dock was in the usual incredible disarray. Shouting, surly men shunted electric wagons mountained with other people's baggage past stacks of crates and dodging people. The working dockers sent up an uproar from the jungle of baggage. Harried clerks and anxious passengers rapidly flooded the bare concrete floor of the loading shed. I walked to the opposite end of the loading shed and watched a very large ship discharge its passengers. I stood outside the enclosure gate and wondered why certain Europeans kissed friends and relatives three times, not twice, not four times. I wondered why the world couldn't be like a passenger off a ship and a waiting brother on the dock, embracing. I walked up and down the loading shed looking at people. Outside it was wet and raining, a cold dark morning, an Army morning.

At the purser's desk outside my own ship I got into a quarrel, a mild one, with two dock laborers and the man behind the desk over a confusion in tagging. I used my voice strongly and got results. I broke off and trailed along the outer edge of the shed below the ship which was peacefully pumping bilge water. On the wall nearest me was written DON'T BRING THE SIU SCABS IN THIS HEAR PLACE. Longshoremen, barrelly, chesty, klaxon-voiced, were loading the ship. At the street end of the pier there was a shape-up. The men standing around in a circle were tense. Some of them turned around to look at me and I walked down the center road of the shed, past the purser, up the gangplank and into the ship which was to take me to Europe. A steward showed me the way to my cabin. It was a small, dark cabin, with large perspiring pipes running at angles on the walls and ceiling. Also there were four men already in the room, and a fifth bunk empty. I walked back up to the deck, the near side, up forward, and watched the dockers load. A sign painted in whitewash stared at me: VOTE ILA. I stood there for about an hour, and then crossed to the river side of the deck and leaned on the rail, looking out at the barges and boats. Soon a boy joined me, about twenty. He stood off shyly to one side. Then he came over and said he was in our cabin. He was from England, he said. He believed in keeping fit. "It always does," he said, "to keep fit." Sure, I said. He said he was a professional window cleaner. He had gone to Canada, emigrated, to seek a new life. His money and prospects ran out. He's returning to England. I asked him how long he had been in Canada. "Week," he said, "a week." Are you sure, I asked, you're giving it a chance? "I couldn't find work," he replied defiantly. Just then a blond boy, about the same age, walked past. He had been wandering the ship as long as I had. A blond boy with pimpled face and searching eyes and innocent mouth and a plastic left hand. The English boy called him over. The boy with the artificial hand, too, shared my cabin. He was very nice. He explained about his hand immediately. The engine room of his ship had exploded. He had been in a Baltimore hospital for two years having plastic surgery, now he was returning home to Bremen. He smiled while he told this story, and then he resumed wandering.

The English boy kept saying that he wasn't sure he was doing the right thing by going back. He pinned me to the rail with speculation, deep and detailed, about whether he had done wrong. He said he knew he would come in for a lot of criticism at home, particularly from his wife. He was tempted, he said, to get off the ship and keep trying but he wouldn't. He did not have any money. I made a vow to myself that under no circumstances would I give him any money. I had an almost physical urge to give him my money. He said he was afraid of what his wife and his brothers would say to him. For quarter hour after quarter hour he tried to juggle the mean details of his situation. Finally, he shrugged and said, "I'll go back." He was in a state of panic and desperately trying not to show it, but he did, by blushing. He was sweating terribly. He kept saying, "I'd stick it out if I wasn't married." I had an equally powerful desire to tell him to stick it out, but I didn't. I said, Look old pal, I think maybe you ought to go home, I think that's what you want to do. He looked at me as though I had just spoken the wisdom of the ages and said, "Yes, yes, I belong at home."

I walked back to the shed side of the ship and began ferociously eating a chocolate bar. I had seven or eight in my pockets.

I watched the unloading for quite some time. The hilarity of the passengers wearing corsages contrasted with the stolid loneliness of the others who looked away with dry, envious eyes. Several of the passengers had even taken to wandering the deck and avoiding each other's eyes, as though actually knowing where they were going instead of pretending. As the day wore on, a kind of quiet settled over the motionless ship. The passengers became restless. The quiet became punctuated by runs of the winch machinery at the forward end and shrill whistles from the hold foreman. I walked up forward to watch the loading. Two young girls on a fling, two girls from the Midwest, were leaning over the rail, and one of them was shouting, "I'll be true to you, Harry." The other seemed to be screaming at the gangplank. I felt utterly incapable of writing a word. In the forward saloon some of the longshoremen were sitting around playing cards. Two of them, one fat, one thin and sleek-haired, were engaged in conning two girls with English accents, causing them to laugh guardedly, and, unconsciously, draw together in the face of this sexual onslaught. I sat down at one of the tables. The longshoremen did not know I was there. I didn't try talking to them.

I went downstairs to the Chief Purser's office and told him I wanted my cabin changed. I paid him an extra ten dollars, and was shown by one of the German stewards to a small, narrow dark cabin. I locked the door and lay down in the top bunk, my hands clasped behind my head. I listened to the sound of the winches. Then I got up and went up into the main saloon. Some of the passengers were already sitting around the bar, and the barman, who was tuning a radio. We nodded to each other. The barman said there would be a delay in sailing. He said five hundred was the ship's normal complement of passengers but she was taking only seventy-five to Le Havre. I asked him if all the stewards and crew members were German, and he said yes, they were all German. I said, I thought the ship was Greek. He said, "The doctor is a Greek. All the others are Germans." He finally got the program he wanted, and after listening he said, "I think there will be another war. A new war." A small man in a brown suit walked over and said, "Yes, maybe." He introduced himself to me as the second mate of a Swedish ship; he, too, was a German. He smiled and said he had four children in Düsseldorf. I said Düsseldorf is a curious place for a sailor to be from, and he smiled and said he had been born there, and also his children. His wife, he said, was a Berliner. The news was coming in over the radio. Two homosexual boys in Italian tight pastel-colored pants looked dreamily at the radio. At the table next to my stool a woman sat reading, an old woman, probably German, in a slouch hat, open mouth, palsied hands, bony frame. She didn't look well. I wondered if she was lonely. The shy young German with the plastic hand sat on another of the stools, down the bar, politely cupping his false hand in his lap, listening to the radio without intensity. The German second mate laughed and slapped the bar and said, "Yes, it is another war. Two cognacs?" he asked me. I wondered, I couldn't help wondering where he had been, what he had done, during the war. I nodded and thanked him. We drank a small single cognac while he listened to the radio. The two young homosexual boys spoke loudly to each other and called each other John. The two girls from the midwest, wearing corsages, came in, looked around aimlessly and sat down. I bought the German second mate a cognac, and in the middle of our drinking it the English boy (the window cleaner) came in and said, half in embarrassment, half eagerly, "There's a commotion up there." The second mate and I and the boy with the false hand and the two girls from the Midwest went upstairs to the deck and lined the rail near the gangplank. The loading party was having to use lights now. The rain had stopped. On the dock, in front of us, two men in black uniforms were dragging a struggling girl towards our ship.

We could hear her screaming. She was saying, I don't want to go. I . . . don't . . . want . . . to . . . *go.* (Later, I found out her name was Wendy. She was blond, especially good-looking, and English. She was being deported from America on a technical violation after having left her husband and child in Arizona. As the ship neared England Wendy and I spent much time together. The last night out she tried to throw herself overboard. She tried several times, until some of us carried her back to her cabin and locked her in. The Greek doctor injected her with a fast-acting sleeping drug. Later, a rather ugly incident took place between the doctor and Wendy, but its description has no place here. At Southampton Wendy had to be dragged off the ship, sobbing and bedraggled, and she became very hysterical on the lighter boat. In the end, I signed a piece of paper which permitted the shore authorities to have Wendy taken to a hospital instead of a police station. Two years later, in a Kensington coffee house, I encountered Wendy again. She had grown much older and quite fat. She remembered me.) Then she started to wail. It made a terrible sound. Most of the longshoremen on the dock stopped working under the lights to watch. A matron, also in a dark uniform, appeared and tried to speak to the blond girl, only to press her lips together firmly and step out of the uniformed men's path. The men heaved the screaming, swearing, hysterical girl up onto the gangplank.

Once she felt the wooden boards under her feet the girl steadied. She tried to shake off the two men but they misinterpreted and held her even more firmly, shoving her forward and causing her to stumble. "Leave go of her," someone shouted in a fury, "she's all right." I saw my fellow passengers eying me and supposed it was I who had shouted. The girl shook loose and sat down on the gangplank, burying her head and crying. The two men in uniform straightened up. One of them then bent down and began to talk to her. His voice snapped her alert and she edged, sitting position, up the gangplank so as to be away from his hands, then stood up, turned around and came up towards us. She was wearing a tight-fitting tweed suit and her bright blond hair was in disarray, her make-up terribly smudged. As she slowly went up the gangplank she hesitated, almost stopped, and said, "I don't want to go. Don't make me go." Then she stepped aboard. Most of the passengers stood around watching for a moment as she groped around on deck, and found a bench, and sat down on it, slumping against a bulkhead. Then they scattered slowly, with backward glances. The two uniformed men, leaving the matron on the dock, walked aboard. One of them went off in search of an official from the ship, and the other stationed himself near the blond girl.

I went over and sat down on the bench. The uniformed man shook his head severely at me. I gave him the gentle fuck-you sign and leaned over close to the blonde. I asked her if there was anything I could get. She shook her head and began to cry again. The guard lost patience and cried, "God's sake, lady." I leaned close and told the blond girl a story, in a low confidential voice. I said it was a story George Orwell found out about. It had to do with two prisoners of war, caught in a Russian contingent attached to a German unit in France. When the British, I said, captured these German troops, they found that in the Russian contingent two of the soldiers did not speak Russian. In fact, these two men did not speak any other language known either to the British or to their fellow prisoners. They could talk only with one another. A military professor of Slavonic languages could not understand them, nor an expert especially brought down from Oxford. Nobody could. But a sergeant who had once served in northwest India overheard the two prisoners and recognized their language. They were Tibetans, he said. This sergeant could speak a kind of pidgin Tibetanese and got the story out of them. Some years earlier these two men had wandered over the Tibetan border into Russia and been drafted into a labor battalion, afterwards being sent to western Russia when the war with Germany broke out. They were taken prisoner by the Germans and sent to North Africa; later they were sent to France, then exchanged into a fighting unit when the Second Front opened, and taken prisoner by the British. All this time, Orwell relates, they had been unable to speak to anybody but each other, and had no idea of what was happening or who was fighting whom.

The blond girl turned her head to me. I don't think she got the story. She said, dazed, "What?" I said, eagerly, Just think now, what if these two Tibetans had been conscripted into the British Army and sent to fight the Japanese, ending up somewhere in central Asia, or even their native village in Tibet, and all the time they still wouldn't be knowing how they had gotten there, but still, they would have got home. The guard standing near the girl looked down at me, frowned and set his jaw. The girl shook her head. Then the other guard came back and asked me if I would move off so they could talk to the girl. I did so, but before I did I touched her shoulder and made her look at me and then gave her the British wartime thumbs-up sign.

When I returned to the rail, on the loading shed side, it was dark and raining again. I had been on that motionless boat since early morning, but it certainly did not feel like it. I leaned on the rail and watched the loading go on under the wet, blackish glare of the searchlights. I leaned on the rail and thought, I am an injured man. I didn't know how or why or by whom (it is the style to say by oneself). I would go to Europe to understand this injury and, if luck were with me, to relieve myself of it.

I leaned on the rail under the dark rain and watched them pull in the gangplank, and thought of the book I was to write and that I did not feel I would write. I was committed to the writing of a book which was to be the sum and total of all that I knew of myself and the worlds in which I had grown up. How dare I? I write a book? I, who don't even know why a man and a woman, a husband and wife, decide to have a child. I must be mad.

And yet, I loved America. Although I could point to few or none of its parts as justification, I felt ineradicably convinced of the direction of America, of the uncertain majesty of its momentum and yes, even that most dangerous of words, destiny. I was part of that direction, beneficiary, critic. The relationship was too complicated. I had to leave. I had outlived my time, had lived too faithfully according to the code of my generation. A new way of life was appearing in America I was no longer equipped to understand, new qualities I was not equipped to see. But who was I to offer myself as arbiter, interpreter, putter of the question? Had I ever, in my heart, trusted and accepted Americans? Or was it not that the real Americans I had always mistrusted and feared? No. I belonged nowhere. I was on the outside. My only qualification for writing of my country was a deep need to immolate myself in some continuity, and this I knew I shared with everyone, but because this was a thing that was slowly, and now with more rapidity, doing me to my death, I knew, I *knew*. I had always known. I had become like an old man before the age of thirty, scanning anxiously among the new generation for the peculiar virtues of my own.

I thought of Swede and his Nazi son.

I thought of the protagonist of my book. As I had written him he was to be a technician of the moral dilemma. Moral dilemma of what? He, I, was not yet a thinker. A moral dilemma is not a mere ingathering, a voracious eating of experience.

No. I spoke for no one but myself. Not a subgeneration, not a group, not a legion of in-betweens. I spoke only for myself.

The one thing I knew was this, that if I ever wrote this book I would not, under pain of knowing myself as liar, disguise or brazen the pity I felt for the world, my friends and myself. I would deal with it directly and in its own terms. I would not pretend it was something else.

I thought about the book, in its detail and felt like collapsing weakly with laughter. I had never known a *natural* period, where things had their accustomed place. All my life I had tried to sink myself within some continuity, and all my life blood told. My racial memory was that of the borderer, the outlaw observer, the gangster Essene, the lustful Brook Valleyite, the Proudhonist with finger at side of nose, the irrevocably homeless revolutionary. I had started out to write a true book of the working-class hero, but how could I deny that I, and my family, were not workers in the real sense but agents, agents of revolution, to the working class? Every time I had followed in my parents' footsteps, had actually done that which I was bred up to do, gone into the factory, spoken from the platform, lived and eaten and hoboed with working people, I had become afflicted and appalled with the crudity and meanness of their lives. I wanted to save them, not live among them. Once I left my class I was rootless and superficial. What had I learned . . . I had learned this. That the deepest evil consisted not of corrupting a vision of life but of failing to understand.

The thirties had been my time, and I had been fourteen in 1940. The historic agencies of change are collapsed; and with them I. Why? I must find out.

And yet it came back to this, watching the close-cropped university fraternity boys in their white sweaters singing around a piano and knowing I am not one of them, they are the Americans. And yet who says they are and I am not? Who dare say it?

And yet it came back to this, the sheer shock, in my own country, of walking along the street and seeing faces behind which are no ideas, or even enjoyment.

No. No more of this. It was time to go.

The winches had stopped. I couldn't hear the foremen's whistles. The longshoremen were no longer playing cards up forward. One by one the loading lights blinked off. The dockside became dark and quiet, the rain abated. I turned away from the rail and went inside.

Inside the large saloon were the same people — the old German lady with palsy and a floppy hat, the second mate with four children, the burned German boy, the two girls from the Midwest, the English window cleaner. Everyone was listening to the radio. The bartender kept his hand on the tuning knob. Among the new people in the room were a young man and young woman. She was plump and pretty and wore black slacks. He had a long nose and wore glasses and a sweater and corduroy trousers. They held hands. They were newlyweds.

I asked the bartender to switch off the radio. He said, "No, we are listening. It is important." I walked out of the saloon and down to my cabin. I climbed up on the top bunk and then swung down and went back up to the saloon. More passengers had come in. The blond girl, Wendy, was seated by herself in a far corner table. Nobody was speaking, not even the two girls from the Midwest. They were all looking at the bartender as though he were a prophet.

There was a terrific roaring and jamming and cackle coming from the loudspeaker, and seeming to come from the reddish chrome and mirrors of the saloon. Out of the static came some very clear words, in English, in a halting foreign accent. "This is Budapest. Budapest Radio. Budapest Radio. Help us. Help. Help. Help." Then, silence.

The radio was turned lower by the bartender. It was nothing but static now. Some of the passengers drifted out. The floor under our feet, which had been thrumming, we could feel move. From outside came several blasts of the ship's horn. The shy German boy with the burned hand came over and said, "We are going now." Some of the passengers were at the windows, watching the dark shape of the dock slide by.

Slowly we swung into the Hudson River. I went over to the newlyweds and said, I'm sorry but I'm a little deaf. I wonder if you could help me for the rest of this evening.